Exploring Science

for the new Junior Cycle

Michael O'Callaghan
Pat Doyle
Orla Molamphy
Ger Reilly

Edco
The Educational Company of Ireland

Grace K

Published 2016
The Educational Company of Ireland
Ballymount Road
Walkinstown
Dublin 12
www.edco.ie

A member of the Smurfit Kappa Group PLC

ISBN 978-1-84536-435-9

Editor: Sally Vince
Design: DesignImage
Layout: QBS
Artwork: Michael Philips and QBS
Cover Design: Identikit

Acknowledgements
Acknowledgement is made to the following for supplying photographs and for permission to reproduce copyright photographs: Alamy, iStock photo, Science Photo Library, Shutterstock

06J18

Contents

Contents

Introduction

For the student

Welcome to secondary school and your new science textbook, *Exploring Science*. Your textbook comes with a **Student Portfolio Book,** a **Glossary of Terms** and a range of **digital resources**. This book will build on your learning of science from primary school by helping you to understand the world around you and the wider universe. It aims to develop your learning skills in science. You will develop these skills yourself while also learning from your teacher and your fellow students.

For the teacher

Written for the new Junior Cycle, *Exploring Science* aims to give students a sense of enjoyment and an interest in the learning of science. The book is based on the **Statements of learning** from the NCCA specification (see *juniorcycle.ie*). It develops students' knowledge of and about science through the unifying strand called the **Nature of Science**, and the four contextual strands (or units): **Biological World**, **Chemical World**, **Physical World** and **Earth and Space**.

Features of *Exploring Science*

- The **Nature of Science** strand is explored in the opening chapter and highlighted throughout the text using four different logos (understanding science, investigating in science, communicating in science, and science and society).

- The rest of the book is divided into the **four contextual strands** or units, which are highlighted by different coloured tabs on the side of each page.
- **Learning outcomes** are stated at the beginning of each chapter in student-friendly language.
- **Keywords** are listed at the start of each chapter to allow students to become familiar with important new terms.
- **Activities** allow students to build on their knowledge by completing research.
- **Diagrams** have been fully labelled and are drawn in a simple style so that students can replicate them easily.
- **Questions** are interspersed within the text to offer teachers the opportunity to use different teaching strategies. In particular, there are chances for group work and pair work.
- **Did you know?** boxes feature interesting facts to stimulate students' interest in science.

- The **language** used is clear and simple to allow for use by students of varying reading levels.
- Simple and helpful **logos** are used throughout to enhance student understanding.

Activity

Group work

Question

Key fact

Corresponding page in Student Portfolio

Research

Student Portfolio

The Student Portfolio book provides additional material, activities and tasks. The portfolio book enables students to maintain a record of specific activities and reflect on their learning, as well as focusing on key words and key facts, through mind maps and comprehension and recall activities. It also contains templates for self-assessment and peer assessment. This book works in conjunction with the textbook.

Glossary of Terms Booklet

A comprehensive Glossary of Terms cross-referenced to the Textbook and Student Portfolio Book.

Teacher's Resource Book

The teacher's book works in conjunction with the textbook and the Student Portfolio book by providing:

- An outline of the new specification and NCCA guidelines
- Learning outcomes for each chapter with explanations of how they are incorporated into lessons
- Information on topics, questions and research ideas that can be used to enhance the students' learning
- Answers to all student questions in the textbook and student portfolio book
- Outlines of digital resources for each chapter and suggestions for integrating them into classroom work
- Suggestions of ways to assess student activities with assessment templates

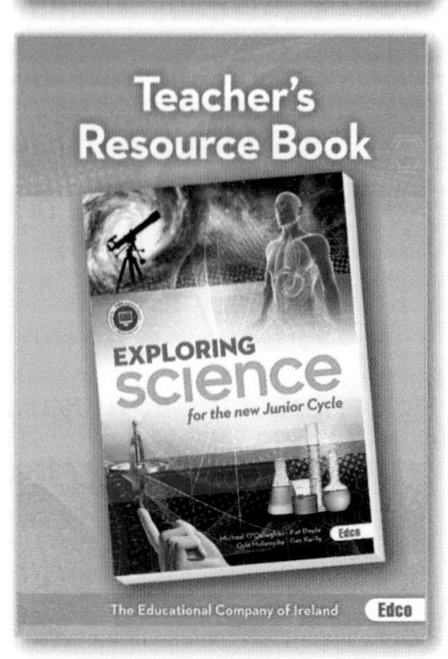

- A range of other information and suggestions to support teachers in the delivery of the new course
- Key skills, statements of learning and literacy and numeracy linked to relevant chapters
- Guidance for the teacher through the chapter and a suggested yearly schedule
- Additional activities and research activities.

Digital resources

The *Exploring Science* **digital resources** will further enhance classroom learning. These resources have been designed to integrate with the student textbook and to complement lessons suggested in the Teacher's Resource Book. Following the Principles for Junior Cycle Education, material is provided to suit a range of learner types and to encourage participation and engagement on the part of the student.

A series of **videos** and **animated diagrams** allows students to observe science in action across all units. These videos reinforce the topic at hand and allow for other perspectives, which may be discussed in class. Similarly, a series of **animated scientist biographies** presents a lively gateway to develop students' interest in science and initiate student-led research.

Further classroom discussion and participation is opened up through **PowerPoint presentations**, including a thematic presentation of information from the student textbook. **Experiment videos** allow for a visual review of activities carried out in the classroom.

A set of useful **report and template documents** geared towards the new curriculum is also available for teachers online. These documents can be used across the course for any year group. Guidance for integration of digital resources in the classroom is provided by the **digital resource symbols** (C6 i2 S9) used throughout the student textbook, as well as the provision of detailed notes and suggestions in the Teacher's Resource Book.

Laboratory equipment

Laboratory safety rules for pupils

The following rules are enforced to keep you and your classmates safe while in a school laboratory.

1. Do not enter the laboratory without permission.
2. Do not use any equipment unless permitted to do so by your teacher.
3. Make sure you know exactly what you are supposed to do. If in doubt, ask your teacher.
4. Make sure you know the position of all safety equipment in the laboratory, e.g. the fire extinguishers, first aid equipment etc.
5. Always wear eye protection or gloves when instructed to do so.
6. Long hair must be tied back during practical classes.
7. Place your bag and other personal items safely out of the way.
8. Never handle any chemicals with bare hands.
9. Nothing must be eaten, tasted or drunk in the laboratory.
10. Any cut, burn or other accident must be reported at once to your teacher.
11. Always check that the label on the bottle is exactly the same as the material you require. If in doubt, ask your teacher.
12. Any chemical spilled on the skin or clothing must be washed at once with plenty of water and reported to your teacher.
13. Test tubes should never be overfilled. When heating a test tube ensure that the mouth of the test tube is pointed away from you and everyone else.
14. All equipment should be cleaned and put back in its correct place after use.
15. Always wash your hands after practical work.
16. Students should behave in a responsible manner at all times in the laboratory.

Safety labels

The following labels appear on bottles in the laboratory. They also appear on many everyday chemicals such as cleaning products and solvents. These labels indicate chemicals that could be dangerous if not used or handled properly. We use these warning symbols on activities in this book.

Toxic		Substances which can cause death if they are swallowed, breathed in or absorbed through the skin. Example: weedkiller.
Harmful or irritant		Substances which should not be eaten, breathed in or handled without gloves. Though not as dangerous as toxic substances they may cause a rash, sickness or an allergic reaction.
Oxidising		Substances which provide oxygen, allowing other materials to burn more intensely. Example: hair bleach.
Highly flammable		Substances which easily catch fire. Example: petrol.
Corrosive		Substances which attack and destroy living tissue, including skin and eyes. Example: oven cleaner.
Warning sign		This sign is used to draw attention to a warning of danger, hazards and the unexpected.
Safety glasses		Wear safety glasses to protect your eyes.

UNIT 1

NATURE OF SCIENCE

CHAPTER 1

UNIT 1 The nature of science

What is science?

Science comes from a Latin word *scientia*, meaning knowledge. Science is the study and knowledge of the (physical and natural) world around us. Science can be divided into different subject areas. In this book we will examine:

- The biological world, by investigating living things
- The chemical world, by investigating substances and how they react
- The physical world, by investigating matter and energy and how they interact
- Earth and space, by investigating the planet Earth and the universe.

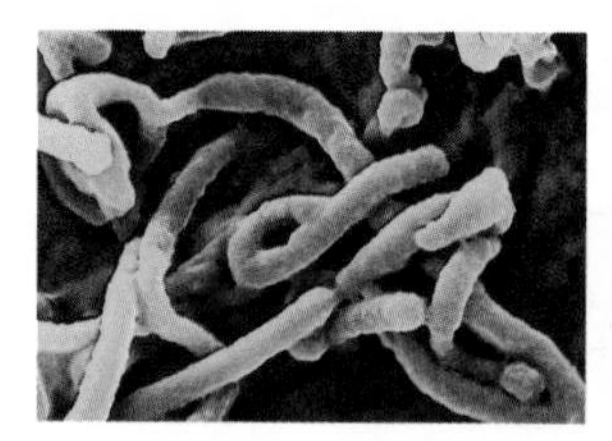

Ebola viruses bursting out of a cell

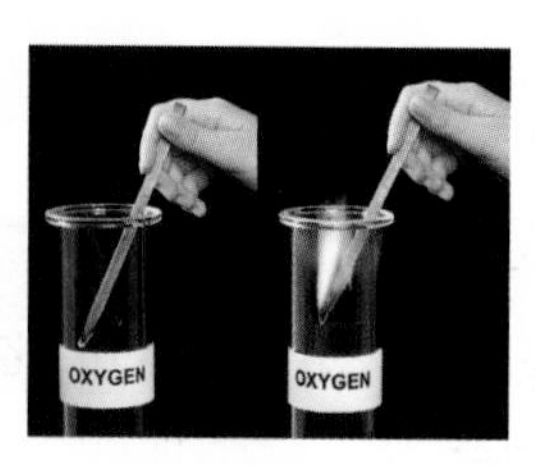

Oxygen relights a glowing splint

The heat given off by an old-fashioned (incandescent) bulb, a light emitting diode (LED) and a compact fluorescent bulb

The lights of Europe from the International Space Station (London is the brightest city shown)

Figure 1.1 *Topics in science*

The nature of science means how scientific knowledge is developed. This mainly involves understanding how science works, carrying out investigations, communicating scientific ideas and considering the role and value of science and scientists to society.

The nature of science will be outlined in this chapter. However, it is not really intended that you should learn all this material in isolation. The nature of science is included in every chapter of this book. It forms the basis of all the content and activities in each chapter. This chapter is included to allow you to understand how science works.

Understanding about science

Curiosity and questions

Science works initially by people being curious. Asking questions and being curious is a key part of being a good scientist. Very often important knowledge has been gained because someone was curious and asked a simple question.

How science answers questions

It is very difficult to answer big questions in science. However, we can ask smaller questions. These questions may be more suited to scientific investigations or experiments and so we might be able to find answers to them.

Question

For example, we could ask the question: 'Is the boiling point of water affected by adding salt?' In answering this question we start by finding out as much as we can about the problem and then suggesting what we think might happen. Such a suggestion is called a **prediction**.

Prediction

We could predict that: *adding salt will change the boiling point of water*. If a prediction can be tested it is called a **hypothesis**.

Hypothesis

A hypothesis is often written as an **If ... then ...** statement. For example: ***If*** *salt is added to water* ***then*** *the boiling point of the water will change.*

A hypothesis is a suggested explanation for something we observe or notice. Examples of hypotheses are:

- If we study then our exam results will improve.
- If drivers use a mobile phone while driving then they are more likely to crash.
- If we practise sprinting then we will get faster.

Having formed a possible explanation or hypothesis, the next step is to design a way to investigate the hypothesis.

Investigating in science

Investigating a hypothesis

A hypothesis is tested by carrying out an investigation or an experiment. Normally two sets of apparatus are set up:

- One set of apparatus is the **investigation**.
- The second set of apparatus is a comparison or **control**. Both sets of apparatus should be identical, *except for one difference*.

For example, returning to our hypothesis above, we could boil some tap water in a beaker and use a thermometer to record the temperature at which it boils. We could then add salt to some tap water and record the temperature at which the salt water boils. When we look at the results:

- If both water samples boil at the same temperature then our hypothesis is incorrect.
- If the salt water boils at a higher temperature than the tap water then our hypothesis is supported.

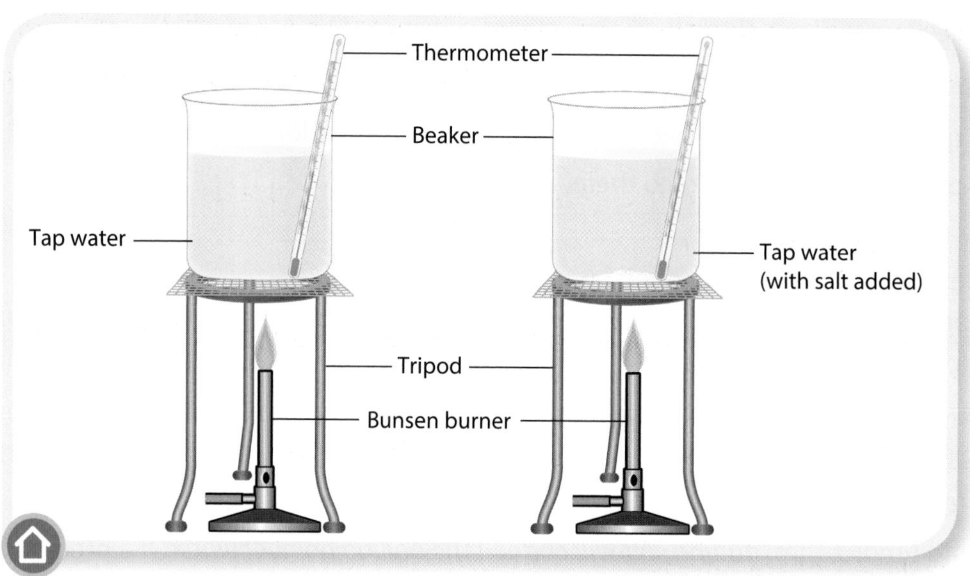

Figure 1.2 *Nature of science – investigating whether adding salt to tap water will change the boiling point of water*

The result(s) of an experiment often causes us to change our hypothesis. So, if the salt water is found to boil at a higher temperature than the tap water, we would revise the original hypothesis by saying: ***If*** *salt is added to water* ***then*** *the boiling point of the water will increase.*

Different types of investigations

Some investigations are laboratory based. However, many investigations take place outside laboratories. Scientists work in all sorts of exciting places, such as outdoors in forest parks and boglands, under the sea, in rainforests, close to volcanoes, near glaciers; or designing spacecraft, cars, computers, phones and a broad range of new technologies.

Some scientists work alone. But many scientists work in groups. That is why it is important for students to be able to work to a high standard alone, but also to be able to co-operate and work as part of a team.

Figure 1.3 *A team of scientists collecting animals in a forest*

Figure 1.4 *Scientists working in a laboratory*

Figure 1.5 *Scientist taking lava samples near a volcano*

The results of investigations

Scientists report on how they carried out their experiments and the results they got in **scientific journals**. These are special types of publications that are read by science experts, e.g. journals such as *Science* or *Nature*. In this way other scientists can read them, think about them and repeat the research if necessary.

If experiments are repeated (or replicated) and the same results are obtained, then they are likely to be valid and reliable. In other words, if investigations are checked by other experts it is more likely that they are genuine and not just made up by the original author or fluke results obtained.

The idea of other scientists reading and checking on investigations is called **peer review**. This acts as a quality control system, i.e. the work and findings are reliable and can be trusted to be true.

Investigations (or experiments)

When investigating a hypothesis the experiments have to be carefully planned. This means:

- Thinking about the problem
- Deciding what methods and equipment are to be used
- Carrying out the investigation so that it is safe, fair and will give reliable results.

Variables

In investigations scientists design an experiment so that the change in one item causes something else to change. These changing quantities are called variables.

There are three kinds of variable:

- **Independent variable**, where one thing is changed (for example when salt is added to the investigation on the previous page) and the results of the one change are observed.
- **Dependent variable**, which is the factor that changes as a result of our investigation. The scientist will focus on the dependent variable (for example the temperature at which the water boils) to see if it responds to the change (the addition of salt).
- **Controlled variable**, where all other factors are the same. For example, this might include using the same amount of tap water and the same size beaker in each case. This makes it a fair test.

Accuracy and precision

In any experiment it is vital that our measurements and readings are as accurate and precise as possible. We should not guess or estimate the volume of water added to each beaker; we should carefully measure the same volume of water using a suitable measuring device.

Data

Data is the information, measurements or observations collected in an experiment. Data can be:

- **Quantitative**, where the data involves the use of numbers. For example, the temperature is 20°C, or the distance is 100 metres.
- **Qualitative**, which describes something without the use of numbers. Very often qualitative data is obtained by using our senses. For example, we say something feels soft, or an object looks green, or a gas smells terrible.

For example, 'We breathe out more carbon dioxide than we breathe in' is a qualitative observation. However, if we say, 'We breathe out 4% carbon dioxide but we breathe in only 0.04% carbon dioxide', this is a quantitative observation or measurement.

The data obtained in any investigation should be analysed to reach a suitable conclusion.

The **analysis** should:

- Try to explain any unusual or strange observations that may have arisen.
- Include consideration of anything that was hard to do or caused difficulty during the investigation.
- Give rise to a discussion of how the investigation could be improved or altered if it was to be repeated, so that more information could be obtained on the topic under investigation.

The **conclusion** is a summary of the findings in the investigation. The conclusion should either support or contradict the hypothesis.

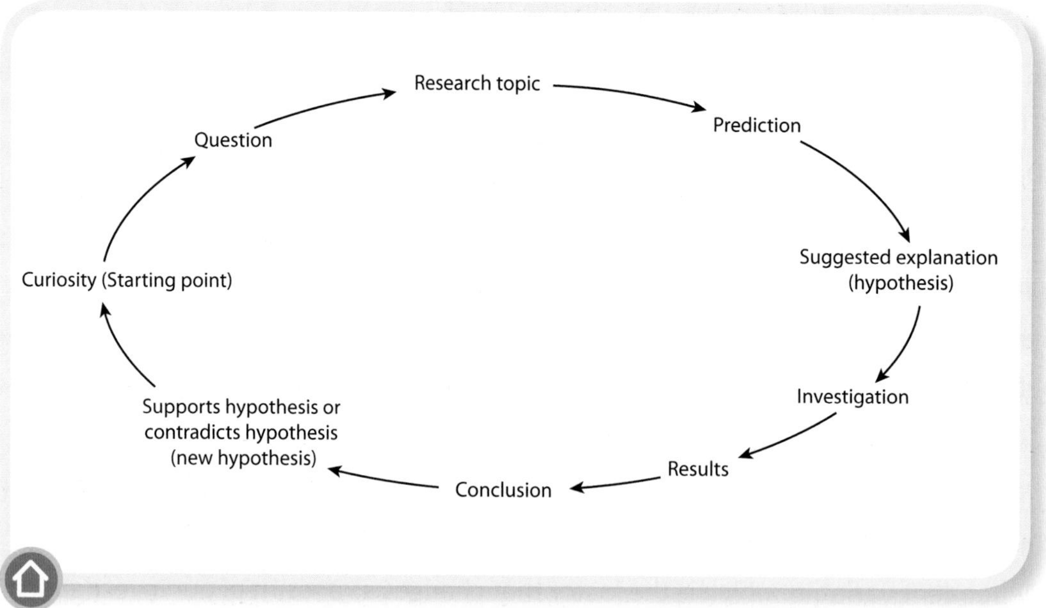

Figure 1.6 *Summary of how science works*

Reviewing and reflecting on investigations

By thinking back over the skills, methods and ideas used to carry out a series of investigations you should become better at applying scientific learning and skills in new and varied ways.

In particular you should be able to think and act like a scientist. This means you should be able to identify questions that are suited to scientific investigations. You should then be able to form a prediction, make a hypothesis that can be tested by investigation and carry out a proper scientific investigation of a new, unfamiliar problem.

Scientific ideas change over time

Science is not a fixed, unchanging set of ideas. It changes all the time. As a result of carrying out investigations our hypothesis is supported or contradicted. Over time a new hypothesis may arise to replace an old, unsupported hypothesis. This means that scientific thinking is constantly changing in line with new investigations that are carried out.

Communicating in science

How to communicate research

An important aspect of science is the ability to tell others what you did, how you did it and what you have discovered. This often involves writing a report of your investigation. In your report it is important that you present your information in a form that is clear, accurate and easy for others to understand.

This may involve a written report, the use of diagrams and photographs, tables to show any numerical data you obtained, or the use of graphs, pie charts or bar charts. Sometimes it involves preparing a poster to outline your work or telling others about your work using a PowerPoint presentation or other multimedia resources.

You will have to adapt your presentation to suit the people to whom you are reporting. For example, a report to your class who shared the investigation with you might be different from reporting to another class or a group of parents.

Conduct research

When carrying out an investigation it is important to find out as much as you can about the topic before you start. This involves researching it using books, libraries, internet and media (such as newspapers, scientific magazines or TV programmes), or any other relevant sources.

Evaluating media-based arguments

Of course you cannot always believe all you see or read. It is important that you make judgements as to how reliable or accurate a source is. A properly conducted scientific report is much more valid than a newspaper report giving a person's (or a group's) point of view. It is very important to be able to detect that a source may be unfair or show bias.

Very often media reports on a scientific issue are based on information given to the media by groups who want to promote their own ideas and plans. It is important to be aware of the source of the information and of the reasons for releasing the information. This is true for all media sources, but is especially true for the internet.

Some of the main features to look for in an internet source you can trust are:

- The name of the author is given.
- The date is given for any research findings that are listed.
- Reliable sources are given (or is the information just personal opinion?)
- In general, websites from universities, governments and organisations such as the BBC or NASA are more reliable.
- Good site design can indicate a more reliable source.
- Good grammar and spelling indicate a more credible site.
- If the information is similar across three different sites it is more likely to be true.

Figure 1.7 *Students studying in a library*

Science in society

Contribution and impact of scientists on society

The nature of science means that it is important to be aware of the role scientists have played in making the world a better place. Through their discoveries and inventions they have expanded our knowledge and understanding of how things work. They have allowed more food to be produced, more diseases to be controlled, new materials to be designed,

Figure 1.8 *Engines are good for transport but bad for the environment*

new technologies to be available and new understandings to be made about our own planet and the rest of the known universe.

You should be able to research and present information on what exactly different scientists have achieved. Some of these scientists are now legends of history. However, many major discoveries are being made by scientists who are still living.

Most of these effects have been for the better but, sadly, sometimes scientific discoveries may be used for negative reasons or have negative results. For example, the invention of engines that could burn petrol has given rise to cars, buses and fast means of transport. However, it has also resulted in carbon dioxide levels rising, which are contributing to global warming and climate change.

Role and importance of science in society

Science and society are deeply interlinked. It is obvious that science affects society by developing new discoveries, processes and materials. Science does not exist simply for itself. It should try to provide solutions that help make the world a better place for everyone. This has been done by developments such as electricity, electronics, digital technologies, communications, disease control, improved healthcare, new materials and drugs, discoveries about our Solar System (and beyond it) and new methods to supply our energy needs as oil and other fuel supplies run out.

However, the link between science and society is a two-way process. Society also relates to science and scientists. Society often guides or encourages scientific research in different areas. This can happen due to laws being passed, public money being made available to fund science and the general interests, values and public opinion as to what science needs to do next. In addition scientists are influenced by the culture in which they grew up. For example, scientists may not want to carry out certain types of research because it goes against what they believe in.

Science has had a huge role in making the world a better place. The role of science will be even more important in the future as we try to come to terms with our growing human population numbers, the need for new forms of energy, our desire to improve our health, our attempts to control disorders such as cancer and Alzheimer's disease, and the need to limit the effects of global warming.

Figure 1.9 *Scientist Stephen Hawking*

These are all huge and complex problems. Remember, however, that science starts in a very simple way: by being curious and asking questions. As Stephen Hawking said:

> 'Look up at the stars and not down at your feet. Try to make sense of what you see and wonder about what makes the universe exist. Be curious.'

UNIT 2

BIOLOGICAL WORLD

CHAPTER

UNIT 2

Living things and cells

Learning outcomes

At the end of this chapter you will be able to:

- Investigate the difference between living and non-living things
- Classify living things into different groups
- Investigate the structures of animal and plant cells and their functions
- Use a microscope to see the structure of animal cells.

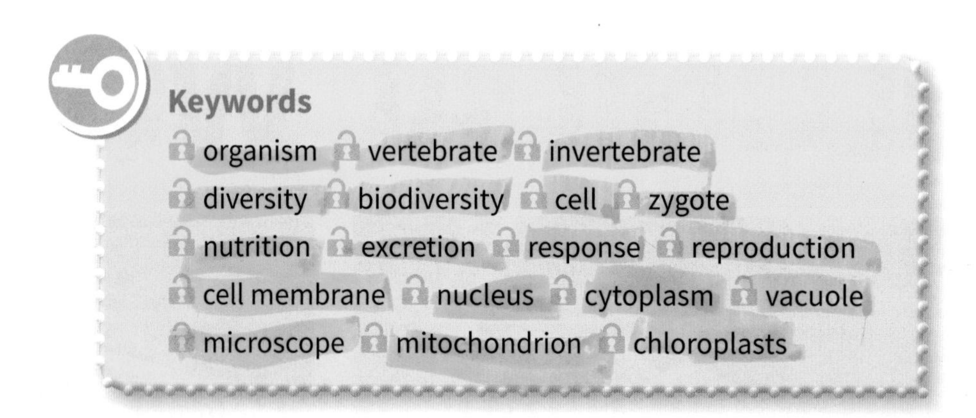

Keywords

organism vertebrate invertebrate
diversity biodiversity cell zygote
nutrition excretion response reproduction
cell membrane nucleus cytoplasm vacuole
microscope mitochondrion chloroplasts

What are living things?

There is no simple way to tell the difference between living and non-living things. In general living things (which in biology are also called **organisms**) must have all of the features or characteristics shown in Table 2.1.

Table 2.1 **The characteristics of all living things**

Characteristic	Meaning
Cells	The basic building blocks of living things
Nutrition	The way in which living things get their food
Excretion	The way in which living things get rid of wastes that they produce
Response	The way in which living things react to changes in their surroundings
Reproduction	The way in which living things produce new living things

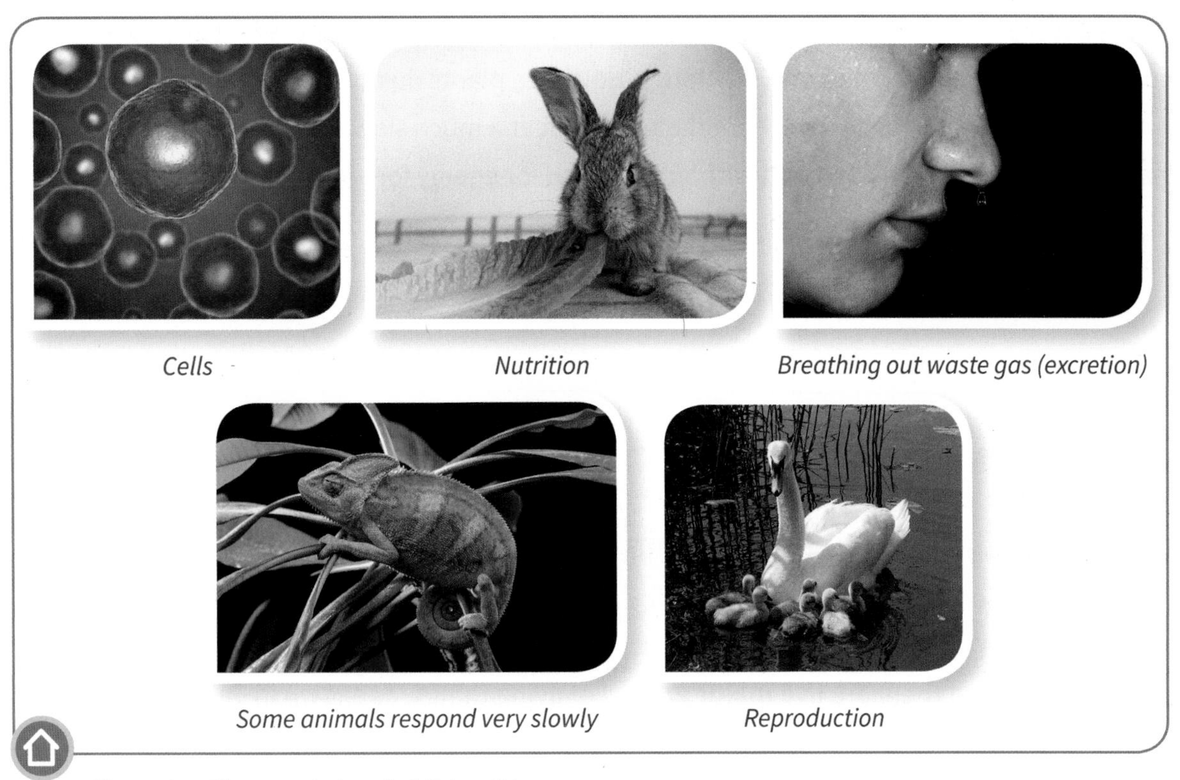

Figure 2.1 *Characteristics of all living things*

2.1 Separate the following into living and non-living things:

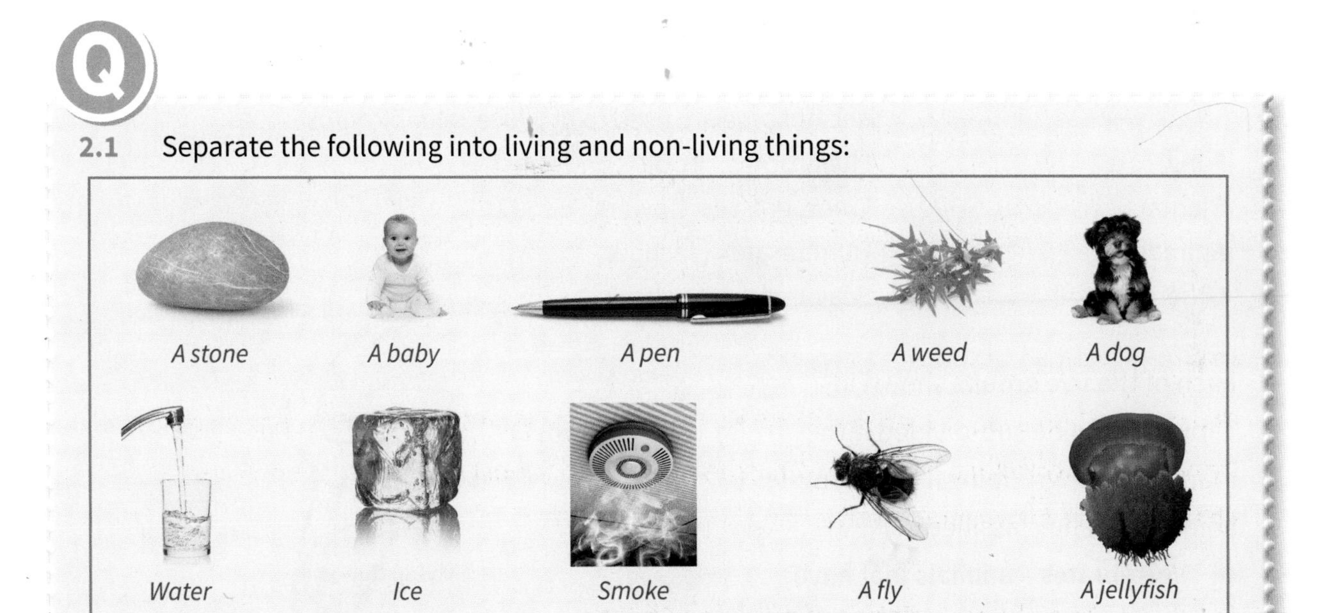

2.2 Why is it difficult to say whether an egg or a piece of fruit is living or non-living?

Some people claim that movement, growth and respiration (which is the **release of energy from food**) are also characteristics of living things. However, plants do not move (from place to place), animals continue growing throughout their lives but at a much slower pace, and the spores of bacteria can remain (be **dormant**) without the need for energy for long periods of time.

2.3 Find some other examples of living things that do not move, grow or get energy from food.

Different types of living things

To make it easier to find music on iTunes it is classified (or grouped) into headings, such as new releases or what's hot or compilations. In the same way living things are classified into groups. In general there are **five major groups** of living things, as shown in Table 2.2. For this book we will focus on plants and animals.

Table 2.2 **Groups of living things**

Group of living things	Examples
Bacteria	Tiny microscopic living things. Some cause disease, some cause decay, some are used to produce valuable substances
Fungi	Mushrooms, moulds and yeast
Plants	Trees, grasses, flowers
Animals	Humans, fish, insects
Others	Seaweeds, amoeba

Each of the five groups shown in Table 2.2 can be sub-divided into many smaller groupings. For example, animals can be classified as:

- **Vertebrates** – animals that have backbones, or
- **Invertebrates** – animals that do not have backbones.

Examples of vertebrates and invertebrates are shown in Table 2.3.

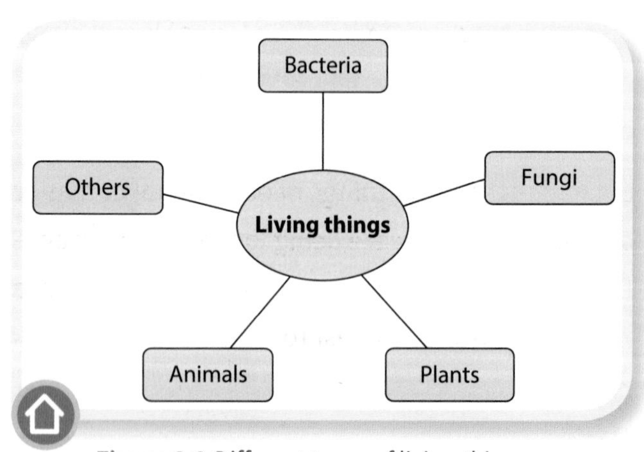

Figure 2.2 *Different types of living things*

Table 2.3 **Types of living things**

Vertebrates	Invertebrates
Horse	Spider
Seagull	Earthworm
Frog	Fly
Snake	Jellyfish

Figure 2.3 *Vertebrates are animals that have a backbone*

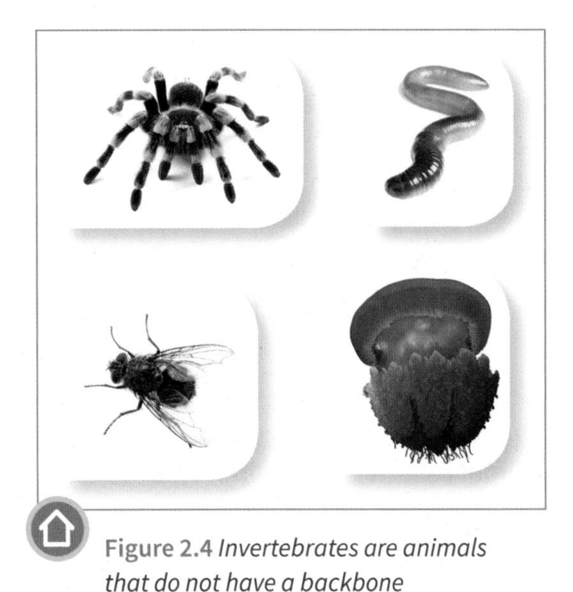

Figure 2.4 *Invertebrates are animals that do not have a backbone*

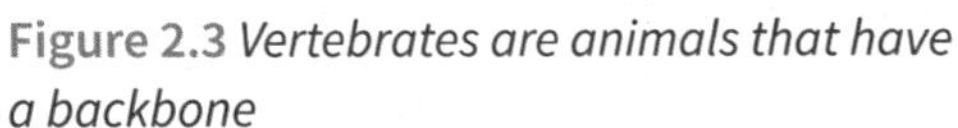

2.4 (a) Work in groups and name three plants and three animals with three, four, five and more than five letters in their name.

(b) Think of an animal in each case whose name starts with the letter *a*, then *b*, then *c*, and so on. How far along the alphabet can you go with your list?

2.5 Work in groups to answer the following questions.

(a) In what way might cars be classified? (For example, by price, by colour.)

(b) In what way might films or movies be classified?

Diversity of living things

There is a huge range (or **diversity**) of living things on Earth. For example, there are many different types of plants, birds, fish and insects. The range of living things is called **biodiversity**.

Each of these living things needs special conditions in which to grow. Unfortunately, many of these conditions are being lost due to human activities. For example:

- Woodlands are destroyed for housing and roads
- Forests are being lost to supply wood for building
- Lakes are destroyed by pollution.

The resulting loss of biodiversity will be examined in chapter 12.

2.6 What other negative impacts to the environment can you think of in addition to the above examples?

Cells

Living things are made of cells. Cells are the basic building blocks of all living things. Most cells are too small to be seen with the naked eye. They can be seen only using a microscope.

Cells can divide to form two cells. This is called **cell division**. Living things grow by cell division. For example, humans grow from a single cell (called a **zygote**) by cell division. As a result, an adult human has a hundred million million cells.

2.7 How many zeros are in a hundred million million?

Animal cells

Animal cells have three main parts:

- A cell membrane
- A nucleus
- Cytoplasm.

Did you know?

Eggs are single cells. An ostrich egg is the largest cell known.

Cell membrane

The cell membrane is a very thin layer that surrounds the cell. Its function (i.e. what it does) is to hold the cell contents in place and control what passes into and out of the cell. For example:

- Cell membranes that are around the cells in the brain allow painkillers to pass into the brain cells. Painkillers cannot pass into many other body cells.
- When we exercise, our muscle cells allow glucose and oxygen to pass in from our blood vessels to supply energy to the cells.
- Wastes can pass out into the blood through our membranes so that we can remove the waste from our bodies.

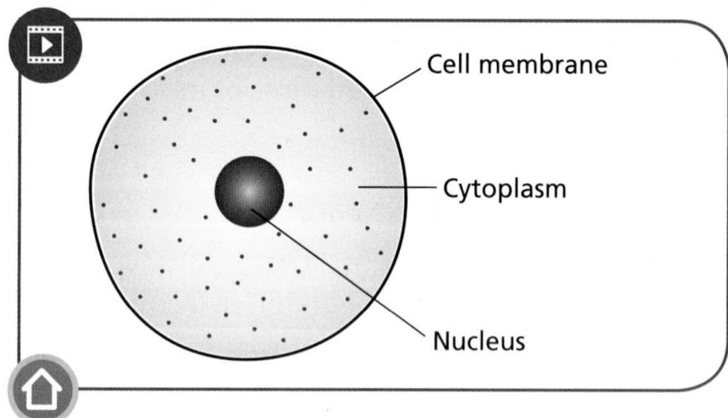

Figure 2.5 *A typical animal cell*

Nucleus

The nucleus is normally round. Its function is to act as the control centre of the cell.

The nucleus controls the cell by means of strands called **chromosomes**. Each chromosome has many genes. Each gene is made of DNA and controls one particular feature. These are the features that are passed on (or **inherited**) from parents to their children.

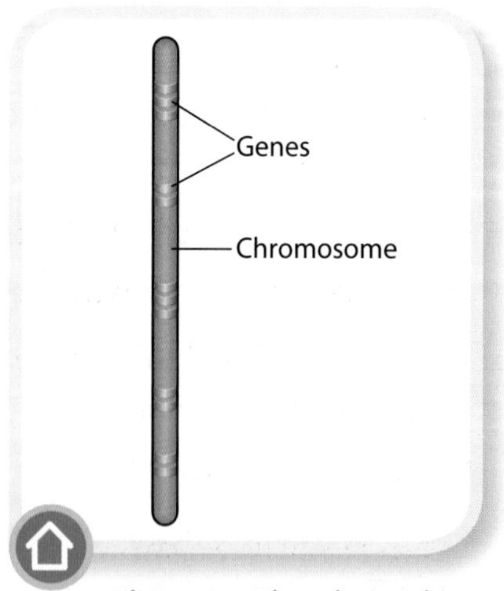

Figure 2.6 *The relationship between chromosomes and genes*

For example, humans have genes to control features such as eye colour, forming nails, height and the formation of fingers and toes.

2.8 Think of a new-born baby and list at least ten features that the baby inherits from its parents.

Did you know?

Human cells have forty-six chromosomes. These chromosomes contain around 20 000 genes.

Cytoplasm

Cytoplasm is a watery liquid found between the nucleus and the cell membrane. Its functions are to carry out some cell reactions and to support tiny cell structures.

These structures carry out many of the vital processes of the cell. They are too small to be seen using a light microscope. (We look at light microscopes later in this chapter.) One such structure is the **mitochondrion**. These tiny structures supply energy to the cell.

Figure 2.7 *Human cheek cells as seen through a light microscope*

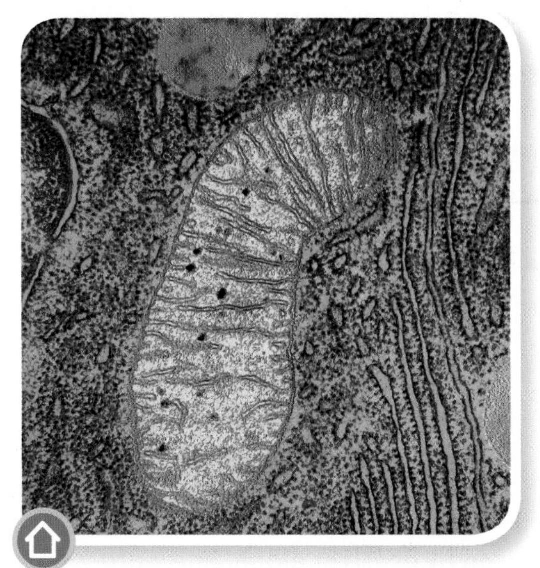

Figure 2.8 *The inside of a mitochondrion as seen under an electron microscope*

Plant cells

Plant cells have five main parts:

- A cell wall
- A cell membrane
- A nucleus
- Cytoplasm
- A vacuole.

Cell wall

A cell wall is found outside the cell membrane in plant cells. The function of the cell wall is to give strength to the plant cell. This is needed as plants, unlike many animals, do not have strong skeletons. The cell walls make plant cells stronger and less flexible than animal cells.

The material in cell walls is called **cellulose**. This forms everyday substances such as paper, cardboard and cotton.

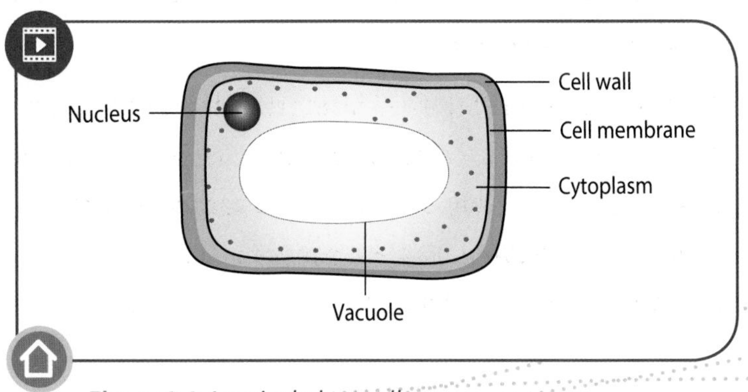

Figure 2.9 *A typical plant cell*

2.9 Why can animal cells (such as skin cells) be stretched, but plant cells (such as lettuce or cabbage leaves) cannot be stretched?

Cell membrane

Plant cell membranes are the same as animal cell membranes.

Nucleus

The nucleus of plant and animal cells is almost the same. However, the genes present in plant cells are different from those found in animal cells.

For example, plant cells have genes for features such as forming a cell wall and making the green chemical (**chlorophyll**) found in many plant cells.

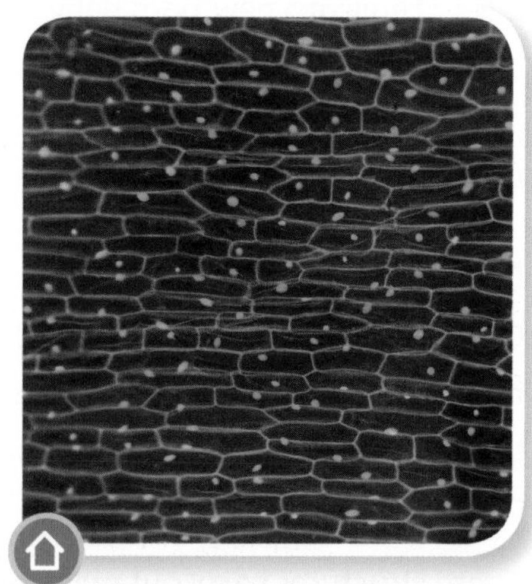

Figure 2.10 *Onion cells as seen using a light microscope*

Cytoplasm

The cytoplasm in plant cells is similar to cytoplasm in animal cells. However, plant cytoplasm may have tiny green structures (**chloroplasts**), which allow the plant to make its own food in a process called **photosynthesis**.

Vacuole

A vacuole contains liquid. If the vacuole is full of liquid it forces the cytoplasm out to push against the cell wall. In this way the function of the vacuole is to give strength to the cell. Normally vacuoles cannot be seen using a light microscope.

The light microscope

A microscope is used to view objects that are too small to be seen by eyesight alone. The word **magnification** means how many times larger the object appears to be when viewed under the microscope.

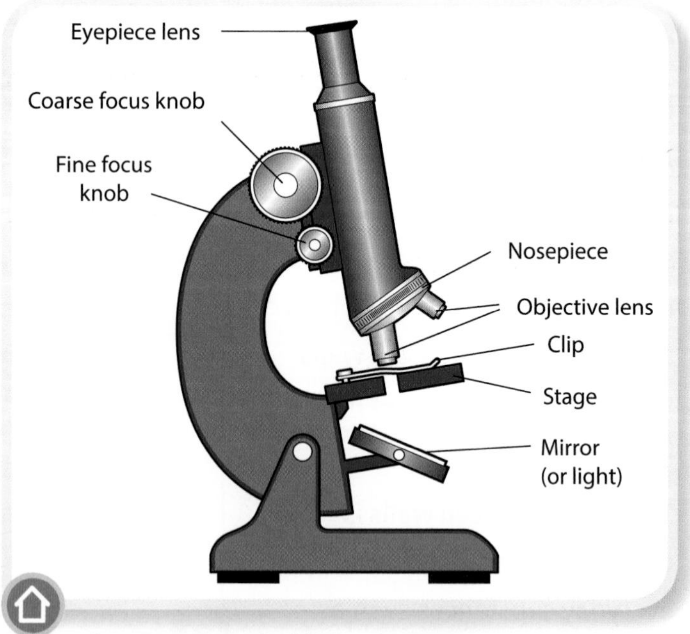

Figure 2.11 *A typical light microscope*

The parts of a microscope

Eyepiece lens

The eyepiece is the lens that is nearest to your eye. If it is marked × **10** it makes the object ten times larger (or it magnifies the object by ten).

Focus knobs

The **coarse** focus knob is used to see the image clearly at low magnification.

The **fine** focus knob is used for delicate focusing at high power.

Objective lens

Each objective lens has a different magnification.

The total magnification is found by multiplying the powers of the eyepiece and objective lenses being used.

Power of eyepiece × Power of objective lens = Total magnification

For example: An eyepiece marked × 10 and an objective lens marked × 20 will give a total magnification of × 200:

10 × 20 = 200

Nosepiece

The nosepiece can rotate to move the different objective lenses into position.

Stage

The stage is used to support the microscope slide. It has a hole in the centre to allow light to pass through.

Clips

The clips are used to hold the microscope slide in place.

Mirror or light

The mirror is used to reflect light from a lamp up through the object. Some microscopes have a lamp instead of a mirror.

Portfolio 19

BIOLOGICAL WORLD

Activity 2.1

Question

How can we examine animal cells?

Equipment needed

Cotton wool buds or wooden spatula (lollypop stick)

Microscope slide

Cover slip

Methylene blue stain

Pen or pencil or seeker

Tissue paper/filter paper

Microscope

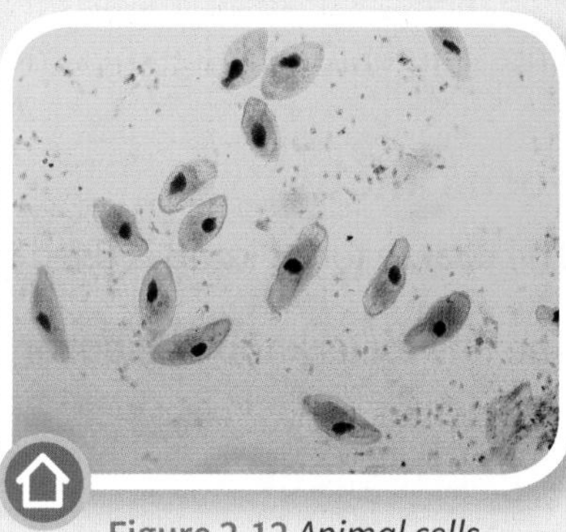

Figure 2.12 *Animal cells*

Safety

- Take care when placing the cover slip as it could break.
- Take care when using the focus knobs not to lower the objective lens onto the slide as it could crack it.

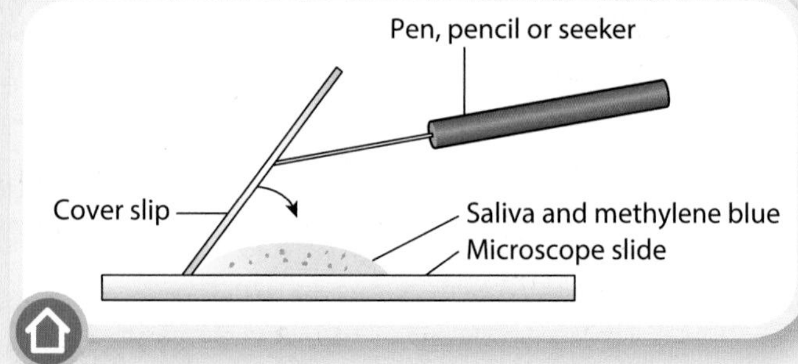

Figure 2.13 *Adding a cover slip to a microscope slide*

Conducting the activity

Preparing the slide

1. Gently scrape the inside of your mouth with the cotton wool bud (or the wooden spatula).
2. Scrape the saliva (which now contains many cheek cells) onto the centre of a microscope slide.
3. Add three or four drops of methylene blue stain to the saliva (this stain highlights parts of the cell, especially the nucleus).
4. Lower a cover slip gently at a 45 degree angle and slowly over the check cells as shown in Figure 2.14.
5. Use the tissue paper to soak up any of the stain that may be outside the cover slip.

Viewing the slide under a microscope

1. Switch on the microscope light (or adjust the mirror so that light is shining through the opening in the stage of the microscope).
2. Turn the nosepiece so that the lowest power objective lens is in place.
3. Place the slide in the centre of the microscope stage and use the clips to hold it in place.
4. Look at the stage from the side and turn the coarse focus knob so that the objective lens moves as close as possible to the slide. (Be careful not to damage the slide or the lens.)
5. Look through the eyepiece and turn the coarse focus knob *slowly* so that the cells become visible.
6. If necessary, move the slide slightly so that you can see the best sample of cells.
7. Draw a diagram of about ten of the cells that you can see. Label the three main parts of one of the cells.
8. Turn the nosepiece to a higher power lens.
9. Use the fine focus knob to get a clear image of one of the cells.

10. Draw this cell and label the three main parts.
11. Observe the cheek cells for features such as:
    - Are they all the same shape?
    - Are they all the same size?
    - What colour is the cytoplasm?
    - What colour is the nucleus?
    - Can you see any particles in the cytoplasm?

2.10 Answer these questions on microscopes.

(a) Give one benefit of using a microscope.

(b) Microscopes are good for examining thin structures (such as cheek cells) but are not good for thick structures.

- (i) Why is this?
- (ii) What colour will thick objects appear under the microscope?

(c) If the focus buttons on a microscope did not work, what problem would you have in viewing objects?

(d) Anton van Leeuwenhoek was a Dutchman who is credited with first using microscopes. In the 1670s he discovered tiny structures such as single-celled living things, cell vacuoles, sperm cells and the structure of muscle cells.

- (i) There was no electricity at the time, so what source of light would he have used?
- (ii) In what kind of cells did he discover vacuoles?

2.11 In 2010 an American businessman/scientist Craig Venter announced the creation of a new type of cell. His team took a bacterium, a virus and parts of other single-celled living things and combined them (and their DNA) to produce a single-celled organism. This organism was never present on Earth before and is an example of 'synthetic life'. He hopes that organisms such as this will be able to produce fuels, medicines and other useful products.

(a) What basic cell parts or structures do you think such synthetic cells would need?

(b) Which of the five groups of living things would they best fit?

(c) Suggest why Craig Venter would want to form a new type of life?

2.12 Some people argue that Craig Venter should not be allowed to form new life types. Can you suggest reasons why they feel this way?

CHAPTER 3

UNIT 2

Passing on characteristics

Learning outcomes

At the end of this chapter you will be able to:

- Describe asexual and sexual reproduction
- Explain characteristics and variation
- Explore patterns in inheritance and variation.

Keywords

asexual and sexual reproduction, gametes, zygote, fertilisation, characteristics, variation, DNA, dominant, recessive, genes, chromosomes

Reproduction

The formation of new living things is called reproduction. This is one of the characteristics of living things. There are two types of reproduction, asexual and sexual:

- **Asexual reproduction** is the formation of living things from one parent cell only.
- **Sexual reproduction** is the production of living things by combining cells from two parents.

Asexual reproduction

Asexual reproduction happens when one cell splits into two, or when one organism divides to form two or more living things. Asexual reproduction does not require sex cells to join together, i.e. it does not require fertilisation.

In asexual reproduction the offspring are identical to the parent cell.

3.1 Antibiotics are drugs that kill bacteria. Bacteria do not reproduce sexually. If you have a sore throat and the antibiotic is effective, why would you expect it to kill *all* the bacteria?

Examples of asexual reproduction

(a) Bacteria are single-celled organisms. When they divide they form two identical cells.

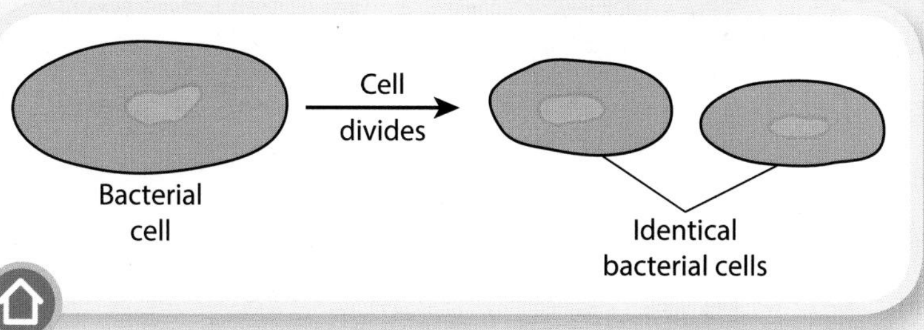

Figure 3.1 *Asexual cell division*

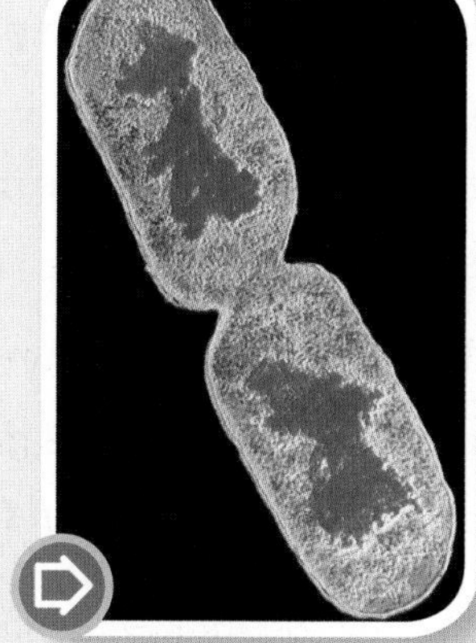

Figure 3.2 *A bacterium reproducing asexually*

(b) Strawberry (and buttercup) plants produce special stems (called **runners**), which grow overground from the base of the parent plant.

Some distance away from the parent plant, the runners form new plants, which are identical to the parent plant.

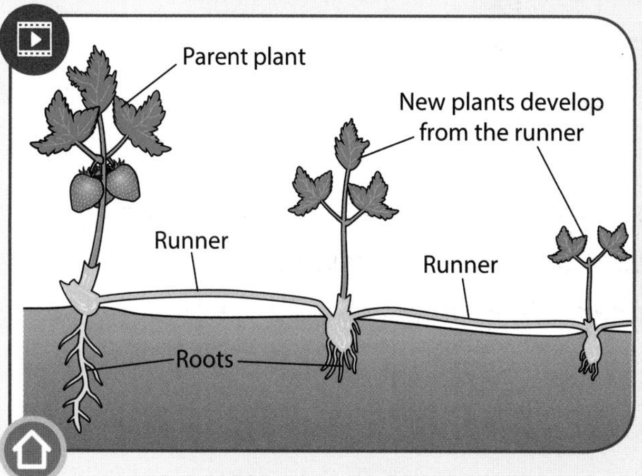

Figure 3.3 *Strawberry runners*

Figure 3.4 *Strawberry runners forming new plants*

Sexual reproduction

Sexual reproduction involves two sex cells (called **gametes**) joining together to form a single cell (called a **zygote**).

3.2 What are the names of the gametes found in humans?

BIOLOGICAL WORLD

The joining or fusion of sex cells is called **fertilisation**.

As a result of sexual reproduction the offspring formed have features or characteristics of both parents. This means the offspring are **not** identical to the parents. This is the main benefit of sexual reproduction.

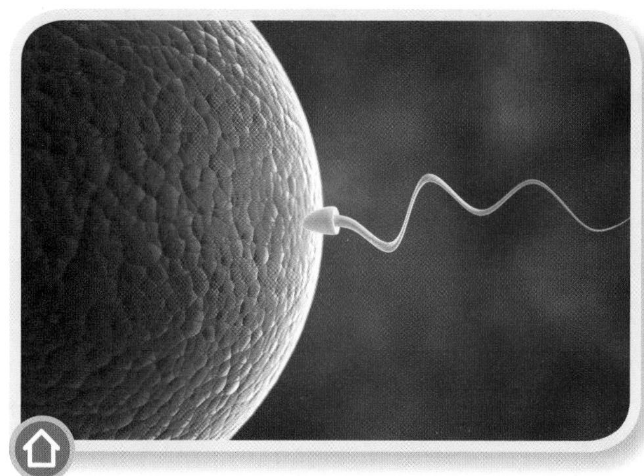

Figure 3.5 *A sperm fertilising an egg*

The most common way animals reproduce is by sexual reproduction (see chapter 11). Plants can reproduce sexually or asexually.

3.3 Would you expect bacteria to have gametes? Explain your answer.

3.4 Brothers (or sisters) may be very similar. However, they normally show some differences due to being formed by sexual reproduction. List five differences that are often visible between brothers or sisters.

3.5 What inherited differences might there be between dog pups from the same parents?

Passing on characteristics

Characteristics are traits or features of an organism that can be passed on from parents to their offspring. Characteristics are controlled by **genes** (which are found on chromosomes). Genes are passed from parents to their offspring during reproduction.

In asexual reproduction the parent passes **exact** copies of its genes to the offspring. This is why the offspring are genetically identical to the parent. For example, strawberries that reproduce by runners will taste, look and grow the same as the strawberries on the parent plant. In sexual reproduction the offspring have different genes.

Examples of characteristics

Humans have many genetically controlled characteristics. These include:

- Eye colour
- The presence or absence of freckles
- Having two eyes
- Having one heart
- The ability to roll the tongue.

Figure 3.6 *Tongue rolling is an inherited trait*

Plant characteristics controlled by genes include:

- Colour of the fruit
- Taste of the fruit
- Colour of the petals
- Height of the plants.

3.6 Discuss the following question in groups and then report back to the class. Growers often prefer fruit that has developed by asexual methods as it is more similar. What features might the grower prefer to be similar in the fruit?

3.7 Plants that reproduce asexually are often all killed by a new fungus infection. Explain why plants that reproduce sexually may not all be killed by a new fungus.

Variation

Humans have many characteristics in common. They have one heart, two eyes and the ability to produce chemicals such as saliva, sweat and hair.

However, humans also have some differences (or variation). There are two types of variations: genetic (or inherited) and non-inherited.

Genetic variation is passed on from parents to their children by genes. This means that genetic variation is inherited from the parents. For example eye colour, the length of our eyelashes and the presence or absence of freckles are all inherited from our parents.

Non-inherited variation is differences that are not controlled by genes. These variations do not pass from parents to their children. They have to be learned or practised. Examples of non-inherited variations are:

- Speaking a language
- Reading
- Texting
- Using a computer
- Tying a lace.

3.8 (a) Inherited variations are controlled by genes. Name the chemical of which genes are made?

(b) In what part of the cell is this chemical normally found?

3.9 Why is the ability to ride a bicycle or play a musical instrument not considered to be genetic variation?

Activity 3.1

Question

How can we investigate some inherited traits?

Note

It is difficult to find human traits that are clearly of one form or another. Most of the following traits are thought to be controlled by single genes. However, it may be difficult to judge some of the following features and put them into a particular category.

Conducting the activity

1. Answer the following questions and tick the boxes on a chart such as the one below to describe yourself. You should work in pairs so you can examine and discuss each other's traits.
   - (a) Have you attached earlobes (do your earlobes attach directly to the side of your head) or detached earlobes (where the earlobes are not attached to the side of your head)?
   - (b) Can you roll your tongue at the sides to form a tube shape or not (as in Figure 3.6)?
   - (c) Have you dimples in your cheeks or no dimples?
   - (d) Are you left-handed or right-handed?
   - (e) Have you freckles or no freckles?
   - (f) Have you naturally curly or straight hair?
   - (g) When you join your hands together by inter-locking your fingers is your left thumb or right thumb on top?
   - (h) Does your hairline form a point at the centre of your forehead (called a widow's peak) or have you a straight hairline?

Trait	Individual results Tick the correct row	Class result totals
Attached earlobes		
Detached earlobes		
Tongue roller		
Not a tongue roller		
Dimples		
No dimples		
Left-handed		
Right-handed		

Freckles		
No freckles		
Curly hair		
Straight hair		
Left thumb on top		
Right thumb on top		
Pointed hairline		
Straight hairline		

2. Combine all the results from your class and put the total number showing each trait into the table.
3. Of the pairs of traits investigated:
   (a) Which trait was the most common?
   (b) Which trait was closest to a 50:50 ratio?

Chromosomes and genes

Chromosomes are thread-like structures found in the nucleus of each plant and animal cell. Most of the time chromosomes cannot be seen in a nucleus because they are stretched out into extremely long, thin threads.

When cells divide, the chromosomes become shorter and thicker and can be seen using microscopes. At this time each chromosome looks like a tiny, thin thread. Chromosomes are made of a chemical called DNA (**deoxyribonucleic acid**) and protein.

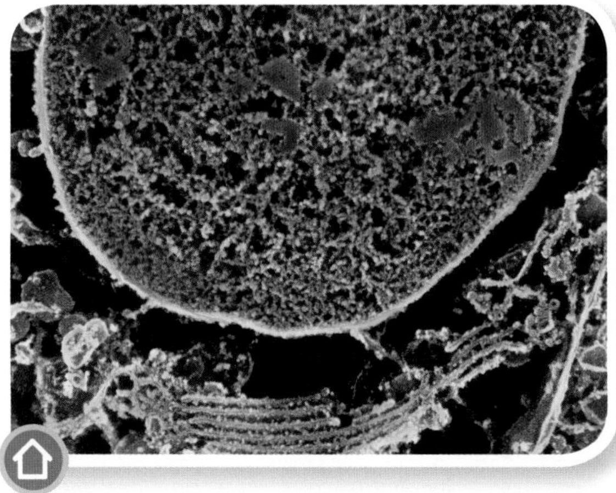

Figure 3.7 *Pink chromosomes in a normal cell*

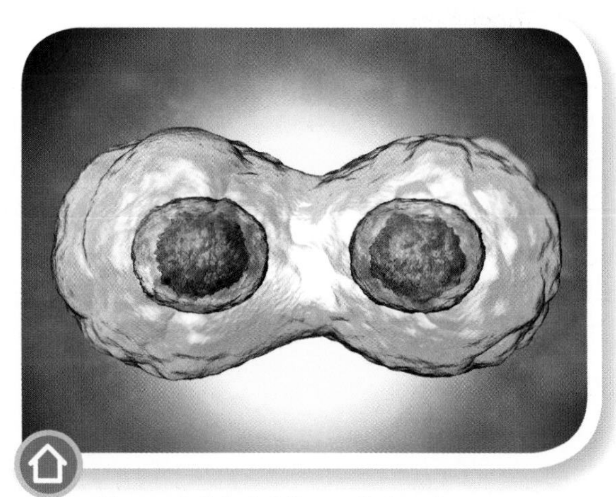

Figure 3.8 *A dividing cell showing chromosomes*

Genes are short sections of DNA located on chromosomes. Genes control the production of inherited characteristics. Examples of human genes include:

- The gene to make acid in our stomach
- The gene to make the coloured chemical in our eyes.

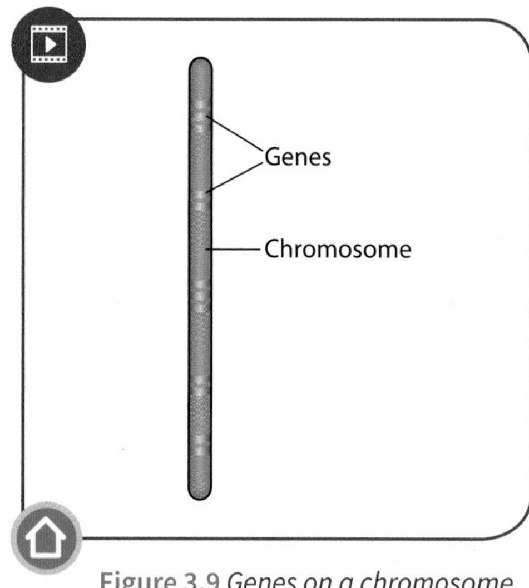

Figure 3.9 *Genes on a chromosome*

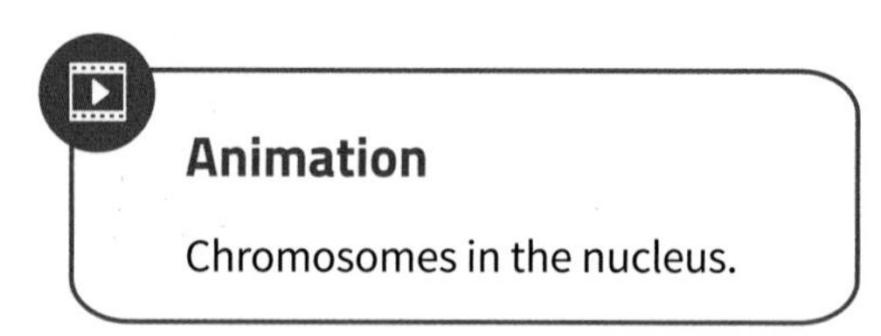

Patterns of inheritance

The inheritance of genetic characteristics often follows a pattern. This is because of the way in which genes may be inherited from each parent. The pattern of inheritance is best understood by following the outcomes of sample genetic crosses.

Introduction to genetic crosses

Eye colour in humans is controlled by a gene. The gene has two versions:

- The **dominant** version represented as **B** causes brown eyes
- The non-dominant version (also called the **recessive** version) represented as **b** causes blue eyes.

This information is often represented as:

- B = brown eyes (dominant)
- b = blue eyes (recessive).

Normally the first letter of the dominant version is used, e.g. for brown eyes, B is used.

The dominant version prevents the non-dominant version of the gene from working.

Each person has two copies of the gene. This means they may have the following combinations:

Gene versions	Eye colour
BB	Brown eyes
Bb	Brown eyes
bb	Blue eyes

In sexual reproduction the number of genes is halved in the production of sperms and eggs. This means the gametes (or **sex cells** or **sperms and eggs**) each contain only one version of the gene.

A person with the combination ...	Will produce gametes (or sex cells) with ...
BB	a single B
Bb	either B or b
bb	a single b

Genetic crosses

Examples of how you can determine the likelihood of a particular genetic variation in the offspring of a family are given in the following crosses.

Cross 1

Question

Show the pattern in eye colour of a family where one parent is BB and the second parent is bb.

Answer

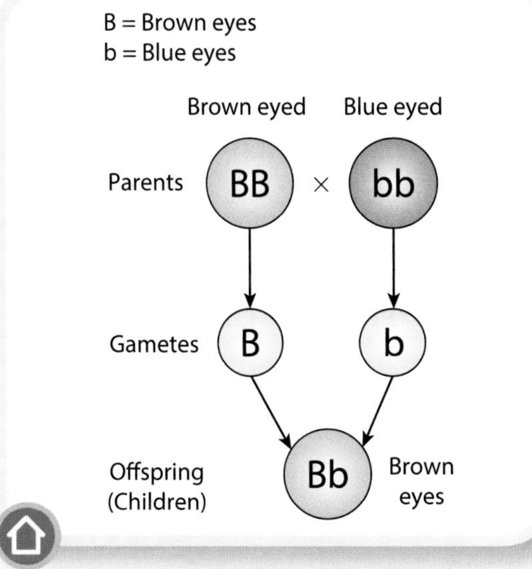

Figure 3.10 *Genetic cross – eye colour*

In this case all the children will have brown eyes.

Cross 2

Question

Show the pattern of inheritance in eye colour in the following family. A brown-eyed parent who is Bb and a blue-eyed parent.

Answer

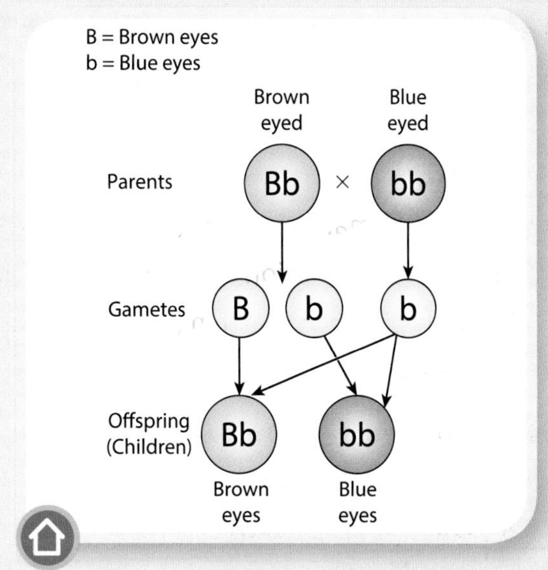

Figure 3.11 *Genetic cross – eye colour*

This cross can also be shown using a Punnett square:

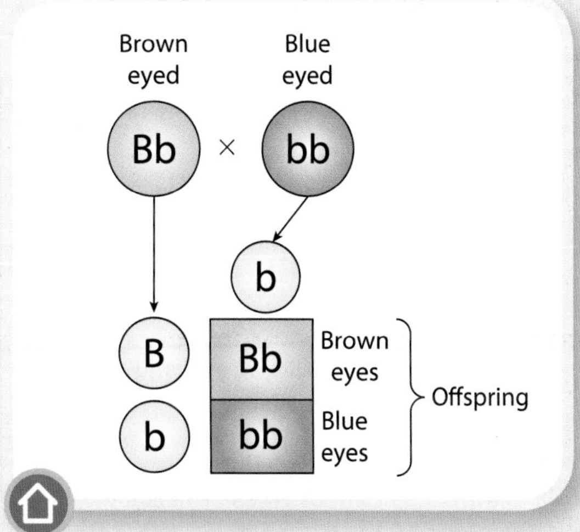

Figure 3.12 *Genetic cross – eye colour*

In this cross there is an equal chance of a brown-eyed or a blue-eyed child. In other words there is a 50% (or 1 in 2) chance of a brown-eyed or a blue-eyed child.

Cross 3

Question

Show by diagrams the pattern of inheritance in eye colour for a family where both parents are brown-eyed (Bb). From the cross predict the percentage chance of the couple having a blue-eyed child.

Answer

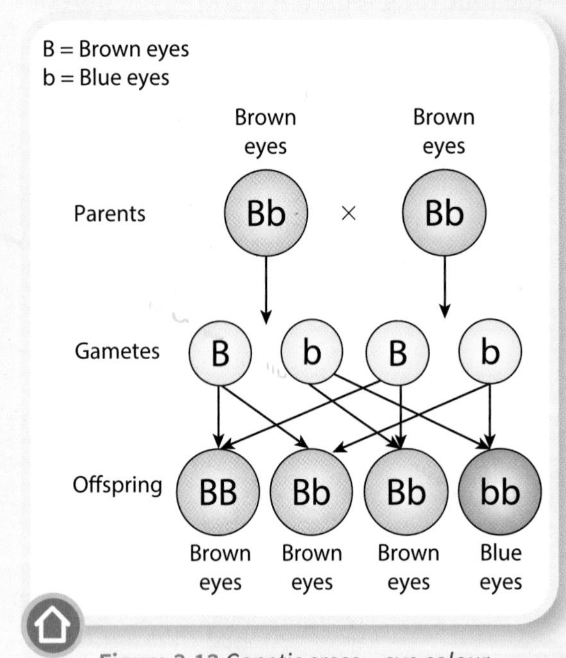

Figure 3.13 *Genetic cross – eye colour*

This cross can also be shown as:

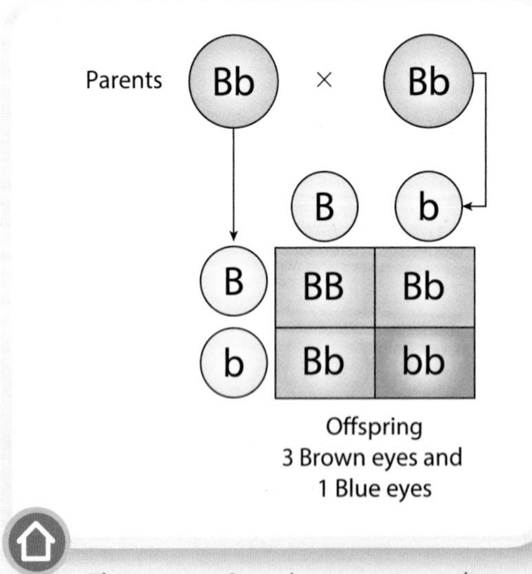

Figure 3.14 *Genetic cross – eye colour*

In this cross there is a 25% (or 1 in 4) chance of the couple having a blue-eyed child.

Cross 4

Question

Freckles are caused by the dominant version of a gene (F). Lack of freckles is caused by the non-dominant (or recessive) version of the gene (f).

(a) Which two of the following genetic combinations could a person with freckles have?

(b) What genetic combination must a person with no freckles have?

(c) If a couple are both Ff, what is the chance of them having a child with freckles? Explain your answer by showing the genetic cross.

Answer

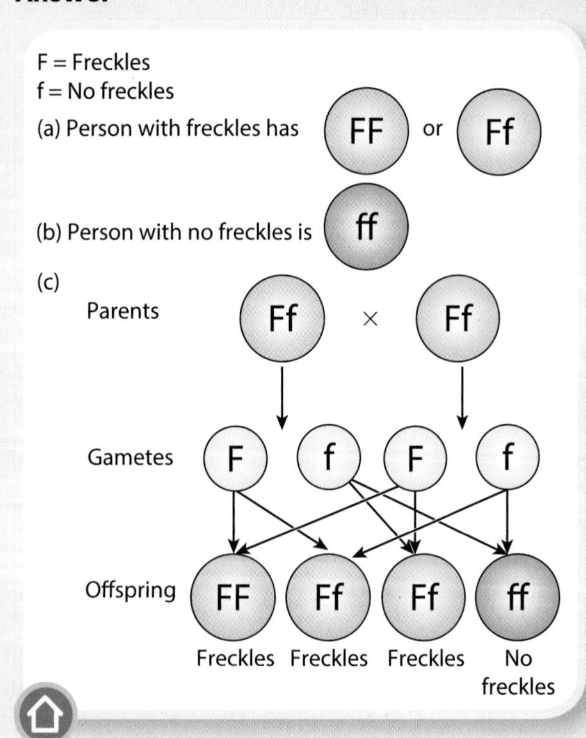

Figure 3.15 *Genetic cross – freckles*

The chance of this couple having a child with freckles is 75% (or 3:1).

The same result would be obtained if this cross was written as a Punnett square.

Cross 5

Question

Full lips (B) are dominant to thin lips (b).
A couple, one with full lips and the other with thin lips, have two children. One of the children has full lips and the other has thin lips.

(a) What are the two possible genetic combinations of a person with full lips?

(b) Only one genetic combination produces thin lips. What is this combination?

(c) Show by diagrams how the pattern of inheritance of the couple and their children could occur.

Answer

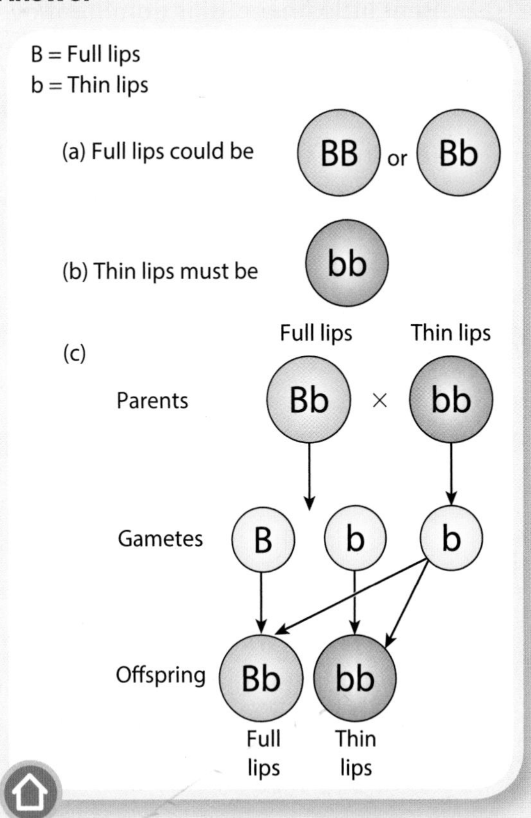

Figure 3.16 *Genetic cross – full lips and thin lips*

3.10 Hitchhiker's thumb refers to the shape of our thumb when we make a fist and extend our thumb into the air. A straight thumb (S) is dominant to a bent thumb (s).

(a) Show the following crosses using diagrams.

(b) For each cross, state the percentage chance of a child with a straight thumb.

(i) 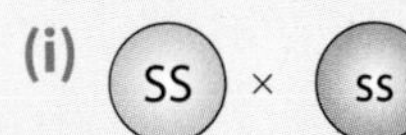

(ii) 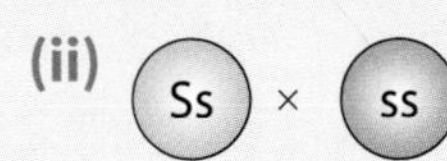

(iii) 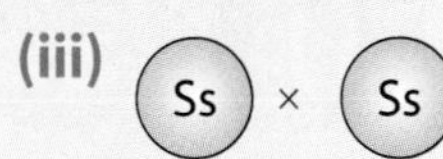

3.11 Gregor Mendel (who is known as the father of genetics) found that in a type of plant red flowers (R) were dominant over white flowers (r). He crossed two red-flowered plants and collected their seeds. He planted the seeds and noticed that most of the offspring plants had red flowers, but some had white flowers.

(a) What was the genetic combination of the plants with white flowers?

(b) If both the parent plants had red flowers but they produced a plant with white flowers, the parents must both have had the same genetic combination. What was the genetic combination of both the parents?

(c) Show this cross using diagrams.

3.12 Bent little finger (B) is dominant over straight little finger (b). A man has the genetic combination Bb and his wife is bb.

(a) What is the shape of the little finger of each person?

(b) Show this cross by means of a diagram and predict the percentage chance of them having a child with bent little fingers.

3.13 Curly hair (C) is dominant to straight hair (c).

(a) Using your knowledge of genes, explain why more people have curly hair than straight hair.

(b) In a family, one parent is CC while the second parent is cc.

(i) What type of hair has each parent?

(ii) What is the chance that their next child will have curly hair? Draw a genetic cross diagram to explain your answer.

3.14 Dimples (D) are dominant to lack of dimples (d). If the parents have the combinations Dd and dd and they have four children, how many of the children do you expect to have dimples? Explain your answer by showing the genetic cross.

3.15 Gregor Mendel is the person who first discovered how the process of genetic inheritance works. Write a biography (life history) of Mendel to include:

- Dates of birth and death
- His nationality
- His background
- Where he lived and worked
- The value of his discoveries.

CHAPTER 4

UNIT 2

The origins of living things

Learning outcomes

At the end of this chapter you will be able to:

- Outline the process of evolution by natural selection
- Explain how evolution leads to the diversity of living things.

Keywords

biodiversity · fossil · extinct · species · natural selection · mutation · evolution · adaptation

Introduction

There is a rich **biodiversity** on Earth. This means there are many different types of living things. Humans have often wondered where all these types of life came from. Were they always present on Earth? Will they always be here?

Evidence from **fossils** (which are the remains of very ancient living things) tells us that some types of living things have been wiped out.

But there are no very old remains of some modern living things.

This suggests that some living things disappear (become **extinct**) and new types of living things emerge, i.e. that life on Earth changes.

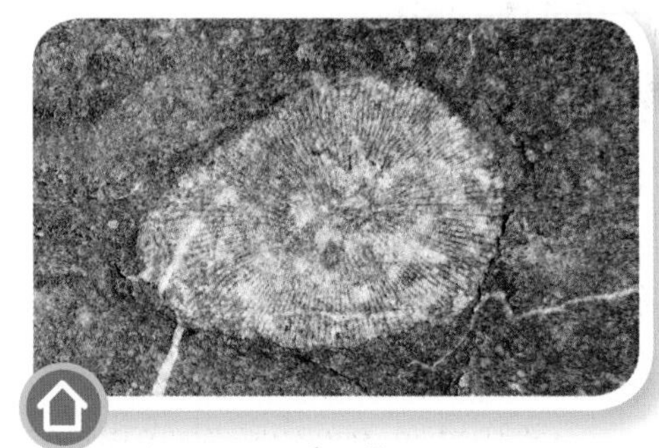

Figure 4.1 *A fossil*

4.1 Name two types of living things that were on Earth but are no longer present (i.e. they are now extinct).

4.2 Name two extinct animal species from Ireland.

4.3 Research how long ago modern humans are thought to have arisen.

Charles Darwin

There are a number of suggestions as to how the variety of living things may have arisen. However, the most widely accepted explanation based on evidence is the **theory of evolution by natural selection**. This theory was first put forward by Charles Darwin (in association with Alfred Russel Wallace) in 1859.

4.4 Write a short biography of Charles Darwin. Include a couple of sentences on each of the following:

- His childhood
- His studies
- The famous ship journey he took
- The islands off South America that he visited
- His health.

Figure 4.2 *Charles Darwin, aged 40*

Animated Scientist Biography

Watch an *Exploring Science* animation to find out more about Darwin and his theories.

Evolution by natural selection

Evolution is the process by which different kinds of living things develop from earlier forms during the history of Earth. Before we look at Darwin's theory of evolution, we need to look at a couple of important terms: species and mutation.

Species

A species is a group of living things that can reproduce together to produce offspring which themselves can reproduce. For example, humans are a species; dogs are a species; so are daffodils, cabbages, cats and rabbits.

A cat and a rabbit cannot reproduce together and so you know they are *different* species.

The members of a species have similar genes and so they have many characteristics in common. However, the members of a species may show variations that are inherited because they are caused by changed genes.

4.5 A cocker spaniel and a poodle can breed together to produce a cockapoo (a 'designer' dog). A poodle and a cat cannot breed together. What does this tell you about:

(a) Cocker spaniels and poodles?

(b) Poodles and cats?

4.6 Name two other 'designer' dogs that humans have developed.

Mutation

We know that characteristics of an organism are controlled by genes and that genes are passed from parents to their offspring during reproduction.

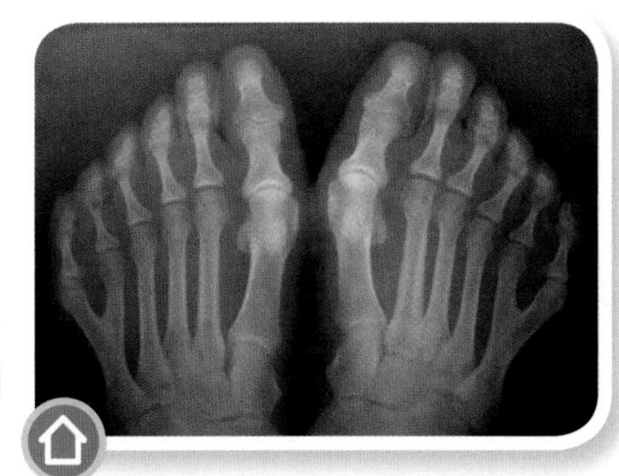

Figure 4.3 *Most humans have five toes: if the gene is altered the person may have extra toes*

Changes in genes are called **mutations**. The genes in the members of a species are different due to mutations and due to events that occur in sexual reproduction.

For example, while humans are similar in having two eyes, they show variations in eye shape and eye colour. These variations are passed on to the next generation because they are inherited or gene-controlled variations.

Theory of evolution

Darwin's theory of evolution is based on three things he noticed (called **observations**) and from these he made two predictions (called **conclusions**).

Figure 4.4 *Theory of evolution of the human*

Darwin's theory of evolution

Observation 1

Living things produce huge numbers of offspring.

For example, a tree may produce thousands of seeds, or a fly may lay thousands of eggs.

Figure 4.5 *A tree can produce thousands of seeds*

Observation 2

The environment (or surroundings) can support only a limited number of living things.

For example, there is not enough space for all the seeds to grow or there may not be enough food for all the flies to live.

Observations 1 and 2 lead to conclusion 1 below.

Conclusion 1

If more living things are produced than can survive, they will struggle to get scarce resources. Darwin called this the **struggle for existence**. It is now often called **competition for scarce resources**.

For example, seeds may struggle to get enough space and light to grow; the flies may struggle for food and water.

BIOLOGICAL WORLD

Observation 3

Darwin studied animals such as pet pigeons and cows on farms. Also, on his voyage around the world he noticed that species showed **inherited variations.** He realised that species could have differences that they would pass on to their offspring.

Observation 3 leads to conclusion 2 below.

Figure 4.6 *Variations in pet pigeons*

Conclusion 2

Suitable variations

Darwin realised that some of the variations would help the living thing to survive better.

For example, if some seeds produced longer or bigger roots, those seeds would grow better; if the wings of some flies developed more quickly, they could fly away to get more food.

An **adaptation** is a characteristic that helps an organism to survive and reproduce. Living things that are best suited or adapted to their environment survive more easily. If they survive, they have a better chance of reproducing and so passing on their genes (and their suitable variations) to the following generations.

Unsuitable variations

However, some variations do not help living things to survive better. These living things are not adapted to their environment and so may die. This means they do not pass their genes (and unsuited variations) on to the next generations.

Natural selection

The way in which organisms whose variations are suited to their environment survive and reproduce is called **natural selection**. Nature selects those organisms that are best suited (or adapted) to their environment.

Table 4.1 Summary of the theory of evolution by natural selection

Observation	Conclusion
1 Living things produce large numbers of offspring 2 The environment can support only a limited number of living things	1 Living things struggle to survive
3 The members of a species have inherited (genetic) variations	2 Nature selects the organisms with variations that help them to live in the environment These organisms survive and reproduce to pass on their genes and their variations

4.7 Find out three major adaptations that have allowed humans to survive in their environment.

Did you know?

Some people believe that Darwin's theory of evolution was the greatest single idea that any human ever had.

4.8 Read about the changes in peppered moths and then answer the questions that follow.

Before the Industrial Revolution (which began around 1780) most of the peppered moths in the north of England were light coloured. This meant they were hard to see on the light-coloured barks of the lichen (a fungus combined with an algae) covered trees. During the Industrial Revolution, for the first time a huge amount of pollution was emitted. This killed off most of the lichens. The barks of the bare trees were now dark coloured. By the 1860s most of the moths were dark coloured.

After more recent pollution control measures were put in place, the lichens grew back on the barks of the trees.

In summary:

Timescale	Moth colour
Before 1780	Light
1780 to 1860	Some light, some dark
After 1860	Mostly dark
Now	?

Figure 4.7 *The light-coloured moth is hard to see on the lichen-covered tree*

Figure 4.8 *The light-coloured moth is very visible on the tree with no lichens*

Now answer questions (a)–(e), based on the information above.

(a) What was the evolutionary change that took place in the moths between 1780 and 1860?

(b) What was the cause of this change?

(c) What might have happened to any light-coloured moths in the late 1800s?

(d) Predict the colour of the moths in recent years. Give a reason for your answer.

(e) Explain how the changes in the moths provide evidence for the theory of evolution by natural selection.

Evolution and the diversity of life

Evolution by natural selection has given rise to all of the different types of living things on Earth today. This happens when a single species evolves to form two (or more) different species. These two species then evolve to form even more species. In time huge numbers of species develop from the original species.

New species

As an example of how new species form, consider the finches on the Galapagos Islands. Darwin studied these birds on his voyage on the *Beagle*. He noticed that the finches on the different islands were similar in many ways, but they showed differences in many features, especially their beak shapes.

Did you know?

Galapago is the Spanish word for tortoise.

Figure 4.9 *Finches*

Darwin concluded that the original finches must have got to the islands from the mainland of South America. On each island the conditions were different. This meant that:

- Where hard seeds were available, those birds with short, strong beaks were better suited to feeding.
- If there were many insects, birds with sharper and more slender beaks were better suited to feeding.
- On an island with many cactus plants, finches with long, pointed beaks were better suited to getting cactus seeds.

On each island those finches that had a beak that was not well suited to feeding on that island got less food. As a result they died out. Those birds with the beaks that were most suited to getting the available food survived. When they reproduced they passed on their beak shape to the next generation.

Darwin concluded that from a single species of finch that flew (or was blown) in from the mainland, many different types of finch evolved. The new beak shapes arose when genes became altered or mutated.

This type of process has happened all over the world to different living things over very long periods of time to produce the wide range of living things found on Earth today.

Did you know?

Over 99% of all species that ever existed have become extinct.

4.9 Research the following:

(a) What country is nearest the Galapagos islands?

(b) How far is this country from the Galapagos islands?

(c) Suggest why the finches did not evolve into as many species in their country of origin.

4.10 Read this information on the evolution of Galapagos tortoises and then answer the questions that follow.

On one of the Galapagos Islands Darwin noticed that most of the giant tortoises had shells with low neck collars. However, he noticed a few tortoises with higher neck collars. All the tortoises feed on plants.

Darwin predicted that in the future (possibly as a result of a long period with no rain) the tortoises with high neck collars would survive better. Over the last hundred or more years the tortoises with low neck collars have become extinct on that island, but many of those with high neck collars have survived.

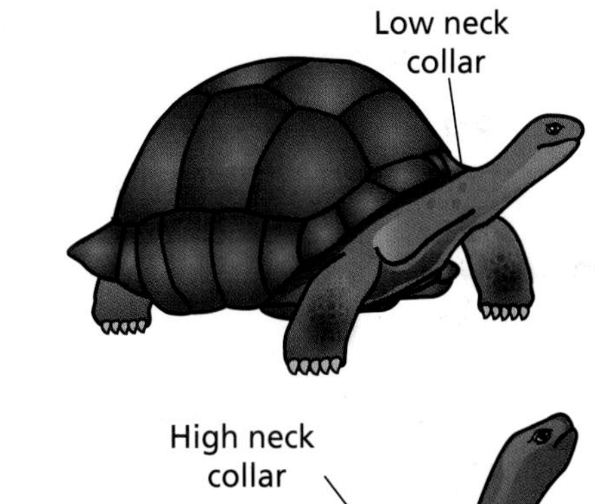

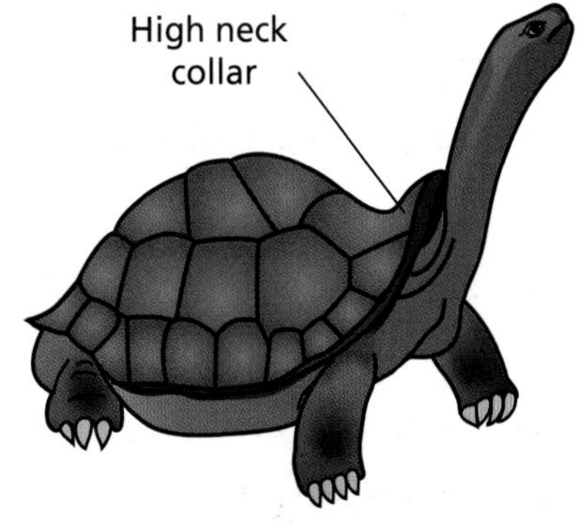

Figure 4.10 *Two tortoises*

(a) How would a lack of rain affect the number of plants on the island?

(b) What advantage might a high neck collar provide for a tortoise in drier conditions?

(c) Apply your knowledge of the theory of evolution to explain why tortoises with high neck collars survived and those with low neck collars died out.

4.11 'Living things that do not reproduce are an evolutionary dead end.' Explain why this is the case.

Work with one partner for this question.

4.12 David and Amanda wanted their future children to be big and strong. So they went to the gym every day for a year and developed really big, strong muscles so that their children would inherit big, strong muscles.

Discuss this with your partner. Do you think their children would have big, strong muscles as a result of their parents' working out in the gym? Explain your answer.

BIOLOGICAL WORLD

Timeline for biodiversity

The planet Earth formed about 4.6 billion years ago. The first forms of life on Earth appeared about 3.8 billion years ago. They were tiny, single-celled bacteria that lived in the sea. For about 90% of Earth's history, living things were found only in the sea or in watery environments.

About 500 million years ago the first plants and fungi grew on land. It is only since then that all the modern life forms have developed. For example, dinosaurs first appeared about 220 million years ago, birds 140 million years ago, and humans only 200 000 years ago.

The examples given show that evolution normally takes place over long periods of time.

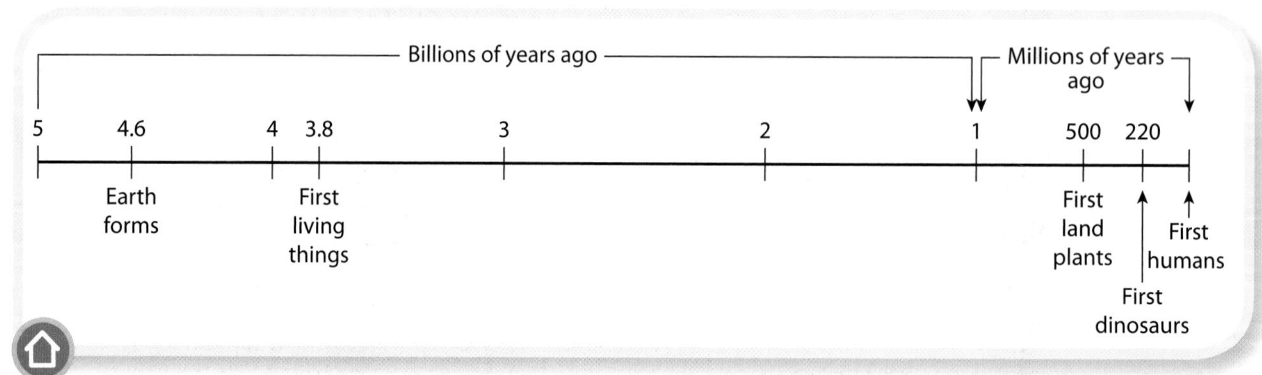

Figure 4.11 *A simple timeline for evolution*

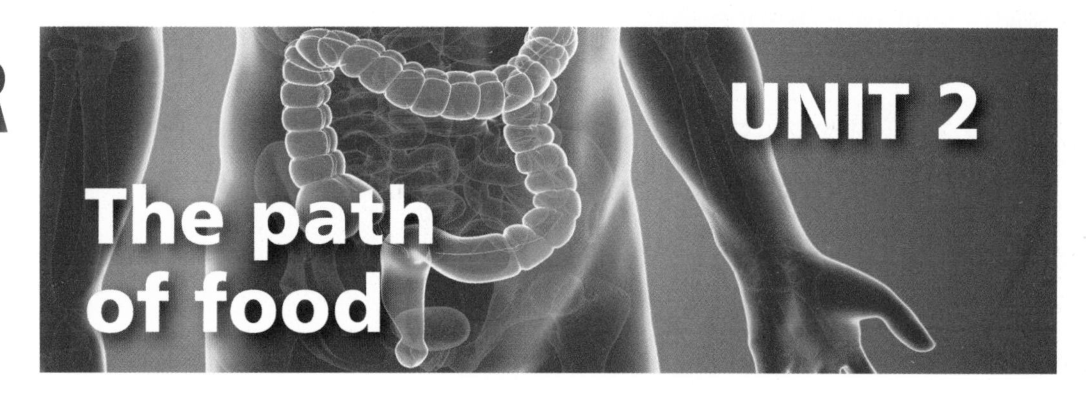

CHAPTER 5

The path of food

UNIT 2

Learning outcomes

At the end of this chapter you will be able to:

- Describe the structure of the organs of the digestive system
- Describe the functions of the organs of the digestive system.

Introduction

The digestive system is a tube that runs from the mouth to the anus. Food is one of our most basic needs. Our digestive system allows us to convert food into a form that the body can use easily.

Digestion is the **breakdown of food**. Our digestive system breaks our food into smaller molecules. These molecules can then pass from our intestines into our blood.

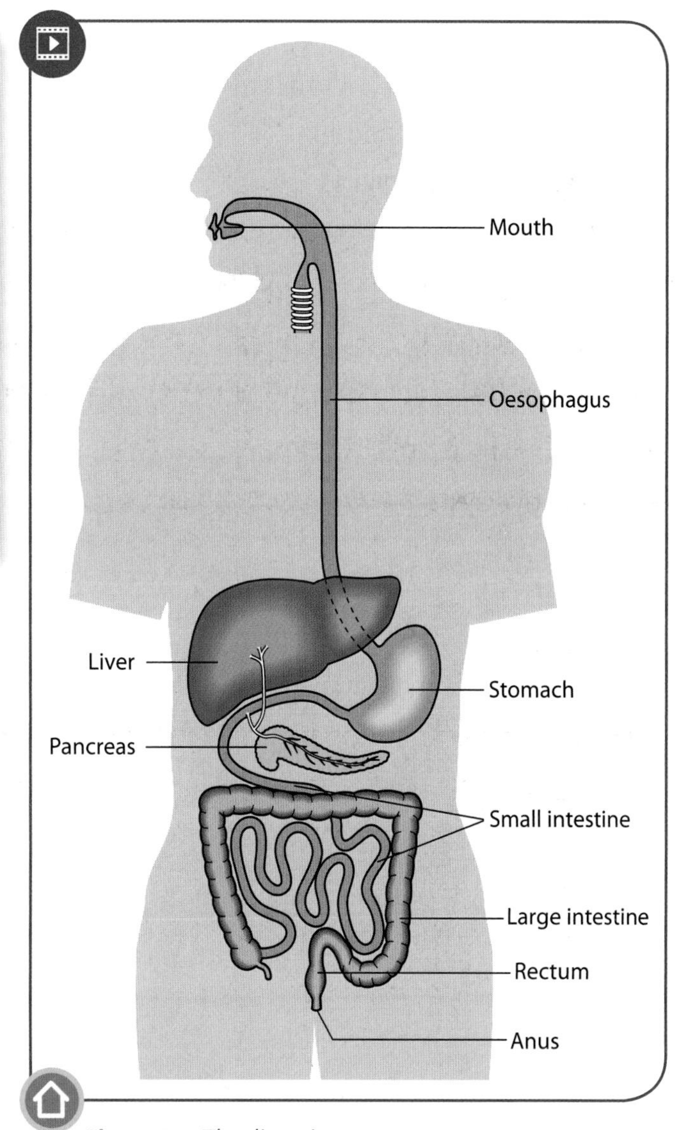

Figure 5.1 *The digestive system*

The blood carries the food molecules to all parts of the body. Any food that does not pass into our blood is removed from our bodies as waste called **faeces**.

Most humans are between 1.5 and 2 metres tall. Our digestive system is up to 9 metres long.

5.1 How do you think such a long tube can fit into a person's body?

5.2 What problem might this arrangement cause for the movement of food through our digestive system?

The functions of the parts of the digestive system

Mouth

The function of the mouth is to take in and digest or break down food. Two types of digestion take place in the mouth:

- Physical digestion
- Chemical digestion.

What is physical digestion?

Physical digestion is the breakdown of food using mechanical or physical methods.
An example of this occurs in the mouth when the teeth cut and chew food into smaller pieces. The smaller pieces of food can be more easily broken down later in the rest of the digestive system.

Teeth

There are four types of teeth in the adult human jaw. The sequence of the teeth from the front to the back of the jaw is given in Table 5.1.

Table 5.1 Teeth in an adult human jaw

Teeth – from the front to the back of the jaw	Appearance and function
Incisors	Sharp edges, like a chisel Used to cut, slice and nibble food
Canines	Long and pointed Used to grip and tear food
Premolars	Large with flat surfaces Used for chewing, crushing and grinding food
Molars	Larger than premolars Used for chewing, crushing and grinding food

5.3 We are advised to chew food many times before swallowing it.
(a) Why might this be important?
(b) What problems might arise for a person who does not chew food thoroughly?

5.4 If a person loses most of their premolar and molar teeth, what problem would they have?

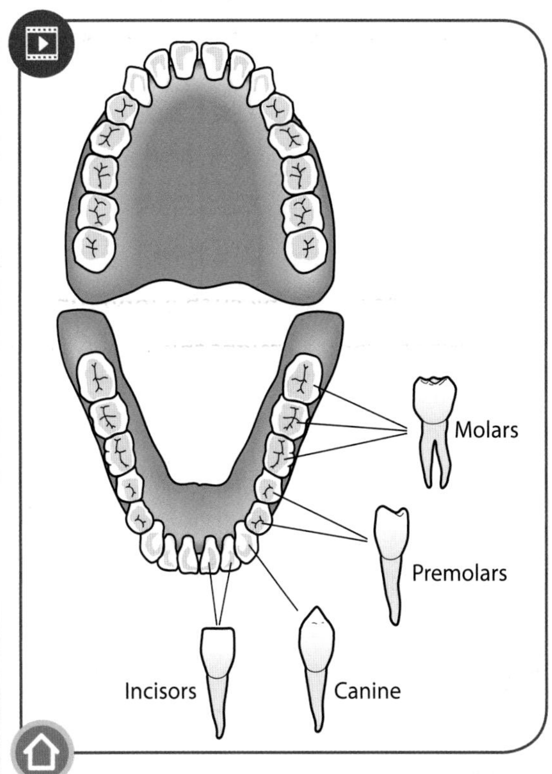

Figure 5.2 *The location and types of teeth in the human jaw*

5.5 Some animals have large incisors and others have large canine teeth. Name one animal in each case and find out why they have such teeth.

What is chemical digestion?

Chemical digestion is the breakdown of food using **enzymes** (or hydrochloric acid in the stomach). We will examine different kinds of food in chapter 9.

An enzyme is a chemical (made of protein) produced by the body that speeds up chemical reactions in the body without the enzyme being used up.

Scientists call substances that speed up reactions **catalysts**. Enzymes are called **biological catalysts**.

Salivary glands are located in the cheeks and under the tongue. They produce liquid called **saliva**. Saliva helps to soften and moisten food.

5.6 Why do we need to soften and moisten food before we swallow it?

Saliva also contains an enzyme called (salivary) **amylase**.

Amylase breaks down starch and turns it into a simple sugar called **maltose**. Our digestive system produces many enzymes, each one breaking down a different type of food.

$$\text{starch} \xrightarrow{\text{amylase}} \text{maltose}$$

Did you know?

Many washing powders and detergents contain enzymes to break down food stains in a short space of time and at a very low temperature.

BIOLOGICAL WORLD

Oesophagus

The oesophagus or **food pipe** is a muscular tube. It forces food down from the mouth to the stomach using a wave of muscular action (called **peristalsis**). This muscular action is stimulated by **fibre** (also called **roughage**) in our diet.

Fibre is material that is not broken down or digested by enzymes in our digestive system. Good examples of fibre include:

- Fruit
- Vegetable
- Cereal grain
- Brown bread
- Muesli
- Porridge.

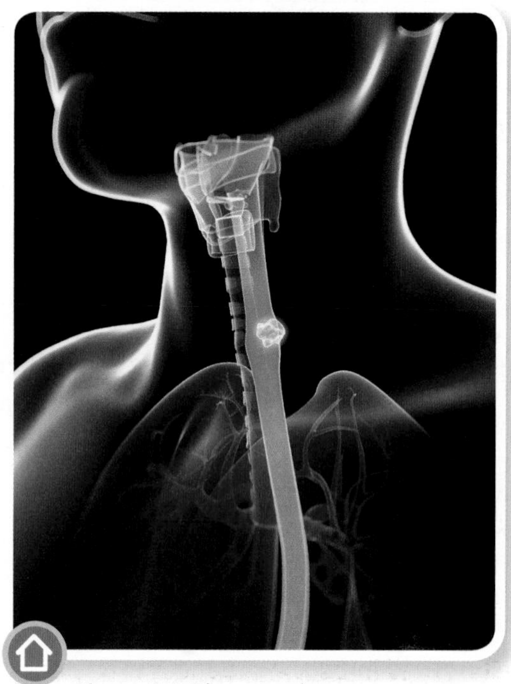

Figure 5.3 *The oesophagus*

5.7 We are told we should eat between five and seven portions of fruit and vegetable every day. Find out:

(a) How big a portion should be.

(b) What the benefits are of eating so much fruit and vegetables.

5.8 If a person standing on their head eats food, the food has to travel upwards. Find out:

(a) What force the food is going against.

(b) How the person can still swallow food.

(c) Astronauts in space experience low (or micro) gravity conditions. Can food pass through their digestive systems in the normal way? Explain your answer.

Stomach

The stomach is a muscular bag that holds food for a few hours.

Hydrochloric acid in the stomach kills bacteria and also softens food.

The stomach produces enzymes that chemically digest food. The stomach also churns and physically digests and mixes the food.

The stomach is an **organ**. An organ is a structure in a living thing that carries out a particular function (or functions).

Did you know?

If stomach acid gets into the oesophagus it causes a stinging sensation called heartburn.

5.9 Food stays in our stomachs for up to four hours. If food passes too quickly through the stomach a person may get many intestinal infections. Why might this happen?

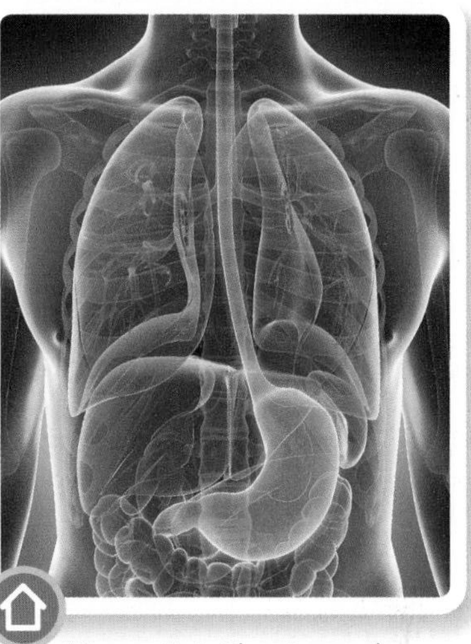

Figure 5.4 *The stomach*

Small intestine

The small intestine produces many enzymes that complete the breakdown of food. Most digestion takes place in the part of the small intestine just below the stomach.

In the rest of the small intestine the food is absorbed from the intestine into the bloodstream. Digested food is then transported all over the body by our blood.

Two organs, the **liver** and the **pancreas**, help to digest food. They pass their products into the small intestine.

Figure 5.5 *The small intestine*

Liver

The liver is a complex organ that carries out a range of functions. One of its many functions is to produce a liquid called **bile**. Bile passes from the liver into the small intestine. Bile helps to digest fat in the small intestine.

The liver is the largest organ inside the body.

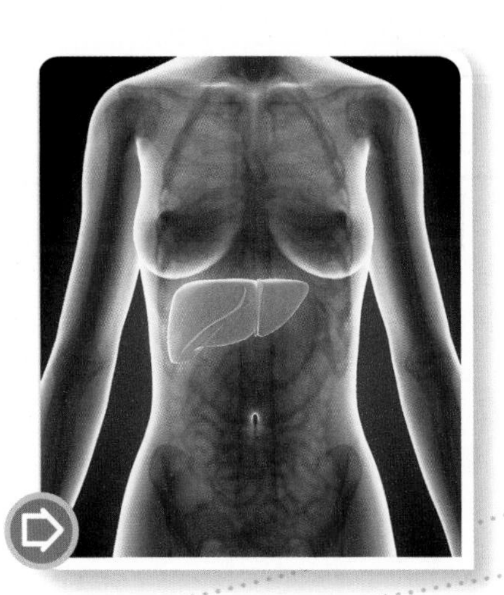

Figure 5.6 *The liver*

5.10 People who have pain and discomfort after eating fried or fat-rich food are often suspected of having a liver problem. Explain why this might be suspected.

Pancreas

The pancreas produces many digestive enzymes. These enzymes pass from the pancreas into the small intestine where they help to digest food.

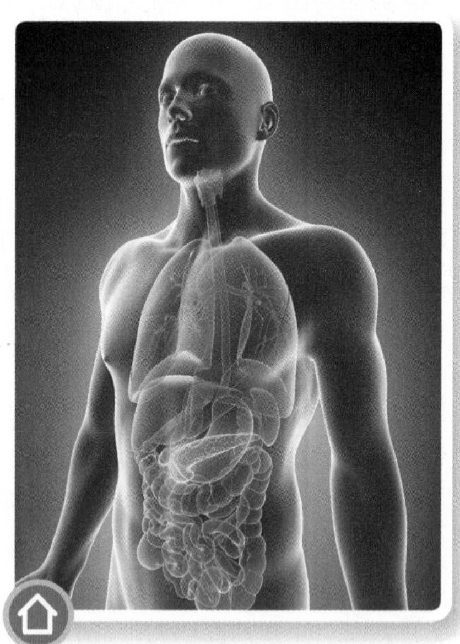

Figure 5.7 *The pancreas*

Large intestine

The material entering the large intestine contains a lot of liquid along with unabsorbed waste material. The large intestine takes water back into the bloodstream (**reabsorbs** water).

The semi-solid waste material left in the large intestine is called **faeces**.

- If too much water is taken back the waste becomes too solid, a condition called **constipation**.
- If too little water is taken back we produce liquid waste and suffer from **diarrhoea**.

Faeces are stored in the rectum and pass out of the intestine through the anus. The loss of unabsorbed food is called **egestion**.

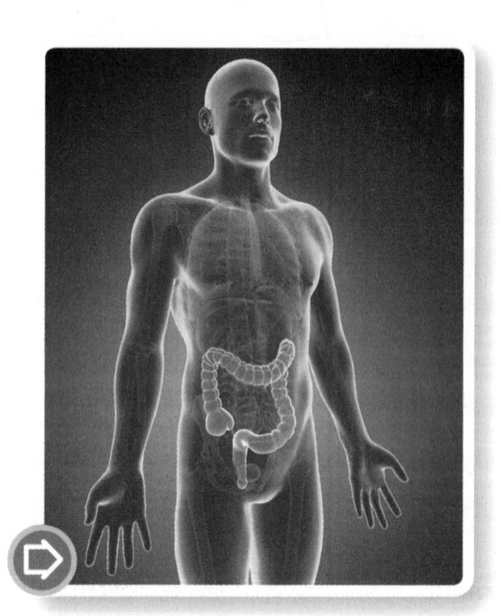

Figure 5.8 *The large intestine*

5.11 Research fibre in the diet:

(a) Find out why a low-fibre diet might cause us to feel bloated and full.

(b) High-fibre diets are thought to reduce the risk of bowel cancer (cancer of the large intestine). Find out why this might be the case.

5.12 Why might children with diarrhoea often suffer from dehydration?

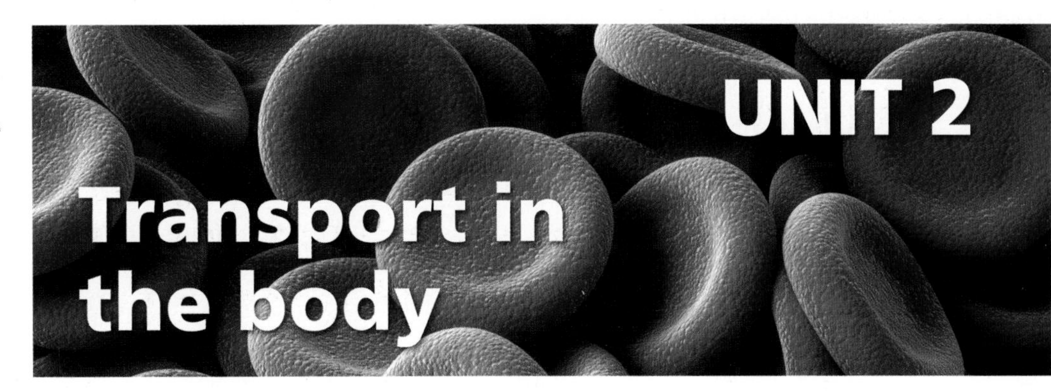

CHAPTER 6

UNIT 2

Transport in the body

Learning outcomes

At the end of this chapter you will be able to:

- Describe the functions of the parts of blood
- Describe the structure and functions of the blood vessels
- Describe the structure and functions of the heart
- Describe the path of blood around the body.

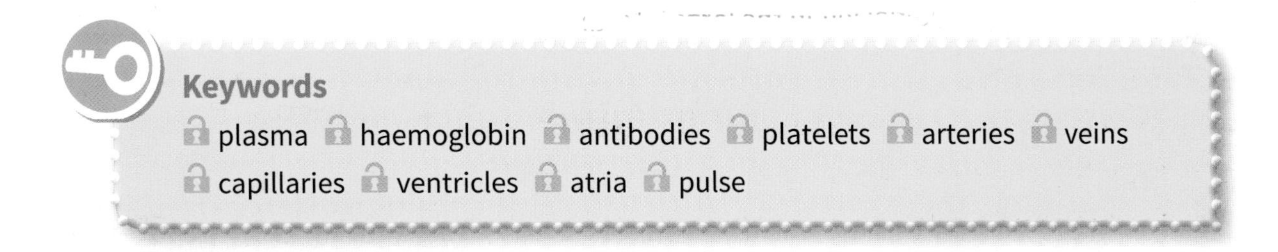

Keywords

plasma haemoglobin antibodies platelets arteries veins capillaries ventricles atria pulse

How do materials pass around our body?

The human body needs a transport system to move materials from one place to another. For example, food, oxygen and waste products have to be moved to and from all the cells in our body.

Our **circulatory** or transport system is made up of:

- Blood
- A system of tubes or blood vessels
- The heart, which is needed to pump blood through blood vessels.

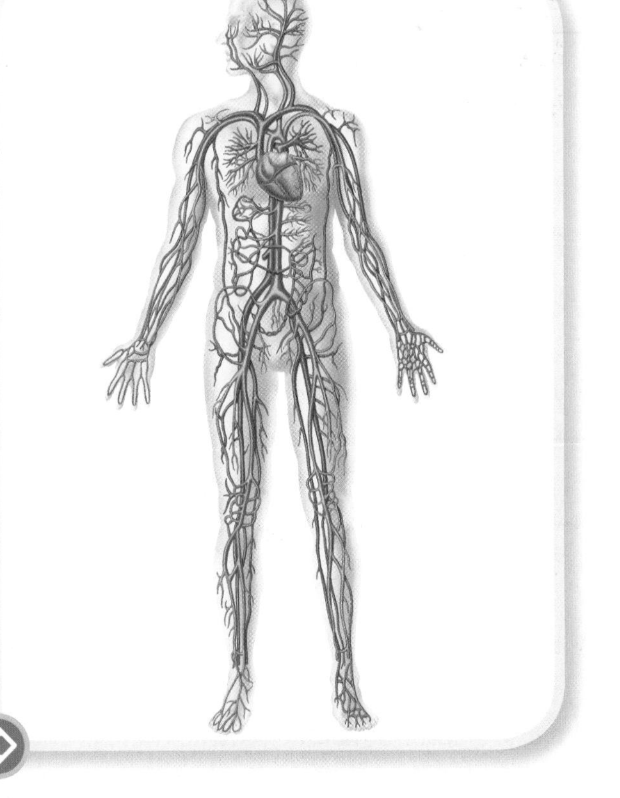

Figure 6.1 *The circulatory system*

BIOLOGICAL WORLD

What is in our blood?

Blood is made up of four parts or components:

- Plasma
- Red blood cells
- White blood cells
- Platelets.

Plasma

Plasma is the liquid part of blood. It is a pale yellow colour and is mostly made of water.

Plasma transports many dissolved chemicals around the body. These chemicals may be:

- Useful materials, such as foods and oxygen
- Wastes, such as carbon dioxide and salts.

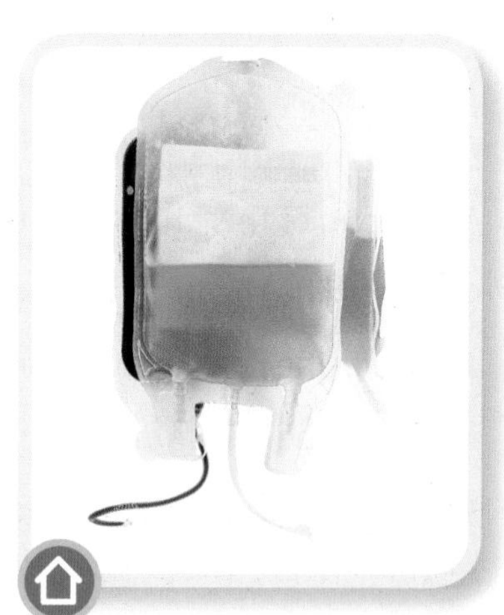

Figure 6.2 *Blood plasma in a bag*

Plasma also transports heat from one part of the body to another. Heat is produced by chemical reactions in all our body cells. By transporting heat our blood plays an important role in maintaining our **body temperature at 37°C.**

Plasma also carries:

- Red blood cells
- White blood cells
- Platelets.

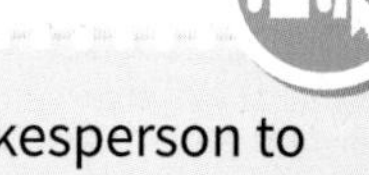

6.1 Discuss the following questions in groups. Each group should elect a spokesperson to report the group's findings to the class.

(a) What causes humans to get too hot?

(b) List the changes that take place in our bodies when we get too hot.

(c) Explain the benefit of the changes listed in (b) above.

How plasma affects body temperature

When we are **too hot**, extra blood (plasma) is sent to our skin (especially to the face, causing it to go red). This allows more heat to pass out of our body and we cool down. This can happen when we are ill. In this case our body temperature may rise (we have a fever). The high temperature helps to destroy the bacteria and viruses that are causing us to be ill.

When we are **too cold**, blood vessels in our skin become smaller. Blood also moves from our extremities to our core. This means we lose less heat from our body.

6.2 Apart from blood plasma there is another type of plasma.

(a) What is the second type of plasma? (Hint: see states of matter in chapter 13.)

(b) Give an example of where it may be found.

6.3 Since blood plasma is pale yellow, why is our blood red?

Red blood cells

Red blood cells are made in **bone marrow** located in the centre of bones. Red blood cells contain a red-coloured chemical (or pigment) called **haemoglobin**. To make haemoglobin we need iron. Our blood contains huge numbers of red blood cells.

6.4 Find out the answers to these questions on iron.

(a) Name any food in our diet that we need to eat in order to get iron.

(b) What is anaemia?

(c) How can you tell if someone is anaemic?

Haemoglobin, and therefore red blood cells, carries oxygen. We will see in chapter 10 that oxygen is needed to release energy from food.

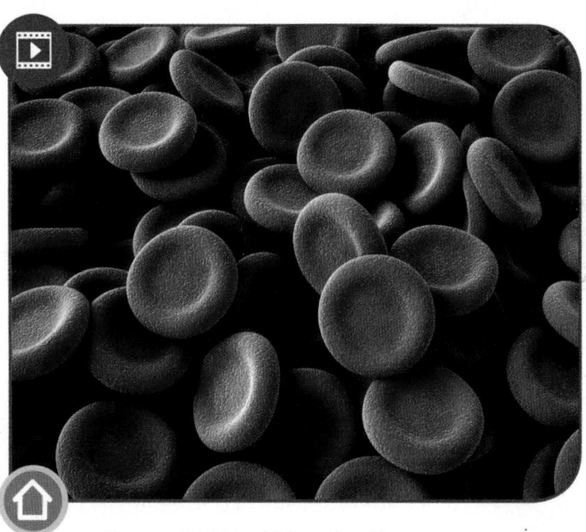

Figure 6.3 *Red blood cells*

The path of oxygen

Oxygen enters our red blood cells in the lungs. It attaches to haemoglobin in the red cells. When blood reaches cells in other parts of our body (such as our muscles or the brain) haemoglobin releases the oxygen into these cells.

White blood cells

White blood cells are also made in bone marrow. White blood cells fight infection. They do this by:

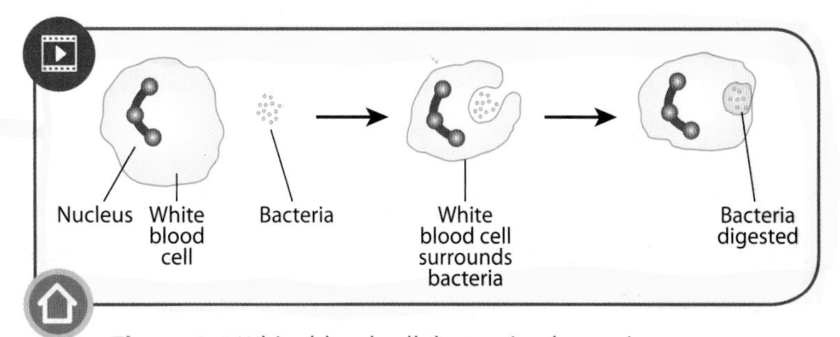

Figure 6.4 *White blood cell destroying bacteria*

- Some white blood cells surround micro-organisms (such as bacteria and viruses) and destroy them.
- Other white blood cells form proteins called **antibodies**. Antibodies help to destroy micro-organisms that have entered the body. Antibodies are very important. AIDS is a condition where the body does not produce any antibodies.

6.5 Since blood contains white blood cells, why is blood not white instead of being red?

BIOLOGICAL WORLD

Platelets

Platelets are formed in bone marrow when large cells break down into smaller pieces. Platelets help to form blood clots. In this way they help to prevent:

- Loss of blood
- Micro-organisms entering the body.

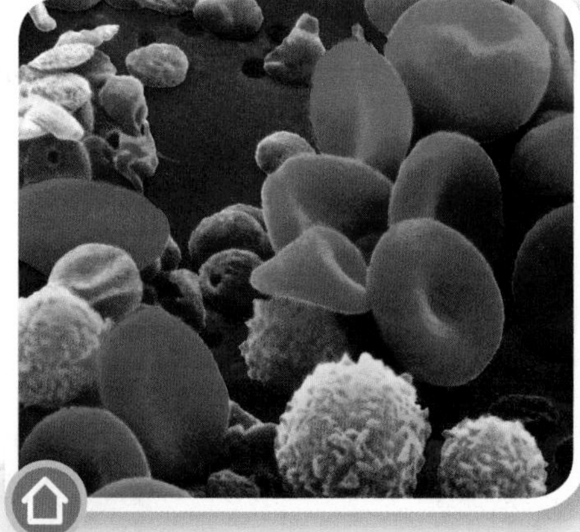

Figure 6.5 *Red blood cells (red), white blood cells (yellow) and platelets (pink)*

6.6 Work in groups to find out what problems each of the following would cause. Each member of the group should report on at least one of these problems to the class group.

(a) A lack (or shortage) of iron
(b) A lack of red blood cells
(c) A lack of white blood cells
(d) A lack of platelets
(e) A lack of blood.

Why do we need blood?

We need blood for a number of reasons. Each of the four parts of blood has its own role (or function) as shown in Table 6.1.

Table 6.1 **What blood does**

Part of blood	Function
Plasma	Transports materials such as foods and wastes
	Transports heat around the body
Red blood cells	Transport oxygen
White blood cells	Fight infection
Platelets	Clot the blood

What are blood vessels?

There are three main types of blood vessels:

- Arteries
- Veins
- Capillaries.

Figure 6.6 *Arteries, veins and tiny capillaries.*

Arteries

Arteries carry blood **away from** the heart. (Remember **a** is for artery and **a** is for away.)

As a result of carrying blood away from the heart, there is a strong flow of blood in arteries. We say that the blood in arteries is under **high pressure**.

Veins

Veins carry blood **to** the heart. The blood flow or pressure in a vein is **low**.

6.7 Apply your knowledge of arteries and veins to identify:

(a) Which of the two needs the thicker, stronger wall.

(b) Which of the two needs valves to prevent blood flowing backwards.

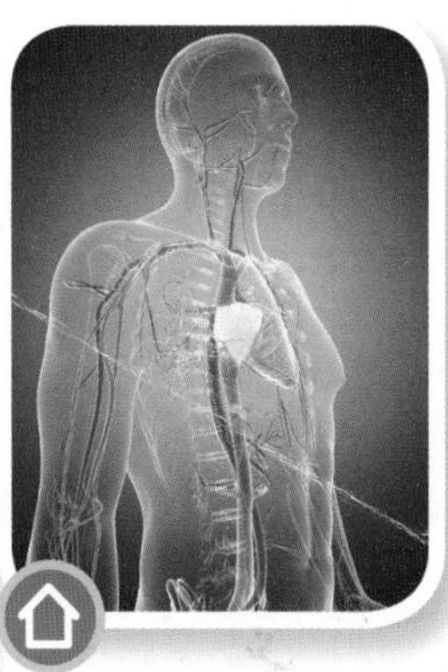

Figure 6.7 *Arteries and veins*

Capillaries

Capillaries are tiny blood vessels. They are found between arteries and veins.

There is a huge number of capillaries in the human body.

The walls of a capillary are very thin. This allows materials to pass into and out of capillaries. For example, in our intestines food passes *into* blood capillaries. This food is carried by the bloodstream to all the cells of the body. The food later passes *out of* the capillaries to enter the body cells.

6.8 The following diagram represents a number of different blood vessels.

(a) State whether each of A, B and C is an artery, a vein or a capillary.

(b) Which way do you think the blood is flowing (i.e. from A to C or from C to A)? Give a reason for your answer.

(c) Name one substance that might pass from the structures labelled B into the cells.

(d) Name one substance that might pass from the cells into the structures labelled B.

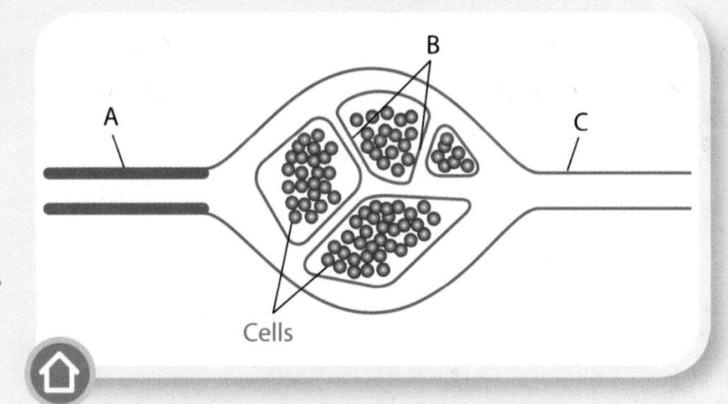

Figure 6.8 *Different blood vessels*

The heart

The heart is about the size of a clenched fist. It is located between the middle and the left-hand side of the chest.

The heart is made of a special type of muscle called **cardiac muscle**. Cardiac muscle is very strong and does not tire easily.

The heart contracts in order to pump blood around our body in blood vessels. The force of this blood causes a pulse.

When we are resting, the average rate of an adult heartbeat is **70 beats per minute**. When we exercise, the heart beats faster. This causes blood and the materials it carries to move faster around our bodies.

6.9 Why do we need to pump blood around the body faster during exercise?

Structure of the heart

Parts of the heart

Chambers: The heart contains **four** chambers. The top two are the right and left **atrium** (plural atria) and the bottom two are the right and left **ventricle**.

Septum: The two sides of the heart are separated by a muscular wall called the septum.

Heart valves: Valves in the heart make sure that blood can flow only in one direction. In this way, they are similar to valves in a car tyre or football (which let air pass in, but not out).

How blood flows through the heart

- Blood from the arms, legs and other parts of the body enters the right atrium of the heart through the **vena cava**. This blood is low in oxygen.
- The **right atrium** contracts to pump the blood down through a valve into the **right ventricle**.
- When the right ventricle contracts, the valve shuts to prevent the blood from going back into the right atrium. As a result, blood is pumped out of the heart in the **pulmonary artery** to the **lungs**.

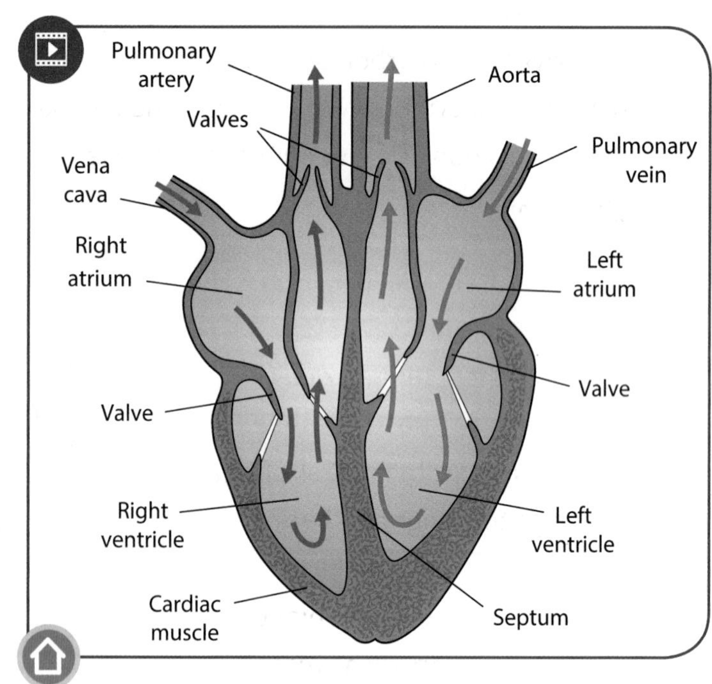

Figure 6.9 *Structure and blood flow of the heart*

- In the lungs, the blood gains oxygen (and also loses carbon dioxide and water vapour).
- Blood from the lungs flows back into the **left atrium** of the heart through the **pulmonary vein**. This blood is now rich in oxygen.
- The left atrium contracts to pump the blood through a valve and into the **left ventricle**.
- The left ventricle contracts, the valve snaps shut and blood is forced out of the heart through the **aorta**. It then passes all around the body.
- Eventually this blood will lose oxygen to the body cells. It will return to the heart in the right atrium. The cycle then starts all over again.

- **The ventricles of the heart**
- The **right ventricle** pumps blood from the heart to the lungs. This is a reasonably short distance and so the muscular walls of the right ventricle are fairly thin.
- The **left ventricle** pumps blood from the heart all around the body. This is a very long distance and so the muscular walls of the left ventricle are very thick.

Pulmonary artery and vein

- Most of the arteries in the body carry oxygen-rich blood. However, the pulmonary artery is an exception to this rule as it carries blood low in oxygen.
- Most of the veins in the body carry blood low in oxygen. However, the pulmonary vein is an exception to this rule as it carries oxygen-rich blood.

6.10 Why are the walls of the atria thinner (and weaker) than the walls of the ventricles?

6.11 Many people suffer from problems caused by damage to the valves in their heart. In terms of blood flow, what problems might they have?

6.12 Compare blood in the pulmonary artery and in the pulmonary vein in terms of:

(a) Pressure

(b) Oxygen and carbon dioxide contents.

6.13 Why do most arteries contain oxygen-rich blood?

6.14 Why does blood in the pulmonary vein have lower pressure than the blood in the pulmonary artery?

The two blood circuits

The circulatory system consists of two circuits:

- In the **lung circuit**, blood flows from the heart to the lungs and back to the heart.
- In the longer, **body circuit**, blood flows from the heart to the rest of the body and back to the heart again.

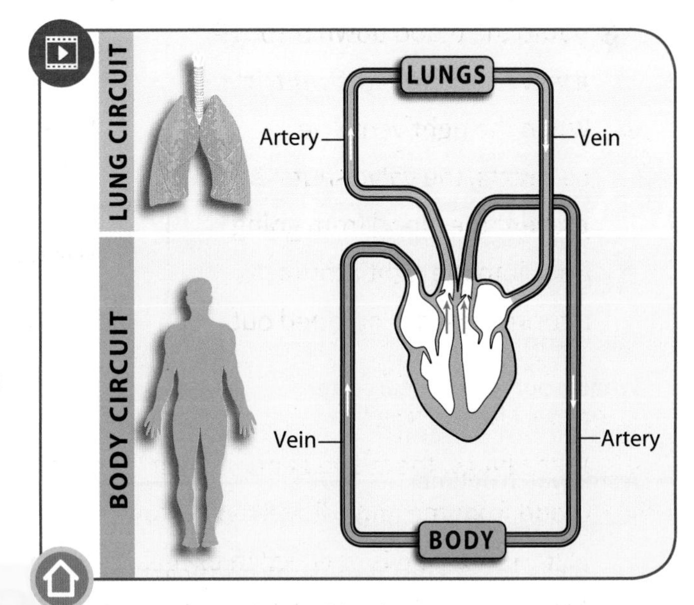

Figure 6.10 *The two blood circuits*

What is a pulse?

When blood is pumped through the arteries it causes a wave of pressure. This wave of pressure is called a **pulse**.

A pulse can be felt in areas of the body where the arteries are close to the surface, for example at the wrist and in the neck.

The pulse rate is used to measure the rate of heartbeat.

How exercise affects pulse rate

When we exercise, the cells in the body (especially in the muscles) need increased supplies of food and oxygen. In addition, the cells need to get rid of extra amounts of carbon dioxide and heat. As a result, exercise causes the heart to beat faster and our pulse rate increases.

6.15 The heart rate (in beats per minute, BPM) and average lifespan of different animals is given in Table 6.2.

Table 6.2 Heart rates and average lifespan of selected animals

Animal	Mouse	Rat	Small dog	Human
Heart rate (BPM)	650	410	120	72
Average lifespan (years)	2	2.5	10	75

(a) Suggest an explanation (or hypothesis) for the variations in the heart rates.

(b) How many times does a human heart beat (on average) every: (i) minute, (ii) hour, (iii) day, (iv) year, (v) 75 years, the average lifespan?

(c) Calculate the number of heart beats in the average life of each of the other animals.

(d) Some people say that every animal has roughly the same number of heartbeats in its life. Some of the figures given above support this idea, but the figures for one of the animals contradicts it. Which is the contradictory animal?

Figure 6.11 Measuring heart rate

Portfolio 45

Activity 6.1

Question

What is our resting heart rate?

Equipment needed

A stopwatch or timer

Conducting the activity

1. While you are resting, use the first finger and middle finger to locate your pulse in your wrist or neck. The pulse rate is a measure of the heart rate.
2. Count the number of pulses for one minute.
3. Repeat this three times.
4. Add the three values together and divide by three to get the average resting pulse rate. Getting an average rate is more reliable than taking a single reading.

5. Record your pulse rates in a table such as the one below.

Number of pulses per minute at rest	Total number of pulses in three minutes at rest	Average pulse rate per minute at rest

Activity 6.2

Question

What is the effect of exercise on heart rate?

The plan is to record the heart rate at rest and then record the heart rate after exercise. This is done by counting the pulse rates at rest and after exercise.

Equipment needed

A stopwatch or timer

Safety

- The exercise should be carried out in a safe environment (i.e. where the person exercising cannot trip or come to harm).
- The type of exercise should be controlled so that it is safe.
- The person being tested should be in good general health.

Conducting the activity

1. Record your resting pulse (or heart) rate as in activity 6.1. If you prefer, you can use the information (or data) you collected in activity 6.1.
2. Provided you are fit and healthy, exercise strongly for two minutes (e.g. step up and down on a step or run on the spot).
3. Immediately after exercising count the number of pulses per minute.
4. Continue to record the number of pulses per minute until the rate returns to the average resting rate.
5. Record how long it takes for the pulse rate to return to normal after exercise.
6. Record your results in a table such as the one below.

Number of pulses per minute at rest	Total number of pulses in three minutes at rest	Average pulse rate per minute at rest	Pulse rates per minute after exercise

What pathway around the body does the blood take?

Figure 6.11 is a model of the system that is used to circulate blood around the body.

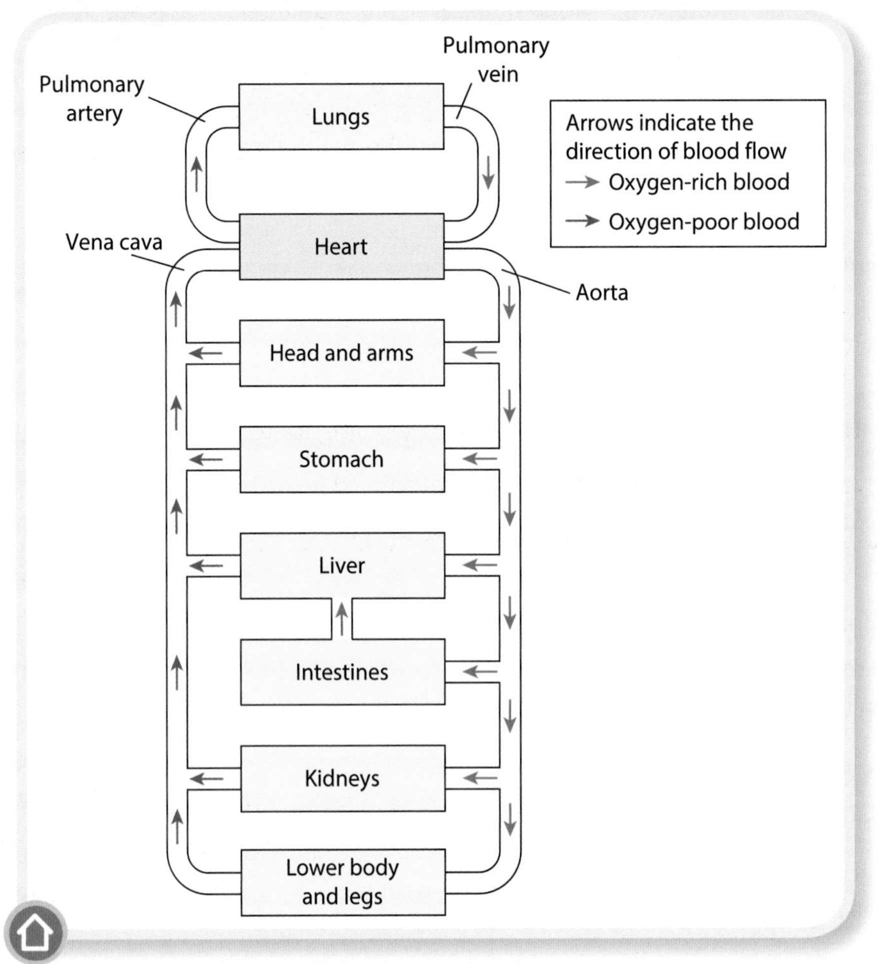

Figure 6.12 *The path of blood around the body*

What happens to blood in different parts of the body?

This is summarised in Table 6.3.

Table 6.3 **What happens to blood in different parts of the body**

Organ	Blood gains	Blood loses
Lungs	Oxygen	Carbon dioxide and water
Intestines	Food, water and carbon dioxide	Oxygen
Head/arms	Carbon dioxide and water	Oxygen and food
Lower body/legs	Carbon dioxide and water	Oxygen and food

6.16 Describe the changes in the blood that take place in:

(a) The heart (b) The intestines (c) The lungs.

6.17 Name the blood vessel that takes blood:

(a) From the heart to the lungs. (b) From the arms and legs to the heart.

6.18 Blood pressure is measured as *x* **mm Hg**. Human blood pressure is given as 120 mm Hg. The blood pressure in a giraffe is given as 300 mm Hg. Why is the blood pressure of a giraffe so high?

Chapter 7 The breathing system

Learning outcomes

At the end of this chapter you will be able to:

- Explain why we breathe
- Describe the structure and functions of the breathing system
- Investigate the carbon dioxide levels of air breathed in and out
- Investigate our breathing rate at rest and after exercise.

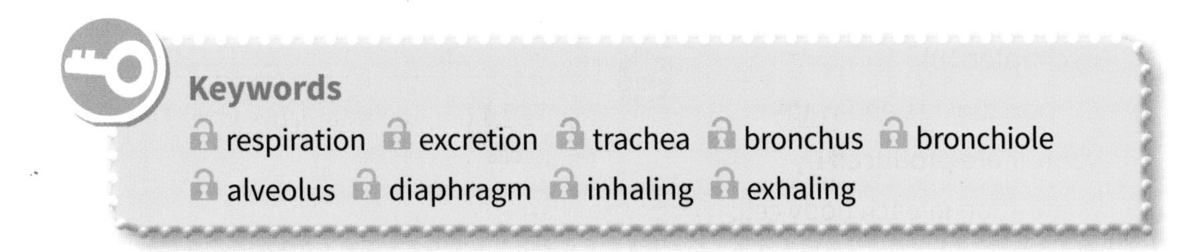

Why do we breathe?

Activity 7.1

Question

What happens to our chests when we breathe?

Conducting the activity

1. Place your hand on your chest.
2. Breathe in (inhale) and breathe out (exhale) deeply and slowly a few times.
3. What do you feel? Do you notice your hand changing position?
4. When you breathe in does your chest get bigger or smaller?
5. When you exhale how does your chest change?

This is what takes place when we breathe:

- When we breathe in, air fills our lungs – this is why in **Activity 7.1** your chest was getting bigger when you breathed in and smaller when you breathed out.
- Oxygen from the air passes from our lungs into our bloodstream.
- The blood carries oxygen to all the cells of our body, where it is used to release energy from food. The release of energy from food is called **respiration** (and is explained in chapter 10).
- Carbon dioxide and water vapour are produced by respiration in each body cell. They enter the bloodstream and are carried by the blood to the lungs.
- Carbon dioxide and water vapour pass from the blood into the lungs and are then breathed out.

Figure 7.1 *Gas exchange between the lungs and body cells*

In this way the breathing system supplies oxygen for respiration and gets rid of the waste products of respiration (i.e. carbon dioxide and water).

The breathing system is also called the **respiratory system**.

Excretion is the getting rid of the waste products of reactions from the body. Carbon dioxide and water vapour are excreted by the breathing system.

7.1 Name the blood vessels that carry blood from:

(a) The heart to the lungs.
(b) The lungs to the heart.
(c) The heart to the rest of the body.
(d) From the body cells to the heart.

7.2 **(a)** Why does our body need oxygen?
(b) Name two substances excreted by the body.

Did you know?

The left lung is slightly smaller than the right lung (to allow space for the heart).

The breathing system

What is the function of the parts of the breathing system?

The breathing system is made up of the following:

- Nose
- Trachea or windpipe
- Bronchus and bronchioles
- Alveolus
- Diaphragm
- Ribs and intercostal muscles.

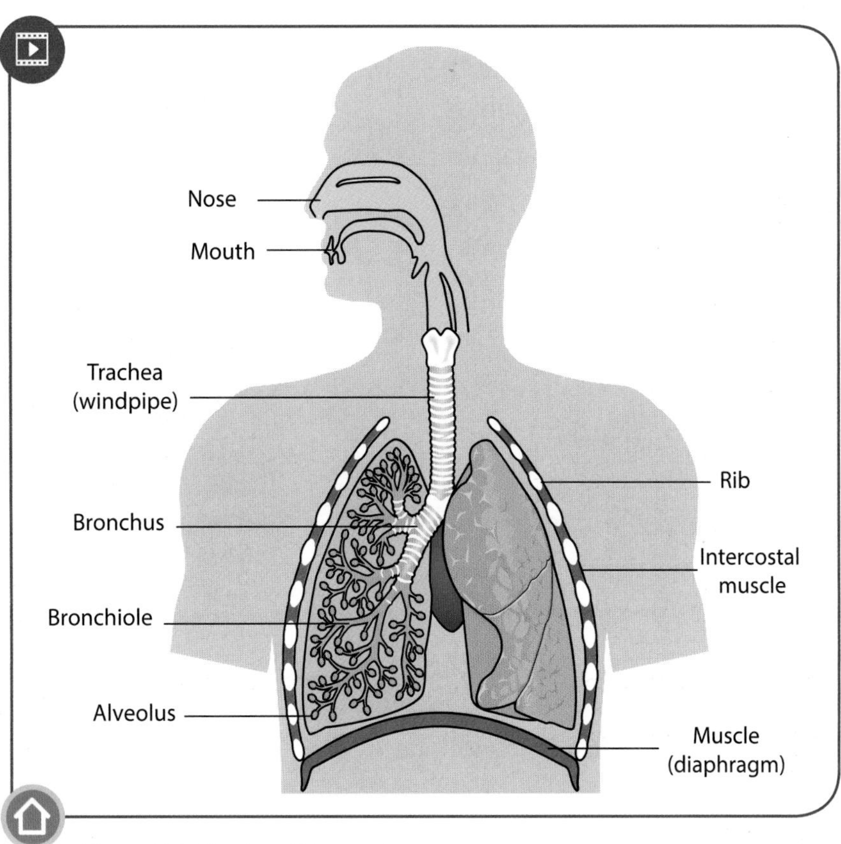

Figure 7.2 *The breathing system*

Nose

We are supposed to breathe in (**inhale**) through our noses. The reasons for doing this are:

- Hairs and mucus trap dirt particles and bacteria in the nose.
- Air is warmed and moistened as it passes through the nose. Warm and moist air helps oxygen to pass from the lungs into the bloodstream more easily.

Trachea or windpipe

The trachea or windpipe carries air to and from the lungs.

Bronchus and bronchioles

We have two bronchi. Each bronchus carries air between the windpipe and a lung.

The two bronchi subdivide many times to form tiny tubes called bronchioles. Bronchioles carry air to and from the air-sacs or alveoli.

BIOLOGICAL WORLD

Alveolus

Each lung contains millions of tiny air-sacs called alveoli. Each alveolus has a thin lining and is surrounded by many tiny blood vessels called **capillaries**. The function of the alveoli is gas exchange:

- Oxygen passes from the air in the alveolus into the blood vessels.
- At the same time carbon dioxide and water pass from the blood vessels into each alveolus.
- The gases pass in each direction by a process called **diffusion**.

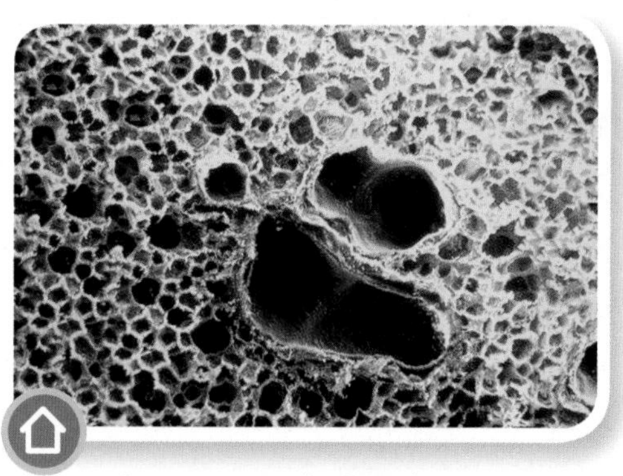

Figure 7.3 *Each of our lungs contains millions of alveoli*

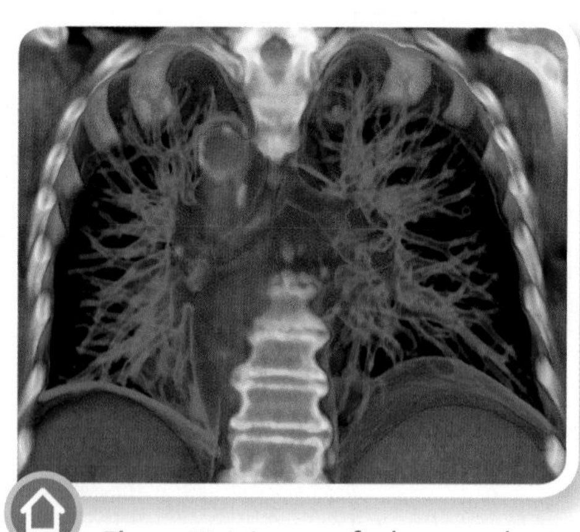

Figure 7.4 *A scan of a human chest, showing the lungs*

7.3 Research diffusion:

(a) What is meant by diffusion? (Hint: see chapter 13.)

(b) Find out if diffusion works better:

(i) At high or low temperatures.

(ii) Across a dry or a moist surface.

(c) Based on your answers to part (b), how is our breathing system adapted to provide the conditions for diffusion to work best?

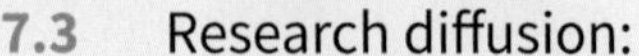

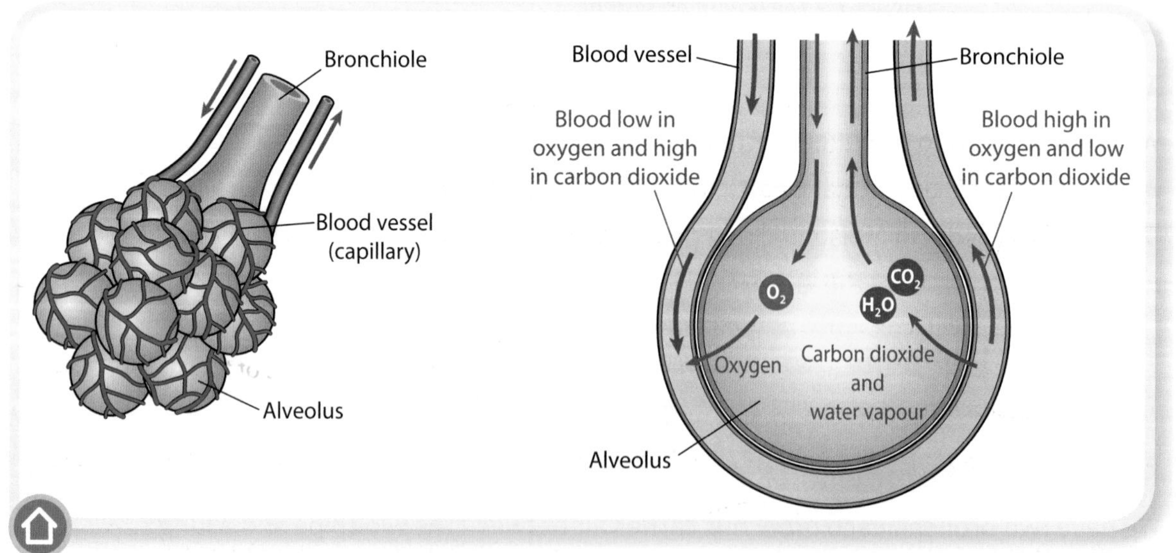

Figure 7.5 *Gas exchange in an alveolus*

Diaphragm

The diaphragm is a sheet of muscle that forms the base of the chest. Along with the ribs and **intercostal muscles** (located between the ribs) the diaphragm causes air to move into or out of the lungs.

Activity 7.2

Question

Can a model of the chest show how we get air in and out of the lungs?

Equipment needed

Large (2 litre is best) empty soft drink plastic bottle to represent the chest

Balloon to represent the lungs

Rubber band

Plastic bag to represent the diaphragm

Scissors

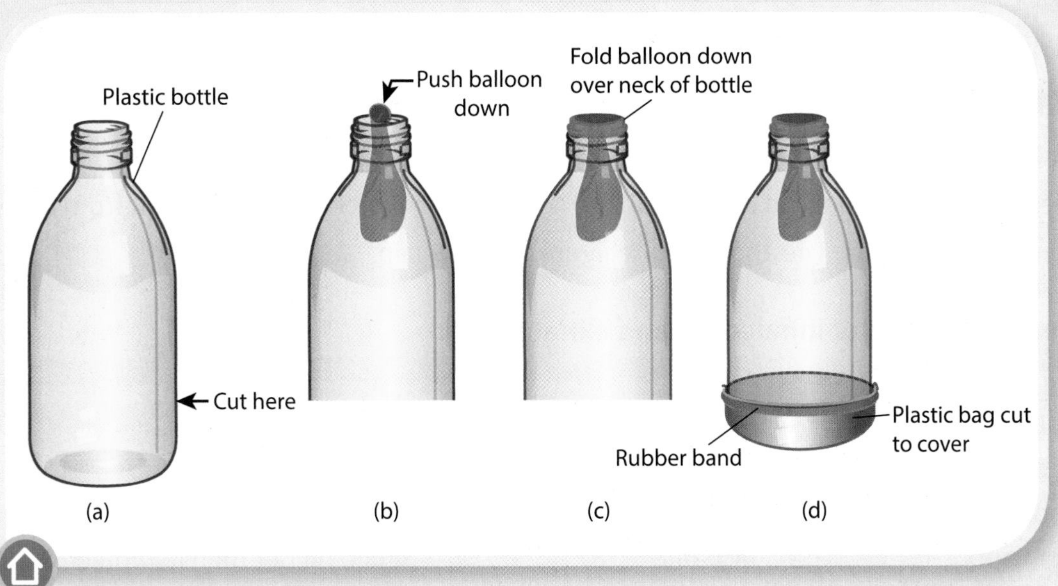

Figure 7.6 *Model of chest and lung*

Conducting the activity

This can be carried out alone, in pairs or in groups.

1. Cut around the plastic bottle about two-thirds of the way down and discard the bottom half.
2. Push the balloon down through the top or neck of the bottle.
3. Fold the top of the balloon down over the neck of the bottle.
4. Cut the plastic bag so that it covers the base of the bottle with about 4 cm spare all round.
5. Use the elastic band to hold the plastic over the base of the bottle so that it is flat but loose.
6. Pinch the middle of the plastic cover at the end of the bottle and pull down gently. What happens to the size of the balloon? Does this represent breathing in or out?
7. Push up gently on the middle of the plastic cover. What happens to the size of the balloon? Does this represent inhalation or exhalation?
8. We have two lungs. This model has only one 'lung'. Discuss in a group how you might alter this activity so that you could make a model with two lungs.

7.4 (a) Why do we have two bronchi?
(b) Why do you think we have so many alveoli?
(c) State two ways that the structure of the alveoli is adapted to allow for gas exchange.

7.5 (a) Inhaled air contains lots of dust and disease-causing organisms. Suggest one way that these unwanted materials are prevented from entering the alveoli.
(b) Name the gas that passes from the alveoli into the blood.
(c) What part of the blood does this gas enter?
(d) Name an excretory product that passes from the blood into the alveoli.
(e) By what process do gases pass into and out of the alveoli?

What is the difference between air breathed in and air breathed out?

As a result of gas exchange in the alveoli, the contents of inhaled air are different from the contents of exhaled air. The approximate figures are given in Table 7.1.

Table 7.1 Makeup of inhaled air and exhaled air

Substance	% in inhaled air	% in exhaled air
Nitrogen	78	78
Oxygen	21	14
Carbon dioxide	0.04	5
Water vapour	Variable	Much higher than in inhaled air

7.6 What is the normal concentration of carbon dioxide in the air?

7.7 Why does exhaled air contain more carbon dioxide than inhaled air?

7.8 The table below shows the exhaled carbon dioxide concentrations of three people. One of the people was resting, one was walking and the third was running. Answer these questions based on the figures in the table:
(a) From the table, match up the three people with the three activities.
(b) Which person would have the greatest demand for oxygen?
(c) Why do you think that the person in part (b) required more oxygen? Identify in your answer any part(s) of the body that needed a higher supply of oxygen.
(d) Which person would have the lowest breathing rate (number of breaths per minute)?
(e) Why do you think that the person in part (d) requires less oxygen?

Person	Percentage of carbon dioxide in exhaled air
A	7
B	4
C	9

BIOLOGICAL WORLD

Activity 7.3

Question

Can we compare the carbon dioxide levels of inhaled and exhaled air?

Limewater turns milky or cloudy in the presence of carbon dioxide. We will breathe in through one container of limewater and breathe out through a second container of limewater.

Equipment needed

Two test tubes
Two stoppers with holes
Tubing or straws
Clear limewater

Safety

- Glass tubing may crack and break. If possible use plastic tubing or straws.
- If you use tubing, it should be washed to make sure it is clean.
- Make sure that the tube or straw that you breathe in through is not in the limewater (to prevent you sucking in limewater).
- Care should be taken when inserting the stoppers into the test tubes (in case the test tubes break).
- Care should be taken to suck air in or blow air out through the correct tubes.
- The apparatus should not be shared, to reduce the risk of passing infections.

Conducting the activity

1. Place equal volumes of clear limewater in two test tubes, as shown in Figure 7.7.
2. Suck air in through tube X and hold your breath for as long as possible.
3. Breathe air out through tube Y.
4. Repeat steps 2 and 3 until the limewater in one of the test tubes turns milky.
5. In which test tube did the limewater first turn milky?
6. Why does the limewater in the second test tube eventually turn milky?

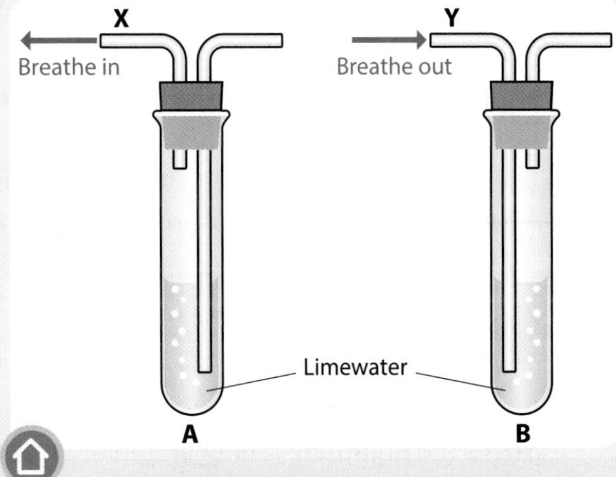

Figure 7.7 *Comparing CO_2 concentration*

What is breathing rate?

The breathing rate is how many breaths a person or animal takes per minute. One breath is one inhalation and one exhalation.

Activity 7.4

Question

How can we find our breathing rate at rest?

Equipment needed

A stopwatch

Conducting the activity

1. Count the number of times you breathe in (inhale) per minute while you are at rest.
2. Repeat step 1 two more times, so you have three counts.
3. Add the three values together and divide by three. This gives the average number of breaths per minute at rest. This gives a more reliable result than a single measurement.
4. Record your breathing rate in a table similar to the one below.

Number of inhalations (breaths) per minute at rest	Total number of inhalations (breaths) in three minutes at rest	Average number of inhalations (breaths) per minute at rest

Did you know?

The normal breathing rate for an adult at rest is from 8 to 16 breaths per minute. For an infant, the normal rate is up to 44 breaths per minute.

7.9 Why is the breathing rate of an infant greater than that of an adult?

7.10 (a) Research the breathing rates of other animals.

(b) Can you see a pattern relating breathing rate and the size of the animal? If so, then state the relationship.

(c) Can you see a pattern relating breathing rate and the life span of the animal? If so, then state the relationship.

7.11 In general, fitter people have lower breathing rates. Their breathing rate also returns to normal faster after exercise than for unfit people. What does this suggest about the size of their lungs?

7.12 Breathing rates increase as people go higher up a mountain, even if they are inactively sitting in a car. Suggest an explanation (or hypothesis) for this change.

Did you know?

A **hypothesis** is when a scientist provides a suggested explanation for something when there is very little evidence. It is the basis for further investigation to find out whether the hypothesis is true.

Activity 7.5

Question

How can we investigate the effect of exercise on the rate of breathing?

Equipment needed

A stopwatch

Safety

- Carry out an appropriate exercise (i.e. an exercise that is safe and not too strenuous for the person being tested). You should carry out this activity only if you are in good health.

Conducting the activity

1. Record your resting breathing rate as in activity 7.4. If you prefer you can use the information (data) collected in activity 7.4. This value acts as a control or comparison.
2. Exercise strongly for two minutes (e.g. jump up and down on the spot or run on the spot).
3. Immediately after exercising count the number of inhalations (breaths) per minute.
4. Continue to record the number of inhalations (breaths) per minute until the rate returns to the average resting rate.
5. Note how long it takes for the breathing rate to return to normal after exercise.
6. Record your results in a table similar to the one below. On a separate sheet of graph paper, or in your Student Portfolio book, draw a graph to show the results you obtained (putting time on the x-axis and the number of breaths per minute on the y-axis).

Number of inhalations (breaths) per minute at rest	Total number of inhalations (breaths) in three minutes at rest	Average breathing rate per minute at rest	Breathing rates per minute after exercise

7.13 The bar chart in Figure 7.8 shows the breathing rate of three people, A, B and C, at rest and after exercise. Answer the following questions based on the bar chart.

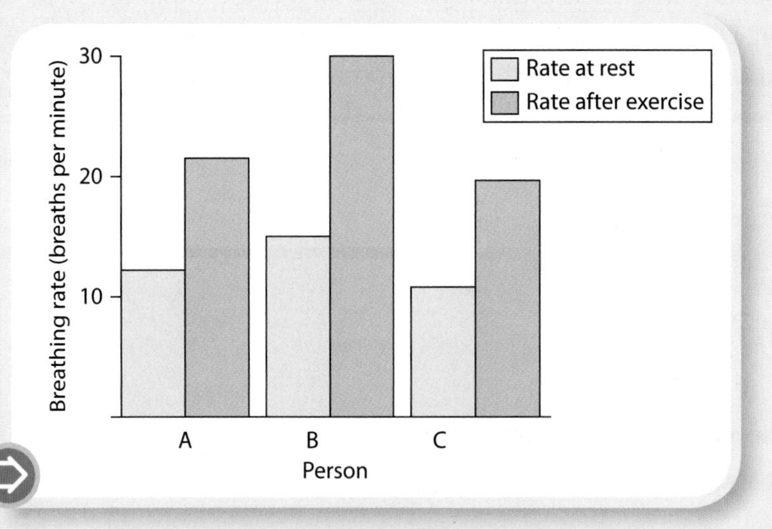

Figure 7.8

(a) Which person has the lowest breathing rate at rest?

(b) Which person has the highest breathing rate after exercise?

(c) Which person shows the greatest range of breathing rates?

(d) What is the percentage increase in breathing rates for person A?

(e) Calculate the average (mean) breathing rate for the three people:

(i) At rest

(ii) After exercise.

(f) Which person do you think is the fittest? Suggest two pieces of evidence from the chart in support of your answer.

7.14 John breathes in and out through the tube labelled X in Figure 7.9.

(a) Through which test tube will inhaled air pass?

(b) Name a liquid that could be used in the test tubes to detect a difference in composition between inhaled and exhaled air.

(c) After some minutes of breathing, how would the liquids in tubes A and B differ in appearance?

(d) What conclusion could you reach based on this difference?

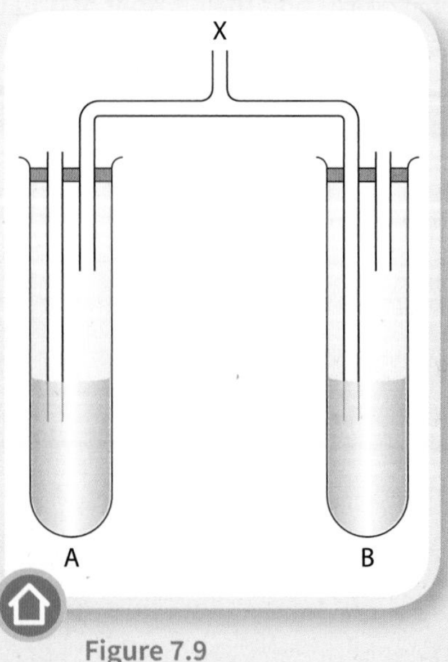

Figure 7.9

CHAPTER 8

UNIT 2

The study of a habitat

Learning outcomes

At the end of this chapter you will be able to:

- Identify different habitats
- Conduct a habitat study by:
  - Measuring environmental features
  - Using keys to name plants and animals
  - Collecting organisms in a habitat
  - Estimating the number of plants in a habitat
- Discuss adaptations, competition and interdependence of organisms in habitats
- Explain how energy and matter flow through an ecosystem.

Keywords

ecology, environment, ecosystem, habitat, environmental (abiotic) factors, identification key, ethics, pooter, sweep net, beating tray, pitfall trap, quadrat, adaptations, community, competition, interdependence, producers, consumers, herbivores, carnivores, omnivores, decomposers, food chain, food web, energy flow, matter flow

What are ecosystems and habitats?

Ecosystems

Ecology is the study of how plants and animals interact with each other and with their surroundings (or environment). The living world is divided into ecosystems, which are similar groups of plants, animals and environments. Examples of major ecosystems are:

- Deserts
- Tropical rainforests
- Grasslands
- Seashores.

Figure 8.1 *Examples of major ecosystems*

Habitats

Ecosystems are large areas containing similar types of environments and living things. Normally an ecosystem is too large to study. Instead, a small, local part of the ecosystem called a habitat is studied. A **habitat** is the place where an organism lives.

There are wide varieties of habitats that can be studied. These include:

- Grassland
- Hedgerow
- Rocky seashore
- Woodland
- Bog
- Local park
- School field
- Pond.

This chapter will deal with one sample habitat, a **grassland**.

8.1 Answer these questions on habitats:

(a) What is the difference between an ecosystem and a habitat?

(b) Which is larger, an ecosystem or a habitat?

(c) Name three different types of habitats found in Ireland.

How to carry out a habitat study

The study of a local habitat is called **fieldwork**. If possible, the habitat should be visited during different seasons. This will show how the habitat changes over the course of a year.

There is a recognised **countryside code** and when investigating any habitat it is important to follow this code.

The countryside code

- Get permission to enter private property.
- Close gates behind you.
- Do not disturb livestock.
- Do not damage gates, fences or crops.
- Do not light fires.
- Do not leave litter.
- Where possible you should 'leave only footprints and take only memories'.

Figure 8.2 *Make sure you follow the countryside code*

8.2 The countryside code is simple, but very important.

(a) Why is it important to follow the countryside code?

(b) Give three problems that might arise if people did not follow the countryside code.

The **study of a habitat** involves the following five steps:

1. Draw a simple map of the habitat (or photograph it if possible).
2. Measure and record the environmental (non-living) features in the habitat.
3. Identify and name all the organisms in the habitat.
4. Collect samples of those organisms in the habitat that cannot be identified.
5. Estimate the number of each plant in the habitat.

Step 1: Map the habitat

Draw a simple map to show the main features of the habitat, e.g. walls, fences, ponds, large trees, hedges or paths. If possible, photograph the habitat.

Step 2: Measure environmental features

The environmental or non-living features of a habitat are called **abiotic** features. Some of the non-living features that you can measure and the equipment used are given in Table 8.1.

Table 8.1 **Measuring environmental features of a habitat**

Feature	Equipment
Temperature	Thermometer or data logger with a temperature probe
Light intensity	Light meter or data logger with a light intensity probe
Soil pH	pH meter or universal indicator paper, or a data logger with a pH probe
Wind direction	Ribbon and compass
Rainfall	Rain gauge

Measure and record as many of the environmental features as possible.

Step 3: Identify the organisms

If possible, organisms in the habitat should be named and listed on site. Plants and animals should be removed from the habitat *only* if they cannot be identified there and then.

Organisms can be identified by comparing them to drawings or pictures in a book or by using a suitable key.

Figure 8.3 *Using a pH and temperature meter*

Activity 8.1

Question

How can we name (identify) plants and animals?

Compare the plant or animal to pictures or descriptions in field guides or use an **identification key**. A key contains a number of questions. By answering each question the name of the living thing can be discovered.

Equipment needed

Plant and animal guide books

Plant and animal keys

Conducting the activity

Plant key Use the key below to name each of the four plants shown in Figure 8.4.

Figure 8.4 *Name the four plants using the key below*

1	Leaves have parallel veins	Plantain
	Veins are not parallel in the leaves	Go to 2
2	Edges of leaves not jagged	Daisy
	Leaves have jagged edges	Go to 3
3	Long leaves growing from a the base of the stem	Dandelion
	Leaves more rounded and growing along the length of the stem	Buttercup

Animal key The following key can be used to name the six invertebrate animals shown in Figure 8.5.

1	Legs present	Go to 2
	Legs absent	Go to 3
2	Six legs present	Insect
	Eight legs present	Spider
3	Body divided into segments	Go to 4
	Body not divided into segments	Go to 5
4	Long body with many segments	Earthworm
	Shorter body with fewer segments	Caterpillar
5	Shell present	Snail
	No shell present	Slug

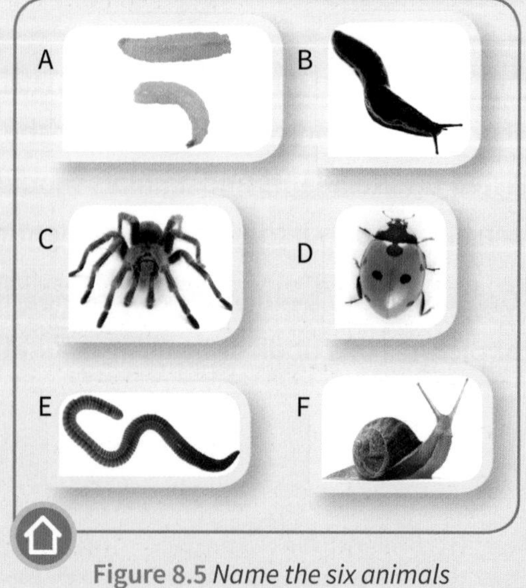

Figure 8.5 *Name the six animals using the key left*

8.3 Figure 8.6 shows four different animals that were found in a habitat study.

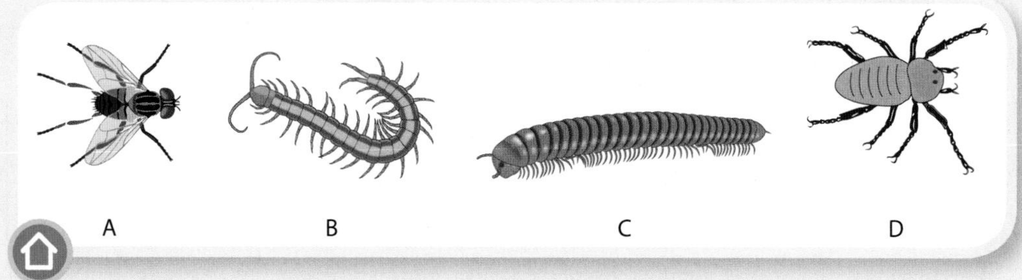

Figure 8.6

(a) What identifies all four animals as invertebrates?

(b) Use the key below to name the four animals.

1	Wings present Wings absent	Housefly Go to 2
2	More than 8 legs Not more than 8 legs	Go to 3 Spider
3	One pair of legs per segment Two pairs of legs per segment	Centipede Millipede

Step 4: Collect organisms for identification in the laboratory

Plants are easy to collect as they do not move away. Slow or non-moving animals can be collected easily. Most animals will have to be trapped or collected using special devices.

Activity 8.2

Question

How can we collect plants and animals in a habitat?

Equipment needed

Knife	Sweep net	Tin or jar	Pitfall trap
Small trowel	Beating tray	Pooter	

Safety

- All equipment should be unbreakable so that it does not cause harm in the habitat.
- Suitable clothing and footwear should be worn.
- Care should be taken if the habitat is wet or rough.

Ethics

Ethics means the study of whether conduct is right or wrong. In this case:

- Is it right to enter someone's property?
- Is it right to remove plants and animals from a habitat?
- What can we do to reduce any damage to the habitat?

Conducting the activity

Plants

Use a knife or small trowel to collect samples of plants and place them in labelled bags.

Remove only small sections of a plant. Remember to collect the leaves, twigs, flowers, seeds and fruits of each plant if they are present.

Use a suitable book or key to name the plant. Make a list of the names of all the plants you found.

Animals

Some animals are collected easily. For example, use a tin or jar to collect slow-moving animals such as slugs, snails and earthworms. Sometimes you can find signs (or evidence) of an animal, e.g. feathers, fur or hair attached to bushes, droppings, nests, burrows etc.

Special apparatus is needed to collect fast-moving animals. Examples of some of the methods used to collect animals are given in Figure 8.7.

Use a suitable book or key to name the plant. Make a list of the names of all the animals (or evidence that they were present) that you found.

8.4 What observations did you make that suggest unseen animals were present in the habitat?

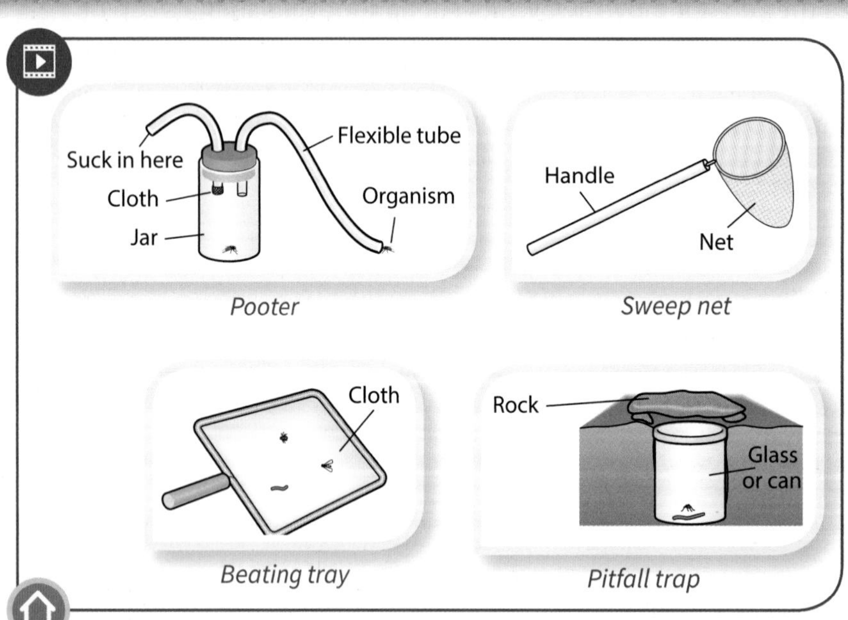

Figure 8.7 *Apparatus used to collect animals*

8.5 Why are animals more difficult than plants to find and collect in a habitat study?

8.6 Why do you think it is important to replace animals that you collected in the same place as you found them?

Figure 8.8 *A pitfall trap with a clear cover to prevent rain getting in*

Step 5: Estimate the number of plants

It is not normally possible to count all the plants in a habitat. Instead, the number of plants is calculated from samples taken at random in the habitat. We can then calculate how often a plant is likely to be found in the habitat (i.e. its **frequency**). The most common method of calculating plant numbers is to use a **quadrat**.

A quadrat is a square frame that is thrown at random in the habitat. Quadrats come in different sizes (e.g. their sides may measure 0.5 m or 0.25 m). They may be made of wood, metal or plastic, or they can be marked out using string or rope.

Portfolio 67

Activity 8.3

Question

How can we estimate the number of plants in a habitat?

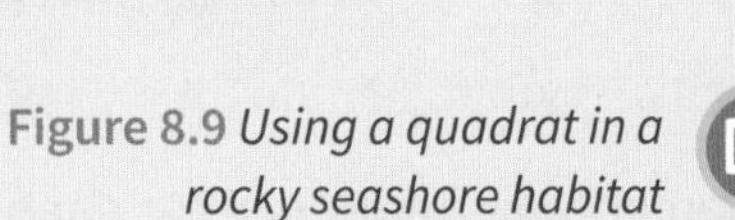

Figure 8.9 *Using a quadrat in a rocky seashore habitat*

Equipment needed

Ball or pen

Quadrat

Pen and notebook

Name of Plant	Quadrat Number										Total	Percentage Frequency
	1	2	3	4	5	6	7	8	9	10		
Grass	✓	✓	✓	✓	✓	✓	✓	✓	✓	✓	10	10/10 = 100%
Buttercup	✗	✓	✓	✗	✓	✗	✓	✗	✗	✗	4	4/10 = 40%
Daisy	✓	✓	✓	✓	✗	✗	✗	✓	✓	✓	7	7/10 = 70%
Clover	✗	✗	✗	✗	✗	✓	✓	✓	✗	✗	3	3/10 = 30%
Dandelion	✗	✓	✗	✓	✓	✗	✗	✓	✓	✗	5	5/10 = 50%
Thistle	✗	✗	✗	✗	✗	✗	✓	✗	✗	✗	1	1/10 = 10%

Figure 8.10 *Recording the names of plants in a quadratic study*

Conducting the activity

1. Throw a ball or pen carefully over your shoulder in the habitat. Ensure that you do not throw the ball or pen too far in case it should land beyond the habitat you are studying.
2. Place a quadrat on the ground wherever the ball or pen lands. This ensures that the quadrat is placed at random in the habitat. This will allow the samples to represent the habitat more accurately.
3. Record the names of the plants in your quadrat.
4. Repeat this ten times in different parts of the habitat.
5. Record the results as shown in Figure 8.10.
6. Calculate the percentage frequency of each plant in the habitat. This is done by adding the number of quadrats in which the plant is found and expressing this as a percentage of the ten quadrats (e.g. buttercups were found in 4 out of 10 quadrats, i.e. 40%).
7. The frequency of each type of plant can also be shown on a bar chart (as in Figure 8.11).

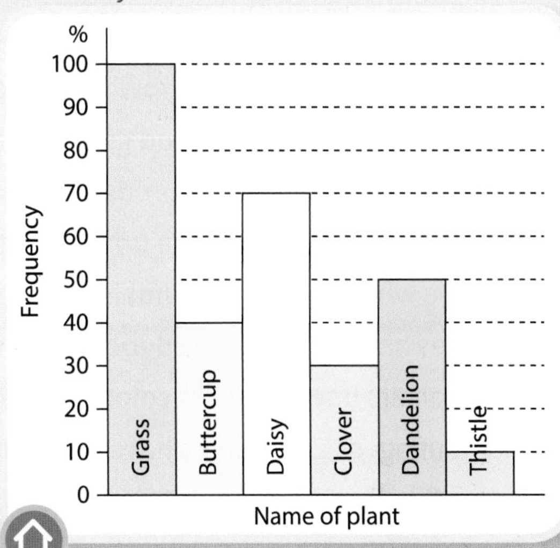

Figure 8.11 *A bar chart showing the percentage frequency of plants in a habitat*

BIOLOGICAL WORLD

8.7 Answer these questions on the use of a quadrat:

(a) What shape is a quadrat?

(b) Why should quadrats not be placed wherever we like in a habitat?

(c) How can you ensure that the quadrat is placed at random points in the habitat?

(d) Why are quadrats of little use in estimating animal numbers?

8.8 When estimating the number of plants in a grassland habitat Declan and Grace got the following results:

Plant name	Quadrat number									
	1	2	3	4	5	6	7	8	9	10
Clover	×	×	×	✓	×	✓	×	×	×	✓
Buttercup	✓	✓	×	×	✓	✓	✓	×	×	✓

(a) Calculate the percentage frequency for each plant.

(b) If one more quadrat was placed in the habitat at random, how likely would it be:

(i) To contain clover? (ii) Not to contain buttercups?

What are adaptations?

In order to survive, living things must adapt to their environment. An **adaptation** is a structure or habit that helps an organism to survive in its habitat or within its community.

A **community** consists of all the organisms living in a particular area.

Adaptations to their environment are very important in allowing organisms to live longer. If they continue to breed they will produce more offspring and the adaptation will pass on to the next generation. This is central to the process of evolution by natural selection (see chapter 4).

For example, adaptations shown by grassland organisms are:

- Plants such as primroses grow and produce flowers early in the spring. This means primroses get more light and grow better than the other plants in their habitat, because the other plants have not produced their leaves in early spring.
- Grasses grow from the base (most plants grow at their tips). This means grasses can survive when grazed by animals.
- Grasses have very branched roots. This means they are not easily pulled out of the ground.
- Caterpillars have a similar colour to the plants they feed on; this allows them to be well camouflaged. Caterpillars have strong mouth parts, so they can bite and chew leaves.
- Butterflies have long tubular mouth parts, so they can drink nectar (sugary water) from flowers.

8.9 Suggest the benefit of each of the following adaptations:

(a) Rabbits have large ears. (b) Foxes have brown coats.

Figure 8.12 *A butterfly drinking nectar*

Figure 8.13 *A caterpillar chewing on a leaf*

8.10 Animals and plants in different habitats show many adaptations. Research and explain the benefit of each of the following adaptations.

Animals:

(a) Hedgehogs have spines.
(b) Hawks have good eyesight.
(c) Rabbits can run fast.
(d) Foxes have large ears.
(e) Frogs hibernate in winter.
(f) Swallows migrate to Africa in winter.

Plants:

(g) Dandelions have long, deep roots.
(h) Seaweeds are very flexible.
(i) Some seaweeds have air bladders.
(j) Blackberry plants have thorns.
(k) Ivy can cling to the bark of a tree.
(l) Buttercups have bright yellow flowers.

What is competition?

Competition takes place when two or more organisms require something that is in scarce supply. In any habitat:

- **Animals** compete for space, food, water and partners.
- **Plants** compete for light, space, water and minerals from the soil.

Figure 8.14 *Red deer competing for a mate*

Types of competition

Competition can occur between plants and animals of the same type. For example:

- Grasses compete with each other for light and space.
- Foxes compete with each other for food.

Competition also occurs between different types of plants and animals. For example:

- Grass and dandelions compete with each other for light.
- Robins and blackbirds compete with each other for food.

8.11 Figure 8.15 shows a sea bird nesting on a rocky cliff. Name two things for which sea birds such as this might compete.

Figure 8.15 *Sea bird nesting on a cliff*

What is interdependence?

All the organisms in a habitat depend on other organisms for their survival. Examples of how plants and animals are interdependent include:

- Animals depend on plants, e.g. rabbits depend on grass for food.
- Plants depend on animals, e.g. flowers depend on bees for pollination.
- Plants depend on each other, e.g. plants depend on each other for shelter.
- Animals depend on other animals, e.g. foxes depend on rabbits for food.

Food interdependence

One of the main ways in which living things depend on each other is for food. Organisms get their food in different ways, and can be categorised as:

- Producers
- Consumers
- Decomposers.

Producers

Producers are green plants that make their own food. Examples of producers are:

- Grasses
- Buttercups
- Nettles.
- Dandelions
- Daisies

Consumers

Animals do not make their own food. Instead, they get their food by eating (or consuming) plants or other animals. For this reason animals are called consumers. Depending on what they eat, consumers can be placed into three different groups:

- **Herbivores** are animals that eat plants only, e.g. rabbits, sheep, slugs and snails.
- **Carnivores** are animals that eat other animals, e.g. foxes, hawks and ladybirds.
- **Omnivores** are animals that eat both plants and other animals, e.g. badgers, thrushes, blackbirds and humans.

Figure 8.16 *A slug is a herbivore*

Figure 8.17 *A sparrowhawk is a carnivore. It is Ireland's most common bird of prey*

Figure 8.18 *Badgers are omnivores*

Decomposers

Decomposers are organisms that feed on dead plants and animals. Decomposers include a range of small animals (such as woodlice and earthworms) along with bacteria and fungi.

Decomposers are of great value as they release chemicals back into the environment. This allows other organisms to use these chemicals.

Figure 8.19 *A barn owl in flight*

8.12 Barn owls (shown in Figure 8.19) feed on small animals, which they hunt at night. Their feathers are specially arranged so that they can fly silently.

(a) Is this an example of adaptation, competition or interdependence?

(b) What is the possible benefit to barn owls of being able to fly silently?

What is a food chain?

A food chain is a list of organisms in which each organism is eaten by the next one in the chain. It is a simple way of explaining how energy and nutrients pass from one living thing to another. The arrows in a food chain show the direction in which the energy and nutrients pass.

An example of a simple food chain is where grass is eaten by a rabbit and the rabbit is then eaten by a fox. This food chain is shown below:

grass ⟶ rabbit ⟶ fox

This food chain has three feeding levels:

1. Grass – normally the first feeding level is a plant or a producer.
2. Rabbit – it is a herbivore and a consumer.
3. Fox – it is a carnivore and it is also a consumer.

Figure 8.20 *A fox chasing a rabbit – this is part of the food chain*

A summary of this food chain is given in Figure 8.21.

Figure 8.21 *A simple food chain*

An example of another food chain is given in Figure 8.22.

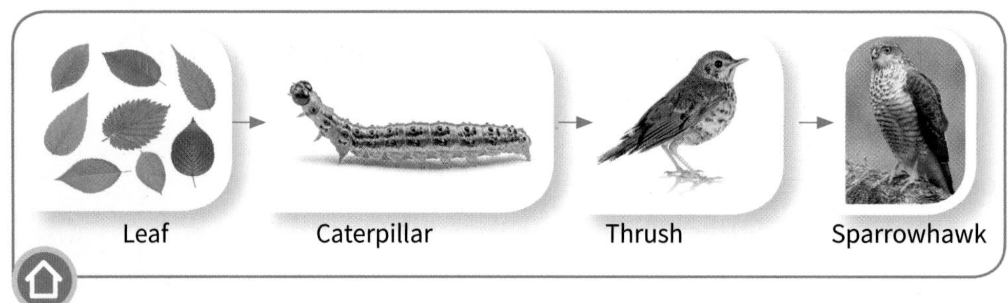

Figure 8.22 *Food chain from a hedgerow*

Do food chains involve decomposers?

Another way to show a food chain is to refer to the decomposers. Decomposers act on dead plants and animals and on the waste products (such as urine and faeces) of animals. The food chain in Figure 8.23 shows the role of the decomposers.

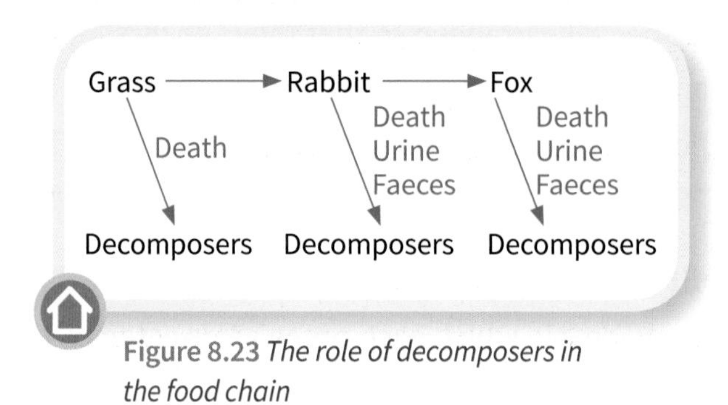

Figure 8.23 *The role of decomposers in the food chain*

What is a food web?

Food chains are a simple way to show how organisms feed in a habitat. For example, the simple food chain described earlier (grass → rabbit → fox) suggests that grass is eaten only by rabbits. It also suggests that rabbits are eaten only by foxes. Both of these situations are untrue.

Figure 8.24 *A kestrel with a mouse*

A food web consists of a number of interlinked food chains. A food web provides a more complete and realistic explanation of the way in which organisms in a habitat feed.

In all food webs, the dead plants and animals are broken down by decomposers. Examples of food webs are given in Figures 8.25 and 8.26.

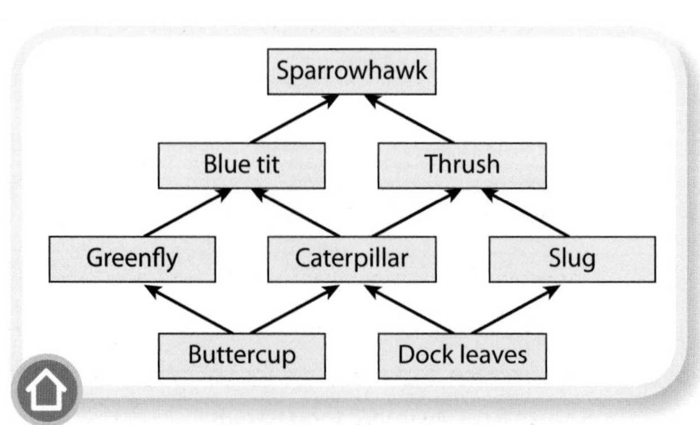

Figure 8.25 *A food web*

8.13 Answer the following questions in relation to the food web shown in Figure 8.26.

(a) Write out a food chain with four organisms in it.

(b) Name the producer in the web.

(c) Name two consumers in the web.

(d) Name a herbivore in the web.

(e) Name two carnivores in the web.

(f) Give one example of competition shown in this web.

(g) Give one example of how mice depend on the ash tree.

(h) Give one example of how the ash tree depends on mice.

(i) If all the robins died, what might happen to the number of:

(i) Owls (ii) Caterpillars.

(j) How many organisms feed on the ash tree?

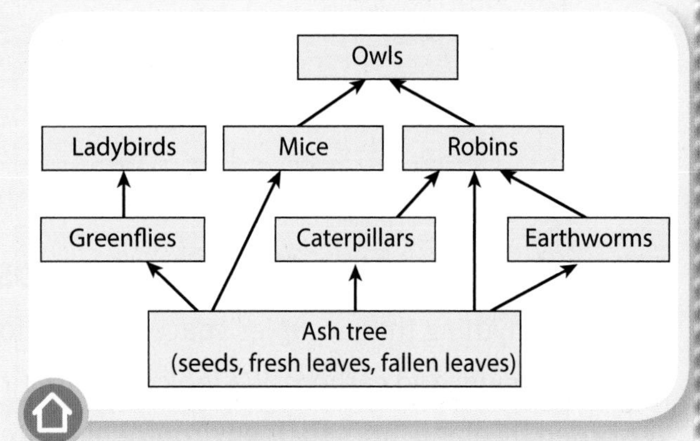

Figure 8.26 *A food web*

How does energy flow in an ecosystem?

Energy is the ability to do work. It can change from one form to another, which we will look at in more detail in chapters 10, 28 and 40.

The main source of energy for every ecosystem is the Sun (or **solar energy**). The Sun's energy is converted into food by **photosynthesis** (which we look at in chapter 10).

Energy flows along a food chain when each organism eats the previous one in the chain. However, not all of the energy flows from each organism to the next one. Some of it is lost:

- The organisms lose heat to their environment.
- The organisms may excrete waste such as urine and faeces (both contain energy).
- Some parts of organisms are not eaten (e.g. roots, bones, fur, teeth).
- Lots of energy is lost as heat when dead things decompose.

Only about 10% of the energy passes from organism to organism in a food chain. This means about 90% of the energy is lost at each step. As a result food chains cannot be too long as there will be very little energy available at the end of a long food chain.

Energy is lost from ecosystems (mainly as heat). Energy is said to **flow through** an ecosystem.

8.14 Tests show that for every 100 kJ of food eaten by a cow it gains only 5 kJ in weight. Wastes (such as faeces, urine and gases) account for 60 kJ. The remaining energy is lost as heat in respiration.

(a) How much energy (expressed as a %) is lost as heat?

(b) How efficient (as a %) is a cow at transferring food into body weight?

BIOLOGICAL WORLD

8.15 In the following food chain the grass was calculated to contain 10 000 kJ of energy. Assuming a 90% energy loss at each step of the food chain, calculate how much energy would be available to the hawk.

grass ⟶ grasshopper ⟶ frog ⟶ hawk

How does matter flow in an ecosystem?

Matter is anything that occupies space (such as food, chemicals and elements or minerals such as calcium and carbon). We look at matter in some detail in chapter 13. Matter is absorbed by plants from their environment. For example:

- Calcium is absorbed by the roots from the soil.
- Carbon is absorbed from the air in the form of carbon dioxide.

Matter passes from one organism to another in a food chain as each organism is eaten, e.g.:

- Calcium passes from grass to rabbits to foxes.
- Carbon (in the form of food) passes from grass to rabbits and from rabbits to foxes.

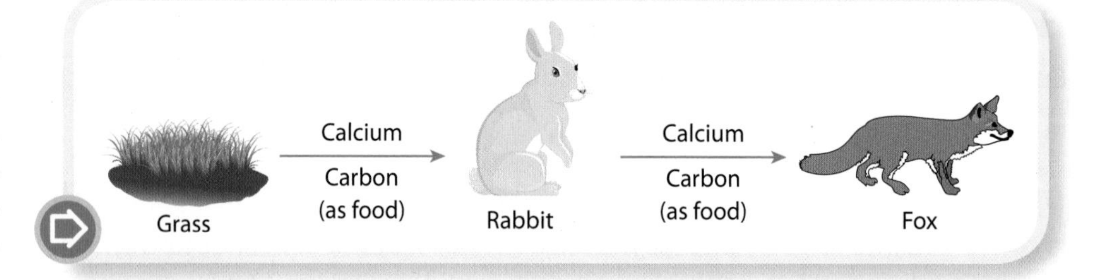

Figure 8.27 *Calcium and carbon passing through a food chain*

Matter is not normally lost from an ecosystem (unless living things leave the ecosystem). Matter is said to be **cycled** in the ecosystem (you will look at nutrient cycling in chapter 39).

In a food chain, for example, any waste and the parts that are not eaten pass into the soil. Here it is broken down (by decomposers) and the elements are released into the soil. These elements may then be reabsorbed by plants and the cycle starts all over again.

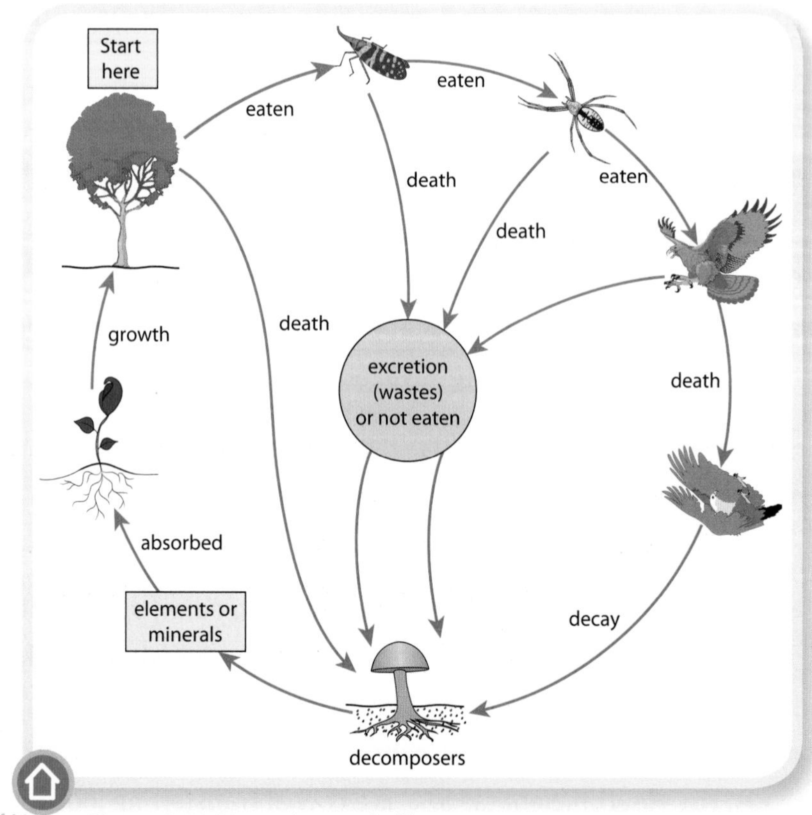

Figure 8.28 *Matter is recycled in an ecosystem*

UNIT 2

Factors affecting human health

Learning outcomes

At the end of this chapter you will be able to:

- Evaluate how inherited factors affect human health
- Evaluate how environmental factors and lifestyle choices (such as nutrition, smoking, exercise, drink, drugs, sleep and work/life balance) affect human health
- Examine the role of micro-organisms in human health.

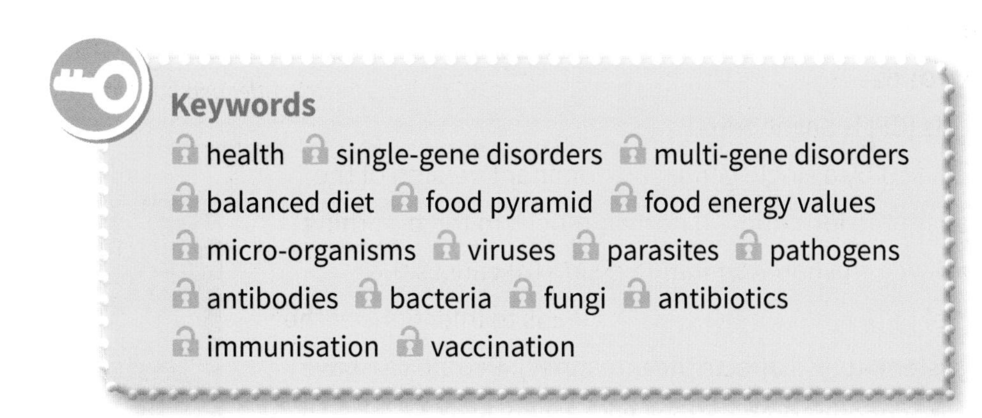

What is health?

Health is a **state of complete physical, mental and social well-being**. It is not just the absence of disease or sickness. In general, health can be considered as:

- Physical (dealing with the body), and
- Mental (dealing with the mind).

9.1 Research and name three common mental illnesses. For one of the illnesses you named describe the main symptoms of the condition.

9.2 Research and name three common physical illnesses. For one of the illnesses you named describe the main symptoms of the condition.

BIOLOGICAL WORLD

What factors affect human health?

Human health is affected by a wide range of factors. Some of these are shown in Figure 9.1.

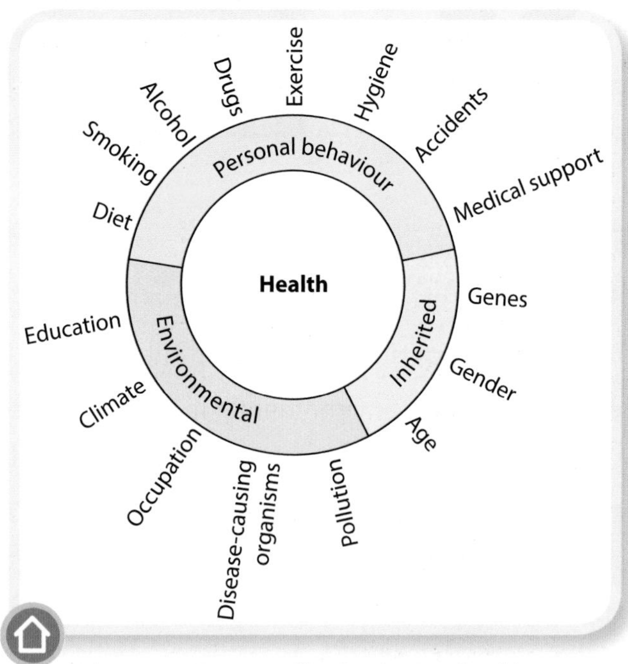

Figure 9.1 *Factors affecting human health*

How do inherited factors affect our health?

In chapter 3 we saw that inherited features are controlled by genes. Normally there are two versions of each gene: the dominant and the non-dominant (or recessive) version. The dominant version of a gene prevents the non-dominant (or recessive) version from working.

Are there single-gene disorders?

Cystic fibrosis

Cystic fibrosis (CF) is an inherited condition caused by a single gene. The dominant version of the gene (N) causes the formation of normal mucus in the breathing system. However, the non-dominant version (n) causes the production of thick, sticky mucus, which leads to infections of the breathing system (it also affects the intestines). People can have three different genetic combinations with respect to CF:

- NN = normal mucus
- Nn = normal mucus
- nn = cystic fibrosis.

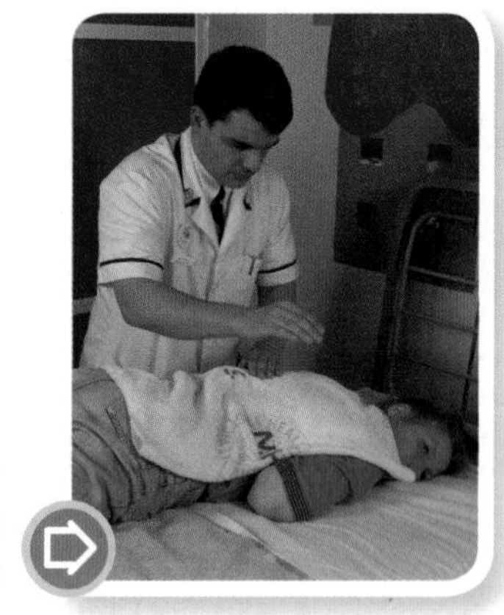

Figure 9.2 *People with cystic fibrosis have to have massages to break up mucus in the lungs*

9.3 Why do you think a person who has the combination Nn does not have cystic fibrosis?

9.4 Why do you think that most genetic diseases are caused when the person has two copies of the non-dominant or recessive gene?

9.5 In terms of mucus production the dominant version of the gene (N) produces normal mucus. The non-dominant (or recessive) version of the gene produces abnormal mucus, which causes cystic fibrosis. Referring to chapter 3 if necessary, explain the following by showing the genetic crosses:

(a) Why there is no possibility of children having cystic fibrosis if the parents are Nn and NN.

(b) Why two parents who do not have cystic fibrosis could have a child with cystic fibrosis.

Other single-gene disorders

Genes cause many other conditions. Some of these are:

- Sickle cell anaemia – where red blood cells are wrongly shaped
- Coeliac disease – the inability to process gluten, which is found in wheat
- Huntington's – where nerve cells die, which affects movement
- Haemophilia – the inability to form blood clots.

Work in groups and present your results to the class.

9.6 Choose one of the disorders listed in the previous paragraph and research it under the headings:
- Cause
- Symptoms
- Treatment.

9.7 During your searching you probably came across some sites that you felt unsure were giving you information that you could trust. Select a site that you think provides reliable information and one that you suspect might not be reliable. Note the addresses of these sites and give reasons for your choice in each case.

Are there disorders caused by many genes?

Cancer

Cancer is a range of conditions (about two hundred) where cells lose control of how fast they divide and for how long they divide. This causes the uncontrolled, rapid growth of cells.

Cancer requires a number of genes to change. Some people are born with one or more of these alterations already in place. They are more likely to get cancer.

Other factors that speed up the risk of alteration of genes are:

- Ultra-violet radiation (e.g. sunlight or sun-beds) or excess X-rays
- Diet (e.g. too much red or processed meat and not enough fruit and vegetables)
- Being overweight
- Viruses
- Smoking
- Lack of physical activity
- Problems with white blood cells that normally should prevent cancer.

Other multi-gene disorders

It is thought that there are many (altered) genes involved in:

- Heart disease
- Alzheimer's disease
- Diabetes
- High blood pressure
- Arthritis
- Obesity.

In addition, some inherited disorders are caused by having an extra or a missing chromosome. An example of this type is Down's syndrome (which results in altered mental and physical development).

Figure 9.3 *Down's syndrome is caused by an additional chromosome*

Did you know?

Down's syndrome is named after a British doctor, John Langdon Down, who first described the condition in 1866. It was only in 1959 that it was discovered that the cause was an extra copy of chromosome 21.

Work in groups and present your results to the class.

9.8 Choose one of the disorders listed as a multi-gene disorder in the previous paragraphs and research it under the headings:

- Cause
- Symptoms
- Treatment.

9.9 During your searching you probably came across some sites that you felt unsure were giving you information that you could trust. Select a site that you think provides reliable information and one that you suspect might not be reliable. Note the addresses of these sites and give reasons for your choice in each case.

How do environmental factors affect our health?

Many environmental factors affect our health (as outlined in Figure 9.1). We will consider two of these factors: nutrition and lifestyle choices.

What are the effects of nutrition on health?

Nutrition is how an organism gets its food. All living things need food. Plants make their own food. Animals take in food when they eat plants or other animals.

Food is needed to:

- Supply living things with energy
- Allow them to grow and repair damaged body parts
- Prevent them from getting diseases.

Humans must ensure that they take in the correct types of food. These foods must also be eaten in the correct amounts. We do this by eating a **balanced diet**.

What is a balanced diet?

A balanced diet contains the right amounts of each of the six different types (or constituents) of food. The six constituents of a balanced diet, the functions of these constituents and the foods that contain them are given in Table 9.1.

9.10 Research one nutrient (a vitamin or a mineral) needed in our diet. For this nutrient:

(a) List three common sources.

(b) Explain its function.

(c) List the common symptoms of a deficiency (or shortage).

Table 9.1 **The functions and sources of the parts of a balanced diet**

Constituent	Function	Common source
Carbohydrates		
Sugars	• Fast supply of energy	• Fruits, soft drinks, sweets, honey
Starch	• Slower supply of energy	• Bread, potatoes, rice, pasta
Fibre (or roughage)	• Helps to move food through the intestines	• Cereals, brown bread, fruit, vegetables
Fats	• Stored in the body • Insulate the body	• Butter, cream, margarine, milk, oil, fried food
Proteins	• Form muscle, hair, nails, enzymes, antibodies	• Meat, fish, egg white, milk, cheese, nuts, peas, beans
Vitamins There are 13 different vitamins	Each vitamin has a different function	Each vitamin has its own sources; generally found in: • Fruits, vegetables, meat, milk, grain
Minerals We need up to 20 different minerals	Each mineral has a different function	Each mineral has its own sources; generally found in: • Fruits, vegetables, meat, milk, grain
Water	• Cell reactions • Transport • Digestion • Controlling temperature	• Drinks, fruit, vegetables

Failure to eat a balanced diet results in a person being malnourished and unhealthy. For example:

- Too many high-energy foods may cause a person to be overweight or obese.
- Not enough energy in a diet may cause a person to be tired and sluggish.
- Lack of fibre may result in constipation (and may increase the risk of bowel cancer).

Food pyramid

The food we eat can be put into the following five food groups:

- Cereals, bread, rice and potatoes
- Fruit and vegetables
- Dairy products
- Meat and fish
- Other types of food.

In order to maintain a balanced diet it is necessary to eat different amounts of each food group. The number of servings of each food group that we should eat each day is given in a **food pyramid** (see Figure 9.4).

Foods at the top of the food pyramid do not contain minerals or vitamins. They should be eaten rarely as they are high in fats and cause people to be overweight. They also lead to heart conditions and may cause diabetes.

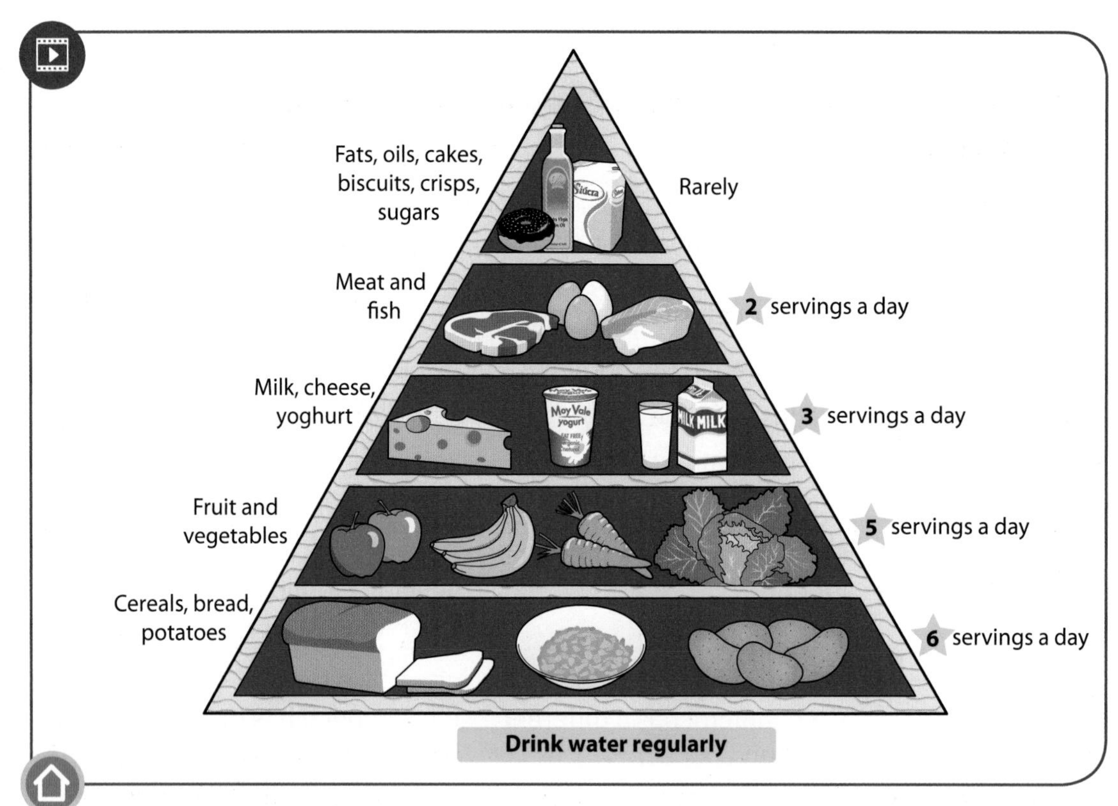

Figure 9.4 *The food pyramid*

9.11 Complete a food pyramid diary, similar to this one, for seven days.

Food groups	Mon	Tues	Wed	Thurs	Fri	Sat	Sun
Fats, oils, cakes, biscuits, crisps, sugar, sweets							
Meat, fish, peas, beans							
Milk, cheese, yoghurt							
Fruit, vegetables							
Cereals, bread, rice, potatoes							
For every portion of a particular type of food you eat, place a tick (✓) opposite that food type in the chart.							

People need different amounts of food

The amount and type of food needed by each person varies according to factors such as:

- Age (younger people need more food than older people)
- Gender (males need more food than females)
- Activity levels (active people need more food than inactive people)
- Health (sick people need smaller portions and softer food).

9.12 Why do you think each of the following groups need more food?

(i) Younger people
(ii) Males
(iii) Active people
(iv) Healthy people
(v) Pregnant women

9.13 Give a reason why a female might need more food than a male.

Energy values

Different foods contain different amounts of energy. The amount of energy in a food is known as its **energy value**.

Energy is measured in units called joules (J). However, the normal unit used for the energy value of a food is **kilojoules per gram** (**kJ/g**).

In general, carbohydrates and proteins have the same energy values, while fats have over twice the energy value of the other two.

Although carbohydrates and proteins have the same energy values, the human body uses protein for energy only when it is close to starvation. This prevents the body from digesting its own body parts such as muscles and the heart.

Typical daily energy needs (kJ) for 12 to 15-year-olds are:

	Inactive	Active
Girl	10 000	11 000
Boy	12 000	15 000

The energy content of different foods is often given on nutrition information panels on the side of the food containers, as shown in Figure 9.5.

JAM Nutritional information Typical values per 100 g	
Energy	1127 kJ
Protein	0.1 g
Carbohydrate	65.5 g
(of which sugars)	65.4 g
Fat	0.0 g
(of which saturates)	0.0 g
Fibre	1.0 g

SOUP Nutritional information Typical values per 100 g	
Energy	205 kJ
Protein	1.0 g
Carbohydrate	4.0 g
Fat	3.3 g
Fibre	0.0 g

BEANS Nutritional information Typical values per 100 g	
Energy	326 kJ
Protein	4.3 g
Carbohydrate	13.8 g
Fat	0.5 g
Fibre	2.9 g

BISCUITS Nutritional information Typical values per 100 g	
Energy	1616 kJ
Protein	2.8 g
Carbohydrate	66.2 g
Fat	13.6 g
Fibre	0.4 g

Figure 9.5 *Examples of nutrition information panels*

9.14 Answer these questions, based on the information on the labels in Figure 9.5.

(a) If an active girl drinks 200 g of soup, what percentage of her daily energy needs is she getting?

(b) If an inactive boy eats 300 g of biscuits, how much of his daily energy needs is he getting?

(c) Which of the four foods do you consider is the unhealthiest? Give a reason for your answer.
(d) Which of the foods would you recommend for a person trying to build up muscle? Give a reason for your answer.

What happens if you eat too much food?

Eating too much food means that the surplus food is converted to fat and stored in the body. This leads to problems such as becoming overweight or obese (which means severely overweight). In turn this can lead to:

- Increased risk of heart disease
- High blood pressure
- Diabetes
- Gallstones
- Breathing difficulties
- Some forms of cancer.

What happens if you eat too little food?

Eating less food than the body needs results in weight loss. In addition it causes:

- Mood swings
- Depression
- Inability to think clearly
- Heart and circulatory problems
- Low blood pressure
- Reproductive problems
- Weak bones.

What are the effects of lifestyle choices on health?

The main lifestyle choices that affect our health, and which we will look at in this chapter, are:

- Diet (which we have already studied)
- Smoking
- Exercise
- Drink and drugs
- Sleep
- Work/life balance.

Smoking

Smoking is bad for our health. This fact is recognised by the health warning printed on all packets of cigarettes. In addition smoking is banned in an increasing number of locations and advertisements for cigarettes are strictly controlled.

Smoking has the following effects:

- Smoke clogs up the tiny hairs in the nose. This allows more dirt particles to enter the lungs.
- Smoke irritates the nose and bronchioles. This causes increased mucus to form, which leads to 'smoker's cough'.
- Smoking results in increased lung infections such as pneumonia and bronchitis.
- Smoking increases the risk of getting lung cancer and other cancers.
- Gases in cigarette smoke enter our blood. Some of these gases reduce the ability of our blood to carry oxygen. As a result our heart must pump harder and faster. This strains the heart and often leads to heart attacks.
- If a pregnant woman smokes, the chemicals in her blood will enter the baby's body. This can affect the development of the baby.

Figure 9.6 *A normal, healthy lung (left) and a smoker's lung (right)*

There are over 7,000 chemicals in cigarette smoke; several hundred of these chemicals can cause cancer.

9.15 In small groups work through the following. In your group, discuss:

(a) Why young people start to smoke cigarettes, and

(b) What are the best ways to prevent young people from starting to smoke.

9.16 Research and list the chemicals and products that are used to make up a cigarette.

9.17 Present your findings to the class using suitable support methods (e.g. PowerPoint, charts, a mind map, summary notes, etc.).

Exercise

Regular exercise has many benefits. This exercise might be organised, e.g. in terms of a sport or training or working out in a gymnasium. However, it can also be informal and carried out as part of our lifestyle. For example, walking or cycling to and from school, and using the stairs instead of taking a lift are valid forms of exercise.

It is suggested that everybody should take at least thirty minutes' exercise five days a week.

Benefits of exercise:

- Helps with weight loss if needed, and prevents weight gain.
- Reduces the risk of developing conditions such as stroke, heart attack, diabetes, depression, some cancers and arthritis.
- Increases energy. Regular exercise improves the efficiency of our lungs, heart and blood vessels, which gives us more energy.
- Improves mood. Physical activity stimulates many brain chemicals that cause us to be happier and more relaxed. It also improves our appearance, confidence and self-esteem.
- Improves sleep, by helping us fall asleep and stay asleep.

Drink and drugs

Alcohol

It is illegal for anyone under the age of eighteen in Ireland to purchase alcohol. What are the problems caused by alcohol?

- It is a depressant (it slows down the working of the brain). This can result in altering our emotions, perceptions, vision, hearing and movement.
- It is a toxic substance. This means that it causes us to feel sick, lose co-ordination, stagger, slur our speech and slow our reaction times.
- It changes our mood. Some people become more friendly and talkative, but some people become aggressive and angry.
- Large amounts of alcohol taken in a short period of time may result in alcohol poisoning. This may result in vomiting, extreme sleepiness, loss of consciousness and even death.
- It is addictive. Anyone who takes alcohol may become dependent on it.

Drugs

The effects of drugs depend on:

- The type of drug
- The amount of the drug
- The size of the person
- How often it is taken
- How fast it gets to the brain
- What other drugs, substances or food are taken at the same time.

Some drugs are illegal for very good reasons: they can have serious effects on our physical and mental health.

9.18 Select and research one of the following common illegal drugs:

- Cannabis
- Cocaine
- Ecstasy
- Heroin.

Explain the effects and dangers of the selected drug.

Sleep

In general, young people need more sleep than adults. Most young people need about eight hours' sleep each night.

Sleep is vitally important to our health. It:

- Improves our concentration
- Makes us more alert
- Increases our energy levels
- Allows our body to recover and heal.

Work/life balance

An important lifestyle choice is to allow enough time for relaxation and play. We all need to have fun and a laugh. This is often best done in the company of good friends. We need to be aware of what makes us feel good and happy and to include this in our daily routine.

What are micro-organisms?

Micro-organisms are small living things. Most of them are too small to be seen with the naked eye. They can be seen only using special microscopes.

Micro-organisms are found in huge numbers almost everywhere. For example, they are present in the air, water and soil, on our skin, and inside plants, animals and humans.

There are three types of micro-organism:

- Viruses
- Bacteria
- Fungi.

Viruses and bacteria are too small to be seen by eye, but we can see some fungi.

Are all micro-organisms harmful?

Most micro-organisms are of benefit. For example, they are important as they play crucial roles in:

- Decomposition – which allows living things to be broken down and their minerals released so they can be recycled into new living things.
- Food production – they are involved in making many foods, alcohol, baking.
- Biotechnology – this is the use of living things, or parts of living things, to produce useful products such as drugs, flavourings, colourings, vitamins, artificial cloth, fuels.
- Water treatment.
- Digestive systems – they make vitamins, prevent the growth of disease-causing organisms and break down some foods.

What is the role of micro-organisms in human health?

Some micro-organisms (often called microbes or germs) are **pathogens**. This means they cause disease.

What diseases do micro-organisms cause?

Viruses

Viruses are the smallest micro-organisms. Up to one million viruses may fit across the thickness of a thumbnail (1 mm). Viruses cannot reproduce by themselves. For this reason it can be argued that they are not living things.

Viruses increase in numbers by invading other cells. They cause the other cell to form new viruses. For this reason all viruses are said to be **parasites** (i.e. they live on or in another living thing).

Examples of human diseases caused by viruses include:

- Measles
- Mumps
- Chicken pox
- Polio
- Colds
- Flu (influenza)
- Cold sores
- AIDS (caused by HIV)
- Ebola.

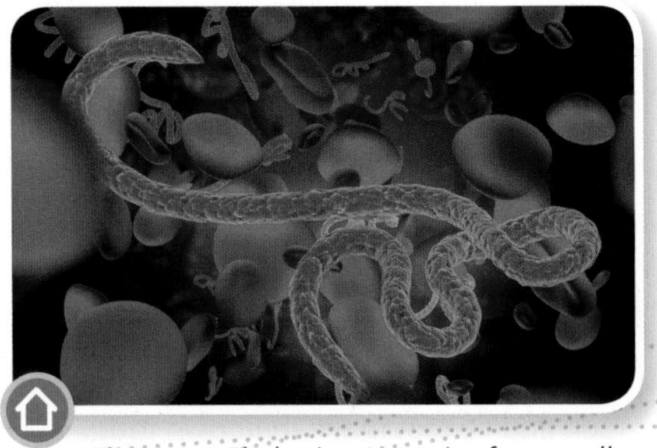

Figure 9.7 *Ebola virus emerging from a cell*

BIOLOGICAL WORLD

Very few chemicals or medicines can kill viruses. For example, antibiotics prevent bacterial infections but have no effect on viruses.

Our bodies fight off most virus infections when our white blood cells produce chemicals called antibodies.

Bacteria

Bacteria are larger than viruses. They are very simple organisms; for example, they do not have a proper nucleus.

In order to grow, bacteria need the following:

- Food
- Water
- A suitable temperature
- A suitable pH.

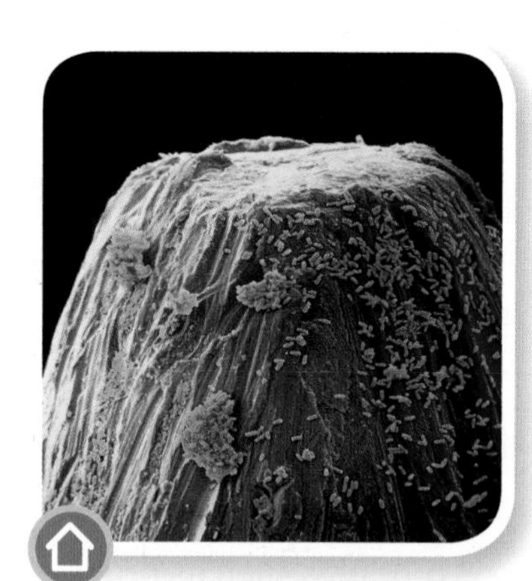

Figure 9.8 *Bacteria on the sharp tip of a pin*

Under ideal conditions bacteria can reproduce very rapidly. Bacteria reproduce asexually. Many bacteria can double their numbers every twenty minutes.

Examples of human bacterial diseases are:

- Tetanus (lockjaw)
- Tuberculosis (TB)
- Pneumonia
- Sore throats
- Tooth and gum decay
- Food poisoning
- Cholera
- Anthrax.

Antibiotics are chemicals made by bacteria and fungi, which kill or prevent the reproduction of other bacteria. Penicillin is an example of an antibiotic.

9.19 Why are antibiotics of no value in treating the flu?

9.20 What is the difference between antibiotics and antibodies?

9.21 It is suggested that the misuse of antibiotics has resulted in the evolution of antibiotic-resistant bacteria.

(a) Find out the name of two of the most common antibiotic-resistant bacteria in Ireland.

(b) Research the ways in which antibiotics have been misused.

(c) What is the main danger of misusing antibiotics?

Fungi

Fungi are simple organisms that do not contain chlorophyll. For this reason they are not green and cannot make their own food.

Some fungi are parasites on plants, on animals and even on humans. Many fungi feed on dead material and act as decomposers. Some fungi are single celled (e.g. yeast), while many form long threads. Very often these threads are underground and only come to the surface as reproductive structures such as mushrooms.

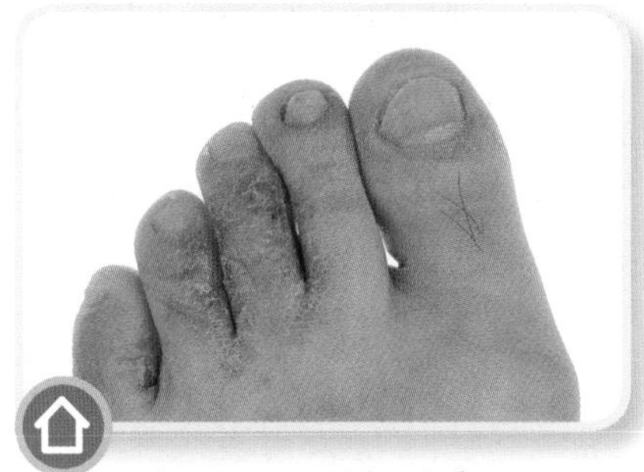

Figure 9.9 *Athlete's foot infection*

Examples of human fungus diseases are:

- Athlete's foot
- Ringworm.

How do we reduce the risk of infections?

Most pathogens spread through the air when we sneeze or cough. Some spread when we touch something and a small number spread in body fluids such as sweat, saliva, blood or semen. In addition some pathogens enter our body when we eat improperly cooked food.

The best ways to reduce infections are to:

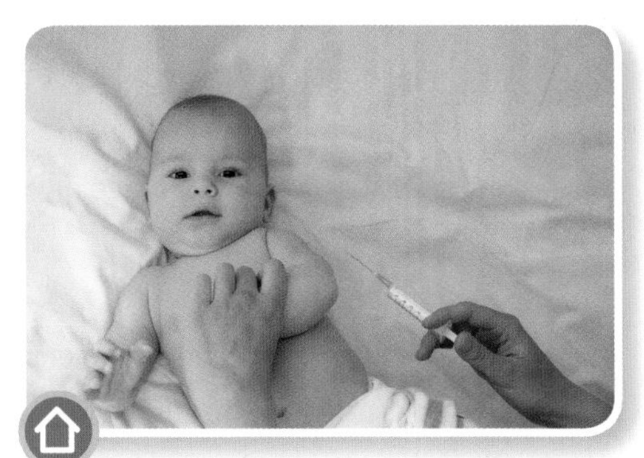

Figure 9.10 *Some vaccinations are given to babies*

- Wash our hands in soap and warm water for at least 15 seconds. This is important before eating or preparing food and after we cough, sneeze, use the toilet, touch animals, play outside or visit a sick person.
- Make sure we get all our immunisations (often called vaccinations). These introduce a small amount of the pathogen into the body. This allows our bodies to produce antibodies against the pathogen. This means we will have long-term resistance to the pathogen. As the pathogen cannot reproduce, the vaccination will not cause us to suffer all the symptoms of the infection.
- Cook food properly. High temperatures kill micro-organisms.
- Eat a proper diet, get regular exercise and get enough sleep, which all help our bodies to fight off pathogens.

9.22 Research the most common diseases against which we can be immunised or vaccinated.

9.23 Explain why vaccinations give us long-lasting resistance to infection but antibiotics give only short-term resistance.

Did you know?

It is suggested that we wash our hands for the same length of time it takes us to sing one verse of the 'Happy Birthday' song.

Portfolio 75

Activity 9.1

Question

How can we show that micro-organisms are present in different locations?

We will take samples from different locations and grow them on nutrient agar in petri dishes. Nutrient agar is a solid, jelly-like substance that contains food that micro-organisms need to grow.

Equipment needed

Nutrient agar	A beaker with boiled water	Disinfectant
Petri dishes (also called plates)	Masking tape	Basin
Cotton wool buds	Pen or marker	

Safety

Micro-organisms can cause disease so we have to reduce the risks by:

- Washing our hands before and after the activity
- Not putting anything dirty in or near our mouths
- Covering any cuts with a bandage or wearing plastic gloves
- Taping the dishes shut
- Killing any micro-organisms at the end of the activity by soaking the dishes in sterilising liquid or disinfectant.

Figure 9.11 *Micro-organisms growing on agar in a petri dish*

Conducting the activity

1. Dip a clean cotton wool bud in boiled water in a beaker. Rub the damp cotton wool bud over the surface to be tested. Sample surfaces are a door handle, a computer keyboard, a desk surface, a phone, the sink in a bathroom, a bin, the sole of your shoe, the inside of your mouth, under your finger nails, etc. Use a separate cotton wool bud in each location.
2. Open the lid of the plate slightly so that micro-organisms in the air do not enter. Rub the cotton wool bud gently over the surface of the agar in a petri dish. If you wish you could use half of each dish for two different samples, just remember which side has which sample. (You could also press your unwashed fingers gently on the surface of the agar in one dish and repeat this in a second dish after washing your hands.)
3. Place the lid on the dish and seal it closed with tape.
4. Place a piece of (masking) tape across the base of the dish and use it to label the source of the sample(s) and your name.
5. Tape a petri dish shut without opening it. This dish will act as a control or comparison for the other dish(es).

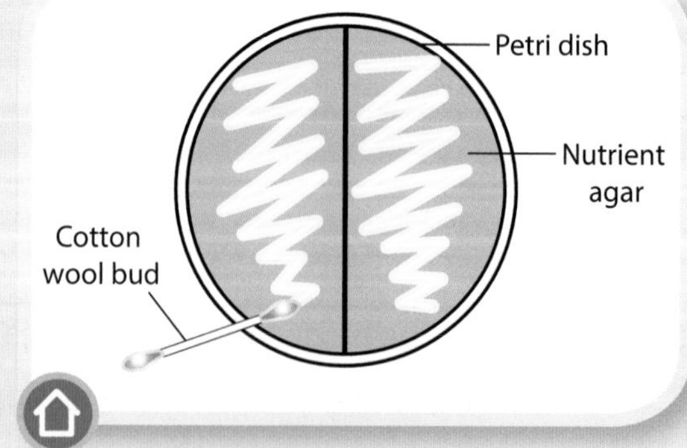

Figure 9.12 *Rubbing a cotton wool bud over the surface of the agar in a petri dish*

6. Leave the dishes in a warm place (between 20°C and 30°C) to allow micro-organisms to grow.
7. Leave the dishes upside down to prevent water from dripping onto any micro-organisms that grow.
8. Leave the dishes for 4 to 7 days.
9. Examine the dishes, but do *not* open them.
10. Take a note of which locations had:
    (a) The greatest and least numbers of different types of micro-organisms.
    (b) The greatest and least amounts of overall growth of micro-organisms.
11. Record your results in a table similar to the one below.

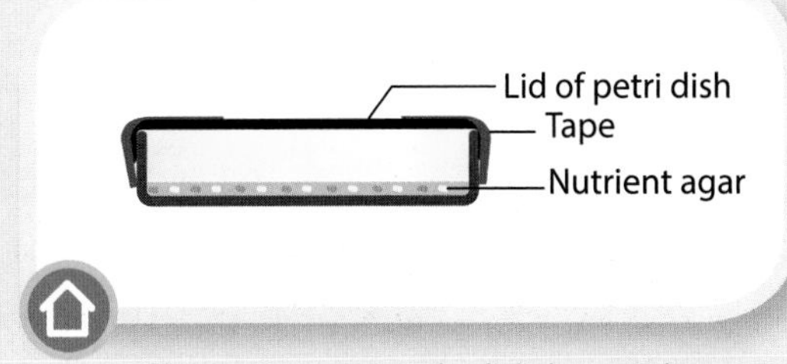

Figure 9.13 *Tape the lid shut and turn the dish upside down*

Observation	Location
Greatest number of different types of micro-organisms	
Least number of different types of micro-organisms	
The dish(es) with the most overall growth	
Dish(es) with no visible growth	
Control dish	

12. When you are finished, the dishes should be soaked in sterilising liquid or disinfectant before being placed in a bin (unless your teacher instructs you otherwise).

9.24 Why did you use nutrient agar?

9.25 Why is it better to use a damp cotton wool bud rather than a dry one?

9.26 What problem might arise if the petri dishes were left in a cold place?

9.27 Why were the petri dishes left lying on their lids?

9.28 Name two types of micro-organisms that might grow on the agar.

9.29 You are asked to compare how effective two liquid hand sterilisers are in killing micro-organisms. Work in groups to plan how you might carry out this investigation. Each group should present their findings to the class and then change their plan if necessary to respond to any good ideas they took from other groups in the class.

BIOLOGICAL WORLD

CHAPTER 10 Respiration and photosynthesis

UNIT 2

Learning outcomes

At the end of this chapter you will be able to:

- Describe respiration as a chemical and biological process
- Describe photosynthesis as a chemical and biological process
- Write the word equations for photosynthesis and respiration
- Investigate the factors that affect respiration and photosynthesis.

Keywords

respiration · aerobic respiration · enzymes · anaerobic respiration · lactic acid · photosynthesis · solar energy · chemical energy · stomata · chlorophyll

Biochemical processes

Respiration and photosynthesis are chemical processes *and* biological processes. Because they are both, they are often described as **biochemical** processes. They both involve energy conversions: in respiration energy is released from food; in photosynthesis energy is used to make food.

What is respiration?

High-energy drinks give you an extra burst of energy when you are getting tired. Have you ever wondered, how does energy in food end up as energy that keeps you moving?

Respiration is the way in which food is broken down to release energy in each body cell.

- If this process needs oxygen it is called **aerobic respiration**.
- If oxygen is not needed the process is called **anaerobic respiration**.

What is aerobic respiration?

Living things need energy to allow them to move, grow, stay warm and repair damaged parts. They get their energy from food in a process called respiration. Respiration for the majority of living things is aerobic.

Aerobic respiration can be summarised by the word equation:

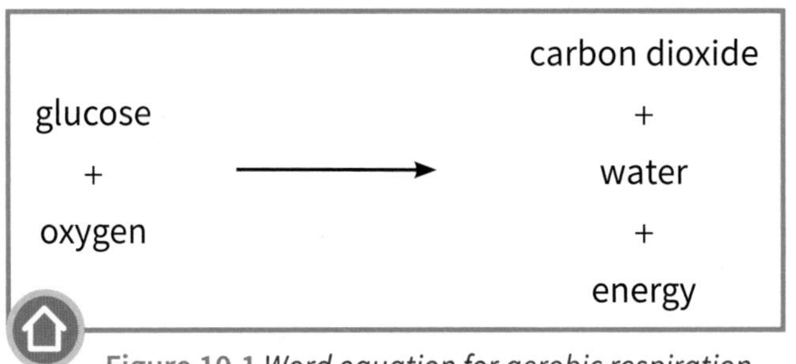

Figure 10.1 *Word equation for aerobic respiration*

Figure 10.2 *Food gives us energy*

10.1 Respiration is vital to life.

(a) Why do all living things need respiration?

(b) Why do humans normally have higher rates of respiration by day than they do by night?

(c) What are the end products of aerobic respiration?

To allow aerobic respiration to take place cells need a supply of glucose and oxygen. In humans:

- Glucose is carried by blood plasma from the small intestine to all the cells of the body.
- Oxygen is carried by haemoglobin in red blood cells from the lungs to all the cells of the body.

In all living cells glucose combines with oxygen to release energy and the waste products carbon dioxide and water (vapour). Some of the energy is used by the cells, while some is lost as heat.

The waste products are carried by blood plasma to the lungs from where they pass out of (or are excreted from) the body.

As well as taking place in all the living cells in the human body, aerobic respiration also takes place in most animal and plant cells.

10.2 What do we use energy for?

10.3 When we take in more energy than we need what happens to the surplus energy?

10.4 Active people need larger amounts of food than inactive people. Explain why this is the case.

10.5 Suggest two reasons why we breathe faster when we exercise.

10.6 Oxygen gas is held in the atmosphere by the force of gravity. This prevents it from escaping from Earth. Suggest why people who live at high altitudes have greater concentrations of red blood cells than those who live at sea level.

Figure 10.3 *Activity uses energy*

Figure 10.4 *Much less energy is needed while resting*

What factors affect respiration?

The main factors affecting respiration are:

- Temperature
- Oxygen
- Water.

Temperature

Respiration is a process that occurs in living things. This means it is a biological process. Most biological reactions are controlled by **enzymes**. These are proteins that speed up reactions without being used up in the reaction.

Above a certain temperature enzymes change shape, which means they do not work so well. This means that the rate of the reaction slows down. These changes are shown in the graph in Figure 10.5.

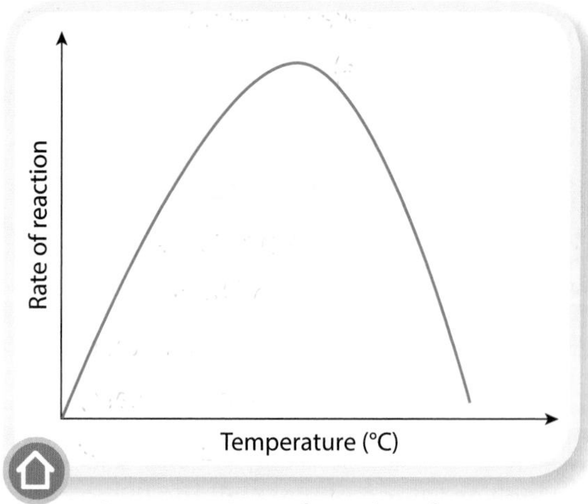

Figure 10.5 *Rate of reaction of enzymes at different temperatures*

Human enzymes have their maximum rate of reaction at 37°C, while plant enzymes work best between 20°C and 30°C. This means the rate of respiration is highest at these temperatures in humans or in plants.

Oxygen

Oxygen is essential for aerobic respiration. When we exercise we breathe faster and deeper to take in more oxygen and release more energy and carbon dioxide.

If there is a shortage of oxygen (e.g. when we exercise vigorously, or if a plant's roots are in waterlogged soil) the rate of respiration may not supply enough energy. Then cells can respire **anaerobically**; this means they break down glucose in the absence of oxygen. This supplies a small amount of extra energy to the cells. However, it also produces harmful waste products.

In humans anaerobic respiration produces lactic acid, as shown in the equation below:

glucose ⟶ lactic acid

Lactic acid causes muscles to cramp, which forces us to stop the exercise.

In yeast cells anaerobic respiration produces alcohol and carbon dioxide:

glucose ⟶ alcohol + carbon dioxide

Did you know?

Lactic acid forming in our chest muscles causes a stitch: if it forms in our heart muscles it causes pain in the chest before a person experiences a heart attack.

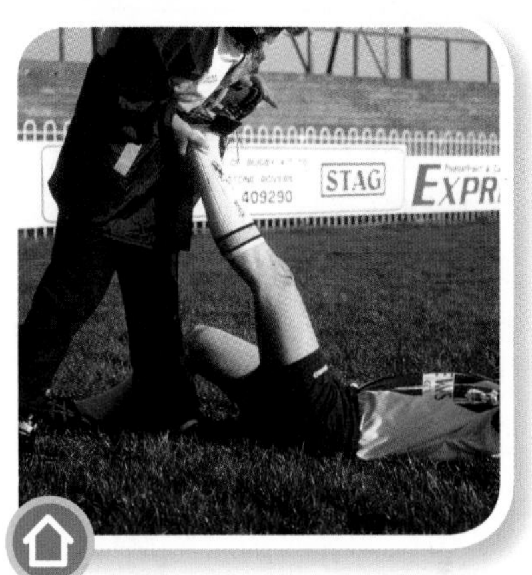

Figure 10.6 *Cramp can often occur when we play sports, which forces us to stop exercising*

Water

Water is essential to allow enzymes to work. This means a lack of water in cells will slow down the rate of respiration.

This is why we must ensure that we drink enough water, especially when we lose water as sweat (e.g. in hot weather or during exercise).

What are the products of respiration?

We have seen that the products of respiration are:

- **Energy** This is why all living things carry out respiration. The more active an organism is, the more respiration it needs to carry out.
- **Carbon dioxide** This is a waste product of respiration.
  - Animals release carbon dioxide into the air.
  - Plants may use some of the carbon dioxide they produce for photosynthesis; any carbon dioxide not used in photosynthesis is released into the air.
- **Water (vapour)** This is another waste product of respiration. Both plants and animals release water vapour into the air.

Did you know?

Yeast is a fungus and is used to make alcohol (beers and wine) and can also be used in baking (the carbon dioxide causes dough to rise).

Can we show that energy is released by respiration?

When seeds germinate (or start to grow) they carry out respiration. This produces heat. If we can trap this heat and measure any temperature change we may see that energy is released. This is what we will try to do in Activity 10.1.

Portfolio 81

Activity 10.1

Question

How can we show that respiration produces energy?

We will try to trap and measure the heat from germinating seeds to see that energy is released.

Equipment needed

2 vacuum flasks
Pea seeds
2 thermometers or temperature sensors connected to data loggers
Disinfectant solution
Sieve
Cotton wool

Safety

- Be careful when boiling the seeds and when rinsing the flasks with boiling water.
- Be careful not to break the thermometer or temperature sensor.
- Do not force the cotton wool into the top of the flask too tightly as you may break the flask.
- Be careful when clamping the flasks that you do not break them.

Conducting the activity

1. Soak some pea seeds in water for 24 hours. This allows them to absorb the water they need for germinating or growing.
2. Boil half of the seeds in water for 5 minutes. This kills the seeds so they act as a control.
3. Soak the live seeds in disinfectant solution for 5 minutes. This kills any micro-organisms on the surface.

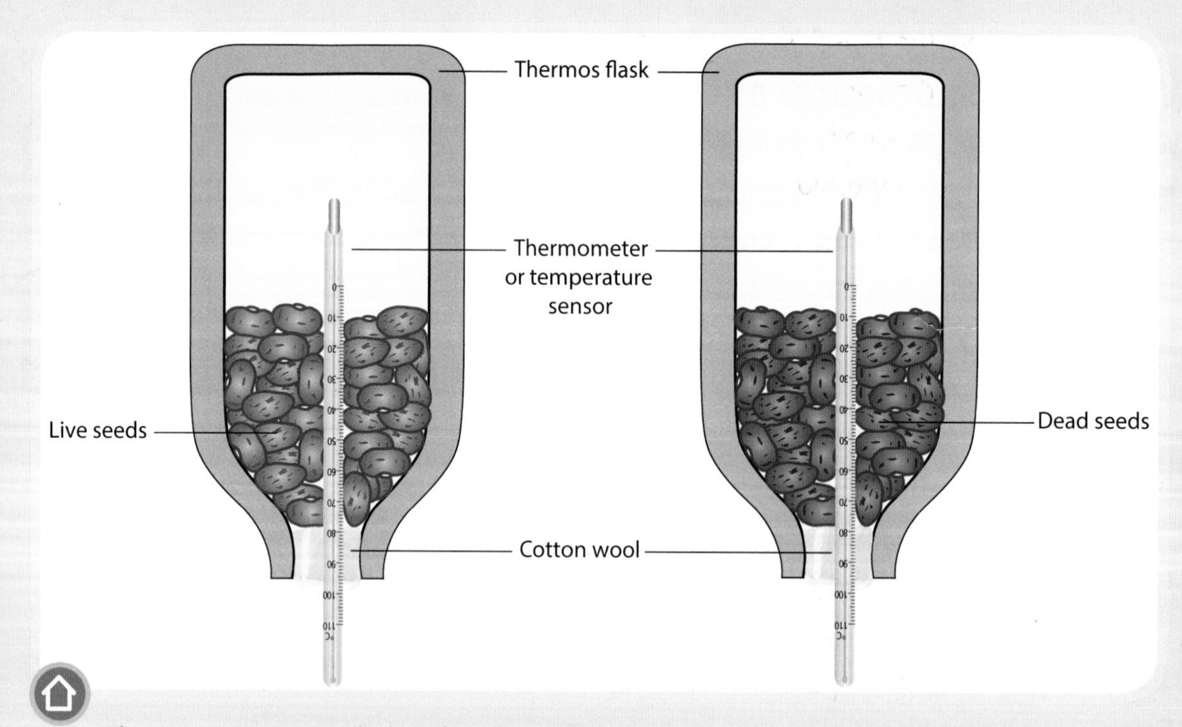

Figure 10.7 *Measuring the heat from germinating seeds*

4. Pour the live seeds into a sieve over a sink. Rinse the seeds to wash off any disinfectant.
5. Rinse out two vacuum (or thermos) flasks with boiling water. This kills any micro-organisms.
6. Half fill one vacuum flask with live seeds.
7. Place a thermometer or temperature sensor in the flask and seal the flask with cotton wool.

8. Half fill the second vacuum flask with dead seeds and place a thermometer or temperature sensor and cotton wool in the flask as before.
9. Leave the flasks upside down for 4 to 7 days.
10. Record the output from the data logger or record the temperature in each flask on as many days as possible.
11. Record your data in a table similar to the one below.

	Temperature (°C)	
Day number	Live seeds	Dead seeds
1		
2		
3		
4		
5		
6		
7		

12. Draw a graph of your results. Place the day number on the x-axis and temperature on the y-axis.

10.7 Why were thermos flasks used instead of glass containers?

10.8 Why were the unboiled seeds disinfected?

10.9 Why was there no need to disinfect the boiled seeds?

10.10 Why were the thermos flasks placed upside down?

Portfolio 83

Activity 10.2

Question

Can we show that a gas is produced by respiration in yeast?

Yeast breaks sugars down to form alcohol and carbon dioxide. If we carry out this reaction in a plastic bottle covered by a balloon then the gas formed may cause the balloon to inflate.

Equipment needed

Small, clear plastic drinks bottle
Balloon
Yeast
Sugar
Warm water

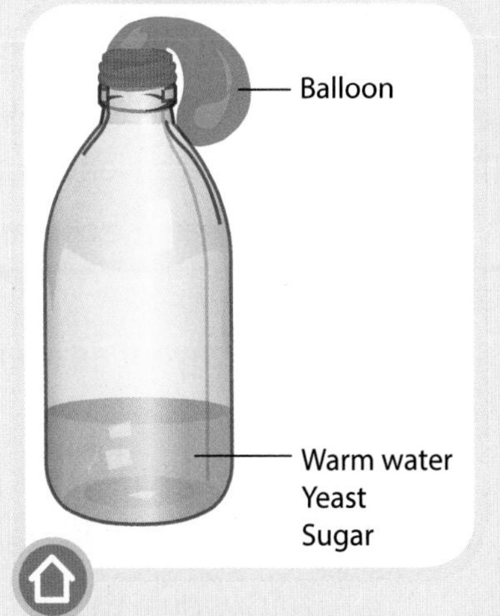

Figure 10.8 *To show that gas is produced by respiration in yeast*

BIOLOGICAL WORLD

Conducting the activity

1. Blow the balloon up and let it deflate a few times to stretch and loosen it.
2. Pour some warm water into the bottle to a depth of about 3 cm.
3. Add a teaspoonful of dried yeast and swirl it around a few times to dissolve it.
4. Add a teaspoonful of sugar to the yeast solution and swirl it to ensure it is dissolved.
5. Place the balloon over the neck of the bottle to seal it.
6. Leave it in a warm place and observe what happens over the next 30 minutes (or longer).
7. As a control, set up a second bottle in the same way but leave out the sugar.
8. Record the results in a table similar to the one below.

Contents of bottle	Amount of expansion of balloon (e.g. none / some / most)
Water, yeast, sugar	
Water, yeast (no sugar)	

10.11 Apart from respiration, what other factor might cause either balloon to expand?

10.12 The balloon with the yeast and sugar will stop expanding after some time. Why do you think this happens?

10.13 Why is it better to use warm water than cold water?

10.14 Suggest how you might adapt this activity to investigate the effects of carrying out respiration at different temperatures.

Investigating i5

10.15 The equipment in **Figure 10.9** was set up to investigate gas exchange in animals.

(a) After some time the drop of coloured liquid was seen to move. In which direction do you think it will move?

(b) Explain why the drop moved in the direction you stated.

(c) Will the concentration of carbon dioxide in the container change over time?

(d) Explain your answer to part (c) above.

(e) If the container was placed in a water bath at 10°C and later at 20°C, would this affect the speed at which the drop of liquid moves?

(f) Explain your answer to part (e).

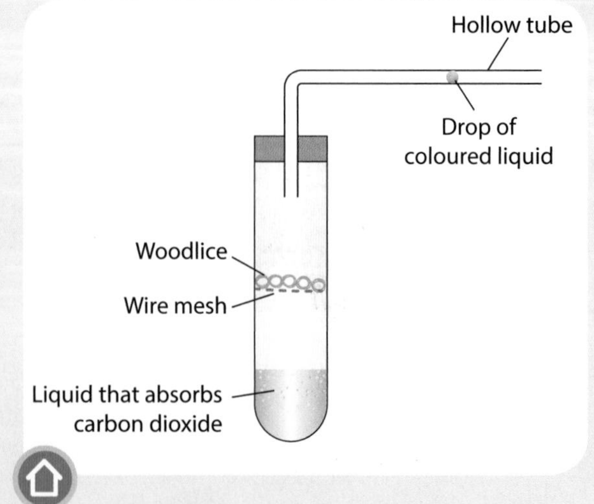

Figure 10.9 *Investigating gas exchange in respiration*

What is photosynthesis?

The Sun is the source of most of the energy on Earth. It provides heat to keep our planet warm. It also provides energy in the form of light.

Plants use solar (sun) energy to make food in a process called photosynthesis. In this way, they convert energy from one form (light) to another form (the chemical energy in food). One of the main differences between plants and animals is that plants can make their own food, while animals cannot.

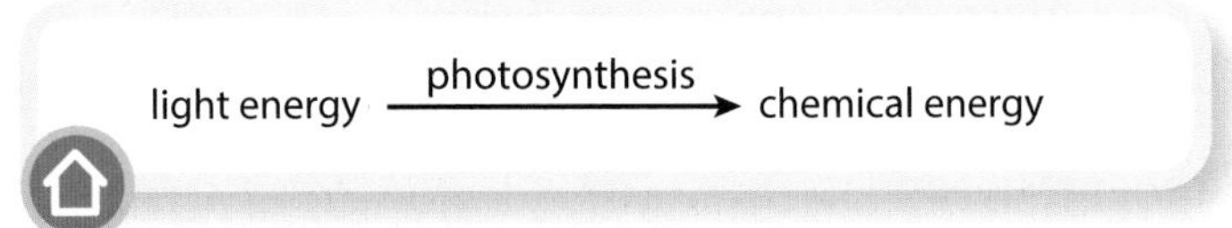

Figure 10.10 *The conversion of energy by photosynthesis*

10.16 What term is used to describe organisms that make their own food?

10.17 What term is used to describe organisms that cannot make their own food?

What is the word equation for photosynthesis?

Photosynthesis can be summarised by the word equation shown in Figure 10.11.

carbon dioxide + water —(light / chlorophyll)→ glucose + oxygen

Figure 10.11 *Word equation for photosynthesis*

Figure 10.12 *Photosynthesis requires light*

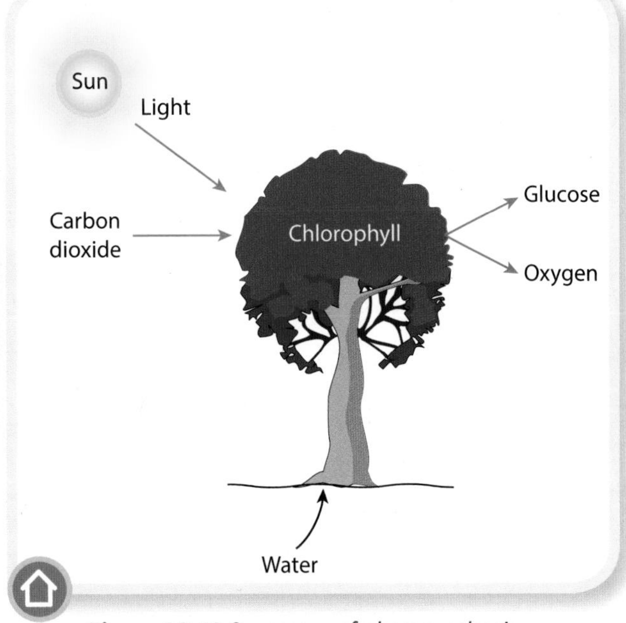

Figure 10.13 *Summary of photosynthesis*

10.18 Photosynthesis has many benefits.

(a) What is the main benefit of photosynthesis to plants?

(b) Photosynthesis has two main benefits for animals. What are they?

What are the factors that affect photosynthesis?

Photosynthesis is affected by the following factors:

- Light
- Carbon dioxide
- Water
- Chlorophyll
- Temperature.

Light

Plants get light from the Sun, and:

- Sunlight is absorbed by leaves.
- Leaves have large flat surfaces to allow them to absorb as much light as possible.
- Light provides the energy needed to form food.

The effects of increasing light intensity (brightness) on the rate of photosynthesis are shown by the graph in **Figure 10.14**.

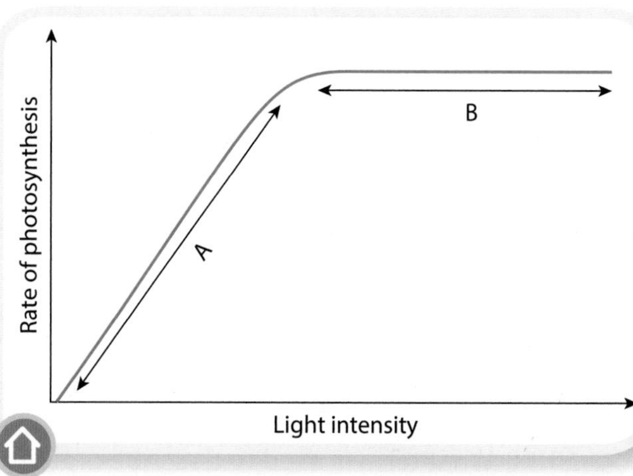

Figure 10.14 *The effects of increasing light intensity on the rate of photosynthesis*

- At low light intensities, increasing the light intensity will increase the rate of photosynthesis (as shown in part A of the graph).
- Above a certain light intensity the rate of photosynthesis remains constant (as shown in part B of the graph). This is because the plant cannot get enough of a necessary factor, e.g. carbon dioxide.

10.19 Why do many leaves have large flat surfaces?

Carbon dioxide

Plants get carbon dioxide from the air.

- Carbon dioxide passes into leaves through tiny openings called **stomata**.
- Stomata are mainly found on the lower surface of a leaf.

The effect of increasing carbon dioxide concentrations on the rate of photosynthesis is shown by the graph in **Figure 10.15**.

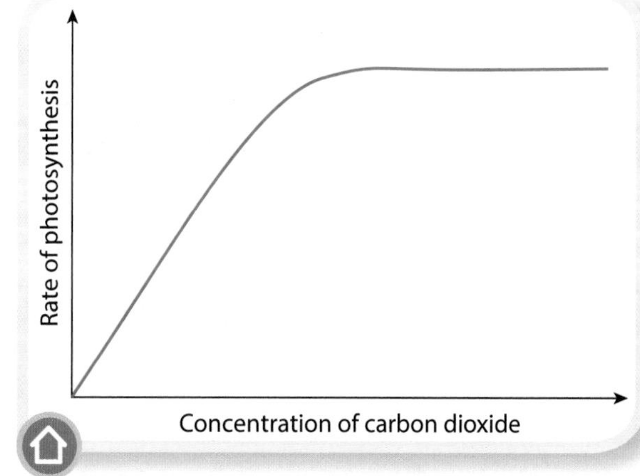

Figure 10.15 *The effect of increasing carbon dioxide concentrations on the rate of photosynthesis*

- If plants are short of carbon dioxide the rate of photosynthesis will slow down.
- Increasing the concentration of carbon dioxide increases the rate of photosynthesis.

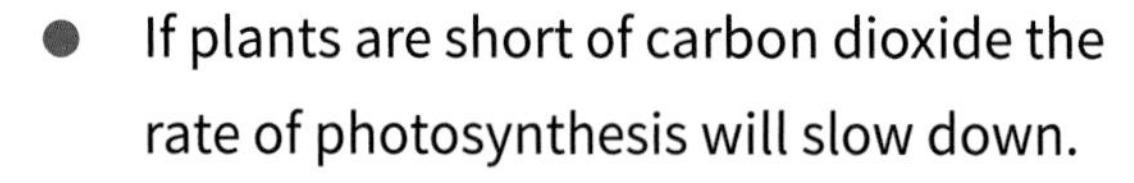

- Above a certain concentration of carbon dioxide the rate of photosynthesis remains constant. This is because the plant cannot get enough of another factor, such as light.

Water

Plants get water from the soil. Water from the soil enters the roots and then passes from the roots up through the stem to the leaves. Water is needed to allow glucose to be made, and it allows enzymes to work so that photosynthesis can take place.

Chlorophyll

Plants make chlorophyll. Chlorophyll is a green dye or pigment that is mostly found in the leaves (and other green parts) of a plant. It absorbs light and allows photosynthesis to take place.

Chlorophyll is not used up in the process of photosynthesis. In this way it acts as a **catalyst** (a catalyst speeds up a reaction without being used up in the reaction).

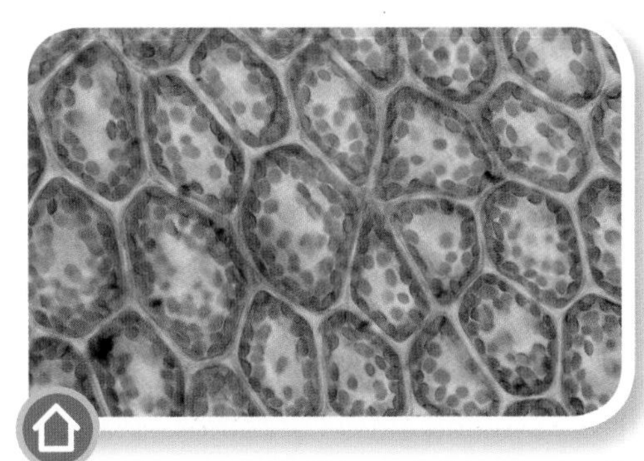

Figure 10.16 *Chlorophyll in plant cells*

Plants lacking chlorophyll are often yellow(ish) and have reduced rates of photosynthesis.

Temperature

Photosynthesis is an enzyme-controlled reaction. This means it is affected by temperature. The ideal temperature for photosynthesis in most plants is between 20°C and 30°C.

Other factors

Other factors that affect photosynthesis are:

- The surface area of the leaves
- The number of leaves
- The distribution of leaves (i.e. whether they are blocking light from each other)
- The number of tiny openings (called stomata) on the leaves.

10.20 Suggest two reasons why the rate of photosynthesis is greater in summer than in winter.

10.21 In a sealed glasshouse the concentration of carbon dioxide was measured over 24 hours. The concentration was found to be at its minimum around the middle of the day and reached a maximum just before dawn.

(a) Give reasons for these two observations.

(b) Suggest why small gas flames are sometimes left alight for a period of time in glasshouses.

What are the products of photosynthesis?

Glucose

The food made by a plant is called glucose. Glucose made in a leaf may be used:

- To provide energy in respiration
- To form starch in different parts of the plant
- To form new cells and allow for growth.

BIOLOGICAL WORLD

Oxygen

The gas made by photosynthesis is oxygen. The oxygen made in this way may be used as follows:

- For aerobic respiration, to provide energy in the leaf
- Released out of the leaf and into the air.

Figure 10.17 *Joseph Priestley (1733–1804)*

10.22 In 1771 Joseph Priestley placed a potted plant in a sealed glass container. He placed a mouse in a second sealed glass container. After a short time he found that the plant was still alive but the mouse had died.

He later placed a similar plant and a mouse in a third sealed glass container. He found that both survived.

(a) Suggest why the plant on its own in the sealed container remained alive.

(b) Suggest why the mouse on its own in the sealed container died?

(c) Suggest why both organisms lived if they were in the same sealed container.

(d) For ethical reasons, why should this experiment not be repeated?

10.23 Photosynthesis occurs only when there is a sufficient level of light. Respiration occurs in light and dark. In the light the rate of photosynthesis is much greater than the rate of respiration.

(a) What gas does photosynthesis take in?

(b) What gas does respiration give out?

(c) What gas or gases does a plant take in during:

(i) Daylight? **(ii)** Darkness?

(d) In the past plants were often placed in a sick person's room by day but taken out of the room at night. Why might this have been done?

Summary

Table 10.1 shows that respiration and photosynthesis are largely opposite processes.

Table 10.1 Comparison of respiration and photosynthesis

	Respiration	Photosynthesis
Gases required	Oxygen	Carbon dioxide
Gases produced	Carbon dioxide and water (vapour)	Oxygen
Energy required or released	Released	Required
When it takes place	Daylight and darkness	Daylight
Where it occurs	Plants and animals	Plants

CHAPTER 11

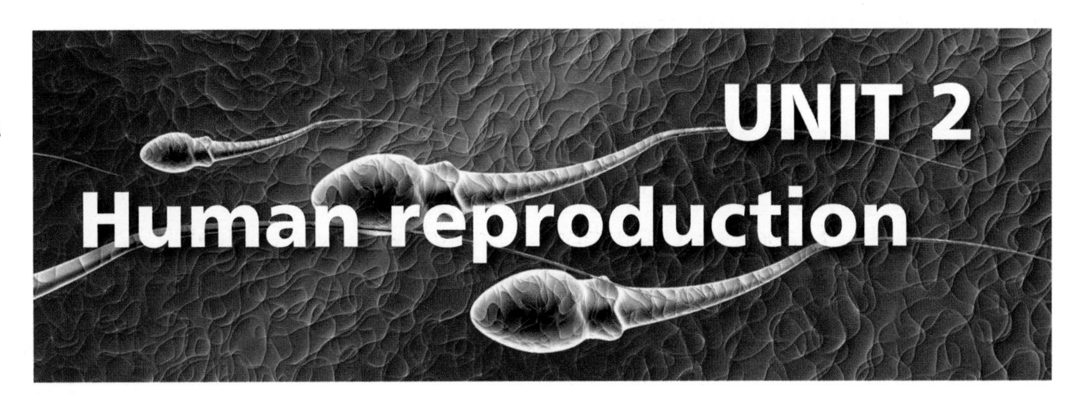

CHAPTER 11 Human reproduction

Learning outcomes

At the end of this chapter you will be able to:

- Describe the structure and functions of the male and female reproductive systems
- Explain what happens in a menstrual cycle
- Explain how pregnancy occurs and develops
- Explain what happens at birth
- Discuss some medical, ethical and societal issues associated with sexual reproduction.

Keywords

gametes · testis · puberty · sperm · scrotum · penis · ovary · fallopian tube · uterus · cervix · vagina · menstrual cycle · menstruation · ovulation · fertile period · intercourse · fertilisation · implantation · pregnancy · amnion · amniotic fluid · placenta · umbilical cord · birth · contraception · IVF · stem cells

What is reproduction?

Reproduction is the production of new individuals.

Humans reproduce sexually. Sexual reproduction involves two parents. Each parent produces sex cells (also called **gametes**). The male gametes are the sperm. The female gametes are the eggs.

Figure 11.1 *A male zebra and a female horse produce a zorse*

11.1 Figure 11.1 shows a zorse. This is the result of crossing a male zebra with a female horse.

(a) Name the male and female gametes that form a zorse.

(b) What structures in the gametes cause the zorse to have features of a horse and of a zebra?

(c) While zorses are produced by sexual reproduction, they cannot reproduce (i.e. they are sterile). Give two other examples of sterile animals produced by crossing two different species?

The male reproductive system

What are the functions of the parts of the male reproductive system?

Testis

The testis (plural *testes*) makes **sperm**. The testes start to make sperm between the ages of 12 and 14. This is the age of sexual maturity (or **puberty**) in boys.

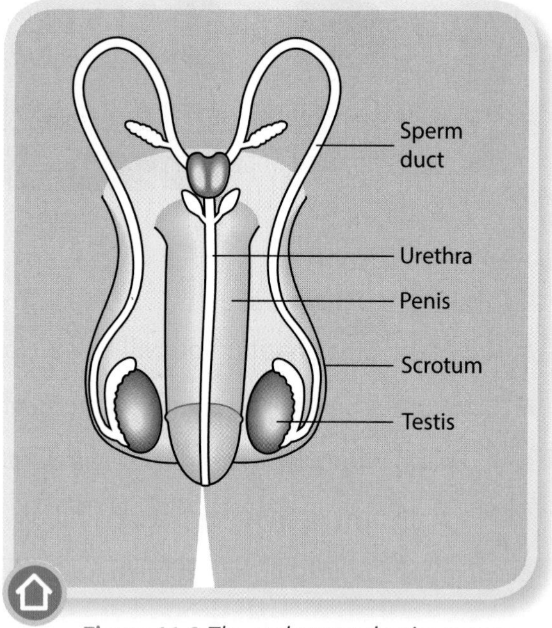

Sperm duct
Urethra
Penis
Scrotum
Testis

Figure 11.2 *The male reproductive system*

Along with making sperm other changes take place in a boy's body at puberty. These include:

- The enlargement of the penis and testes
- A rapid growth spurt
- The voice box (or larynx or Adam's apple) enlarges causing the voice to deepen
- The growth of hair on the body.

Sperm are the male sex cells (also called the male gametes). Each sperm cell is tiny and they are produced in huge numbers by the testes.

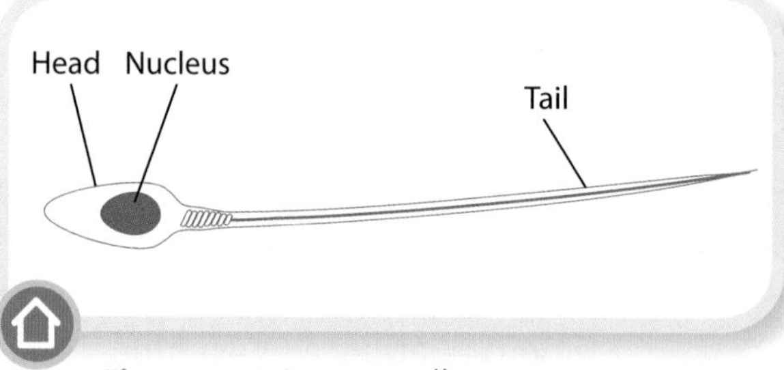

Figure 11.3 *A sperm cell*

Scrotum

The scrotum is a sac in which the testes are held. The scrotum holds the testes outside the body, allowing them to be kept at a temperature just lower than body temperature. This allows sperm to be made successfully.

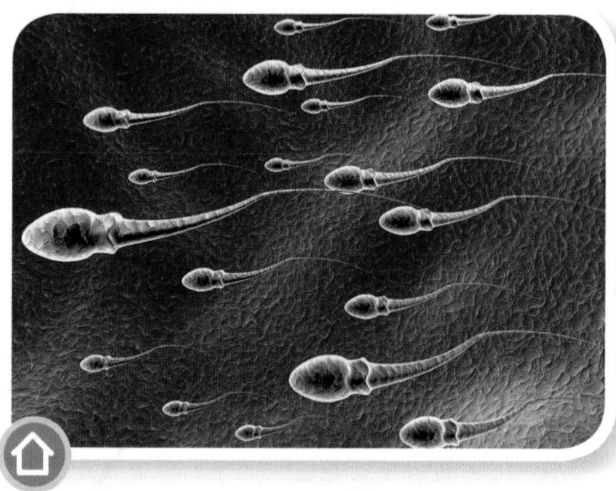

Figure 11.4 *Sperm cells*

Sperm ducts

Two sperm ducts carry sperm from the testes to the penis.

A number of glands are located beside the sperm ducts. These glands produce a liquid called seminal fluid. The mixture of sperm and seminal fluid is called semen.

Penis

The sperm ducts join a tube called the **urethra**. Sperm pass through this tube, which is located in the centre of the penis.

The penis allows semen (or sperm) to pass out of the male body and into the body of the female.

11.2 Rewrite the words below in the correct order to describe the path taken by sperm cells: sperm duct/penis/testis

11.3 Name the structure in males responsible for each of the following:
(a) Making sperm
(b) Controlling the temperature at which sperm are produced
(c) Transferring sperm to the female
(d) Carrying sperm from the testes to the penis.

BIOLOGICAL WORLD

The female reproductive system

What are the functions of the parts of the female reproductive system?

Ovary

The ovaries produce eggs. The ovaries start to make eggs at puberty. This occurs between the ages of 10 and 13 years. Other changes taking place in the girl's body at puberty include:

- The growth of the pelvis, breasts, vagina and uterus
- The growth of hair on parts of the body.

Eggs are the female sex cells or gametes. Each egg is much larger than a sperm cell.

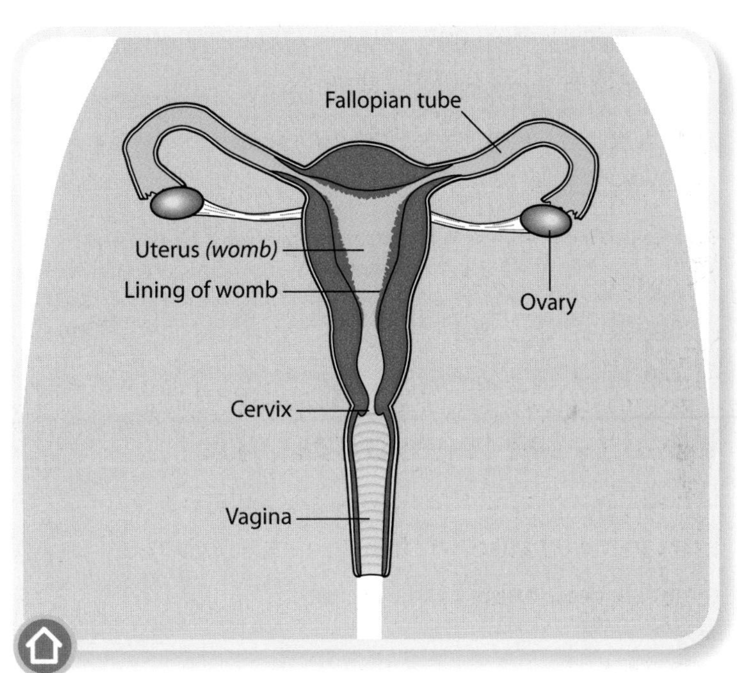

Figure 11.5 *The female reproductive system*

Normally, one egg is formed each month in the female body. Egg production starts at puberty. Beyond the age of 35 the number of eggs in each ovary falls dramatically. Egg production usually stops between 45 and 55 years of age. This stage, where the ovaries have run out of eggs, is called the **menopause** (or the 'change of life').

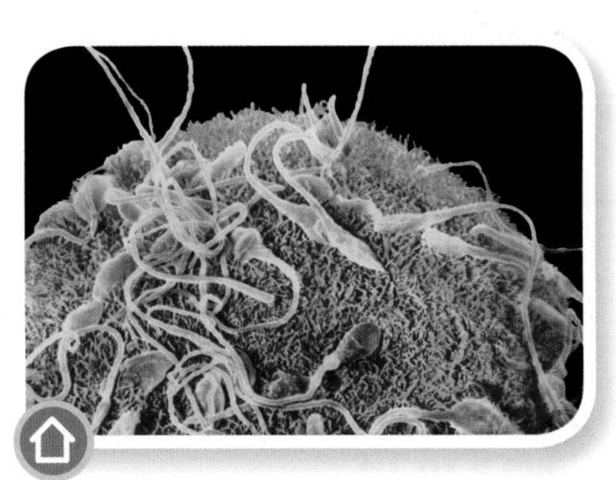

Figure 11.6 *Sperm about to fertilise an egg*

Fallopian tube

The fallopian tube collects the egg from the ovary and carries it to the uterus.

If sperm are present, one of them may join (or fuse) with the egg in the fallopian tube. If there are no sperm present, the egg dies within two days.

Uterus

The uterus or womb is the place in which a baby (or embryo) will develop.

Cervix

The cervix is the opening or neck of the uterus. Sperm pass through the cervix in order to reach an egg.

Vagina

The vagina is a muscular tube into which the penis releases sperm. It forms the **birth canal** when the baby passes down the vagina at childbirth.

11.4 Name the structures in males and females that produce gametes.

11.5 Outline the differences between sperms and eggs in terms of:
(a) Size (b) Numbers formed (c) Structure.

11.6 In order to prevent pregnancy some women have their fallopian tubes closed by surgery. How does this prevent pregnancy?

11.7 Research the name given to a similar procedure as that in question 11.6 for males, where the sperm ducts are cut or sealed.

What is the menstrual cycle?

In females, one menstrual cycle takes place about every twenty-eight days between puberty and the menopause. The menstrual cycle does not take place during pregnancy (i.e. when a baby is developing in the uterus).

What happens during a menstrual cycle?

The main events in the menstrual cycle are outlined below. The times given in this account are average times. These timings can be different in different females and during different months.

Days 1 to 5

The lining of the uterus (which had built up during the previous menstrual cycle) breaks down. This lining, along with some blood, is passed out of the body through the vagina. This process is called **menstruation** or **having a period**.

During these days, a new egg matures in the ovary.

Days 6 to 13

A new lining develops in the uterus. This lining will be needed to nourish a developing baby if the female becomes pregnant.

The egg continues to develop in the ovary.

Day 14

The egg is released from the ovary. This is called **ovulation**. The egg can survive for two days in the fallopian tube.

Days 15 to 28

The lining of the uterus remains in place. It will break down on the first day of the next menstrual cycle.

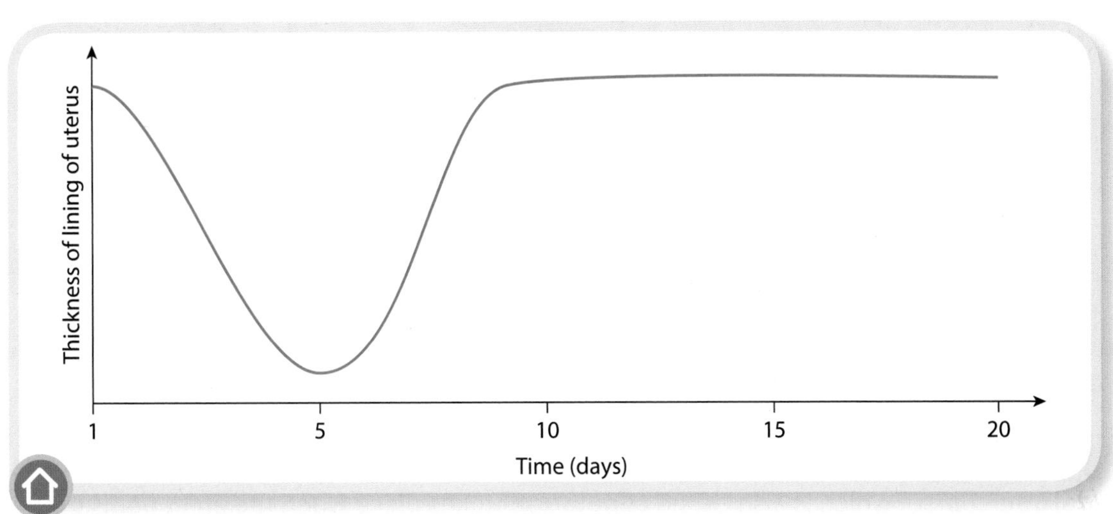

Figure 11.7 *The changes in thickness of the lining of the uterus over part of the menstrual cycle*

11.8 Figure 11.7 shows what happened to the thickness of the uterus lining over part of a menstrual cycle. Refer to this figure to answer some of the following questions.

(a) What is menstruation?
(b) On what day did menstruation finish?
(c) Why does the lining of the uterus thicken?
(d) On what day would you expect the lining to decrease in thickness again as it did on day 1?
(e) What is ovulation?
(f) On what day in a normal menstrual cycle does ovulation normally occur?

The fertile period

The fertile period is the time during the menstrual cycle when a female is most likely to become pregnant if she has sexual intercourse.

- Sperm can survive in the female reproductive system for five to seven days. They survive for such a long time because the female system nourishes the sperm.
- The egg can stay alive for two days.
- The fertile period is the time in the menstrual cycle when pregnancy is most likely to take place. For a twenty-eight-day cycle this is normally from day 9 to 16.
- The fertile period may be different in every female or in every month because menstrual cycles are not always twenty-eight days long. In some females the fertile period could start before day 9 and last beyond day 16.

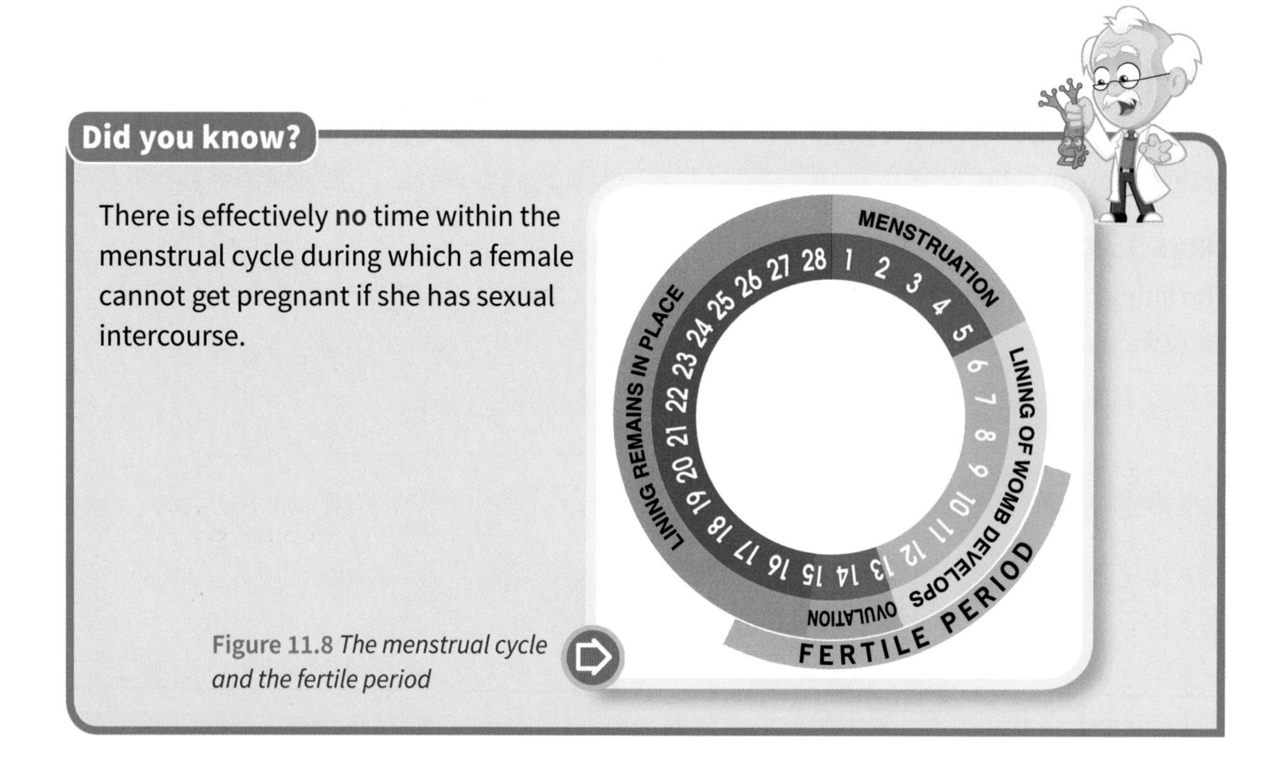

Did you know?

There is effectively **no** time within the menstrual cycle during which a female cannot get pregnant if she has sexual intercourse.

Figure 11.8 *The menstrual cycle and the fertile period*

What is sexual intercourse?

Sexual intercourse (which is also called **copulation**) takes place when the erect penis of the male is placed in the vagina of the female.

The movement of the penis in the vagina causes semen to be released from the penis.

What happens to sperm in the vagina?

Normally, millions of sperm are released into the vagina. The sperm move through the cervix and into the uterus. They then move from the uterus towards a fallopian tube.

After ovulation, the egg is pushed along the fallopian tube by tiny hairs. Many sperm swarm around the egg in the fallopian tube. Soon the head of one of the sperm will enter the egg.

If there is no egg present in the fallopian tube, the sperm die, normally within five days.

11.9 How do the sperm know which ovary has released the egg?

What is fertilisation?

Fertilisation takes place when the nucleus of a sperm joins or fuses with the nucleus of an egg. This takes place in the fallopian tube.

The fertilised egg forms a single cell called a **zygote**.

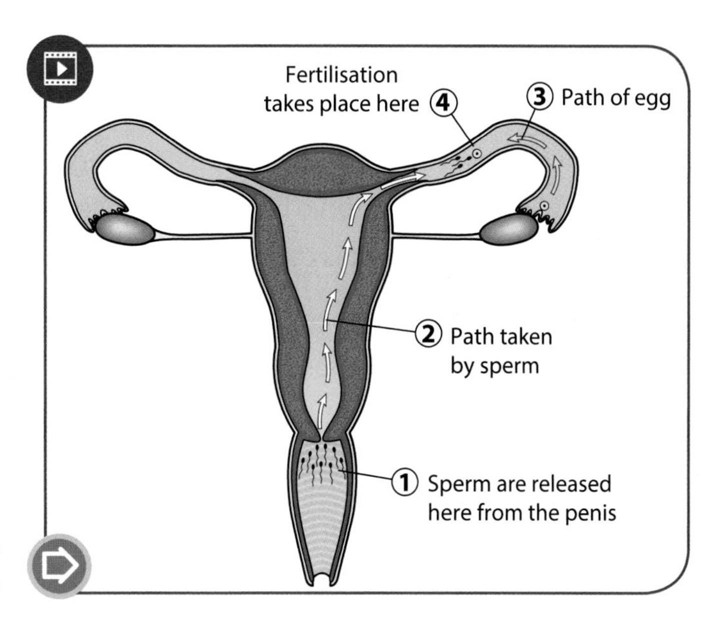

Figure 11.9 *Path of sperm and egg leading to fertilisation*

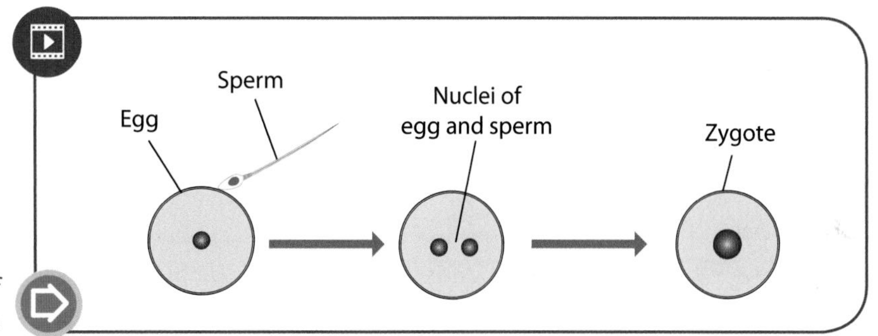

Figure 11.10 *The process of fertilisation*

11.10 Figure 11.11 represents sexual reproduction in humans.

(a) Name the structures represented by the letters A and C.

(b) Name the cells represented by B and D.

(c) Name the process E.

(d) Name the cell F.

(e) In what part of the female reproductive system does process E normally occur?

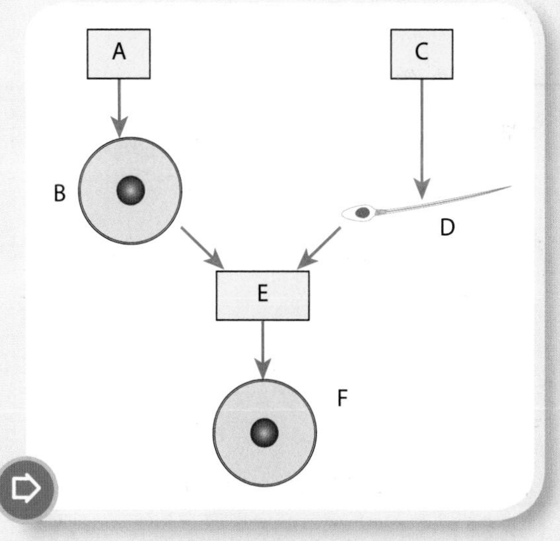

Figure 11.11 *Representation of sexual reproduction in humans*

11.11 How are identical twins formed?

11.12 In what way is the formation of non-identical twins different to the formation of identical twins?

Pregnancy

Once the zygote has formed it goes through many cell divisions to form a ball of cells. These cells then form an embryo. Within a few days of fertilisation, the embryo becomes attached to the lining of the uterus. This attachment is called **implantation**.

Soon after this, the embryo becomes surrounded by a membrane called the **amnion**. This membrane fills up with a liquid called **amniotic fluid**. Amniotic fluid acts as a shock absorber to protect the embryo (or baby) during pregnancy.

After eight weeks, the embryo can be recognised as a human. At this stage, it is called a **foetus**.

Pregnancy normally lasts from implantation until birth. A normal pregnancy lasts around forty weeks (about nine months).

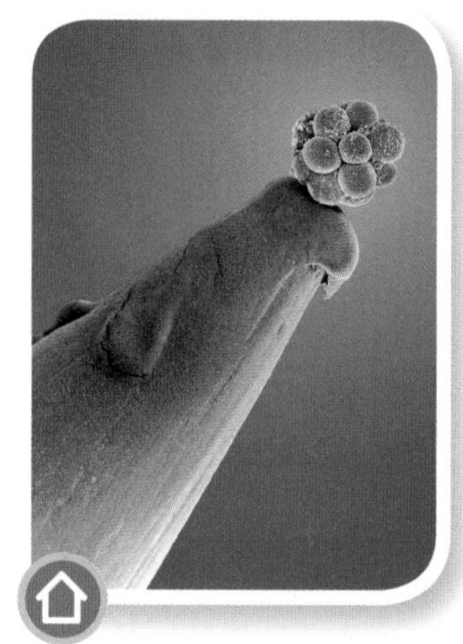

Figure 11.12 *A three-day-old embryo on the tip of a pin*

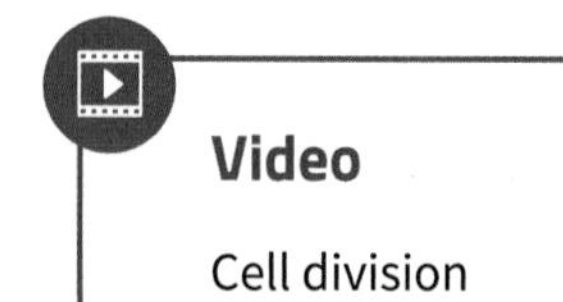

Video

Cell division

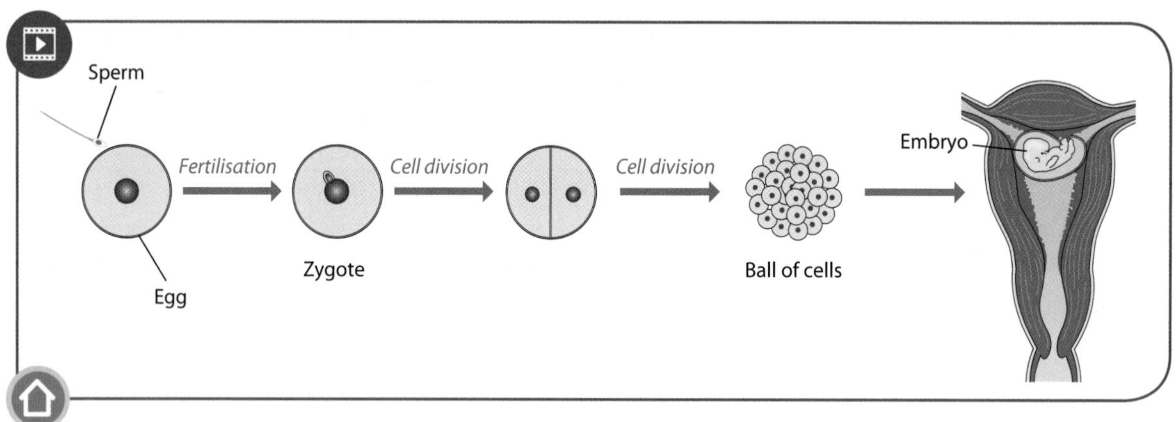

Figure 11.13 *Sexual reproduction*

Figure 11.14 *Embryo at seven weeks*

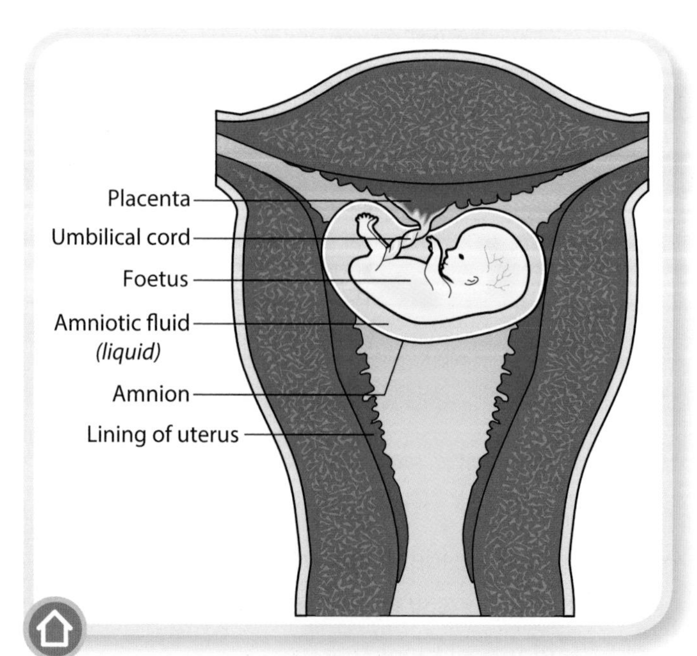

Figure 11.15 *Foetus in uterus*

11.13 Rewrite the following in the order in which they normally take place: implantation/gamete formation/amnion forms/fertilisation/intercourse/embryo forms/zygote forms.

What is the placenta?

A structure called the placenta forms early in pregnancy. The baby's blood passes through the **umbilical cord** to and from the placenta. The placenta attaches to the lining of the uterus.

The umbilical cord attaches to the baby at the navel (belly button).

The functions of the placenta

The function of the placenta is to allow materials to pass between the mother and the baby in the uterus:

- Food and oxygen pass from the mother's blood into the baby's blood.
- Waste products (such as carbon dioxide and salts) pass from the baby to the mother.
- Along with these useful functions the placenta also allows harmful substances, e.g. alcohol, smoke and drugs, to pass into the baby.

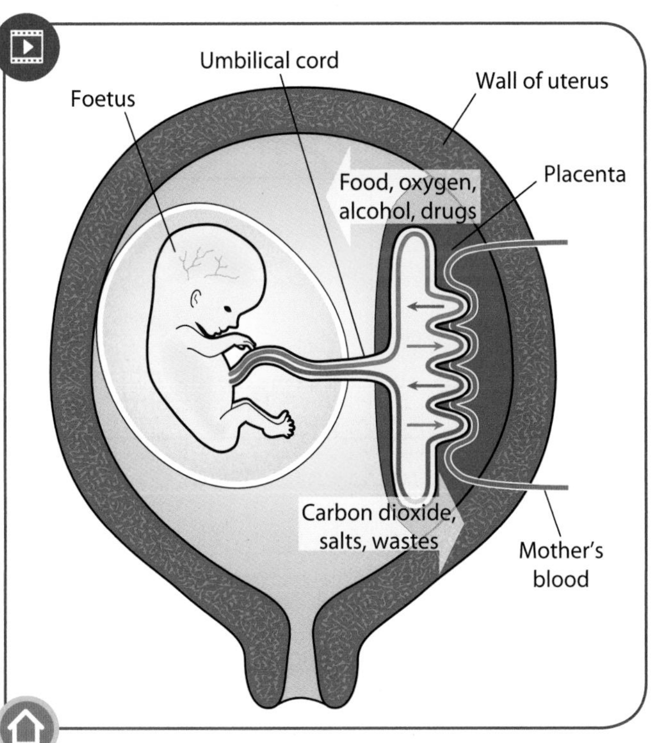

Figure 11.16 *Essential and harmful substances can pass between mother and baby*

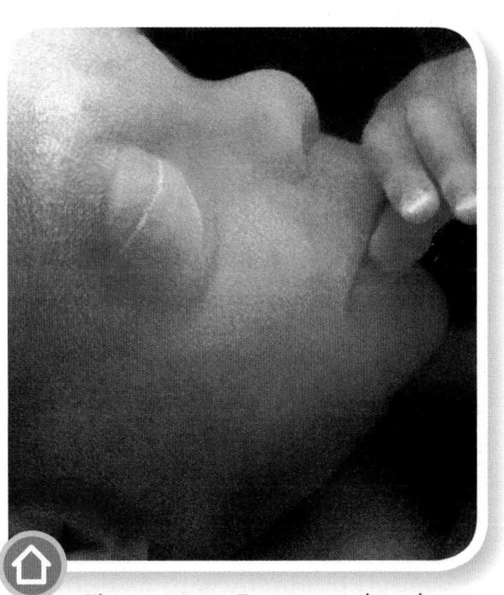

Figure 11.17 *Foetus aged twelve weeks*

11.14 Figure 11.18 represents the links between a mother and her foetus during pregnancy.

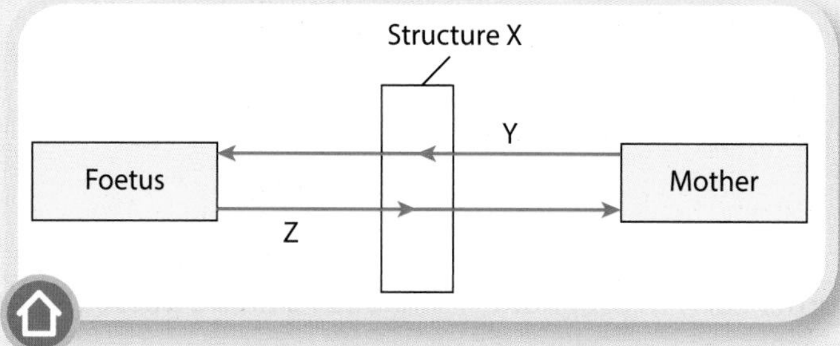

Figure 11.18 *Representation of childbirth*

(a) Name the structure shown as X.

(b) Name a gas that passes in the direction of arrow Y.

(c) Why does the foetus need the gas named in part (b)?

(d) Name a gas that passes in the direction of the arrow Z.

(e) From what organ does the gas named in part (d) pass out of the mother's body?

(f) Why can a foetus in the uterus not breathe through its mouth?

What happens at birth?

Towards the end of pregnancy, muscles in the uterus begin to contract. These contractions are called **labour**. The contractions cause the amnion to burst. The release of the amniotic fluid through the vagina is called 'the breaking of the waters'.

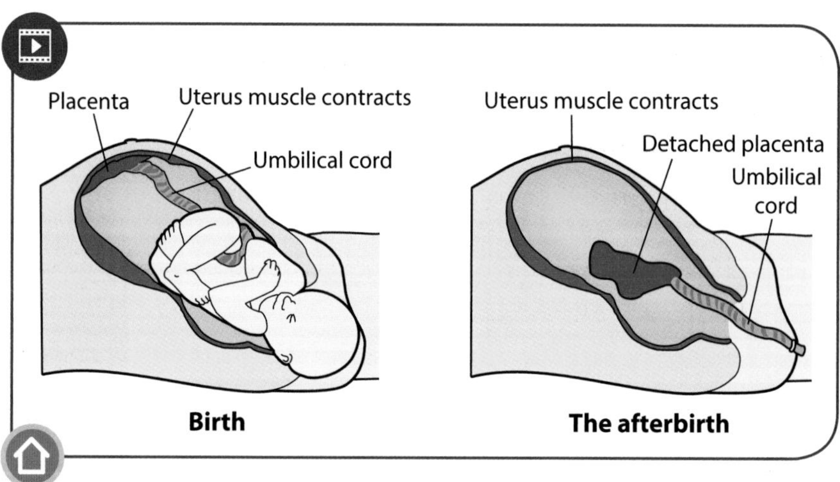

Figure 11.19 *The links between a mother and her foetus*

The cervix gradually widens during these contractions. The contractions cause the baby to be pushed head first out through the cervix and the vagina.

The umbilical cord is clamped (to prevent loss of blood from the baby) and cut. The baby soon starts to breathe through its lungs for the first time.

The uterus continues to contract after the baby is born. These contractions push the placenta and the remains of the umbilical cord out of the vagina. These materials are called the **afterbirth**.

Growth of the baby

The baby may feed on breast milk produced by the mother. The main benefits of breastfeeding are:

- Breast milk is full of the ideal nutrients that a young baby needs.
- Breast milk contains many substances (antibodies) that help to protect the baby from infections.

The remains of the umbilical cord fall away from the baby's navel after about seven days.

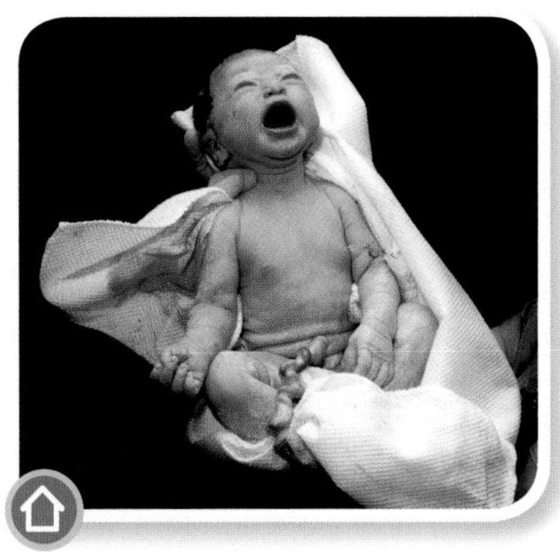

Figure 11.20 *A newborn baby, before the umbilical cord is cut*

11.15 Rewrite the following in the order in which they occur:
amniotic fluid passes out of uterus/baby's feet emerge from vagina/amnion breaks/ cervix expands/baby's head emerges from vagina/placenta expelled from uterus/ contractions of uterus begin

What are the main medical, ethical and societal issues surrounding sexual reproduction?

The area of sexual reproduction presents many issues for debate in terms of topics:

- Relating to our health
- That test our beliefs
- That relate to the society we live in.

Some of these topics are discussed in the following sections. Other topics can be researched and discussed in class groups.

Contraception

Medical issues

Contraception is the deliberate use of artificial methods to prevent pregnancy.

Some couples want to control the number of children they have or to control how soon after each other their children are born. Others wish to have sexual intercourse without the female becoming pregnant.

These couples may use contraception as a method of birth control, or family planning, in order to prevent unwanted pregnancies.

There are two main types of contraception:

- Preventing fertilisation
- Preventing implantation.

Preventing fertilisation

Natural methods Natural methods of preventing the sperm from reaching the egg are based around avoiding intercourse during the female's fertile period. These methods aim to predict or detect the time of ovulation.

Artificial methods Artificial methods of contraception include stopping the female from producing eggs. This can be achieved by the female taking the contraceptive pill.

Other artificial methods involve preventing the sperm from reaching the egg. These methods include:

- The use of a condom, which covers the top of the penis
- A cap, which covers the cervix
- Chemical creams or foams, which kill sperm
- Medical operations in which the sperm ducts or fallopian tubes are cut and sealed.

Preventing implantation

- Some pills prevent pregnancy by stopping the embryo from attaching (or implanting) in the uterus.
- A T-shaped device inserted by a doctor in the uterus also acts in this way.

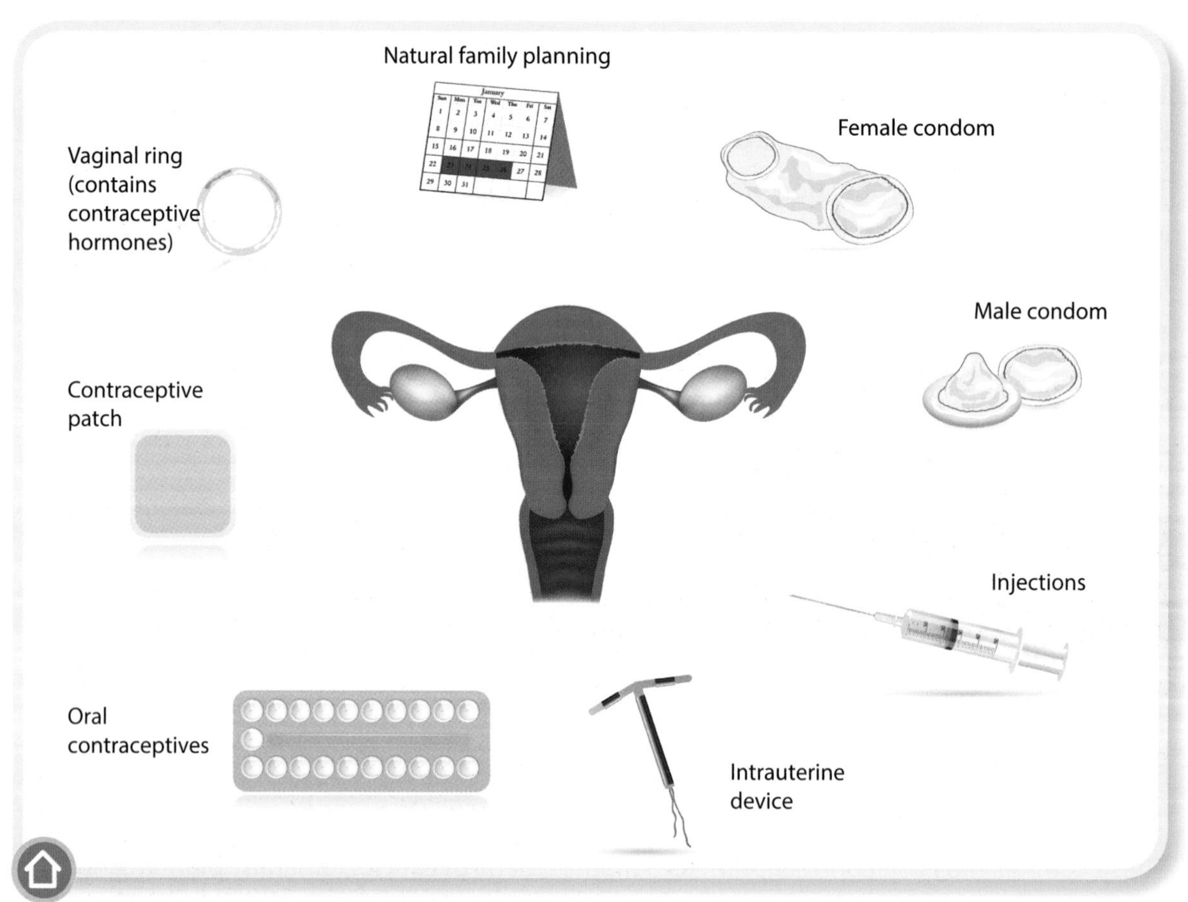

Figure 11.21 *Contraceptive methods*

Ethical issues

Some couples may decide that a number of these methods are not acceptable to them. This may be because they are not reliable enough or that they do not agree with them, i.e. ethically, or because of their religious belief system.

Societal issues

Different societies have different views on contraception. These views are often reflected by the laws in a country or state.

IVF (in vitro fertilisation)

Medical issues

Infertility is the inability to have offspring. Roughly one in six Irish couples is infertile. Some of these couples may use IVF treatment in order to have a child.

IVF involves taking eggs from the female and sperm from the male and allowing them to fertilise outside of the body (i.e. in a container such as a petri dish).

If fertilisation is successful one (or more) of the embryos is placed into the uterus of the female. The hope is that the embryo(s) will implant and develop in the uterus just as would happen in a normal pregnancy.

The process is called IVF or in vitro fertilisation because the sperm and the egg join together outside the body of the female. In vitro means 'in glass'.

Advantages of IVF:

- IVF allows a couple who are unable to achieve fertilisation naturally to have a child.
- The child develops normally in the uterus.

Disadvantages of IVF:

- There is a small risk of more than one embryo developing (and multiple pregnancies increase the risk of premature births or low birth weight). Some people consider multiple births an advantage.
- There may be some side effects of the drugs that are taken to allow IVF.
- There is a slightly higher risk of the baby being born with a birth defect.
- It is a costly process that often does not result in pregnancy.

Ethical issues

Some people feel that IVF is wrong for one or more of the following reasons:

- It is not a natural process.
- Not all of the embryos are used and those that are not used are destroyed or used for stem cell research (see next page).
- There is an increased risk of birth defects.

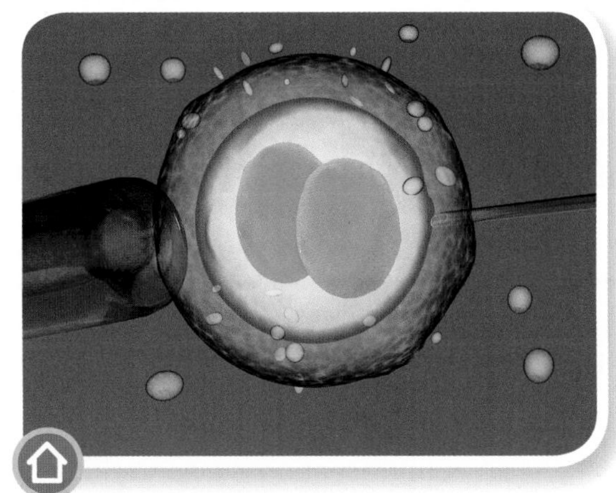

Figure 11.22 *An embryo being selected before being placed in the uterus*

Societal issues

Different societies have different views on IVF. These views are often reflected by the laws in a country or state.

Stem cells

Medical issues

Stem cells are cells that can develop into any type of body cell. They are often used to learn how structures in the body are formed and to test the effect of new drugs.

It is hoped that stem cells will provide treatments for problems such as spinal cord injuries, heart diseases, strokes, Parkinson's disease, and many other disorders. In addition they may be used to form new healthy structures for use in transplants.

Stem cells can be obtained from three- to five-day-old embryos, from umbilical cords and from adult sources such as bone marrow, fat and nose cells.

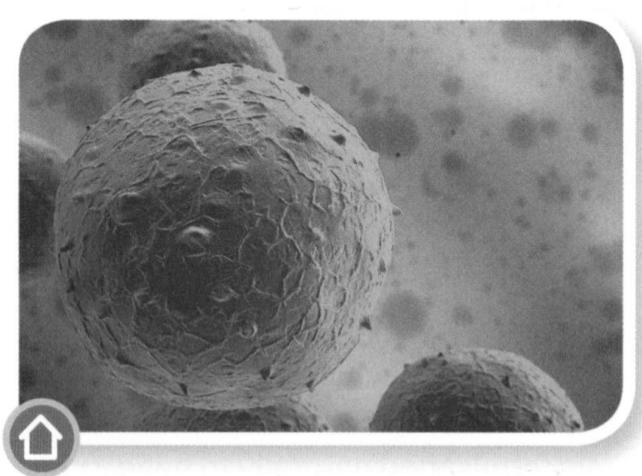

Figure 11.23 *Embryonic stem cells*

Figure 11.24 *A bladder grown from stem cells for transplant*

Ethical issues

Embryonic stem cells are often obtained from embryos left over after IVF treatment. Some people believe that using stem cells from embryos is wrong as it destroys a potential life. Others feel that the possible benefits outweigh this issue.

Societal issues

Different societies have different views on the use of stem cells. The basic problem is the conflict of two sets of values:

- The duty to prevent or reduce suffering.
- The duty to respect the value of human life.

In some countries or states the use of all stem cells is banned by law. In others the use of all stem cells is legal. In yet other countries the use of non-embryonic stem cells is legal. Some countries do not have any clear guidelines on stem cells as it is a relatively new process.

Ethics

11.16 The class should vote on which of the following proposals they will discuss:

- Contraception is a good thing and should be available to those over 18 years old.
- IVF is of more harm than benefit to society.
- Stem cell research should be illegal.

Work in groups to research and discuss the proposal selected. Each group should elect a person to explain its views to the class.

CHAPTER 12 Maintaining biodiversity, benefits of ecosystems and global food production

UNIT 2

Learning outcomes

At the end of this chapter you will be able to:

- Evaluate how humans can conserve ecological biodiversity
- Explain the benefits that people obtain from ecosystems
- Evaluate how humans can contribute to global food production.

Keywords

conservation · biodiversity · pollution · waste management · global food production · reduce · reuse · recycle · ecosystem · food gap

What is conservation?

Conservation is the protection of plants, animals and natural areas from the damaging effects of human activity. If we look after our wildlife and their habitats we can prevent them from being wiped out (becoming **extinct**).

Failure to conserve can result in the death of organisms in their habitats. In some cases the entire species or type of organism may become extinct.

Figure 12.1 *The corncrake's habitat is being destroyed*

For example, birds called corncrakes are in danger of being wiped out in Ireland due to the loss of hay meadows in which they breed. Some orchids are also threatened with extinction because their habitats are being destroyed.

The decrease in the number of types of plants and animals means there is a decrease in **biodiversity** (i.e. the different types of living things). To prevent the loss of habitats and wildlife it is necessary to look after our natural resources. Examples of good conservation practise are given on page 124.

Figure 12.2 *Some orchids are under threat as they lose their habitat*

12.1 Work in groups to discover the names of two plants in Ireland from each of the following categories:

(a) Extinct
(b) Critically endangered (i.e. in danger of becoming extinct)
(c) Endangered (i.e. whose numbers are declining).

12.2 Select one of the plants you have listed and:

(a) Find an image (drawing or photograph) of it.
(b) Explain why it is in danger.
(c) Present your results to the class and vote on the best presentation.

12.3 Work in groups to research what is meant by a **protected species** in Ireland.

12.4 Name two animals in Ireland that are protected species.

12.5 Select one of the animals you have listed in question 12.4 and:

(a) Find an image (drawing or photograph) of it.
(b) Explain why it is protected.
(c) Present your results to the class and vote on the best presentation.

Why do we need conservation?

Conservation is necessary for the following reasons:

- To prevent organisms from becoming extinct. At present, many organisms are facing this threat.
- To maintain the balance of nature. The loss of any one type of organism can cause dramatic results for other types of organisms.
- Future generations have the right to the same natural resources as are found at present, e.g. the world would be a poorer place if elephants, tigers or any other animal or plant became extinct.
- Plants are the source of many medicines. As plants become extinct, we lose the ability to test them for new medications.
- If our natural resources are not protected there is a danger that human lifestyles (and even our survival) would be at risk.

12.6 Give three examples of how the loss of named living things might cause problems for other named living things? (Hint: how is the reduction in honey bees affecting plants?)

12.7 Why would it be a tragedy if elephants (or any animal or plant) became extinct?

What can we do to support conservation?

The only species on Earth that threatens conservation is humans. It is up to us, both as a species and as individuals, to support conservation measures. Humans can support conservation by:

- Making themselves aware of the issues
- Joining conservation groups
- Supporting groups in society that encourage proper conservation
- Refusing to join in any activity that threatens conservation
- Refusing to buy products that have been sourced unethically.

12.8 Sinéad wants to support conservation in Ireland.

(a) Find out the names of three groups that she could join to achieve her aim.

(b) Explain the role of one of these groups in more detail.

Figure 12.3 *Killarney National Park: a centre for conservation and biodiversity*

12.9 Work in groups to research two chemicals, drugs or medicines that we get from plants. Explain the benefit of these substances.

12.10 Work in groups to discover the five most threatened big animals (i.e. larger than a cat) on Earth.

12.11 Discuss why the animals you named in question 12.10 should be conserved and agree on the three most important reasons.

What are the main causes of loss of biodiversity?

Some of the factors that are responsible for organisms being killed off (resulting in a loss of biodiversity) are:

- Habitat loss or fragmentation
- Pollution
- Invasive species (organisms that are introduced to an area and which cause harm)
- Climate change (see chapter 41)
- Over-exploitation (the overuse of wildlife by people)
- Human population numbers.

We will look at some of these in more detail.

Habitat loss or fragmentation

Habitats are being destroyed on a huge scale. For example:

- We cut down forests and woodlands for timber or for housing.
- Bog lands are being drained for farming.
- Grassland is being used up for roads, housing and factories.
- Lakes are being destroyed by pollution.

Figure 12.4 *This habitat in Borneo is being destroyed*

Destruction of habitats destroys the organisms in that habitat. Sometimes the remaining habitat is too small to support any surviving organisms or the remaining habitats are too far apart to allow organisms to move between them.

12.12 Work in groups to find out what habitats were wiped out in the area around your school. For example, what was there before your school was built, before local houses were built, before any local factories or shopping areas were built?

Pollution

Pollution is caused mainly when humans add unwanted material to the environment. The materials that cause pollution are called **pollutants**. There are three main environments that get polluted:

- Air
- Water
- Soil.

Air pollution

The main sources of air pollution are:

- Greenhouse gases
- Acid rain
- CFCs
- Dirt particles
- Smog.

12.13 Work in groups to research the sources of air pollution listed previously.

- **(a)** Explain the source of each pollutant and the effect it has on the environment.
- **(b)** Present your findings to the class in a suitable manner (i.e. a talk, poster, PowerPoint, etc.).

Water pollution

The main causes of water pollution are:

- Badly treated sewage (toilet) waste
- Oil spills
- The dumping of household, farming and industrial wastes.

Figure 12.5 *Air pollution*

Soil pollution

Soil pollution is mainly caused by:

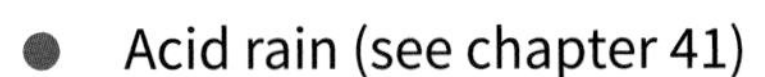

- Acid rain (see chapter 41)
- Overuse of fertilisers and slurry (which is animal waste, such as faeces and urine in a liquid form) on the land
- Improper dumping of wastes.

12.14 One area we can all contribute to is minimising household waste.

- **(a)** Make a list of the main wastes that your family produces each week.
- **(b)** What steps does your family already take to reduce the amount or effect of wastes produced?
- **(c)** What other steps could you take to reduce the amount of wastes produced by your family?

12.15 Work in groups to research *one* of the following causes of loss of biodiversity:

- Invasive species
- Climate change
- Over-exploitation
- Human population numbers.

12.16 Prepare a poster to outline your findings from question 12.15.

12.17 When nutrients enter a water supply (such as a stream, river, pond or lake) they allow more simple plants called algae to grow in the water. This happens because the nutrients are rich in minerals such as phosphates. The extra minerals may result in an overgrowth of algae, called an algal bloom.

(continued)

When the algae die, bacteria cause them to decompose. The bacteria use up all the oxygen in the water as they grow. This results in the death of all the animals and plants in the water.
Nutrients are present in wastes such as animal manure (slurry), fertilisers that are washed off the soil, dumped milk, sewage and washing detergents.

(a) What chemical element is mainly responsible for the death of plants, as described above?
(b) When algae grow in water they carry out photosynthesis. What gas do they add to the water?
(c) The gas you named in part (b) has benefits for fish and other water-based animals. Why do animals benefit from this gas?
(d) Why are farmers advised not to apply fertilisers when there is heavy rain?
(e) Untreated sewage or waste water from kitchen sinks can be examples of poor conservation practice. Explain why this is so.

Figure 12.6 *An algal bloom caused by excess fertiliser*

Figure 12.7 *Fish killed by lack of oxygen in the water*

How can we conserve ecological biodiversity?

To conserve organisms we must control the factors listed earlier (habitat loss and fragmentation, pollution, invasive species, climate change, over-exploitation and human population numbers). Some of the ways these factors can be controlled are considered below.

Preventing habitat loss and fragmentation

Habitats can be preserved by:

- Reducing pollution (which may destroy plant and animal life)
- Planting native vegetation, which will support native animals
- Controlling or limiting building to preserve habitats
- Preventing the entry and growth of invasive (or non-native) species
- Developing national parks and special areas of conservation where wildlife is protected by law.

Controlling pollution

Pollution can be controlled by proper waste management.

Waste management

The large numbers of humans and the modern style of life produce huge amounts of waste materials. These wastes include dirty water, urine, faeces, plastics and packaging, along with agricultural and industrial wastes.

These wastes can be managed by using the **3Rs**. (See also chapter 23.) These are:

- **Reduce** the use of unnecessary goods and packaging (e.g. plastic bags).
- **Reuse** as many materials (e.g. glass or second-hand furniture) as possible.
- **Recycle** as much waste as possible (e.g. paper, glass, metals and plastics).

12.18 List three ways in which you or your family use, or could use, the 3Rs.

12.19 A good example of recycling is composting.

(a) Find out what is meant by composting.

(b) What substances can be composted?

(c) List two advantages and two disadvantages of composting.

(d) Investigate the possibility of your school or class making your own compost. Check out the Green-Schools Ireland website for details and advice.

Figure 12.8 *Garden and kitchen waste in a compost heap*

12.20 At present most Irish household waste is disposed of by **landfill**. However, there are problems associated with this method. Some people suggest that **incinerators** would be a better way to dispose of household waste.

Research the words in **bold** and answer the following questions.

(a) What is meant by landfill?

(b) What are the main problems associated with landfill?

(c) What are incinerators?

(d) What are the main benefits of incinerators?

(e) Why might you not like to live close to an incinerator?

Figure 12.9 *A waste incinerator*

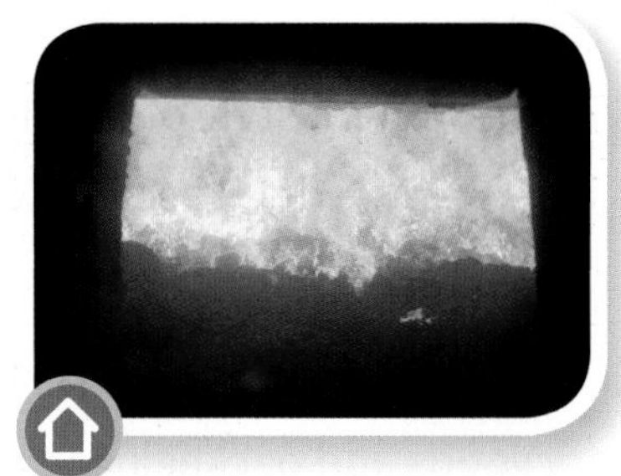
Figure 12.10 *Waste being burned in an incinerator*

Figure 12.11 *A landfill site*

12.21 Giant hogweed and the grey squirrel are two invasive species in Ireland. Research both of these and explain:

(a) How or why they are thought to have entered Ireland.

(b) The problems they are causing.

(c) What can be done to control or prevent them from spreading.

What benefits do people obtain from ecosystems?

An ecosystem is a large area containing similar types of environments and living things (e.g. a woodland, a grassland or a seashore). We obtain many benefits from ecosystems. These benefits can be grouped into four main types:

- Supporting
- Products
- Controlling
- Cultural.

Supporting benefits

Supporting benefits allow the other three types of benefits to exist. Ecosystems support:

- Biodiversity (ecosystems support many types of living things)
- Soil formation
- Photosynthesis (which absorbs carbon dioxide and helps reduce global warming)
- Nutrient recycling (dead materials rot to release valuable elements needed for new growth to occur). You will look at this in more detail in chapter 39.
- Water recycling (water is absorbed by plant roots and released back into the air as water vapour). See chapter 39.

Products benefits

Ecosystems produce valuable substances or products such as:

- Wood
- Fuel (turf/peat or firewood)
- Food (including seafood and wild animals)
- Fresh water
- Medicines
- Useful chemicals.

Figure 12.12 *A wood pile*

Figure 12.13 *A turf pile*

Controlling benefits

Ecosystems help to control features such as:

- Air quality (the plants take in carbon dioxide and give out oxygen)
- Water quality (water is purified as it goes down through the soil)
- Pollination (by supporting insects)
- Soil erosion (roots stabilise soil)
- Flood damage (water is absorbed or diverted)
- Pest control (pests are reduced by being eaten or weakened by parasites).

Cultural benefits

The non-material benefits of ecosystems include:

- Recreation (in parks, mountains and by the sea)
- Sports (swimming, climbing, walking)
- The use of nature in arts (pictures, paintings, films)
- Education (trips to parks, seashore, mountains)
- Scientific (research on habitats and wildlife).

Figure 12.14 *Field trips are educational*

12.22 Research national parks in Ireland.

(a) Name a National Park in Ireland.

(b) What are the five main benefits of this park to Irish society?

(c) Suggest why there are more plant and animal species in national parks than in land outside the parks.

Investigating i2 Investigating i3 Investigating i4 Society S10

Activity 12.1

Question

Can we purify water?

Our drinking water is purified in five steps:

1. It is aerated to add oxygen to the water and to remove unwanted gases (this is called *aeration*).
2. Small dissolved dirt particles are made to clump together (this is called *flocculation*).
3. It is allowed to settle so that large particles sink to the bottom (*sedimentation*).
4. It is filtered to remove tiny particles from the water (*filtration*).
5. Chemicals are added to kill micro-organisms (*disinfection*).

We will carry out the first four steps. Disinfectants are dangerous so we will not use them in the classroom. As a result the water we purify is ***not*** safe to drink.

Equipment needed

- About 1 litre of muddy water (or 1 litre of water with two cups of soil mixed into it)
- Empty 2 litre plastic soft drinks bottle with its cap
- Empty 2 litre plastic bottle cut about halfway down
- Two large beakers
- Filter funnel
- Alum (aluminium potassium sulfate) solution
- Small graduated cylinder
- 250 ml beaker
- Fine sand
- Coarse sand
- Small pebbles
- Filter paper
- Rubber band
- Stirring rod or spoon
- Stopwatch or timer

Safety

- Take care when cutting the plastic bottle – make sure your knife or scissors does not slip.
- The filtered water is ***not*** safe to drink.

Conducting the activity

1. Pour half of the dirty water into a beaker and leave it aside. This acts as a control.
2. Pour the other half of the dirty water into the empty bottle. Close the lid and shake vigorously for 30 seconds.
3. Pour the water into a large empty beaker and back into the bottle ten times. (Steps 2 and 3 aerate the water and remove any smelly gases.)
4. Pour the water into the base of the bottle with the top cut off.
5. Add 30 ml of alum solution to the water and slowly stir it for five minutes. What do you notice about the water as you stir it? (This is flocculation.)
6. Let the water sit without stirring it or moving it for twenty minutes. Observe it every five minutes. What do you notice is happening in the water? (This is called sedimentation.)

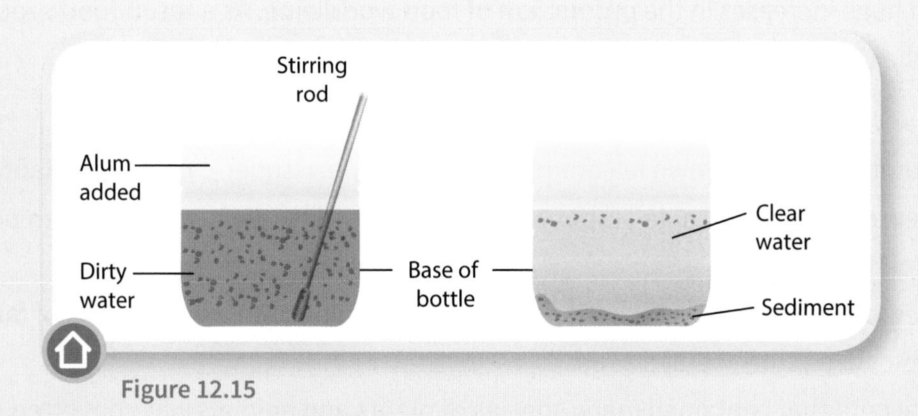

Figure 12.15

7. Place the filter paper over the mouth of the bottle with the bottom cut off and secure it firmly in place using the rubber band. Place it upside down in the beaker.
8. Pour a 250 ml beaker of pebbles into the bottle. Then pour a 250 ml beaker of coarse sand on top of the pebbles. Then pour two 250 ml beakers of fine sand on top of the coarse sand.
9. Pour about 2 litres of clean tap water onto the sand in the upturned bottle. Be careful not to disturb the sand too much. Pour away the water that passes through the filter paper. (This step cleans the filter materials, i.e. the sand and pebbles.)
10. Pour about two-thirds of the dirty water through the filter system. Do not pour any of the sediment into the filter bottle.
11. When all the water has filtered through, compare the filtrate to the original dirty water. What do you notice? How different are the two water samples?
12. Note that the filtrate is ***not*** safe to drink. It may contain micro-organisms that are harmful.

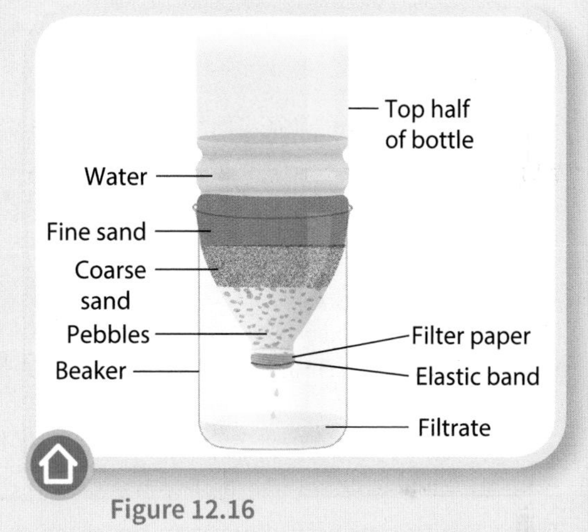

Figure 12.16

12.23 How is water aerated naturally?
12.24 How is water naturally filtered?
12.25 Find out what chemicals are added to our drinking water to disinfect it.
12.26 Why is rainwater that is collected in a barrel not safe to drink but water in a well (or spring water) is safe to drink?

How can humans contribute to global food production?

At present there are slightly over 7 billion people on Earth. It is predicted that the number of humans in 2050 will be between 9 and 10 billion. As the numbers rise it will be necessary to increase the global or world food supply.

This need for more food is not a new problem. In the late 1950s and the 1960s the human population was increasing faster than it is now. However, the 'green revolution' at that time resulted in huge increases in the production of food worldwide. As a result food production matched the rise in human numbers.

The green revolution resulted in some problems also. For example:

- The number of crops grown fell dramatically as the new 'super-crops' were planted widely.
- The new crops needed large amounts of fertilisers and had to be sprayed with pesticides to kill off insect pests.
- The new crops also used much more fresh water and needed a higher level of farm technology (tractors, sprayers, etc.).
- Natural land that contained many species of plants and animals was converted to growing single crops (such as rice, wheat or oil palm). These single crops are called **monocultures** and result in huge loss of biodiversity.

Figure 12.17 *A wheat field in winter*

Figure 12.18 *An oil palm plantation. Note there is only one type of plant growing*

There are two possible ways to produce more food:

- Convert more land to growing crops
- Increase the yield of crops grown on present farm land.

12.27 Research the role played by Norman Borlaug in increasing global food production.

Animated Scientist Biography

Watch an *Exploring Science* animation to find out more about Borlaug and his ideas.

Can we increase the amount of farmland worldwide?

At present only about 10% of the world's surface is used for growing crops (66% of Earth's surface is water, some land is too dry or too hot or too cold, or the soil is too poor to grow crops).

If we use more land for crops it will mean we have to destroy habitats. This will result in loss of biodiversity. For this reason this option is not the best one.

Can we increase the yield of crops?

A huge amount of research is going on worldwide to increase the yield of crops. Some of this involves using older crops that were preserved as seeds (in seed banks). Much of the research is attempting to develop new strains of crops by adding genes to existing plant crops.

It is hoped that the new crops will be able to produce increased yields, resist higher global temperatures, use less fresh water, resist pests and diseases, have improved taste and contain more nutrients. In addition attempts are being made to allow plants to produce more than one crop each year. This could potentially increase food production hugely.

12.28 The photograph in Figure 12.19 shows the entrance to the Svalbard Global Seed Bank. This is a project sponsored by Bill Gates and a number of multinational companies to store seeds from every plant on Earth in a huge underground vault.
Research this project and find out:
(a) Who Bill Gates is.
(b) Where the project is located.
(c) Why they are doing it.
(d) Why some people question this project.

Figure 12.19 *The Svalbard Global Seed Bank*

12.29 Most of the world's food is produced by a small number of plants.
(a) Research the top five food plants worldwide.
(b) Which of the plants named in part (a) can grow in Ireland?

How can we reduce the food gap?

The food gap refers to the difference between the amount of food produced and the amount of food needed worldwide. This gap can be reduced in a number of ways:

- Reduce the loss or waste of food. At present it is estimated that up to 33% of food produced for human use is not eaten.
- Adjust our diets. It takes far more land to produce meat (especially beef) than it does to produce the same energy content in plants. The world's population is increasingly demanding more meat in its diet. This may not be sustainable.

Figure 12.20 *Feeding fish on a fish farm – this is one type of aquaculture*

- Increase our use of poor-quality land.
- Improve how we use our existing land and water resources.
- Control human population increases.
- Increase our use of water-based food production (aquaculture).

12.30 Research food wastage.

(a) Find out how we waste up to one-third of our food.

(b) How much of this waste is avoidable?

12.31 In terms of energy conversions it is said that it is more efficient to eat 'lower down the food chain'. The energy conversions for two food chains are shown in the table below.

Food chain	Energy passing to humans (kJ/hectare of wheat)
Wheat → humans	850 000
Wheat → animal → humans	85 000

(a) Do humans get more energy from eating wheat directly or from eating wheat that is processed through animals?

(b) Give one reason for the difference in energy transfer to humans shown in the table.

(c) Which type of diet is more efficient in transferring energy: a vegetarian diet or a meat-containing diet?

(d) Which of the types of diet named in (c) represents eating lower down the food chain?

12.32 Aphids are flies that harm crops. Ladybirds can be used to limit the number of aphids in a habitat. This is called **biological control.**

Biological control is the use of one living thing to reduce the number of a second living thing. Biological control is more environmentally friendly than the use of pesticide sprays.

(a) Work in groups to find another example of biological control.

(b) Suggest why your example is better than using pesticides.

(c) Why do you think that biological control is not more popular?

Figure 12.21 *A ladybird eating aphids*

UNIT 3

CHEMICAL WORLD

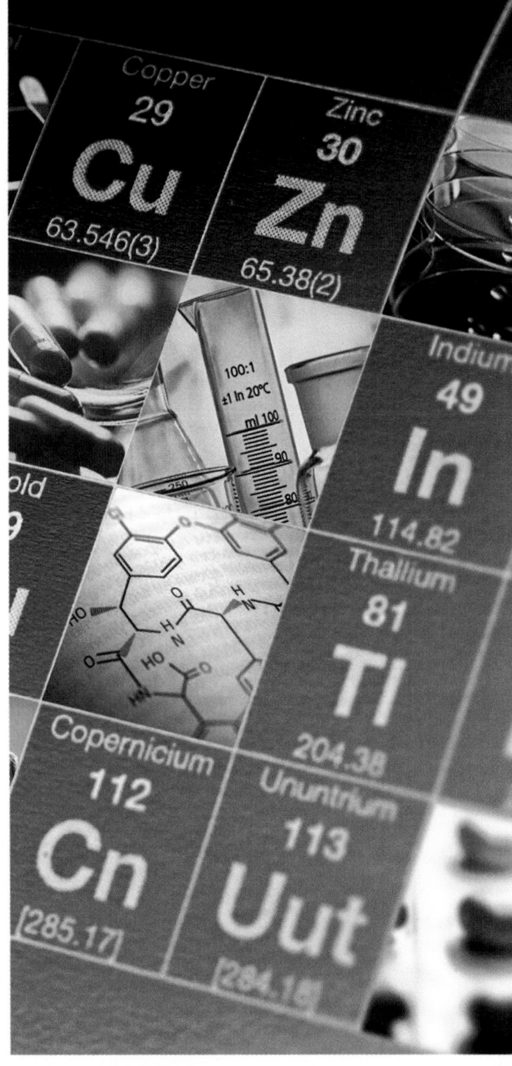

CHAPTER 13 The particle theory

UNIT 3

Learning outcomes

At the end of this chapter you will be able to:

- Describe matter
- Name the three states of matter
- Classify materials as solid, liquid or gas
- Describe how particles are arranged in each state of matter
- Outline the properties of solids, liquids and gases
- Explain changes of states of matter.

Keywords

matter, atoms, volume, melting, boiling, evaporation, condensation, freezing, diffusion

What is matter?

Matter is anything that **occupies space and has mass.** Everything – *everything*: a cat, a leaf, a book, a raindrop, a flea, a pencil, even you! – on Earth is made up of matter.

Did you know?

Nothing is the only thing that is not matter.

Matter has three forms, which are known as the three **states of matter**:

- Solid
- Liquid
- Gas.

13.1 What solids, liquids and gases can you see in this serving of hot food?

Arrangement of particles

One thing that is common between solids, liquids and gases is **particles** (atoms or molecules). The particles in a substance stay the same whether it is a solid, liquid or gas; what changes is the arrangement of the particles and their energy. These particles are like small balls and they behave differently in each state of matter.

Properties of the states of matter

The *properties of a substance* is just a way of defining how it behaves – that is, how it looks, how it feels and how it acts.

Properties of solids

The particles in a solid are closely packed into position. They can vibrate but do not move from their position. As a result, solids keep their shape and volume. As the particles are in fixed places, solids cannot flow and cannot be compressed (squashed).

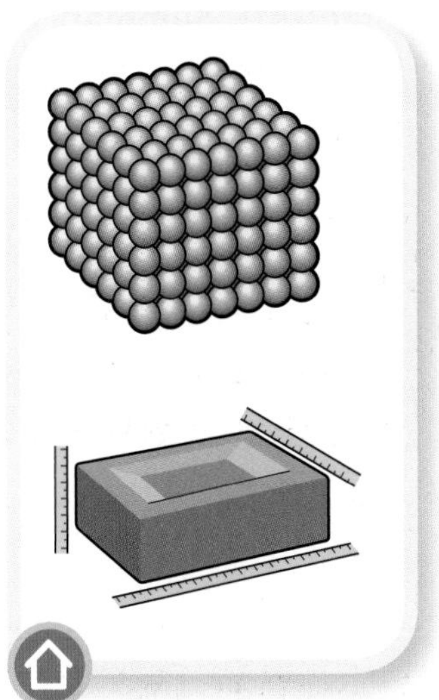

Figure 13.1 *Solids have a definite volume*

Properties of liquid

The particles in liquids are close to each other but are free to move past each other. They do tend to stick together, however. Liquids do have a definite volume, but will take the shape of whatever container they are placed in. They cannot easily be compressed or squashed.

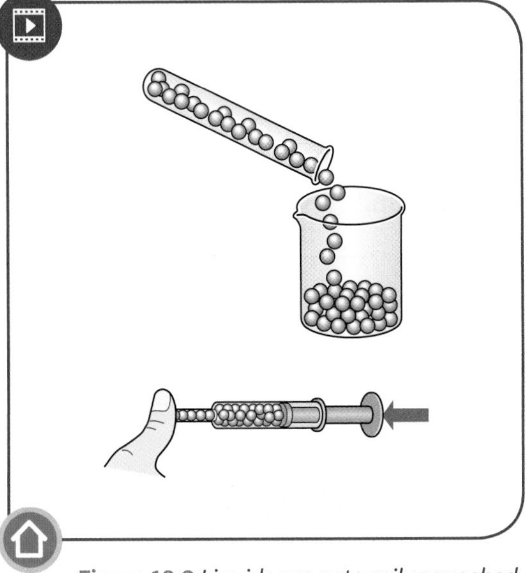

Figure 13.2 *Liquids are not easily squashed*

Figure 13.3 *Liquids have no definite shape and always take the shape of the container they are poured into*

Properties of gases

In gases the particles are free to move in all directions. They don't keep a definite shape or volume and always fill the container they are placed in. As the particles are very spread out it is easy to compress them into a smaller volume.

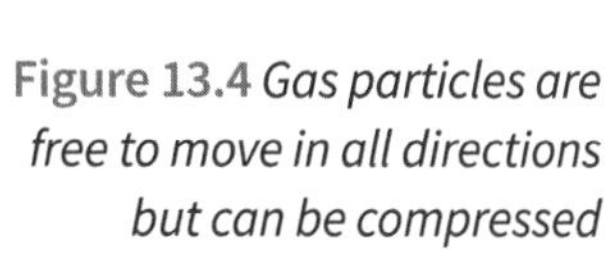
Figure 13.4 *Gas particles are free to move in all directions but can be compressed*

Figure 13.5 *Gases can be compressed*

Table 13.1 summarises the three states of matter.

Table 13.1 Summary of the states of matter

	Solid	Liquid	Gas
Definite shape	✓	×	×
Definite volume	✓	✓	×
Can be compressed	×	×	✓
Can flow	×	✓	✓
	Figure 13.6	Figure 13.7	Figure 13.8

Q

13.2 Write out and complete the following:

(a) Matter is anything that occupies ________ and has ________. There are three states of matter: ________, ________ and ________.

(b) In a solid the particles are packed ________ together. Therefore solids have a ________ shape. In a gas, particles move around very ________ and there are large ________ between them. In a ________, the particles can slide past each other. As a result, they have no ________.

13.3 You have all three states of matter as part of you!

(a) Name a solid that is part of you.

(b) Name a liquid that is part of you.

(c) Name a gas that is part of you.

Properties of states of matter

13.4 Within your group, imagine each person is a particle. Move into position to demonstrate the arrangement of the particles in:

(a) Solids (b) Liquids (c) Gases.

13.5 What arrangement has the most energy: solid, liquid or gas?

Different states – different jobs

13.6 Look at what makes up a car. In your group, discuss each state of matter – where it may be used in the car and why.

13.7 Natural gas from the North Sea is piped into our homes. It is invisible. What has been added to the gas to enable leaks to be detected?

13.8 Temperature is measured with mercury or alcohol thermometers. Do you think water is suitable as a liquid in thermometers? Explain.

Properties of states of matter

13.9 Coal, petrol and butane are three common fuels.

Figure 13.9 *Coal*

Figure 13.10 *Petrol*

Figure 13.11 *Butane*

(a) Divide your class into five groups. Each group answer a question from the list below relating to the different fuels.

(b) Come back together as a class and discuss your answers.

(c) Together, write out the properties of each state of matter.

Group A – What is the state of matter for each fuel?

Group B – Can each fuel move/flow?

Group C – Can each fuel change shape?

Group D – Is it possible for each fuel to change volume?

Group E – Which fuel(s) can be compressed?

Change of state

This is where a material can change from one state of matter to another. There is no change in mass and no new substance is formed.

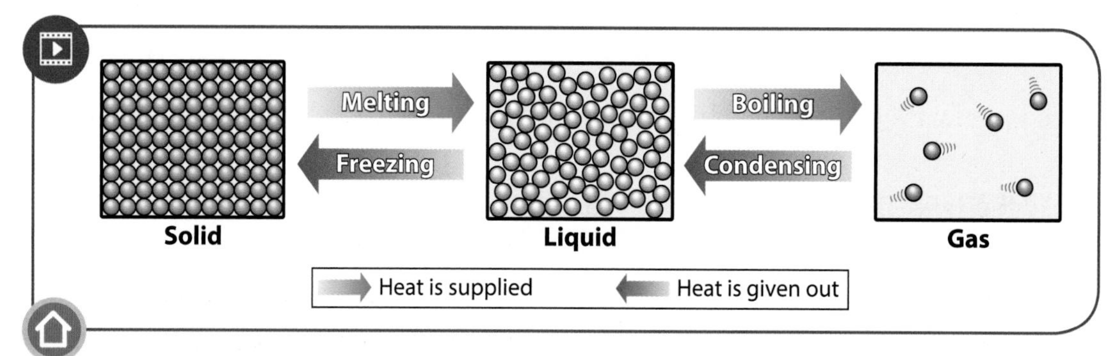

Figure 13.12 *Change of state*

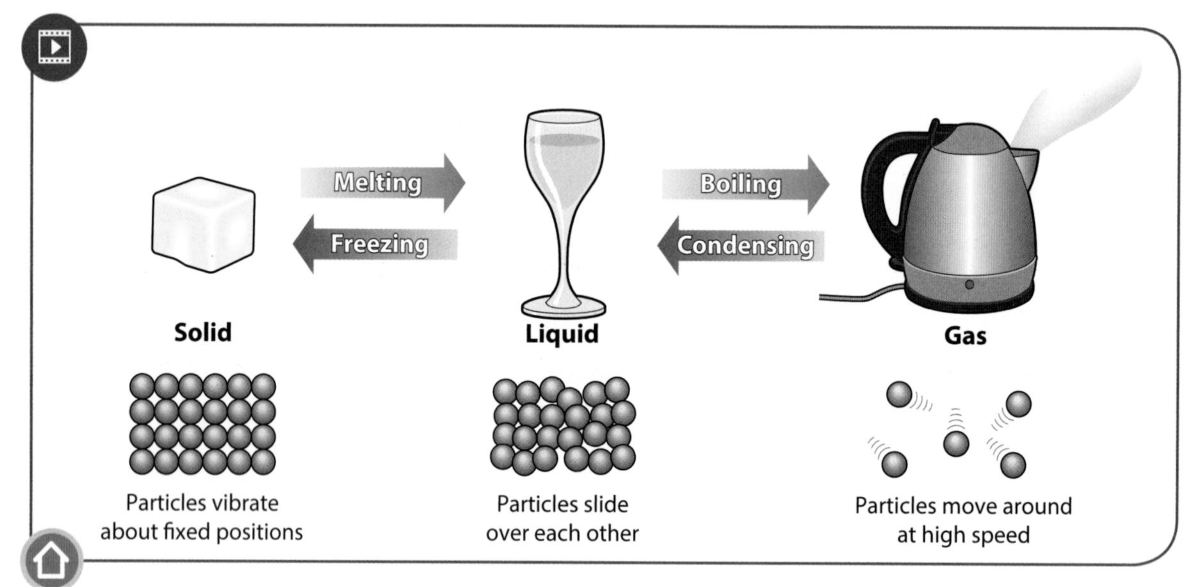

Figure 13.13 *Substances change state when heated or cooled*

Melting

Melting takes place when a solid (ice) is heated (gains energy) and it changes into a liquid.

13.10 From the following list select the correct word to complete the changes of states of matter: freezing, melting, boiling, condensation.

(a) solid ⟶ liquid = ____________

(b) liquid ⟶ gas = ____________

(c) gas ⟶ liquid = ____________

(d) liquid ⟶ solid = ____________

13.11 Can you figure out what is happening to the particles in the solid when they are heated? Write down what you think is happening.

Boiling

Boiling takes place when a liquid is heated and it turns into a gas.

13.12 What is happening to the particles when they change from a liquid to a gas?

13.13 Do the particles in a gas require more energy than the particles in a solid?

Condensation

This is where cooling a gas (removing energy) causes it to change into a liquid.

13.14 Explain what effect the removal of energy may have on the particles and why a gas changes into a liquid.

Freezing

Freezing happens when a liquid is cooled and changes into a solid.

13.15 What do you think is happening to the particles in a liquid that causes them to stop moving and form a solid?

Boiling point of a liquid

The boiling point is the temperature at which a liquid changes into a gas throughout the liquid.

The temperature at which this occurs in water is 100°C and in ethanol it happens at 78°C.

Did you know?

When water boils, water vapour called **steam** is released. Steam is not the white cloud produced – that is tiny droplets of water. Steam is an invisible gas next to the surface of the water.

13.16 Puddles disappear quickly when the sun comes out. This is where the water changes from a liquid to water vapour by evaporation. Investigate how evaporation differs from boiling and why we don't see anything happening during evaporation.

Diffusion

Imagine the smell of a stink bomb! When the bomb is opened (broken) the small particles move from where there are lots of them, to where there are fewer of them. This is how the smell spreads. This is called diffusion.

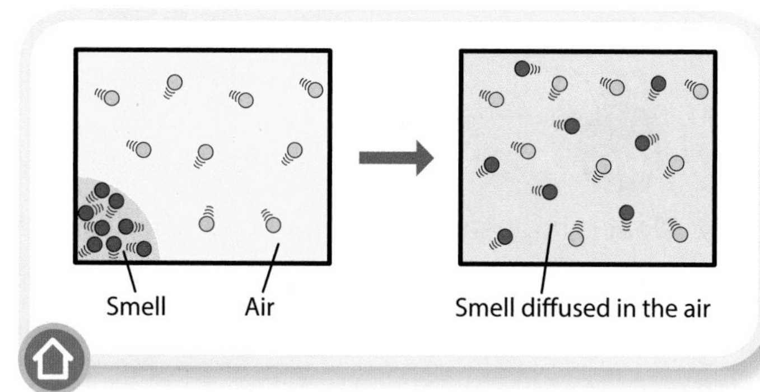

Figure 13.14 *Particles in a gas spread evenly by diffusing*

Diffusion is the movement of particles from an area of high concentration to an area of lower concentration. Diffusion occurs mainly in liquids and gases.

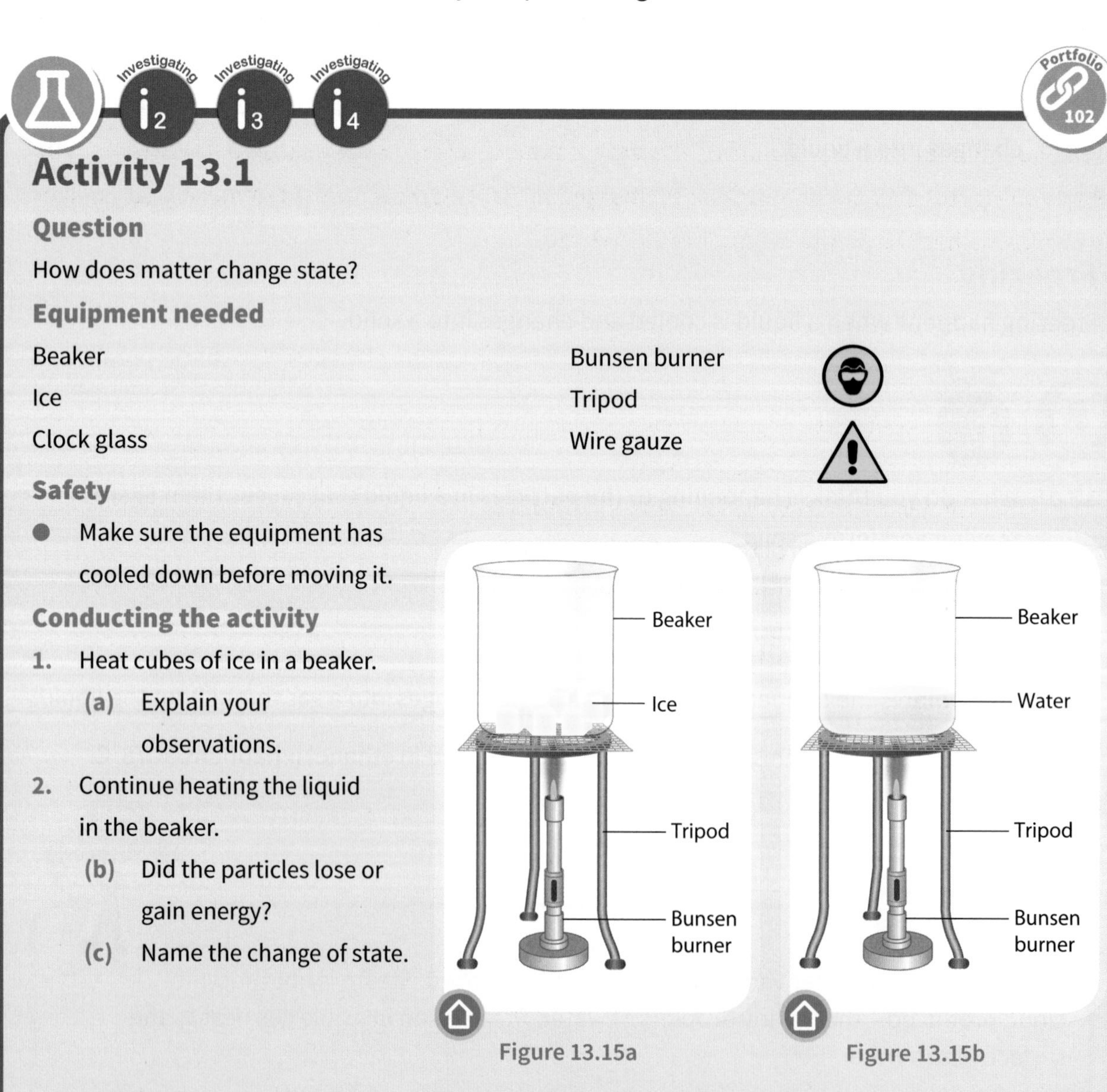

Activity 13.1

Question

How does matter change state?

Equipment needed

Beaker
Ice
Clock glass
Bunsen burner
Tripod
Wire gauze

Safety

- Make sure the equipment has cooled down before moving it.

Conducting the activity

1. Heat cubes of ice in a beaker.
   (a) Explain your observations.
2. Continue heating the liquid in the beaker.
   (b) Did the particles lose or gain energy?
   (c) Name the change of state.

Figure 13.15a

Figure 13.15b

3. Place a clock glass over the beaker.
   (d) Explain what you see.
   (e) Name the change of state.
4. Place the beaker in freezer for a few hours.
   (f) Explain your result.
   (g) Describe what happened to the particles.

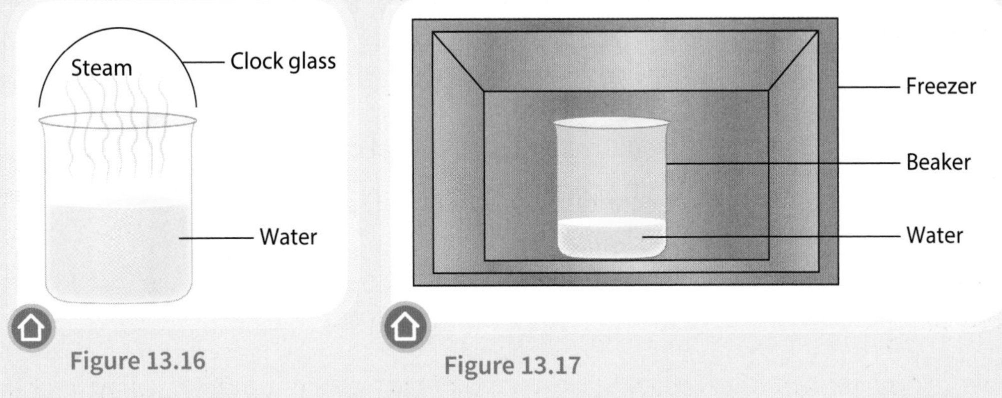

Figure 13.16

Figure 13.17

5. Discuss and evaluate your results and explanations as a whole class.

Fourth state of matter

Plasma is the fourth state of matter. It is very similar to a gas – in fact, plasma is a gas that can carry an electrical charge. Plasma particles spread out and move around randomly but unlike gas, plasma has the ability to conduct electricity.

13.17 Research plasma to find the answers to the following questions:
   (a) Where is plasma found on Earth?
   (b) What is the most common form of plasma?
   (c) What percentage of the universe is plasma?
   (d) Where is plasma used in industry?

CHAPTER 14 UNIT 3 Observing change

Learning outcomes

At the end of this chapter you will be able to:

- Distinguish between a physical change and a chemical change
- Outline the changes that may occur during a chemical reaction
- Describe the law of conservation of mass.

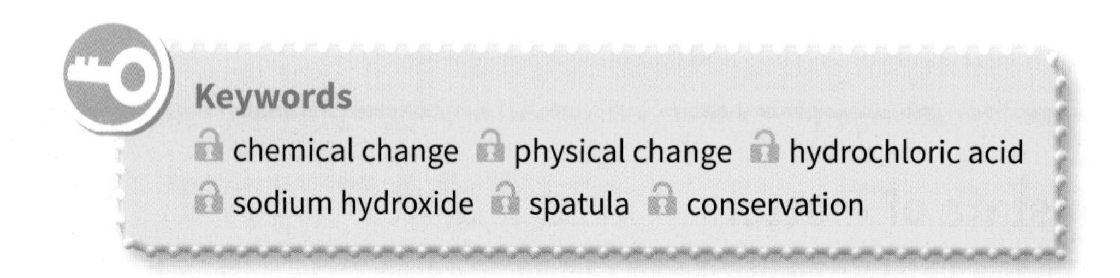

In science there are many changes, but can they always be reversed?

Physical change

Our study of chemistry leads us to a better understanding of our world and the processes by which materials can change and be changed. We know from chapter 13 that matter exists in three states (see Figure 14.1 for a recap).

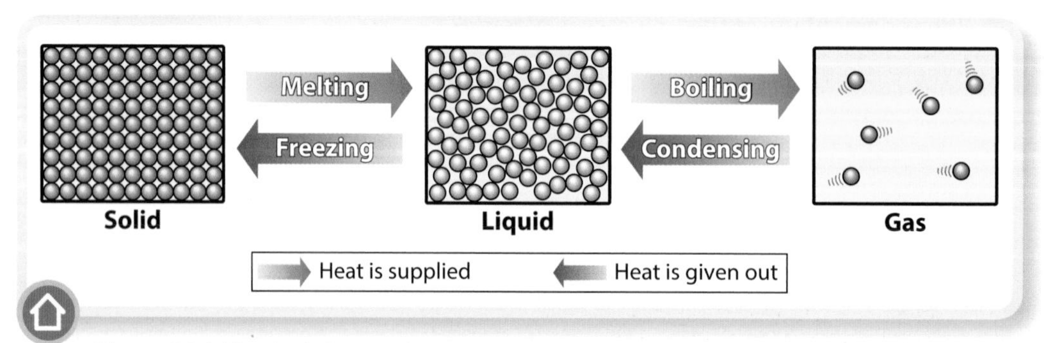

Figure 14.1 *Physical changes in matter*

The changes shown in Figure 14.1 are reversible and no new substance is formed; there is just a change of state. This is called a **physical change**, where there is no change in particles, just their arrangement and their energy.

14.1 Look at the following pictures and discuss in groups why these may be physical changes.
For each of them, discuss the questions:
(a) Are any new substances made?
(b) Can you reverse the changes (that is, go back to what it looked like at the start)?

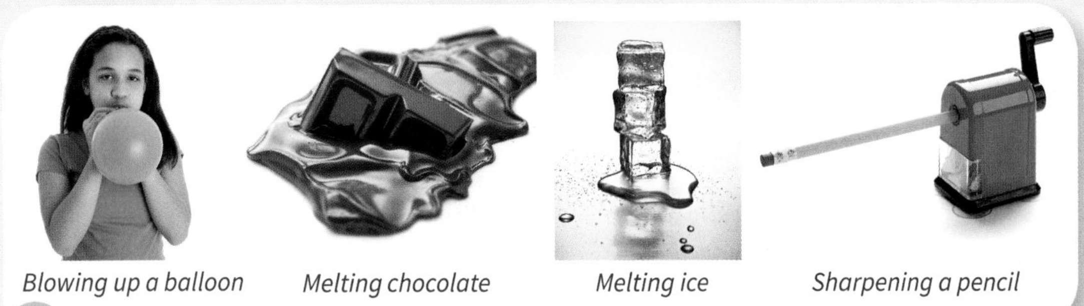

Figure 14.2 *Different matter undergoing physical changes*

14.2 Now consider what might happen when a match is ignited and burning.
Discuss these questions:
(a) What changes occur to the match when it has been lit? List them.
(b) Is energy produced?
(c) What forms of energy have been produced?
(d) Can you reverse this change?
(e) Is this a physical change?

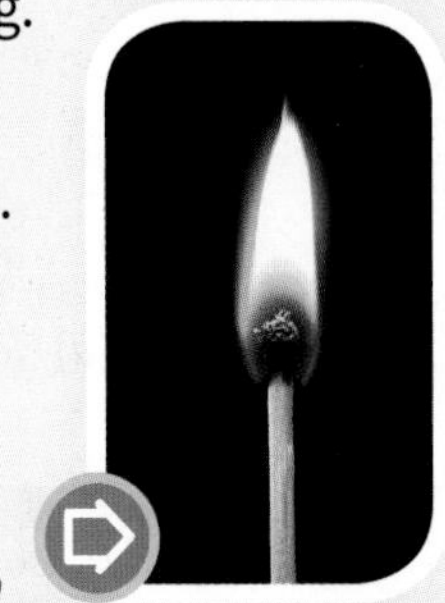

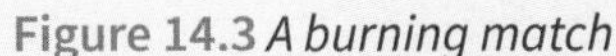

Figure 14.3 *A burning match*

Chemical change

A burning match is an example of a chemical change, where a chemical reaction takes place and a new substance is formed. During a chemical change energy may be released or absorbed. This means chemical changes are usually very difficult to reverse.

Here are some everyday examples of chemical change:

Figure 14.4 *Iron reacts with oxygen and water to form iron oxide (rust)*

Figure 14.5 *When you add a dissolvable tablet to water you may get bubbles*

CHEMICAL WORLD

14.3 List two differences between physical change and chemical change.

14.4 State which of the following changes are physical changes and which are chemical changes:

Burning wood	Dissolving sugar in tea	Baking a cake
Making toast	Dicing potatoes	Cutting paper

14.5 Look at the following pictures within your group and discuss what changes occur.

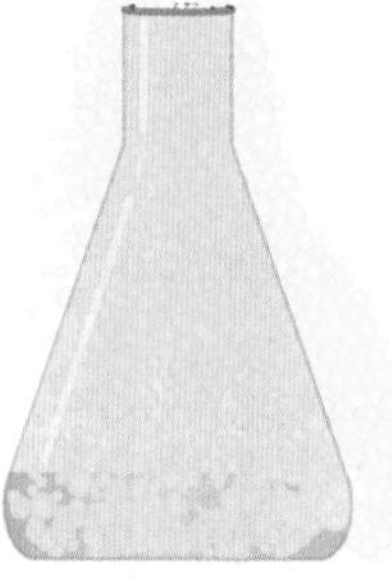

(a) *Raw liver in hydrogen peroxide*

(b) *Ice hotel in Sweden, which is built every year*

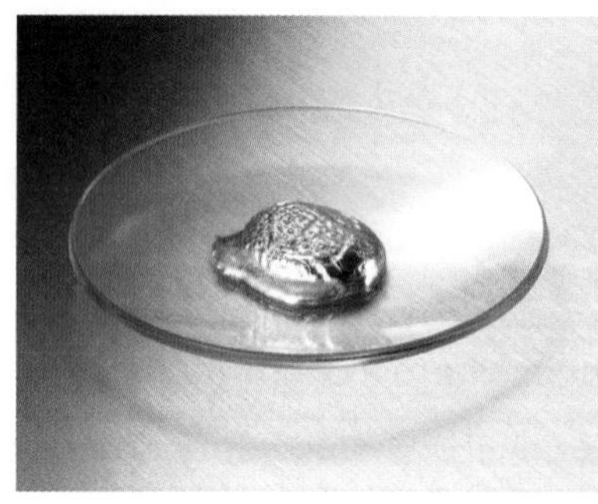

(c) *Melting gallium*

(d) *Combustion engine of a space ship*

Figure 14.6 *What changes are taking or have taken place?*

14.6 Look at this candle.

Which label (A or B) shows a physical change and which shows a chemical change? Explain your answer.

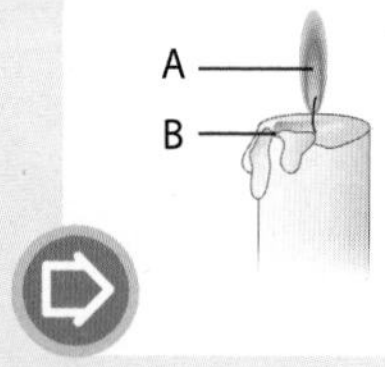

Figure 14.7 *Changes taking place to a candle*

CHEMICAL WORLD

Chemical reactions

Many useful materials are produced from chemical changes (also known as chemical reactions), such as plastics, which are made from reactions with oil.

The chemicals that react together are called **reactants** and the substances formed are called the **products**.

Observing change

During a chemical reaction the atoms rearrange to form a new substance. There are some signs that indicate this has occurred:

- Colour change
- A change in temperature
- Light is emitted
- Bubbles of gas are produced.

Figure 14.8 *A chemical reaction takes place when a firework is lit*

Figure 14.9 *When you add a dissolvable tablet to water and you get bubbles then a chemical change occurs*

Did you know?

Have you ever smelled a rotten egg? It smells completely different from fresh eggs. A chemical change during spoilage of eggs causes this odour.

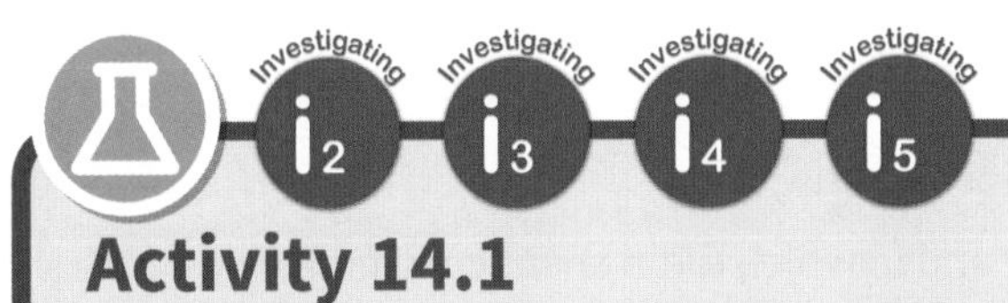

Portfolio 107

Activity 14.1

Question

What changes are taking place in chemical reactions?

Equipment needed

4 test tubes
Test tube rack
Spatula
Iron nails
Thermometer
Sodium hydroxide (0.1 M)
Sulfuric acid (0.1 M)
Vinegar
Baking soda
Copper oxide
Water
Universal indicator

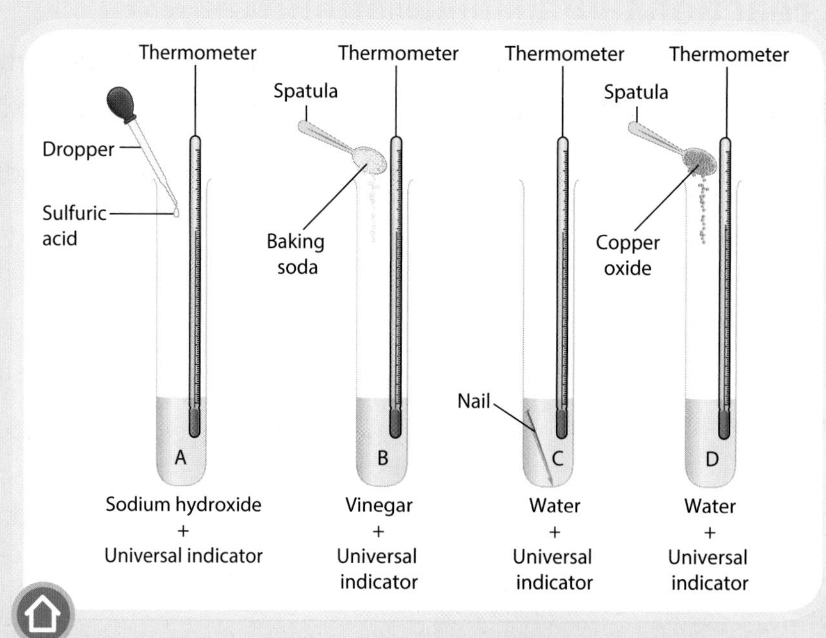

Figure 14.10 *Investigating changes*

Conducting the activity

You are going to add substances to four different test tubes. For each test tube, record:

(a) Any change in temperature
(b) Any change in colour
(c) Any noticeable odour
(d) If there is formation of bubbles.

1. *Test tube A* Place 3 cm^3 of sodium hydroxide into the test tube. Add a few drops of universal indicator. Measure the temperature of the solution.
   Add 3 cm^3 of sulfuric acid. Measure the temperature again. Note any changes.
2. *Test tube B* Place 3 cm^3 of vinegar into a test tube. Add a few drops of universal indicator. Measure the temperature. Add half a spatula of baking soda. Measure the temperature again. Note any changes.
3. *Test tube C* Place 3 cm^3 of water and a few drops of universal indicator into a test tube. Measure the temperature. Add an iron nail. Measure the temperature again. Note any changes.
4. *Test tube D* Place 3 cm^3 of water into a test tube and add a few drops of universal indicator. Add half a spatula of copper oxide. Measure the temperature again. Note any changes.

Results

Look at your results for each test tube and answer the following questions:

(a) In which test tubes did a physical change take place, and in which did a chemical change take place?
(b) Write down the properties that tell you if there has been a chemical reaction (chemical change).

Conservation of mass

We know that matter can be changed from one form into another, but during physical and chemical changes, is there a change in the overall mass of the matter, or does it remain constant? We will investigate this in the next activity.

Portfolio 109

Activity 14.2

Question

Does mass change during physical changes and chemical changes?

Equipment needed

Electronic balance	Spatula	Sugar	Hydrochloric acid (0.1 M)
4 beakers	Water	Sodium hydroxide (0.1 M)	Universal indicator

Conducting the activity

Reaction A

1. Place two beakers (50 ml) on a balance and press the zero button.
2. Place 10 cm^3 of water in one beaker and add a few drops of universal indicator.
3. Place one spatula of sugar into the other beaker.

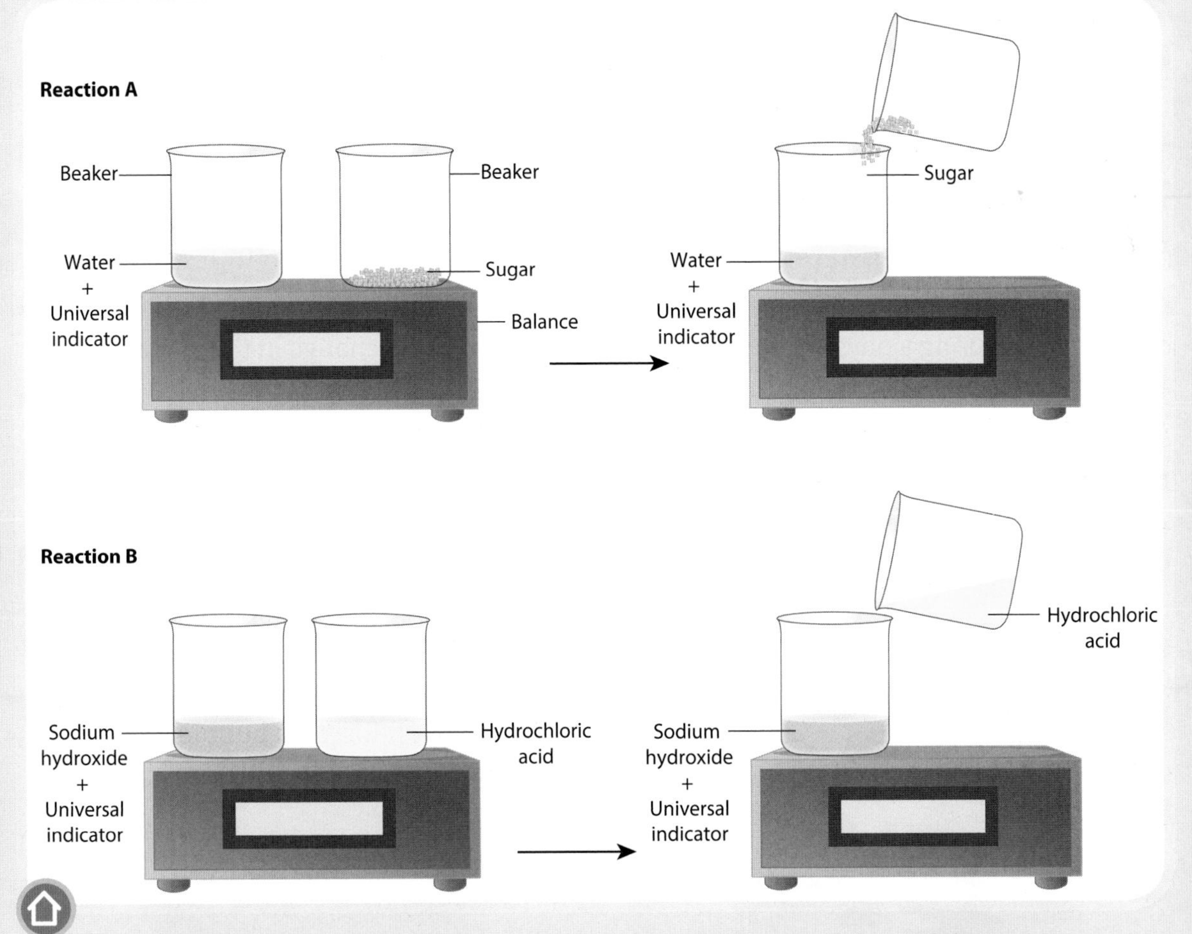

Figure 14.11 *Investigating changes in mass during physical changes and chemical changes*

4. Record the total mass on the balance.
5. Add the sugar to the water and replace the empty beaker on the balance.
6. Record the total mass.

Reaction B

1. Place two beakers (50 ml) on a balance and press the zero button.
2. Add 10 cm^3 of sodium hydroxide into one beaker and add a few drops of universal indicator.
3. Add 10 cm^3 of hydrochloric acid into a second beaker on the balance.
4. Record the total mass on the balance.
5. Add the hydrochloric acid solution to the sodium hydroxide solution and replace the empty beaker on the balance.
6. Record the total mass.

Divide into groups. Within your group, analyse your results and answer the following questions:

14.7 Did you notice any changes during reaction A and reaction B? Which reaction, A or B, showed a chemical reaction? What evidence do you have to support this?

14.8 Was the initial mass the same as the final mass for each reaction?

14.9 During a physical or chemical change is there a change in the overall mass?

Law of conservation of mass

Antoine Lavoisier, a French chemist in the eighteenth century, discovered the law of the conservation of mass. He discovered that the mass of a substance cannot be created or destroyed, so during a physical and chemical change there is no change in the overall mass.

Figure 14.12 *Antoine Lavoisier*

Did you know?

If you leave a can of soda open for a long time the carbonic acid (fizz) decomposes into carbon dioxide and water. It loses its bubbles. This is another example of a chemical change.

Particle model diagrams

A particle model diagram shows how particles (atoms) rearrange to form a new substance during a chemical reaction. Figure 14.13 and Figure 14.14 are examples of these diagrams.

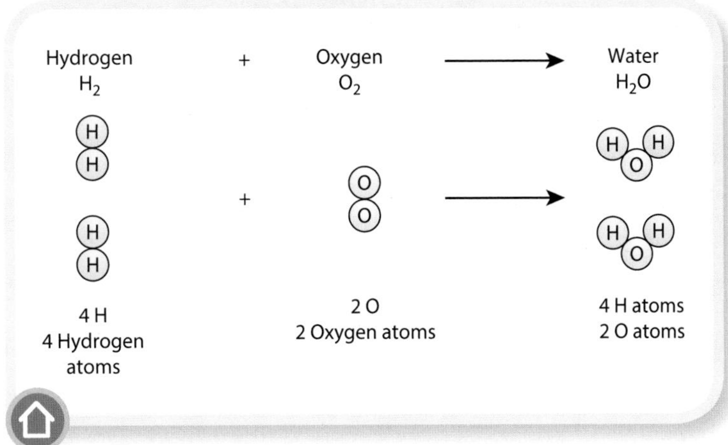

Figure 14.13 *Particle model diagrams*

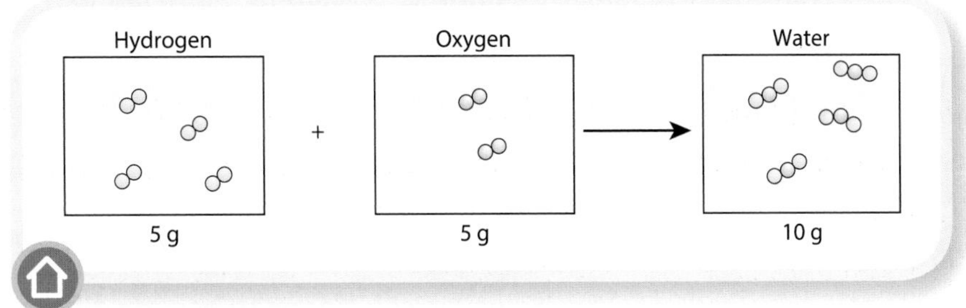

Figure 14.14 *Particle model diagrams*

14.10 Draw a particle model diagram for Figure 14.15:

Copper + Oxygen ⟶ Copper oxide

Figure 14.15

14.11 According to the law of the conservation of mass, how much zinc was produced? (See Figure 14.16.)

Calcium	+	Zinc carbonate	⟶	Calcium carbonate	+	Zinc
68 g		192 g		152 g		*x* g

Figure 14.16

14.12 If 50 grams of sodium reacts with chlorine to form 128 grams of salt, how many grams of chlorine reacted? (See Figure 14.17.)

Sodium	+	Chlorine	⟶	Sodium chloride (salt)
50 g		*x* g		128 g

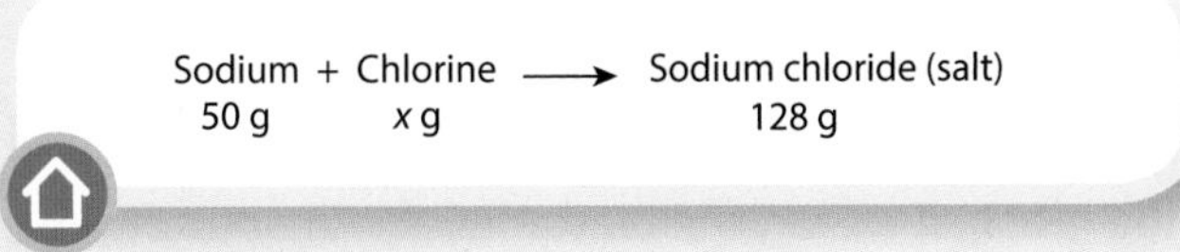

Figure 14.17

CHAPTER 15

UNIT 3

Particles in solution

Learning outcomes

At the end of this chapter you will be able to:

- Distinguish between solute, solvent and solution
- Outline how different mixtures may be separated.

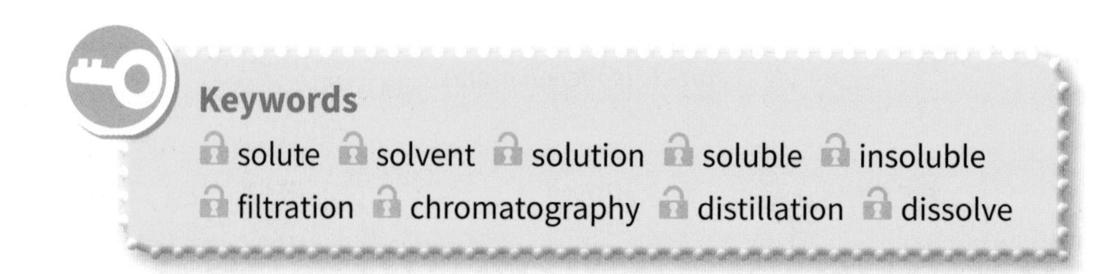

What are solutions?

When we think about solutions we usually think of them as a solid dissolved in a liquid, e.g. seawater contains salt dissolved in water. However, solutions can be very different to this. For example, oxygen dissolves in water to form a solution that allows fish to breathe.

Dissolving

When a substance dissolves in a liquid its particles slip into the gaps between the particles of the liquid and they become completely mixed up together.

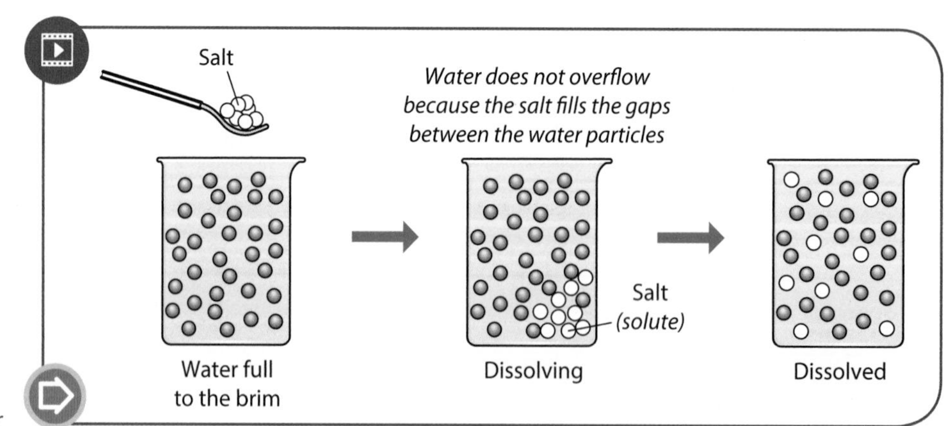

Figure 15.1 *Salt dissolving in water*

Did you know?

If you pour a handful of salt into a full glass of water, the water level will actually go down rather than overflowing the glass. Why do you think this is?

15.1 Look at Figure 15.2. There are certain words we need to know. Explain each of the following words:

(a) Solvent

(b) Solute

(c) Solution.

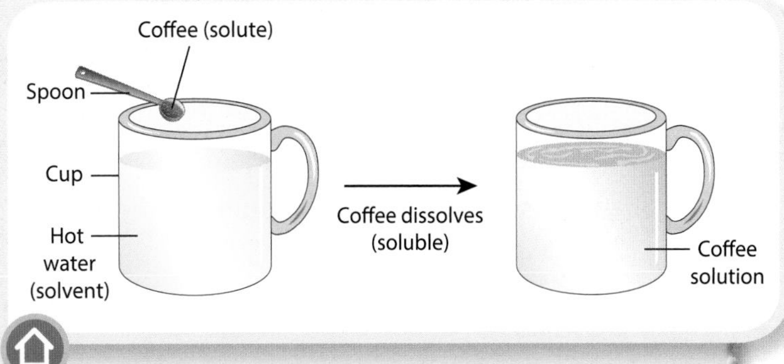

Figure 15.2 *Coffee dissolving in water*

15.2 Write out and complete the following:
Most solutions are made up of a substance called the ______________, which dissolves in the liquid called the ______________. Substances that dissolve are said to be ______________, while those that don't are ______________. A cup of coffee is a ______________, the hot water is the ______________ and the coffee granules are the ______________.

Concentrated and dilute solutions

Have you ever tried tasting fruit squash without adding water first? It tastes unbearably sweet. These types of drinks are **concentrated solutions**. This means there is a lot of solute dissolved in the solvent.

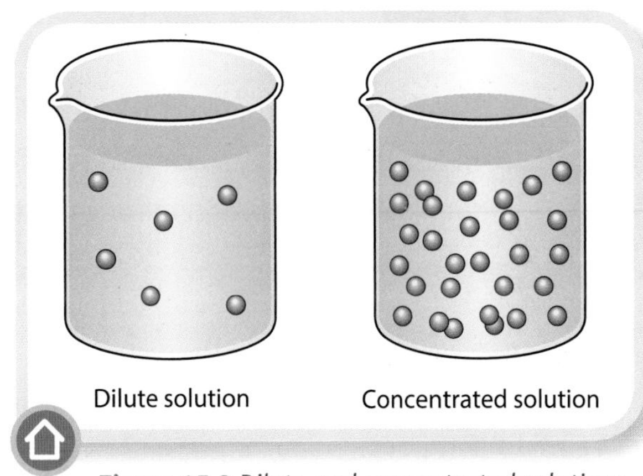

Figure 15.3 *Dilute and concentrated solutions*

15.3 What is the solute in the concentrated solution of squash?

By adding water to the concentrated solution of squash, you are making the solution more dilute and nicer to taste.

If you add too much water, the drink may taste too weak (dilute).

15.4 Briefly explain the difference between a dilute solution and a concentrated solution.

15.5 If you make your glass of squash too dilute, what could you do to make it more concentrated again?

Did you know?

There is about ½ lb or 250 g of salt (NaCl) in the average human body.

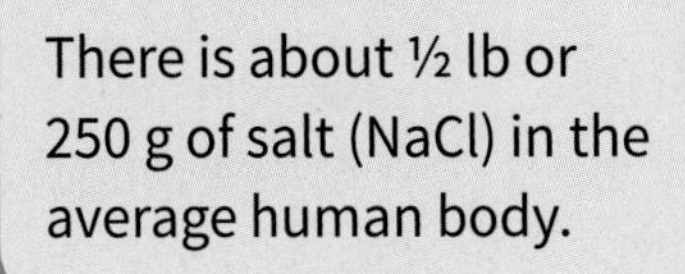

15.6 Give one everyday example of each of the following:

(a) A gas dissolved in a liquid

(b) A liquid dissolved in a liquid

(c) A solid dissolved in a liquid

(d) A gas dissolved in a solid.

15.7 Name a solvent other than water and a substance that dissolves in it.

Did you know?

One bucketful of water contains more atoms than there are bucketfuls of water in the ocean.

15.8 Divide into groups. Within your group outline how you could investigate if there is a change in the overall mass when a solid dissolves in a solvent.

Soluble/insoluble

Solids that dissolve in a liquid are said to be **soluble** and solids that do not dissolve are called **insoluble**.

15.9 Make a list of five solids that are soluble in water and five solids that are insoluble in water.

15.10 In a salt solution you cannot tell if there is any solute present. Draw a particle diagram for a salt solution and for pure water.

15.11 Find out:

(a) What name is given to two liquids that mix, e.g. alcohol and water?

(b) What name is given to two liquids that do not mix, e.g. oil and water?

Activity 15.1

Question

Does the solubility of water change with temperature?

Equipment needed

4 beakers	Vegetable oil	Sugar	Spatula
Water	Food colouring	Sand	Thermometer

CHEMICAL WORLD

Safety

- Take care to add the oil to water, and not the other way round.

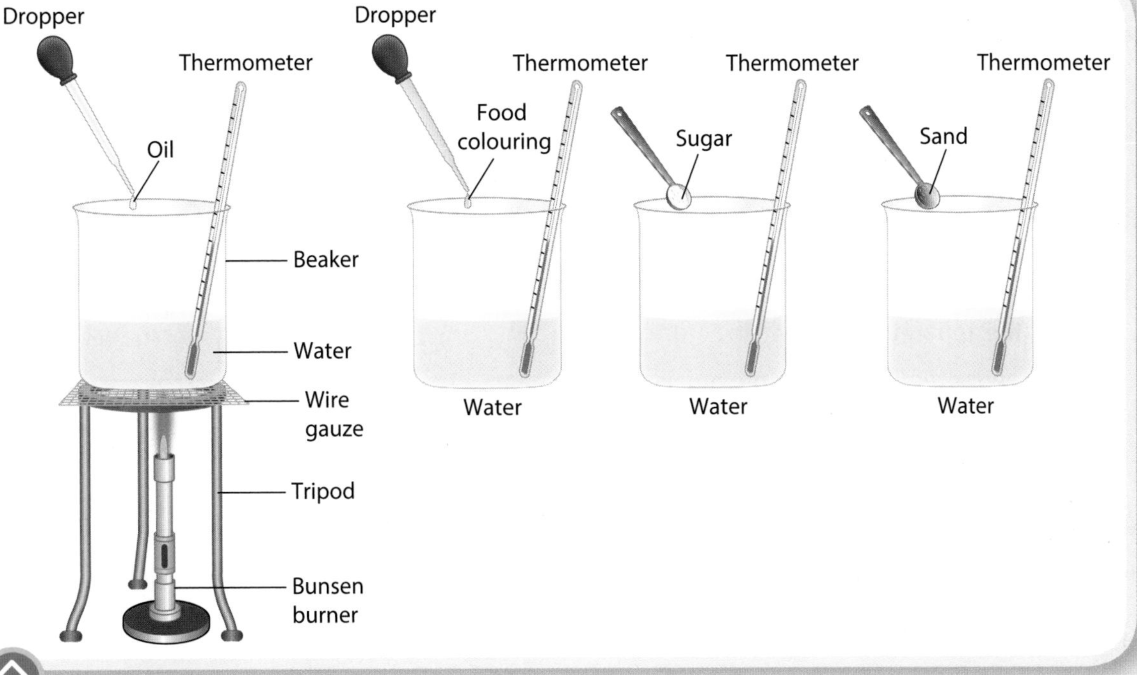

Figure 15.4 *Investigating solubility*

Conducting the activity

1. Place 50 cm^3 of water (at room temperature) into each beaker.
2. Add a small amount of oil to the first beaker. Observe and record what happens.
3. Stir the water and record the result.
4. Repeat steps 1, 2 and 3 for the other three substances, recording the results.
5. Repeat steps 1 to 4 with the water at 40°C.
6. Record your results.

15.12 Referring to your results, answer these questions:

(a) How did hot water affect the ability of each substance to dissolve?

(b) What is the effect of stirring the solution?

15.13 Research why water is such a good solvent and why certain substances will dissolve in water and why other substances will not.

Separation of mixtures

The different substances in mixtures can be separated easily by physical methods. The method depends on the type of mixture.

CHEMICAL WORLD

Portfolio 117

Activity 15.2

Question

How do you separate an insoluble solid and a liquid?

Equipment needed

Conical flask	Test tube or beaker
Filter funnel	Water
Filter paper	Soil sample

Conducting the activity

1. Set up the apparatus as shown in Figure 15.5.
2. Slowly and carefully pour the mixture into the filter paper as shown.
3. Allow time for the water to separate from the soil.
4. Record your findings

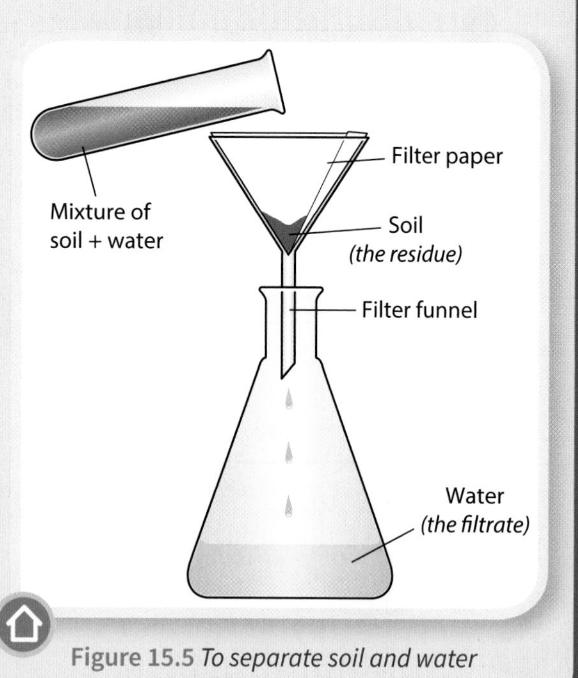

Figure 15.5 *To separate soil and water*

Portfolio 117

Activity 15.3

Question

How do you separate a soluble solid and a liquid?

Equipment needed

Evaporating dish	Tripod	Bunsen burner
Beaker	Wire gauze	Solution of salt water

Safety

- Use tongs for moving the evaporating dish off the tripod.
- Wait for the equipment to cool before removing the salt.

Figure 15.6 *Rapid evaporation*

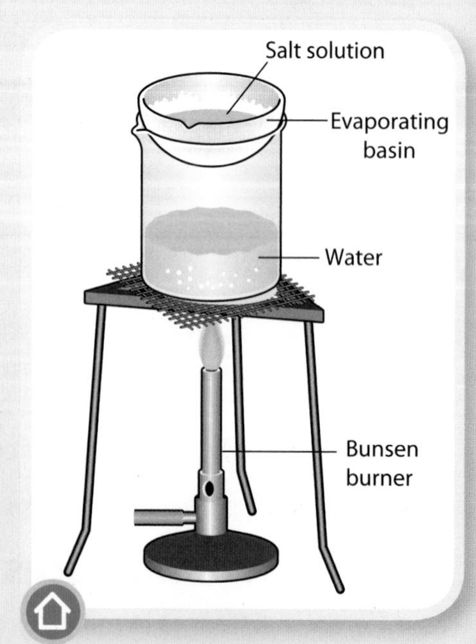

Figure 15.7 *Gentle evaporation*

CHEMICAL WORLD

Conducting the activity

1. Set up as shown in Figure 15.6 and heat directly until most of the water has evaporated.
2. Using tongs, carefully transfer the evaporating dish onto a beaker of boiling water as in Figure 15.7. (This heats the evaporating dish more gently and prevents the salt from spitting out of the dish.)
3. Evaporate the rest of the water (solvent) and remove the salt from the dish when cooled.
4. Record your findings

Portfolio 117

Activity 15.4

Question

How do you separate two substances by distillation?

Equipment needed

Bunsen burner
Tripod
Wire gauze
2 retort stands and clamps
Round-bottomed flask beaker
Thermometer
Tubing
Quickfit distillation apparatus (Liebig condenser)
Salt/water mixture, or water/alcohol mixture

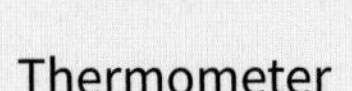

Safety

- Use retort stands for holding the round bottomed flask and the Liebig condenser.

Conducting the activity

1. Set up the apparatus as shown in Figure 15.8.
2. Ensure that water flows into the condenser from the lower end and out of the top end. This ensures that the outer layer of the condenser is fully filled with moving water and kept cool.
3. Heat the round-bottomed flask to boil the solution. The temperature remains at 100°C as the water distils across.
4. Remove the Bunsen burner when all the water has evaporated.
5. Record your findings.

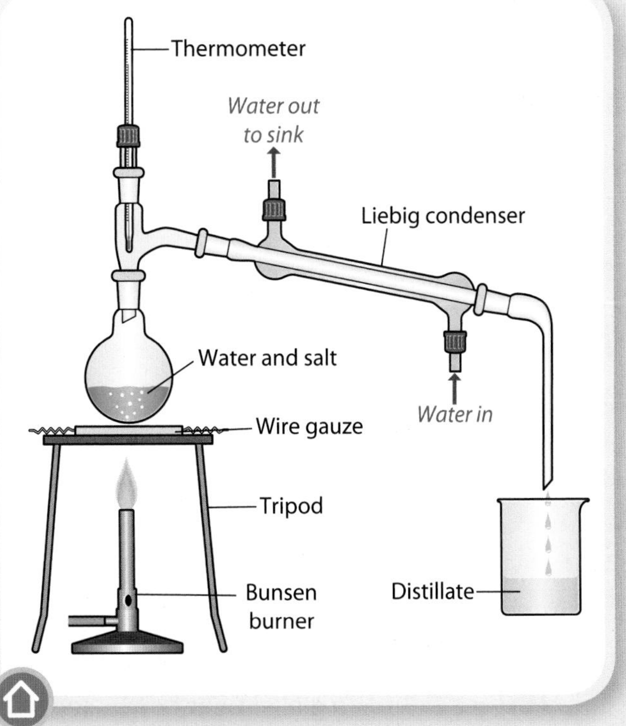

Figure 15.8 *Simple distillation*

Activity 15.5

Question

How do you separate colours in a sample of ink?

Equipment needed

Chromatography paper
Scissors
Gas jar
Paper clip
Glass rod
Capillary tubes
Samples of inks, markers or food dyes
Solvent

Conducting the activity

1. Cut a strip of chromatography paper to fit inside the gas jar as shown in Figure 15.9.
2. Remove the paper and draw a horizontal line 2–3 cm from the bottom of the paper.
3. Using the capillary tube, place a small concentrated spot of the ink/colour to be separated on the centre of the line.
4. Pour a suitable solvent into the gas jar ensuring that the level of the solvent is below the level of the ink.
5. Place the chromatography paper back in the jar and suspend it from the glass rod. Use a paper clip to ensure that the paper does not fall into the solvent.
6. Allow time for the solvent to soak up to near the top (10–15 minutes).
7. Record your findings.

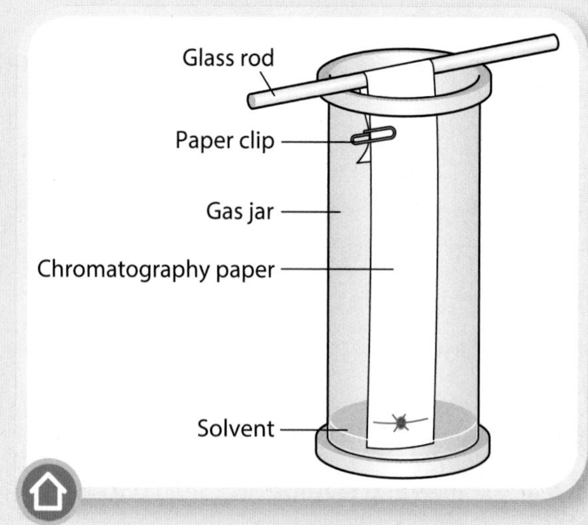

Figure 15.9 *Initial stage*

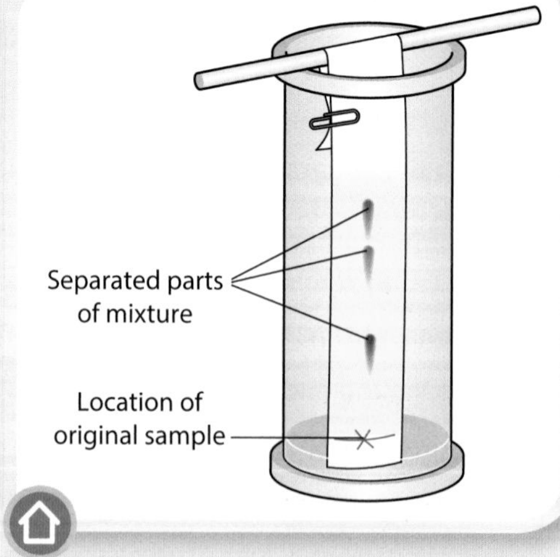

Figure 15.10 *End stage*

15.14 Divide into groups. Discuss the following mixtures within your group and write down what activities you would do to separate each mixture.

Mixture 1: Bag of coloured sweets – sorting out the sweets into the different colours
Mixture 2: Broken glass sugar bowl – separating pieces of glass from sugar
Mixture 3: Drinking water – getting pure water from salty water
Mixture 4: Metal and salt – separating a mixture of aluminium foil, paper clips and salt
Mixture 5: Orange sweet – finding out what colours the orange food colour is made from

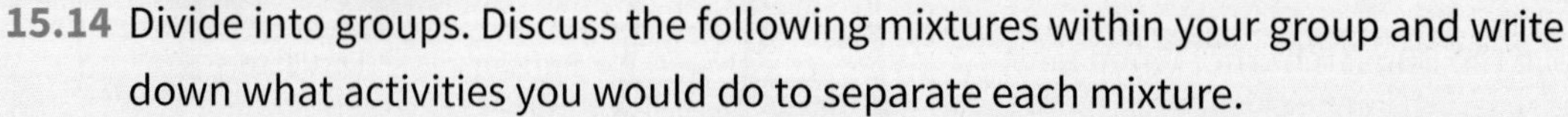

15.15 **Investigation:** In your group, read the following and determine if you can solve the problem using separation methods.

Brand A crisps states that it has less salt than Brand B crisps. Design and carry out an investigation to test and analyse the crisps to see if this is true.

15.16 Research what foods contain large amounts of salt.

15.17 What problems can arise from excess salt in your diet?

15.18 Research the solutes in a fizzy soda drink.

15.19 Water is the most important solvent as it dissolves very many solutes. Make a list of all the different jobs that water is used for around the home. Note how it is being used as a solvent in each job.

Were you surprised at how much we use water?

15.20 Can you resist the mixture we know as chocolate? Chocolate is a mixture of around 300 different substances. Some of these are chemicals that can act like drugs and affect the way your brain works. They are present in chocolate only in small quantities, but this may explain our liking for the confection.
We wouldn't have chocolate without science! Research chocolate to find the answers to the following questions:

(a) What are the main ingredients in a bar of chocolate?

(b) Chocolate gets its taste from the chemicals extracted from cocoa beans. What is the Latin name for the cocoa tree?

(c) A stimulant found in chocolate is also found in coffee. What is it?

Figure 15.11 *Chocolate*

15.21 Chocolate can act as a poison to some animals. Which domestic pet in particular must not be given chocolate, and what will they experience if they eat chocolate?

CHEMICAL WORLD

CHAPTER 16

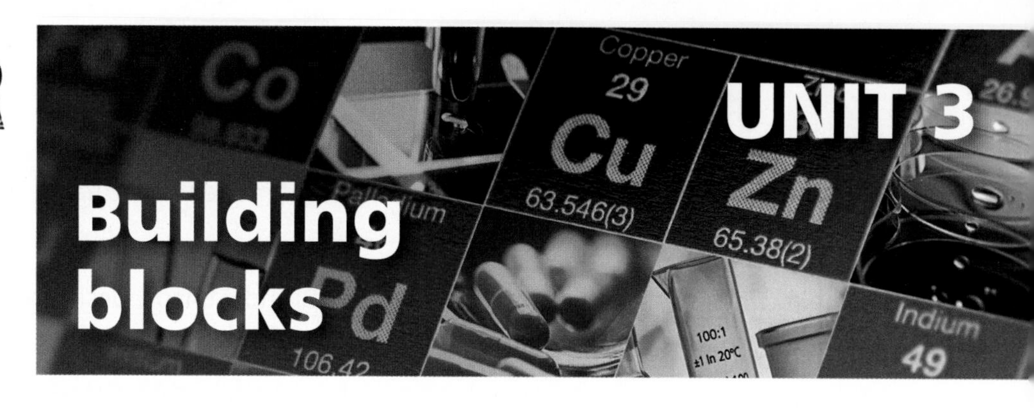

Building blocks

Learning outcomes

At the end of this chapter you will be able to:

- Describe an atom
- Distinguish between elements, compounds and molecules
- Construct a model for any molecule.

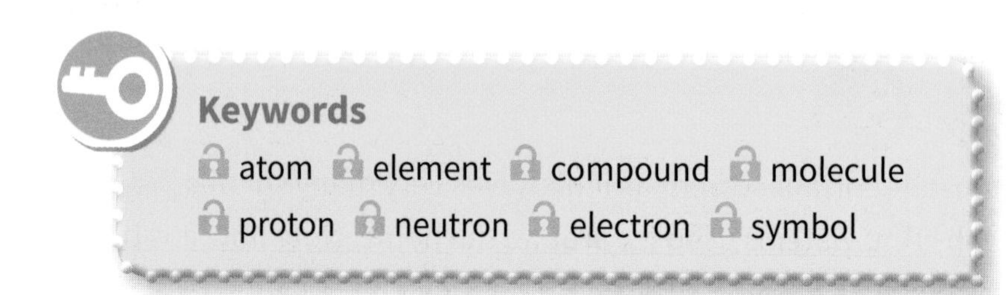

What are atoms?

Atoms are the basic building blocks of all materials. The word 'atom' comes from a Greek word describing something that cannot be divided. When atoms were discovered, scientists thought of them as solid balls, like snooker balls, which could not be split into anything simpler.

Figure 16.1 *When atoms were discovered, they were thought to be solid, like this snooker ball*

Element

An element is a substance made up of only one type of atom.

If you burn a piece of wood, you will get a black solid. That solid is called carbon. Carbon is an element because it is made up of only carbon atoms and cannot be broken down into anything simpler.

Figure 16.2 *The burnt log is carbon, and only carbon*

Did you know?

Hydrogen is the most abundant element in the universe.

Symbol

Each element has a symbol. H is the symbol for hydrogen. Fe is the symbol for iron, which comes from the Latin name *ferrum*.

16.1 What is an element?

16.2 Give three examples of elements and their symbols.

16.3 Who was the scientist who first called the tiny particles in matter 'atoms'?

16.4 Where would you find a list of all the elements, with their symbols?

16.5 List the names of all the elements whose symbols start with the letter C.

16.6 Divide the class into five different groups. Your teacher will give each group four different elements to research.

For each element, find out:

(a) Its symbol

(b) Its state of matter at room temperature

(c) Whether it is a metal, a non-metal or a semi-metal

(d) Its appearance

(e) Where it may be used.

Did you know?

The element helium was discovered on the Sun before it was found on Earth.

16.7 Which of the elements in Figure 16.3 are used in:

(a) Jewellery?

(b) Thermometers?

(c) Plumbing?

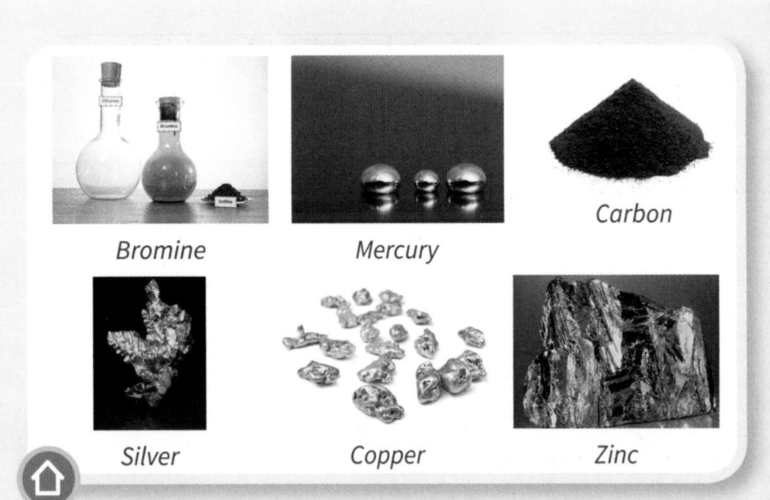

Figure 16.3 *Elements*

Molecules

A molecule is formed when two or more atoms join (**bond**) together chemically.

Compounds

When a molecule is made up of two or more different types of atoms, we call it a compound. All compounds are molecules but not all molecules are compounds.

> **Did you know?**
>
> There are about ten million known compounds that can be made with carbon.

Hydrogen gas (H_2) and oxygen gas (O_2) are not compounds because each is composed of one element. Water (H_2O) and carbon dioxide (CO_2) are compounds because each is made up of more than one type of element. All compounds are **non-elements**.

16.8 State two differences between a mixture and a compound.

16.9 Look at the following and state whether each is an element or a compound.

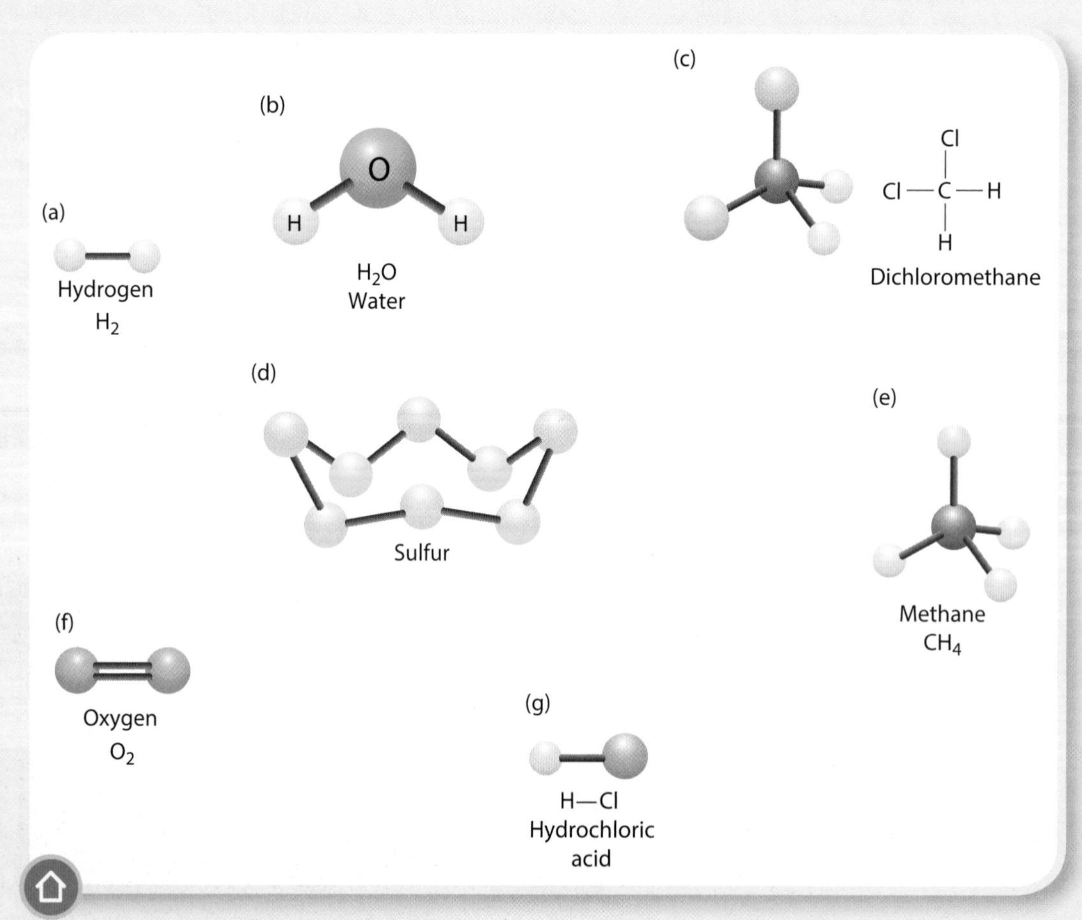

Figure 16.4 *Element or compound?*

Making models

You can use models to show how atoms bond (join) to each other.

Model kits have different coloured balls for each element and sticks to join one ball to another.

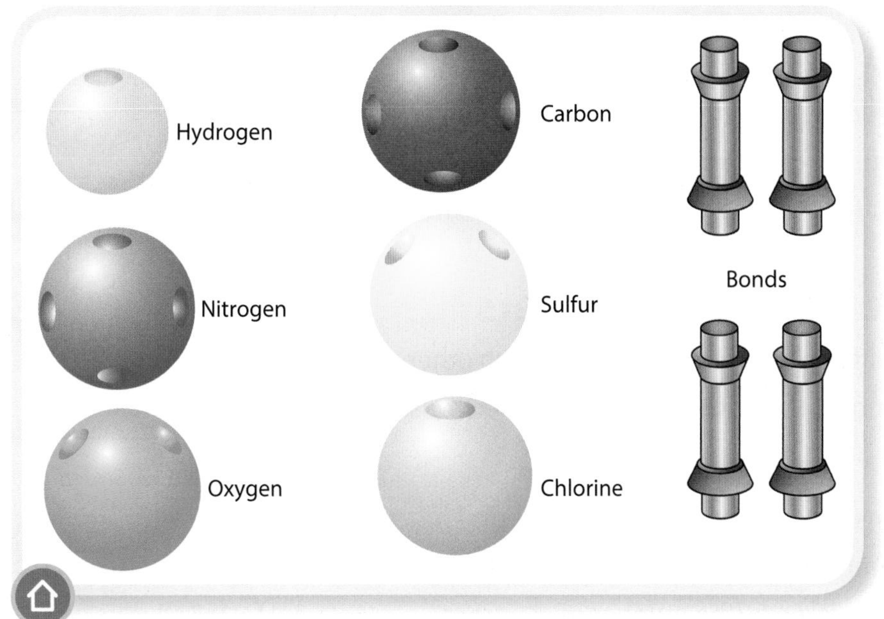

Figure 16.5 *Models are used to show how atoms bond together*

16.10 Make your own model

(a) Using a model kit, design your own model of an element or compound. Remember to use the colours for each element as shown in Figure 16.5.

(b) Compare your model with others in your group. Do the other students know the name of the atoms in your model of an element or compound?

(c) Was the model you made an element or a compound?

(d) Draw diagrams of the molecules everyone in your group made.

Structure of the atom

The atom is made up of smaller particles called **sub-atomic particles**.

These are:

- Protons
- Neutrons
- Electrons.

The three particles in the atom are quite different from each other. Table 16.1 summarises the properties of each.

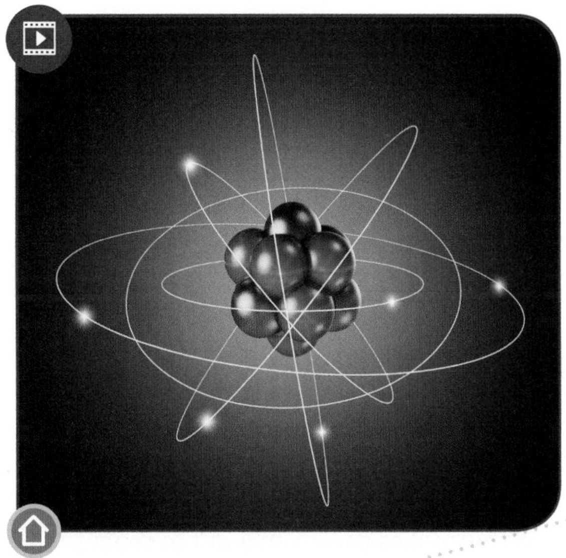

Figure 16.6 *Computer image of the atomic structure*

Table 16.1 **The properties of protons, neutrons and electrons**

Particle	Charge	Mass	Location
Proton	+1	1	Nucleus
Neutron	0	1	Nucleus
Electron	−1	Negligible	Shells

All the particles are extremely small. Electrons are so small it would take almost 2000 of them to have the same mass as a single proton or neutron.

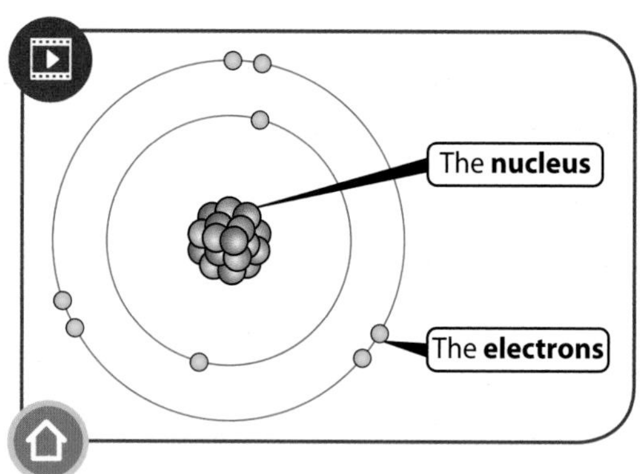

Figure 16.7 *Structure of the atom*

Atomic and mass numbers

Atoms of different elements differ from each other by the number of protons, neutrons and electrons they have.

Every element has its own **atomic number**. The atomic number tells you how many protons (which is the same as the number of electrons) there are in one atom of the element.

There is also the **mass number**. The mass number tells you how many protons and neutrons there are in the atom. Examples are given in Figure 16.9 and Figure 16.10.

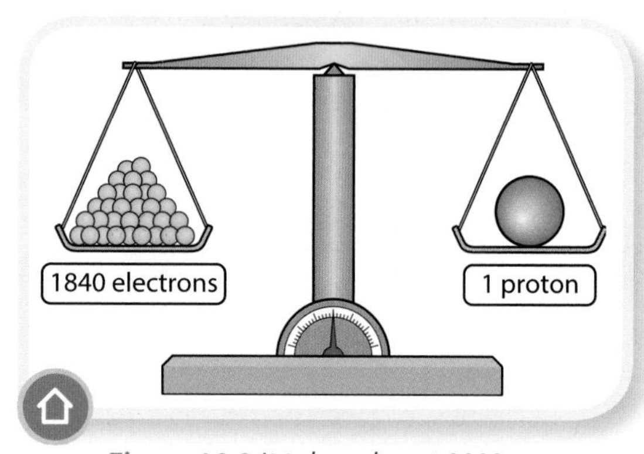

Figure 16.8 *It takes almost 2000 electrons to have the same mass as a single proton (or neutron)*

Figure 16.9 *Atomic and mass numbers of aluminium*

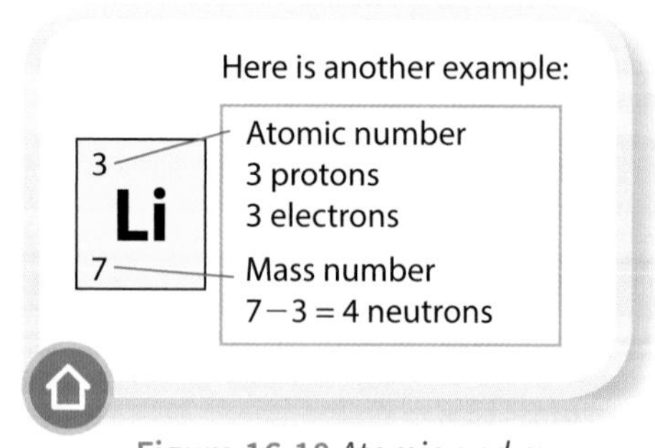

Figure 16.10 *Atomic and mass numbers of lithium*

How electrons are arranged

Electrons whizz around the nucleus in energy levels called **shells** or **orbits**. The first shell can hold only two electrons; the second and third shells can each hold up to eight electrons. Electrons fill up the shells one by one, starting with the first shell. When a shell is full, they start a new one.

All atoms would like to have full electron shells, but in most atoms the outer shell is not full and this makes the atom want to react to fill it.

16.11 Do you think an atom with full electron shells would be more or less likely to react chemically with another material?

Bohr model

A Danish scientist called Niels Bohr was the first person to suggest the idea of electron shells containing electrons orbiting the nucleus. The way these electrons are arranged is called the **electron configuration**. The way they are explained is called the **Bohr model**. Figures 16.12, 16.13 and 16.14 show some examples of atoms of elements using Bohr models.

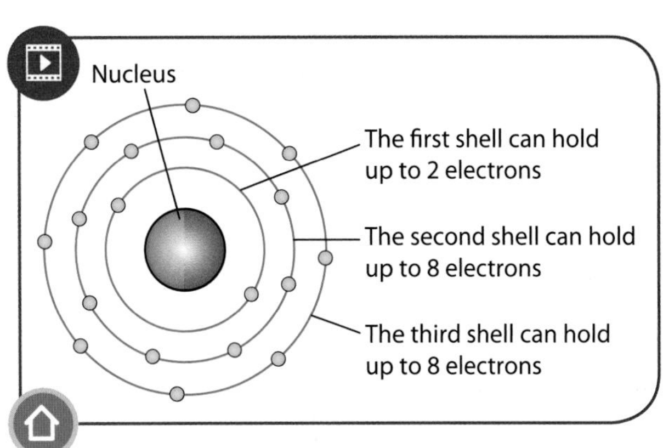

Figure 16.11 *The arrangement of electrons in an atom*

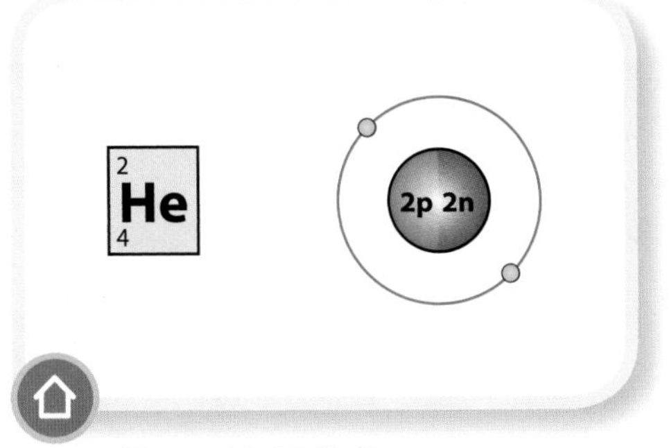

Figure 16.12 *Helium*

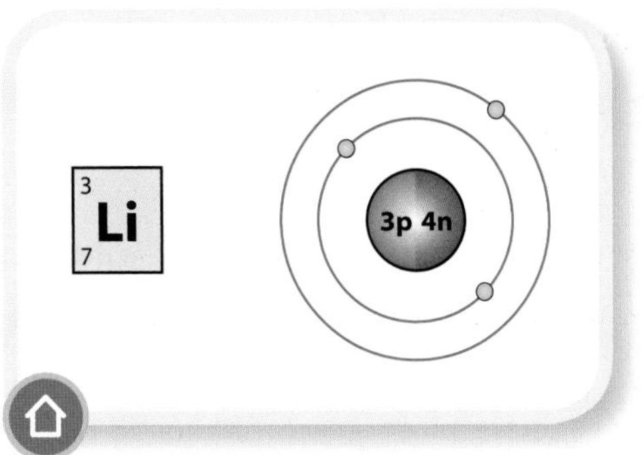

Figure 16.13 *Lithium*

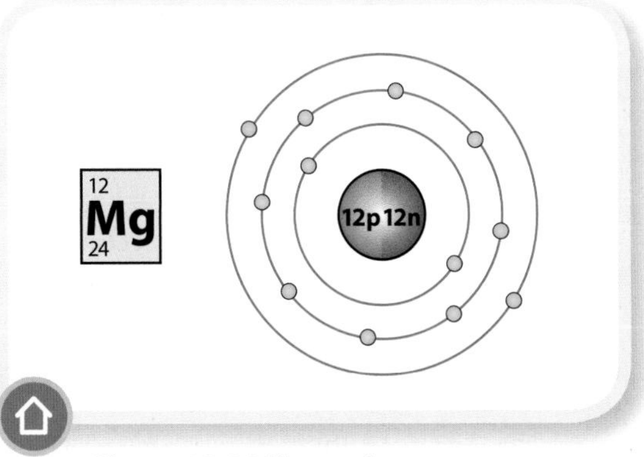

Figure 16.14 *Magnesium*

16.12 An atom is made up of three types of particle. Name them.

16.13 What is the atomic number of an atom?

16.14 What is the mass number of an atom?

16.15 Complete this sentence: The protons and neutrons found in the ______________ and the ______________ spin around in orbits or ______________.

16.16 Use this table to help you answer the questions below.

Element	Atomic number	Mass number
Oxygen	8	16
Chlorine	17	35
Gallium	31	70
Zinc	30	68
Tungsten	74	184

(a) How many protons would you expect to find in an atom of chlorine?

(b) Where in the atom would the protons be found?

(c) How many neutrons would you expect to find in an atom of zinc?

(d) Which element in the table above has atoms that contain the same number of protons and neutrons?

16.17 Give the number of protons, electrons and neutrons in the atoms in **Figure 16.15**.

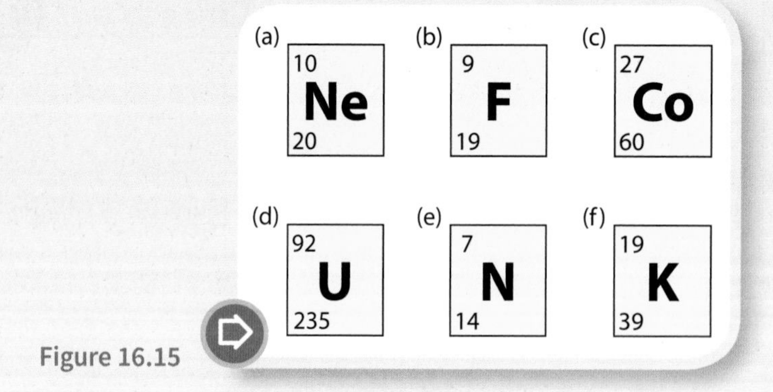

Figure 16.15

16.18 Draw fully labelled diagrams of the atoms in **Figure 16.16**.

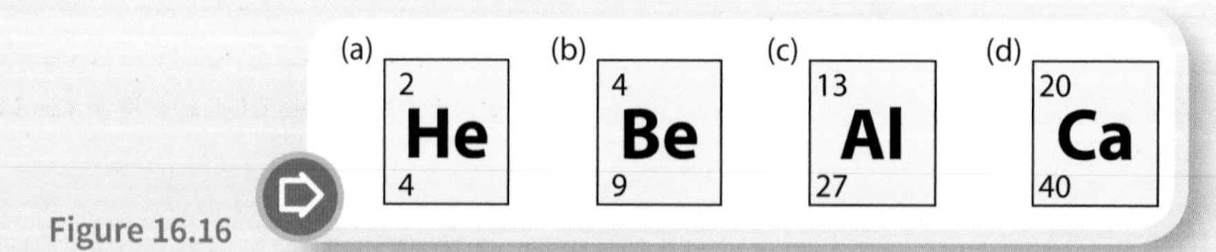

Figure 16.16

16.19 Divide into groups. Each group is to design and construct a model of an atom (element of your choice) showing the exact number of protons, neutrons and electrons.

16.20 Scientists discovered in about 1939 that a powerful explosion might be possible by splitting an atom.

Albert Einstein had many theories that helped scientists in developing the atomic bomb. He was so frightened about what might happen if Hitler and the Germans made the bomb first that he wrote to US President Franklin Roosevelt telling him about the bomb. This led to the Manhattan Project being set up, which involved over two hundred scientists researching and developing the bomb. The first atomic bomb exploded in 1945 in the New Mexico desert. The temperature at the centre of the explosion was three times hotter than the centre of the Sun.

On 6 August 1945 an atomic bomb named 'Little Boy' was dropped on Hiroshima, Japan.

Research the history of the first atomic bomb and answer the following questions:

(a) Who was the United States president who made the decision to use the atomic bomb against Japan?

(b) On 9 August 1945 a second bomb was dropped on Japan.
  (i) Where was it dropped?
  (ii) What was its nickname?

(c) Which elements were used to make the two atomic bombs?

(d) What were the devastating effects of the atomic bombs?

(e) Did the atomic bombs have any long-lasting effects on our society?

(f) Do you think scientists regret creating such a bomb?

Figure 16.17 'Little Boy', the bomb dropped on Hiroshima

Animated Scientist Biography

Watch an *Exploring Science* animation to find out more about Einstein and his discoveries.

CHEMICAL WORLD

CHAPTER 17

UNIT 3 Metals and non-metals – properties and uses

Learning outcomes

At the end of this chapter you will be able to:

- Classify substances as metals or non-metals
- Investigate properties of metals
- Apply the uses of metals and non-metals based on their properties.

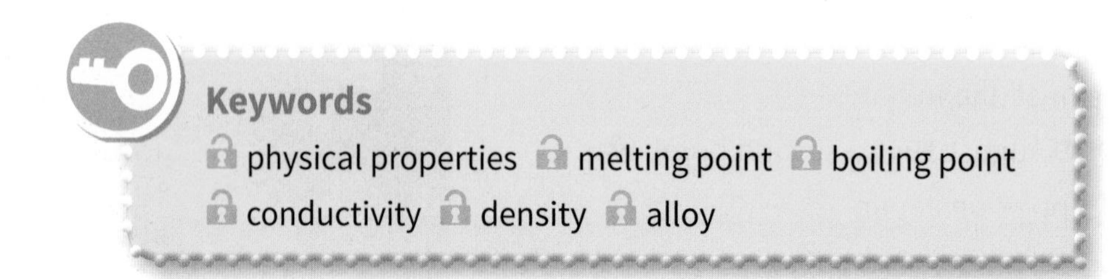

Keywords

physical properties · melting point · boiling point · conductivity · density · alloy

What are physical properties of materials?

Physical properties are the characteristics and features that define any material. Every material has a different set of properties that makes it perfect for some jobs and useless for other jobs. For example, the plastic used in the handle of a brush is hard, strong and stiff, whereas the plastic used in the bristles is soft and flexible.

Figure 17.1 *The handles of the brush and pan are made of hard plastic and the bristles of the brush are made of soft plastic*

Ninety-two elements are found naturally on Earth. These can be classified as:

- Metals
- Non-metals
- Semi-metals or metalloids (e.g. silicon).

There are just a few semi-metals, and in this chapter we will be looking at metals and non-metals.

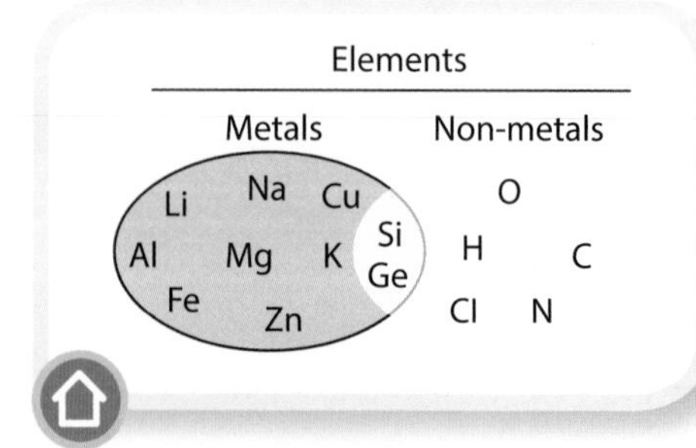

Figure 17.2 *Metals, semi-metals and non-metals*

Metals

Most of Earth's naturally occurring elements are metals. Their different properties make individual elements ideal for a large variety of uses in everyday life. Refer to the periodic table on page 176.

The properties of metals

Metals have a number of physical properties in common, but each metal is slightly different also.

Melting point

This is the temperature at which a solid material turns to a liquid. For example, the melting point of ice is 0°C. Most materials that are pure chemicals have a unique melting point.

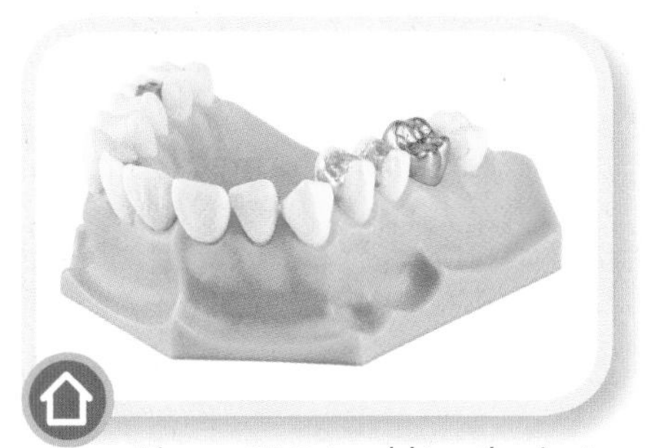

Figure 17.3 *A gold tooth – just one of the many uses of metal*

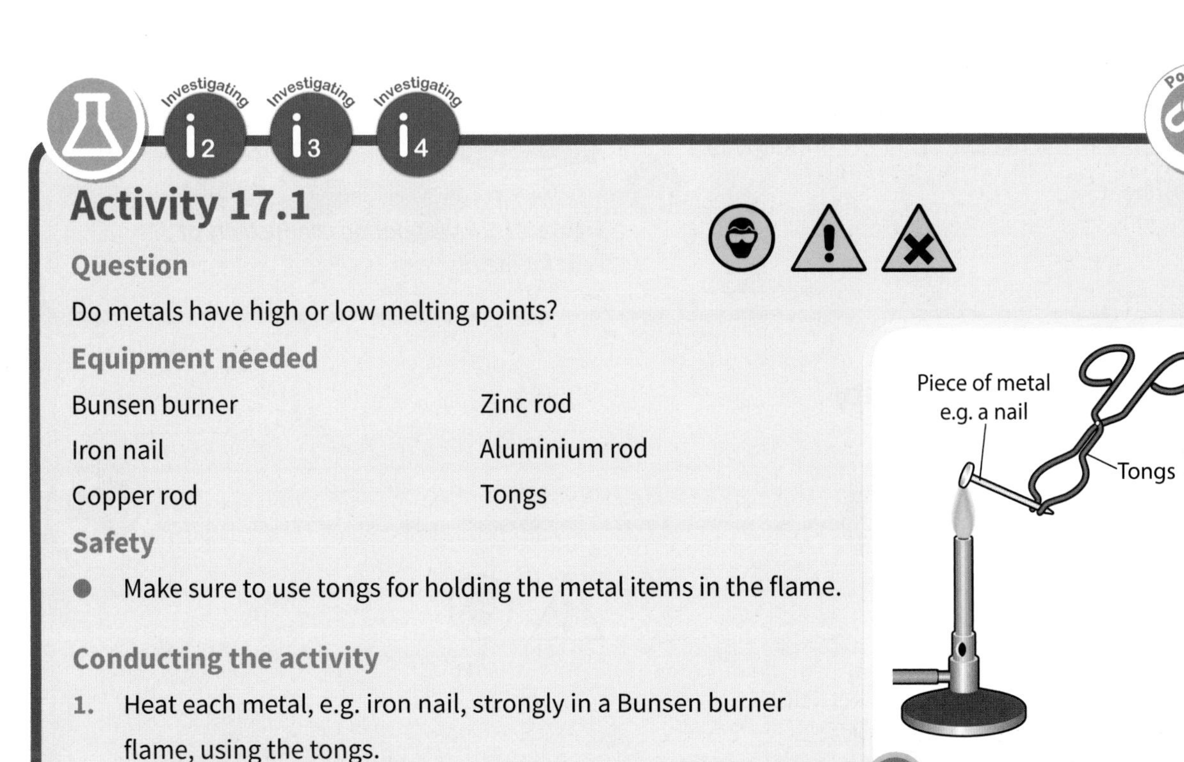

Activity 17.1

Question

Do metals have high or low melting points?

Equipment needed

Bunsen burner
Iron nail
Copper rod
Zinc rod
Aluminium rod
Tongs

Safety

- Make sure to use tongs for holding the metal items in the flame.

Conducting the activity

1. Heat each metal, e.g. iron nail, strongly in a Bunsen burner flame, using the tongs.
2. Make a note of what happens to each metal.
   (a) Do any of the metals melt?
   (b) What can you say about the melting points of these metals?

Figure 17.4 *Investigating the melting points of metals*

Conductivity of heat

Activity 17.2

Question

Are metals good conductors of heat?

Equipment needed

4 metal rods (different metals)
Bunsen burner
Tripod
Grease/wax
Pins

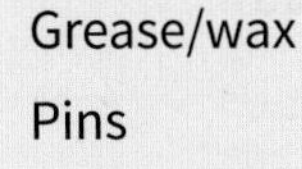

Safety

- Make sure the metal rods are stable on the tripod.

Conducting the activity

1. Set up the apparatus as shown in Figure 17.5.
2. Heat the four rods over a Bunsen burner flame.
3. Note what happens to each pin.
4. When writing up your results, place the metals in decreasing order of conductivity of heat.

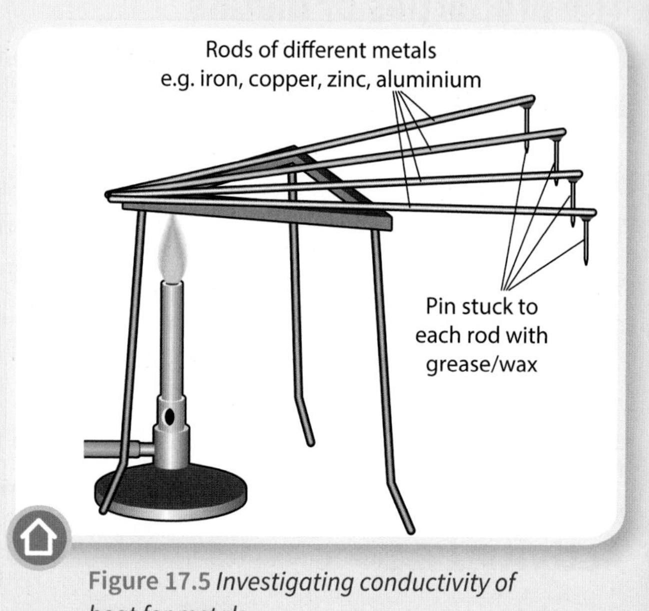

Figure 17.5 *Investigating conductivity of heat for metals*

Conductivity of electricity

Activity 17.3

Question

Are metals good conductors of electricity?

Equipment needed

Bulb
6-V battery or powerpack
Leads
Crocodile clips
Four different metals, e.g. iron, copper, zinc, aluminium

Safety

- Take care when setting up the battery circuit that the crocodile clips don't touch.

Conducting the activity

1. Set up the circuit as shown in Figure 17.6.
2. Place some different metals between the crocodile chips.
3. Note what happens each time.
4. When you write up your results, say whether metals are good conductors of electricity.

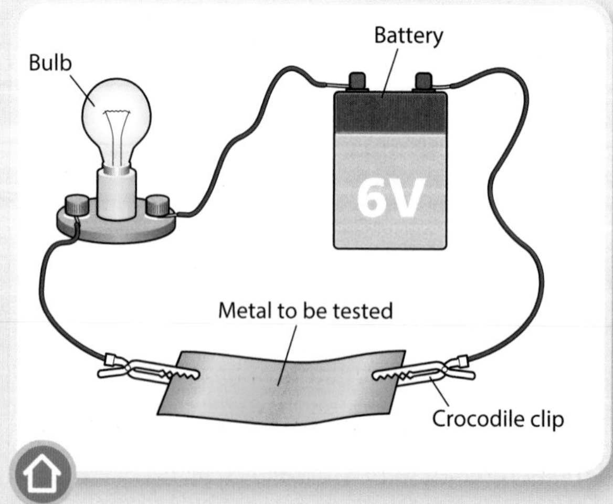

Figure 17.6 *Investigating electrical conductors*

Other properties of metals

The short investigations in the previous activities show some of the physical properties of metals. Metals are also:

- **Malleable**, i.e. they can be hammered into different shapes; e.g. aluminium can be flattened into very thin sheets and sold as 'tinfoil'.
- **Ductile**, i.e. they can be stretched out into wire, e.g. copper.
- Generally **hard and strong** with high melting points.

The physical properties of metals are illustrated in Figure 17.7.

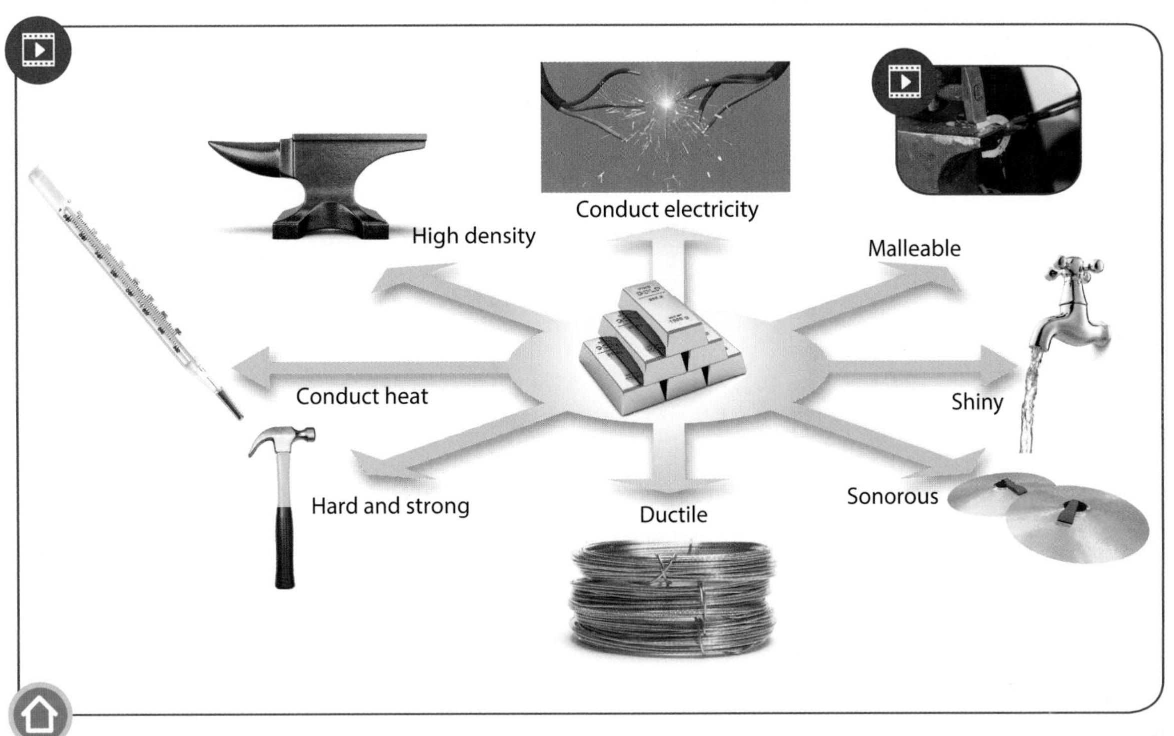

Figure 17.7 *The physical properties of metals*

Not all metals have all these properties. For example:

- The alkali metals are soft with low densities, e.g. sodium and potassium.
- Mercury is a liquid at room temperature.

Metals have high densities

Many metals have a high density. This means they feel very heavy for their size. The reason for this is that there are a lot of atoms packed into a small volume.

Metallic bonding

Metal atoms are held tightly together by **electrons**. These electrons come from the outer shells of the atoms and hold the atoms together.

The metals are hard, strong and can conduct heat because of the atoms held tightly together. Metals can conduct electricity because the electrons are free to move.

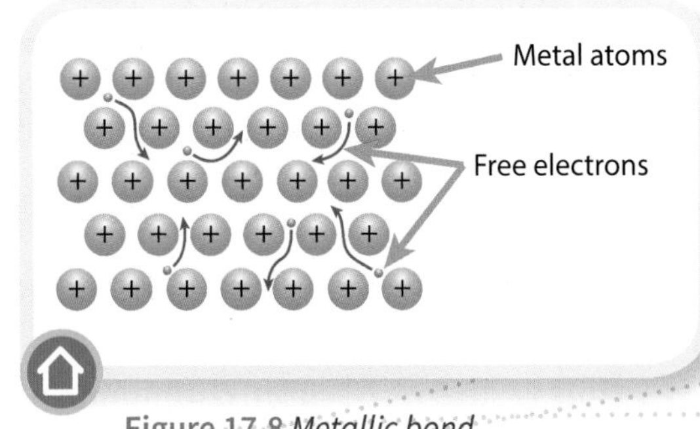

Figure 17.8 *Metallic bond*

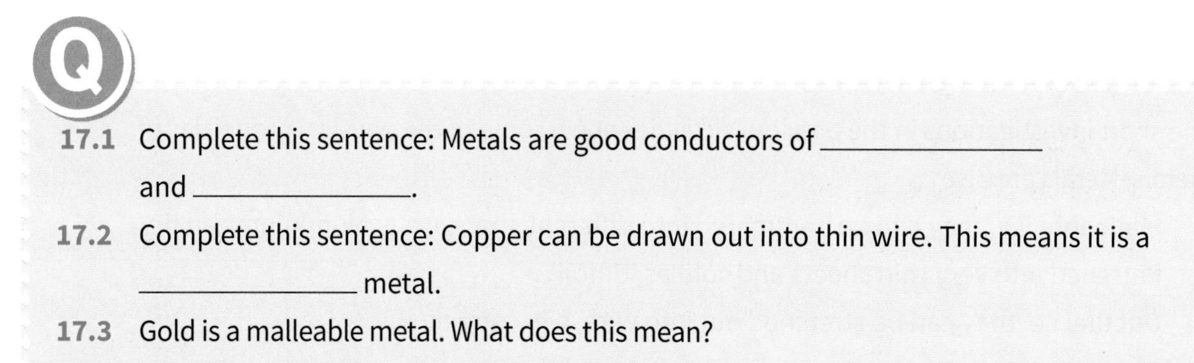

17.1 Complete this sentence: Metals are good conductors of ________________ and ________________.

17.2 Complete this sentence: Copper can be drawn out into thin wire. This means it is a ________________ metal.

17.3 Gold is a malleable metal. What does this mean?

17.4 What is unusual about the metal mercury?

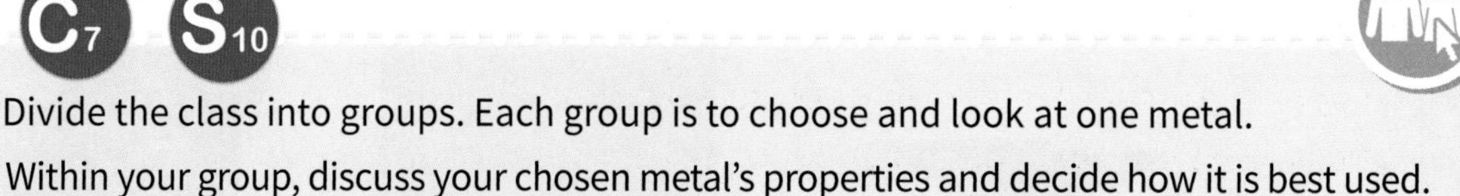

17.5 Divide the class into groups. Each group is to choose and look at one metal. Within your group, discuss your chosen metal's properties and decide how it is best used.

An example is: Aluminium is strong and can be bent into shape but it is also light so it is used to make aeroplanes.

17.6 Titanium is a transition metal that is used in hip replacements. Research the properties of titanium and list three properties that make it suitable for this use.

17.7 Research the properties of the metals listed below, and explain why each has been chosen for its use:

(a) Using copper to make wires.

(b) Using iron to make bridges.

(c) Using gold and silver to make jewellery.

17.8 Give two reasons why metal, rather than plastic, is a good choice for a saucepan.

Alloys

Sometimes metals are more useful when they are pure, e.g. pure copper is much better at conducting electricity than when it is mixed with other metals. However, many metals are better and more useful for certain jobs when they are combined with other metals or a non-metal (such as carbon). These are known as alloys. Some common alloys are listed in Table 17.1.

Table 17.1 **Alloys, their uses and composition**

Alloy	Composition	Use
Brass	Copper and zinc	Musical instruments, ornaments
Bronze	Copper and tin	Statues
Solder	Lead and tin	Soldering
Mild steel	Iron and carbon	Building reinforcement
Stainless steel	Iron, chromium and nickel	Knives, sinks
Alnico	Aluminium, nickel and cobalt	Powerful magnets

17.9 What is an alloy?

17.10 Give two examples of alloys.

Steel

Pure Iron has a regular arrangement of identical atoms. The layers of atoms can slide over each other and this makes the iron soft, which allows it to change shape easily. This makes it unsuitable for most uses.

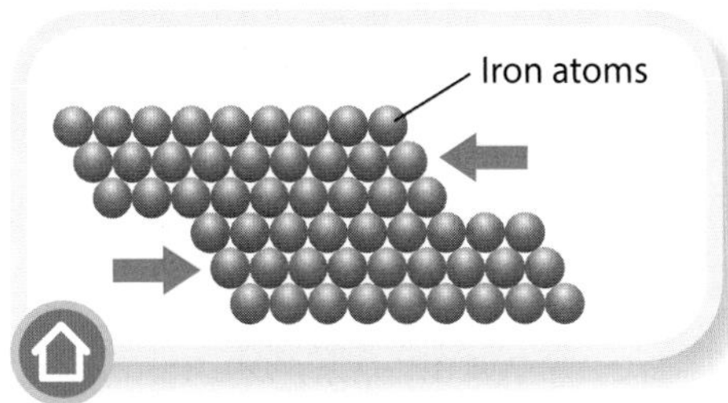

Figure 17.9 *Iron*

Most pure iron is changed into alloys of steel, where small amounts of carbon and sometimes other metals are added to the iron.

The carbon atoms upset the layers of iron atoms, making it more difficult for them to slide over each other. This makes the alloy harder.

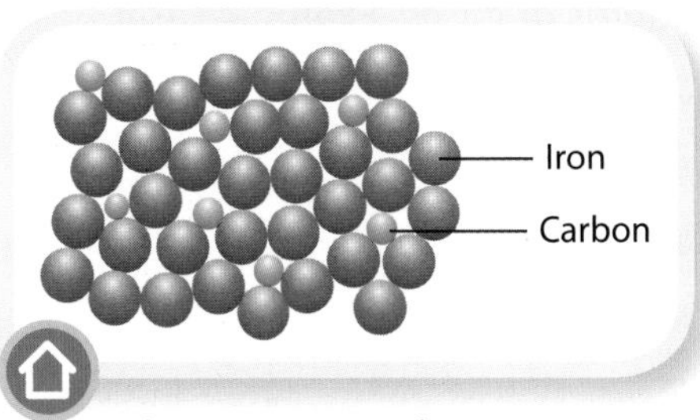

Figure 17.10 *Steel*

17.11 There are three different types of steel, as shown in the table below:

Type of steel	Properties
Low carbon steel	Easily shaped
High carbon steel	Very hard, inflexible
Stainless steel	Corrosion-resistant

(a) Which of these alloys are suitable for car bodies? Give your reasons.

(b) Stainless steel is corrosion-resistant. What does this mean?

(c) Give some everyday uses of stainless steel.

(d) High carbon steel is used for blades for cutting tools and for building bridges. Why is this?

Figure 17.11 *The Eiffel Tower is made of iron and needs repainting every seven years*

Did you know?

The Eiffel Tower is made of iron. Iron goes rusty if air and water get on it. So the Eiffel Tower has to be painted every seven years and it takes an entire year of twenty-five painters working on it. That wouldn't happen with stainless steel!

17.12 Some alloys are called **smart alloys.** One such smart alloy is **nitinol.** Research this alloy, looking particularly at:

(a) What metals are mixed together to form nitinol?

(b) Why is it called a smart alloy?

(c) Where is it used?

Non-metals

There are twenty-one non-metal elements. Many non-metals are liquids or gases. Examples are:

- Carbon
- Sulfur
- Oxygen
- Nitrogen.

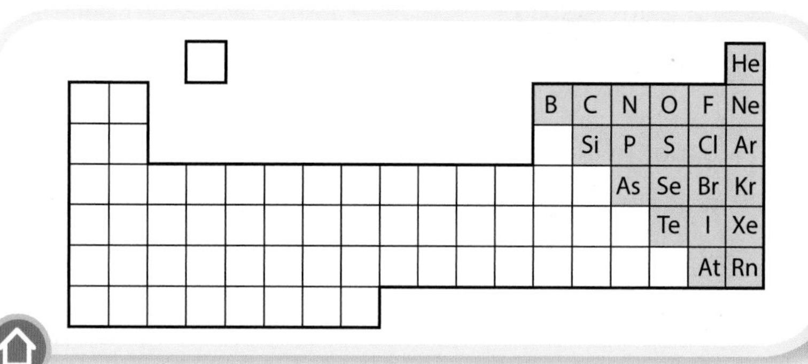

Figure 17.12 *Periodic table for the non-metals*

Properties of non-metals

Non-metals have properties that are generally opposite to those of metals.

Melting point and boiling point

The forces that hold the atoms together in non-metals are weak and this means they melt and boil easily. The melting and boiling points of some non-metals are given in Table 17.2.

Table 17.2 The melting and boiling points of some non-metals

Non-metal	Melting point °C	Boiling point °C
Sulfur	113	445
Oxygen	–218	–183
Chlorine	–101	–35
Helium	–272	–269
Neon	–249	–248

Conductors of electricity

Non-metals are electrical insulators, which mean electrical current cannot flow through them.

17.13 Non-metals combine to make materials that are good insulators. Name one of these materials and state where it may be used and why.

Conductors of heat

Heat does not travel very well through non-metals, so this makes them very good heat insulators.

17.14 Where might non-metals be used in everyday objects? Give five examples.

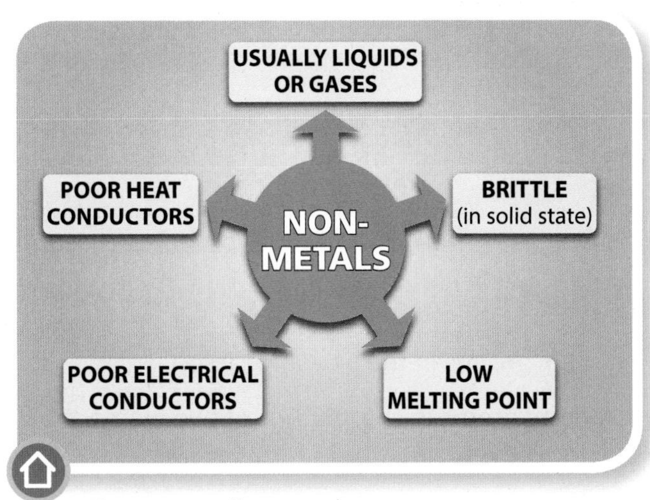

Figure 17.13 *Non-metals*

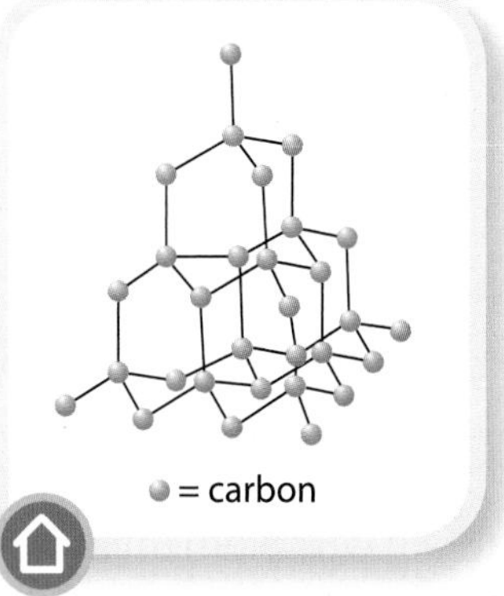

Figure 17.14 *Diamond*

Some exceptions

Not all non-metals have these properties.

For example:

- Carbon in the form of graphite is a good conductor of electricity.
- Carbon in the form of diamond is extremely hard with a high melting point.

Did you know?

The melting point of diamond is 3500°C. The carbon atoms are bonded very strongly, which makes it very hard. Its hardness is ideal for drill bits for cutting glass.

17.15 The table shows the percentage of different metals in the €1 coin:

Coin	Colour	% Copper	% Zinc	Nickel
€1 outer ring	Gold	75	20	5
€1 centre	Silver	75	0	25

(a) Why are alloys, rather than pure metals, used to make coins?

(b) What are the similarities and differences between the different alloys used for €1 coins?

(c) Which metal gives a gold colour to the coins? Explain how you can tell.

(d) Copper has an antibacterial effect. Explain why this is useful for coins.

Figure 17.15 *Euro coins*

CHEMICAL WORLD

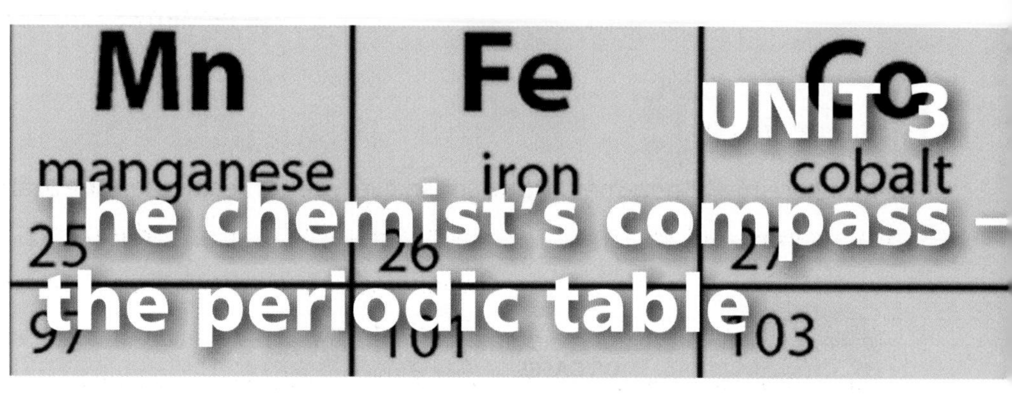

UNIT 3

The chemist's compass – the periodic table

Learning outcomes

At the end of this chapter you will be able to:

- Examine and identify elements in the periodic table
- Explain why elements are placed in certain groups in the periodic table
- Use the periodic table to predict the ratio of atoms in compounds of two elements.

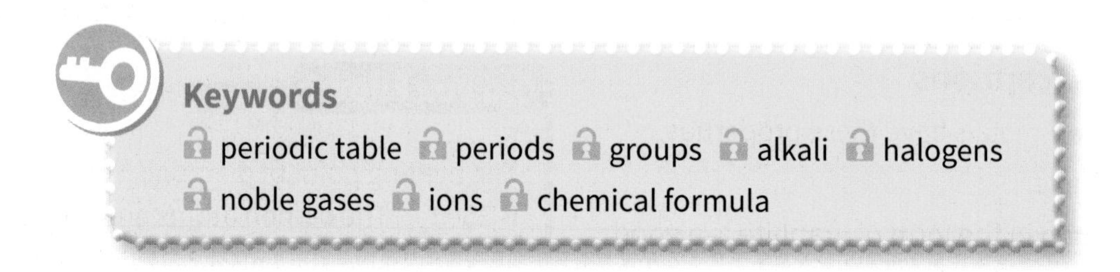

Keywords

periodic table, periods, groups, alkali, halogens, noble gases, ions, chemical formula

What is the periodic table?

The periodic table is considered to be one of the most important tools of the chemist. It shows a list of all the **elements**.

In the 1880s, scientists discovered a number of elements. They realised that some of these elements behaved in similar ways to others. A Russian chemist called Dmitri Mendeleev arranged them in order of the mass of the atoms of each element. He also lined up elements that behaved similarly.

Only about half of the elements had been discovered by this time. Mendeleev left gaps in his table for elements that had yet to be discovered.

18.1 Dmitri Mendeleev was passionate about chemistry. Research him and make notes on:

(a) His life

(b) His periodic table

(c) His other achievements.

The modern periodic table

The modern periodic table has no gaps in it. The elements are not arranged according to atomic mass but by **atomic number**. The table is arranged into:

- Vertical columns, called **groups**, where the elements with similar physical and chemical properties (behaviours) are grouped together
- Horizontal rows, called **periods**, which are in order of increasing proton number.

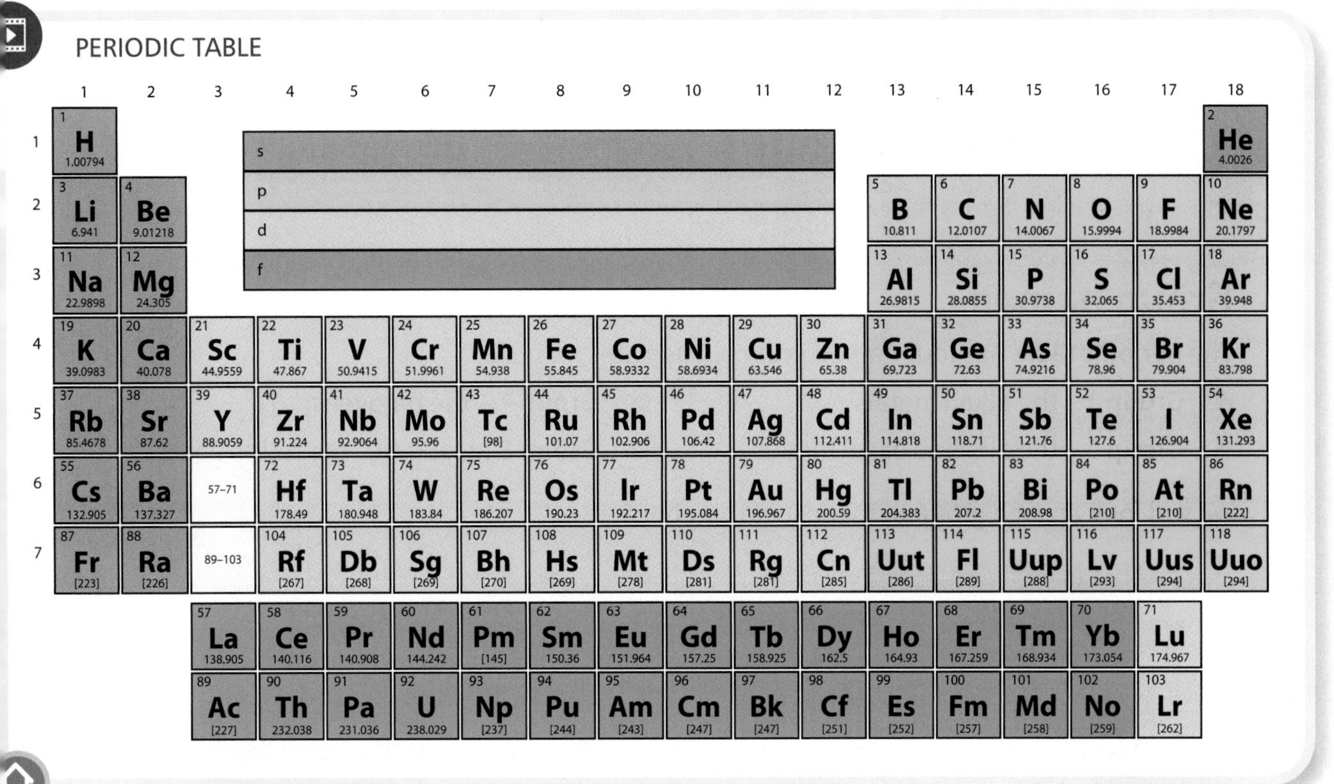

Figure 18.1 *Periodic table* (See page 414 for a larger version)

18.2 Complete the following sentence: Vertical columns of elements are called ______________ and horizontal rows of elements are known as ______________.

18.3 From the periodic table name:

(a) Three elements from group 2.

(b) Three elements from period 2.

(c) The element in group 1 period 3.

Animated Scientist Biography

Marie Curie was a scientist who discovered two new elements: radium and polonium. Watch an *Exploring Science* animation to find out more about Marie Curie and her investigations.

18.4 Refer to Figures 18.1 and 18.2. Complete this table to show that you understand how the periodic table is arranged.

Element	Symbol	Period	Group	Metal	Non-metal
Carbon					
	H				
		2	3		
Barium					
Chlorine					
	He				

Group names

The periodic table has four named groups. They are:

- **Group 1** – the alkali metals
- **Group 2** – the alkaline earth metals
- **Group 7** – the halogens
- **Group 8 (group 0)** – the noble gases.

We will look at each group in the rest of this chapter.

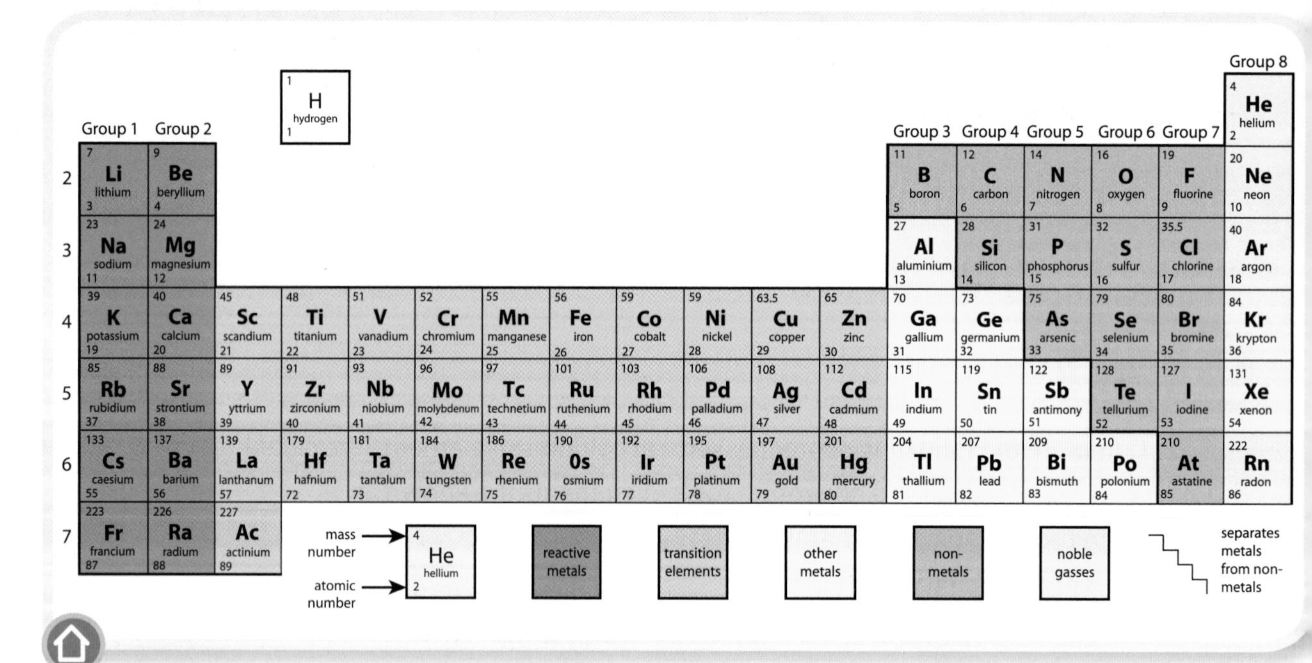

Figure 18.2 *Periodic table – each colour shows elements with similar properties.*
See page 414 for the recently updated table.

Group 1 – the alkali metals

All the alkali metals have one electron in their outer shell. The atoms want to get rid of this loose electron. As a result, the alkali metals are very reactive and behave similarly. Elements in this group include:

- Lithium (Li)
- Sodium (Na)
- Potassium (K).

Reactions of alkali metals with water

When an alkali metal such as **lithium** is added to water it floats on the surface of the water and forms a ball shape. Hydrogen gas is released and lithium hydroxide is formed, which dissolves in the water.

lithium + water ⟶ lithium hydroxide + hydrogen

Did you know?

There are ninety-two elements in the periodic table that occur in nature. All of the other elements are strictly synthetic. Technetium was the first element to be made artificially.

Sodium is more reactive than lithium. It may even catch fire (orange flame) as it fizzes about on the surface.

sodium + water ⟶ sodium hydroxide + hydrogen

Potassium is even more reactive than sodium. Can you predict the products of the reaction between potassium and water?

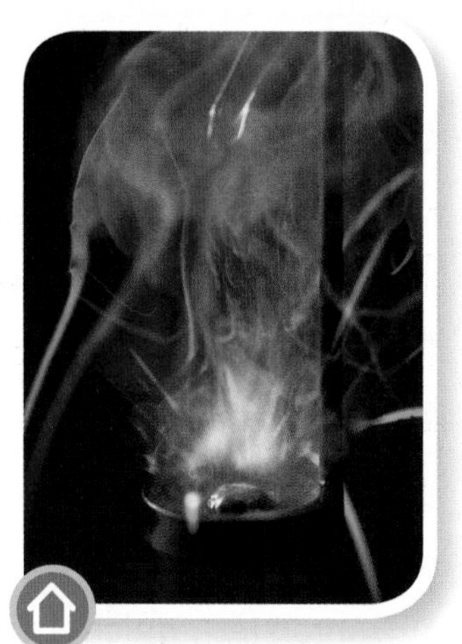

Figure 18.3 *Potassium reacting with water*

Reactions of alkali metals with air

All metals are shiny. Alkali metals look dull, but when they are cut a shiny surface is revealed. This shiny surface quickly goes dull again as the metal reacts with oxygen in the air, forming the metal oxide.

For lithium the reaction with oxygen is:

lithium + oxygen ⟶ lithium oxide

For sodium the reaction with oxygen is:

sodium + oxygen ⟶ sodium oxide

Group 2 – the alkaline earth metals

Elements in this group include:

- Beryllium (Be)
- Magnesium (Mg)
- Calcium (Ca).

All elements in this group have two electrons in their outer shell. Group 2 elements are not as reactive as group 1 elements.

Figure 18.4 *Alkaline earth metals – beryllium, magnesium, calcium, strontium and barium*

CHEMICAL WORLD

CHEMICAL WORLD

Group 7 – the halogens

The elements in group 7 have seven electrons in their atom's outer shell. (The word halogen also contains seven letters!) Elements in this group include:

- Fluorine, in the form of compounds such as sodium fluoride, which is sometimes added to water to strengthen enamel in our teeth.
- Chlorine, which is sometimes added to water to kill bacteria.

Figure 18.5 *The halogens (chlorine, bromine and iodine)*

Elements in this group are trying to gain an electron because they want a full outer shell.

Group 8 (group 0) – the noble gases

The elements in group 8 are all gases and have full outer shells of electrons in their atoms. As a result, the noble gases are unreactive and thus very stable. Members of the noble gases include:

- Helium (He)
- Neon (Ne)
- Argon (Ar), which is used in filament lamps (light bulbs).

Figure 18.6 *Helium, one of the noble gases, is sometimes used in balloons*

18.5 Complete the following sentence: The elements in group ______________ are called the alkali metals. Because they react vigorously with water they are stored under ______________. Lithium, ______________ and ______________ are examples of alkali metals.

18.6 Complete the following sentence: The elements of group 7 are called the ______________. They get ______________ reactive as you go down the group; therefore ______________ is the most reactive.

18.7 Find out how these names were assigned to each of these groups:

(a) The alkali metals
(b) The alkaline earth metals
(c) The halogens
(d) The noble gases.

18.8 Select one element from each group and find out where it may be used.

18.9 How many naturally occurring elements are there?

18.10 Look at Figure 18.7 and answer these questions using the letters A–E *and* the elements' names.

(a) Which two elements are in the same group?

(b) Which two elements are in the same period?

(c) Name the group to which elements A and B belong.

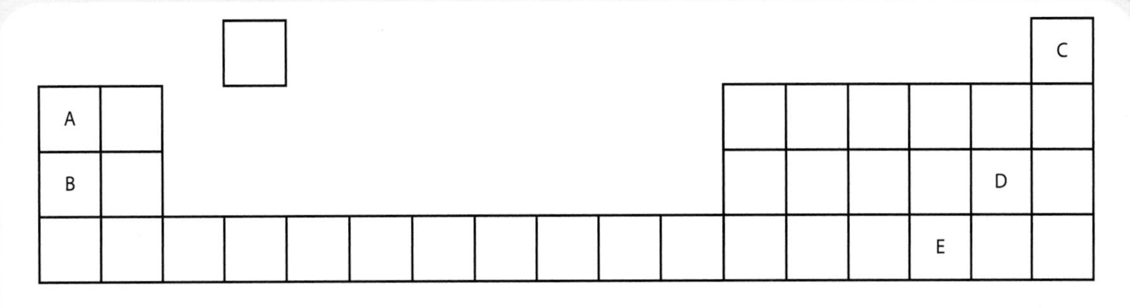

Figure 18.7

18.11 From the periodic table name:

(a) Three elements from group 3.

(b) Three elements from period 3.

(c) The element in group 2, period 3.

How are chemical bonds formed?

A compound forms when two or more elements chemically combine. The question is: why do these elements react and combine with each other? They react to have a full outer shell of electrons. There are two ways for atoms to achieve this:

- **Ionic bonding** This occurs when one atom *loses* and another atom *gains* electrons.
- **Covalent bonding** This occurs when atoms *share* electrons.

Electron shell rules

- Electrons are found in shells or orbits.
- The shells nearest the nucleus are filled first.
- The first shell can hold up to two electrons.
- The second and third shells can each hold up to eight electrons.
- Atoms that have a full outer shell of electrons are stable and do not react.
- In most atoms the outer shell is not full and this makes them want to react.

What are ions?

All atoms would like full outer shells and they will either lose or gain electrons in order to achieve this. When atoms lose or gain electrons they become charged particles and are called ions. The elements that readily form ions make up groups 1, 2, 6 and 7:

CHEMICAL WORLD

- **Group 1** – alkali metals. These have only one electron in the outer shell, which they lose to form a positive ion (+1), e.g. Na^{+1}.
- **Group 2** – alkaline earth metals. These have two electrons in their outer shell so will lose two electrons to form a positive ion (+2) e.g. Mg^{+2}.
- **Group 6** – non-metals. These have six electrons in their outer shell and so will gain two electrons for a full outer shell to form a negative ion (–2) e.g. O^{-2}.
- **Group 7** – halogens. These have seven electrons in their outer shell and so will gain one electron to form a negative ion (–1) e.g. Cl^{-1}.

CHEMICAL WORLD

Forming compounds – chemical formulas

You can use the periodic table to predict the ratio of atoms in compounds.

Combine metal and non-metal

When you combine a metal and a non-metal the name of the metal comes first followed by the name of the non-metal, and the ending is changed to **ide**.

sodium +	chlorine	= sodium chloride
Metal	*Non-metal*	*Compound*

Sodium is in group 1 of the periodic table so it needs to lose one electron. Chlorine is in group 7 of the periodic table so it needs to gain one electron. So the ratio of atoms in the compound sodium chloride is 1:1. One sodium atom bonds with one chlorine atom.

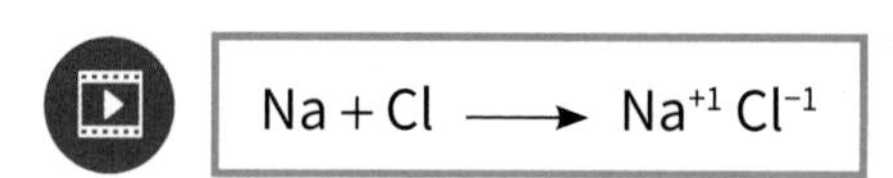
$Na + Cl \longrightarrow Na^{+1}\,Cl^{-1}$

18.12 What are the names of the compounds formed between:
(a) Calcium and chlorine?
(b) Lithium and bromine?
(c) Magnesium and oxygen?

Combine non-metal and non-metal

Again you can use the periodic table to predict the ratio of atoms in compounds. You need to work out the combining power of each atom. This is the number of bonds each atom can form. For example:

- Hydrogen is in group 1 of the periodic table, which shows it has only one electron and needs one more electron in order to be stable so that it can form one bond; so its combining power = 1.

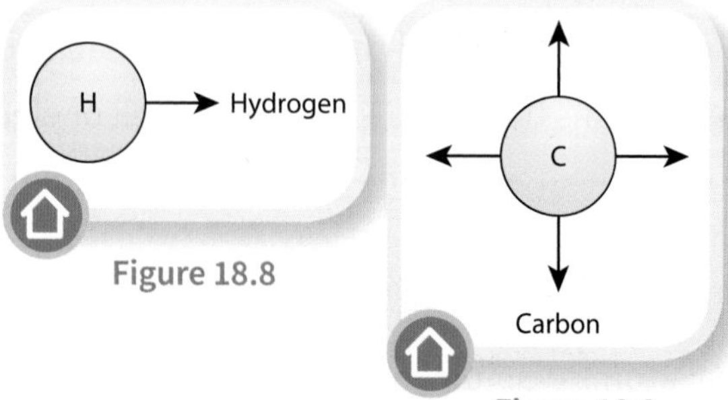

Figure 18.8

Figure 18.9

- Carbon is found in group 4 of the periodic table, which shows it has four electrons in its outer shell and it requires four more electrons in order to be stable so it can form four bonds; so its combining power = 4.

Carbon has combining power = 4 (4 bonds) whereas hydrogen has combining power = 1 (1 bond), so you will need four hydrogen atoms to bond with one carbon. This is methane. Natural gas is mainly methane.

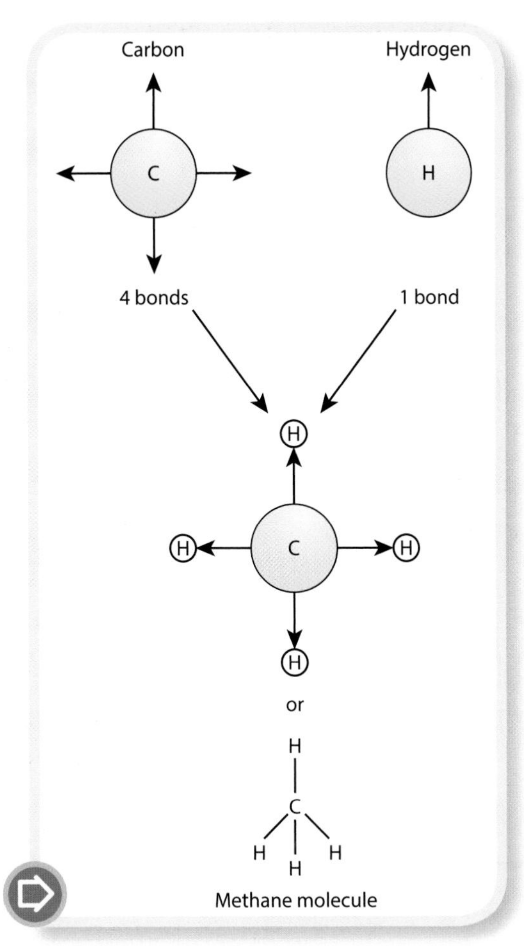

Figure 18.10 *Chemical formula for a compound containing carbon and hydrogen*

Note: Atoms do not always obey the **octet** rule (eight electrons in the outer shell). For example, hydrogen, beryllium and boron have too few electrons in the outer shell to form an octet.

18.13 In your group, copy and complete the following table using the periodic table.

Element	Symbol	Group number	Electrons needed	Combining power	Show bonds
Hydrogen	H	1	1	1	(H)→
Carbon	C	4	4	4	←(C)→ with ↑ and ↓
Nitrogen					
Oxygen					
Sulfur					
Chlorine					

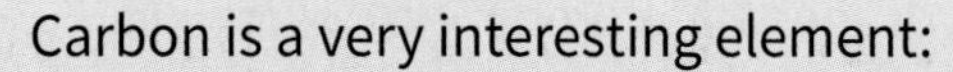

Carbon is a very interesting element:

- It can form about 10 million compounds with almost all other elements in the periodic table.
- The human body's mass is 18.5% carbon.

18.14 Using the periodic table work out the formula and the name of the compound formed between:

(a) Hydrogen and chlorine
(b) Nitrogen and hydrogen
(c) Carbon and oxygen.

18.15 Draw diagrams and show the bonding in a water molecule.

How to combine a metal atom, a non-metal atom and oxygen

The name of the metal comes first. The name of the non-metal comes next with the ending **ate**. This occurs only when an oxygen atom is present. For example:

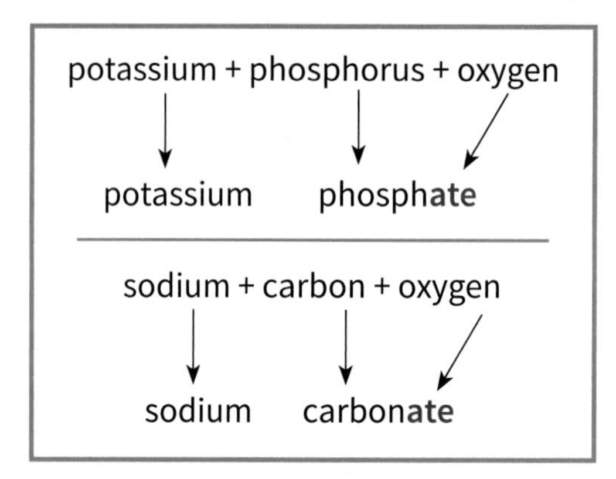

18.16 Write the name of the compounds formed between the following:

(a) Potassium + nitrogen + oxygen
(b) Magnesium + carbon + oxygen
(c) Calcium + sulfur + oxygen
(d) Lithium + phosphorous + oxygen.

18.17 What are the names of the different types of atoms in the following compounds:

(a) Calcium nitrate?
(b) Potassium carbonate?
(c) Sodium bromide?
(d) Sodium carbonate?

18.18 Refer to the periodic table and work out the formula for the following compounds:

- **(a)** Sodium chloride
- **(b)** Magnesium chloride
- **(c)** Sodium oxide
- **(d)** Magnesium oxide
- **(e)** Potassium oxide.

Hydrogen molecule (H_2)

Each hydrogen atom has one electron in its shell, so each atom has a combining power = 1, so two hydrogen atoms will overlap their shells and bond forming a hydrogen molecule (H_2).

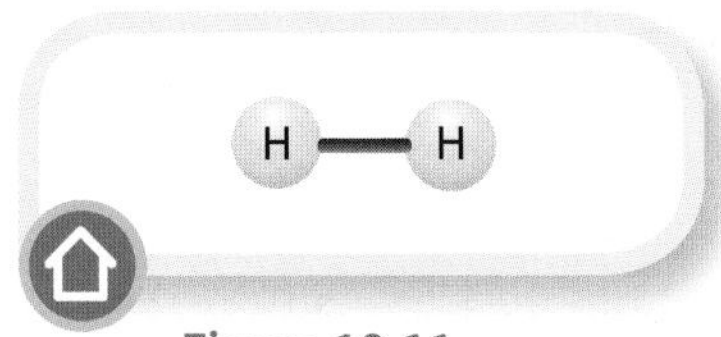

Figure 18.11

Oxygen molecule (O_2)

Each oxygen atom has six electrons in the outer shell so it needs to gain two electrons to fill the outer shell. So each oxygen atom has a combining power = 2; in an oxygen molecule two oxygen atoms are bonded together and there is a **double bond**.

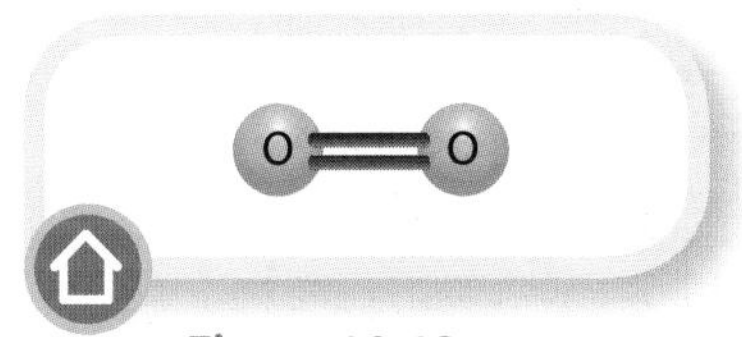

Figure 18.12

18.19 Refer to the periodic table to work out what a nitrogen molecule looks like.

UNIT 3

Materials science – fit for purpose

Learning outcomes

At the end of this chapter you will be able to:

- Classify materials into different groups
- Investigate the properties of different materials
- Identify the choice of a material for a particular purpose and assess its fitness for purpose.

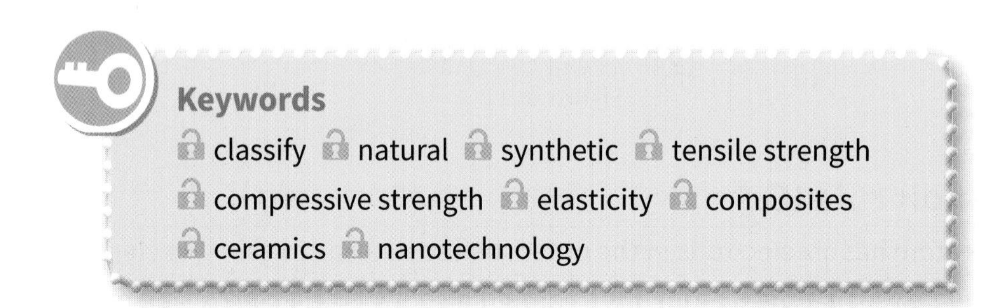

Keywords

classify natural synthetic tensile strength compressive strength elasticity composites ceramics nanotechnology

What is a material?

A material is a substance that things are made from. Materials have different properties and these are very important when choosing which material to use in a particular product.

Figure 19.1 *The material for this mobile phone would have been chosen very carefully for its particular properties*

How do we classify materials?

Materials can be sorted or classified into different groups by looking at their properties. For example:

- Solids, liquids and gases
- Elements, compounds and mixtures
- Metals and non-metals
- Natural and synthetic (manufactured).

19.1 Copy the following table and complete it using your knowledge of everyday materials and chemistry.

Material	State of matter	Element compound or mixture	Metal or non-metal	Natural or synthetic
Plastic				
Wood				
Butane				
Coal				
Glass				
Helium				
China				
Iron				
Quartz				

What are the properties of materials?

Different materials have different properties. The properties can be categorised as:

- Strength
- Hardness
- Stiffness
- Elasticity
- Density
- Melting point
- Ability to conduct heat and electricity.

We look at each of these properties below.

Strength

This is how good a material is at resisting force. You can find out how strong a material is by how much force is needed to either break it or permanently change its shape. There are two different types of strength:

- Tensile strength
- Compressive strength.

Figure 19.2 *A man using a rope on a field study in Patagonia*

Tensile strength

This is by how much a material can resist a pulling force. For example, ropes and cables need a high tensile strength or they could snap.

Compressive strength

This is how well a material can resist a pushing force. For example, bricks need good compression strength or they could be squashed by the weight of the bricks above them.

Figure 19.3 *The bricks in this wall need good compression strength*

Activity 19.1

Question

Which paper has the greatest tearing strength?

We will be hanging a container on different kinds of paper (kitchen paper, napkin, tissue, newspaper, photocopying paper) and putting weights (marbles) into it to see how much weight the paper can take before it tears.

Equipment needed

- Paper clip
- String
- Empty yoghurt carton
- Marbles
- Electronic balance
- Different types of paper: kitchen paper, napkin, tissue, newspaper, photocopying paper

Safety

- Take care that when the paper tears the marbles do not fall out of the container and on to the floor, where people could slip on them.

Conducting the activity

1. Cut out the different types of paper to equal sizes (20 × 20 cm).
2. Make two holes opposite each other near the rim of an empty yoghurt carton.
3. Make a hole at the end of each piece of paper with a hole punch.
4. Using a paper clip and string, hang the carton from the first type of paper, as shown in Figure 19.4.
5. Gradually add marbles gently to the carton until the paper tears. Place the marbles gently in the yoghurt pot, as force will cause the paper to tear too soon.

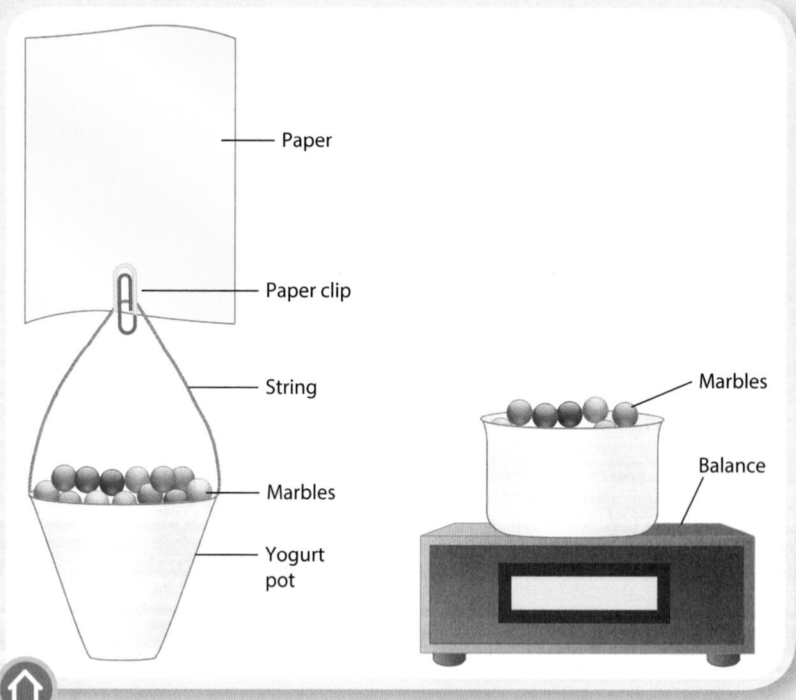

Figure 19.4 *To find the tearing strength of paper*

6. Record the number of marbles and find the mass of marbles on an electronic balance.
7. Repeat steps 4 to 6 for the remaining squares of paper.
8. Record all your results in the following table and compare your results with the rest of the class.

CHEMICAL WORLD

Type of paper	Number of marbles	Mass of marbles (g)
Kitchen paper		
Napkin		
Tissue		
Newspaper		
Photocopying paper		

19.2 List all the different types of paper you can think of. Try to put them in order of how strong you think they are.

19.3 Why would you not make a shopping bag out of tissue paper?

19.4 What happens when paper gets wet?

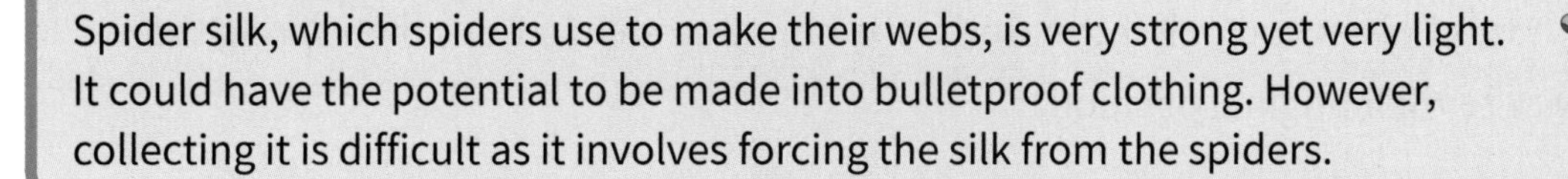

Did you know?

Spider silk, which spiders use to make their webs, is very strong yet very light. It could have the potential to be made into bulletproof clothing. However, collecting it is difficult as it involves forcing the silk from the spiders.

Hardness

The hardness of a material is how difficult it is to cut into. Solids can be hard because their particles are held together by very strong bonds. The hardest material found in nature is diamond. Diamond can cut most materials and this explains why many industrial drills have diamond tips.

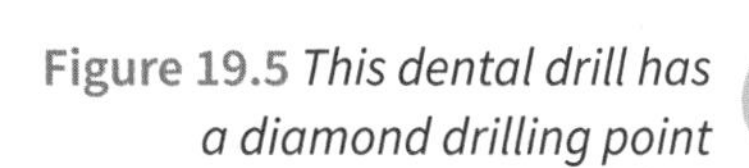

Figure 19.5 *This dental drill has a diamond drilling point*

19.5 What do you think would happen if you rubbed a metal pen tip against the surface of a piece of wood? Make a prediction in terms of the hardness of the metal and the wood that you are comparing and then test it. Discuss what you observed.

19.6 Diamond is one of the hardest materials, so how could you cut a diamond?

Figure 19.6 *The centenary diamond – diamond is one of the hardest materials*

Stiffness

A stiff material does not bend or change shape when a force is applied. This is not the same as strength, because some materials, such as rubber, can be very strong but can bend and stretch very easily. Materials such as steel are very difficult to bend so they are very stiff. This explains why steel bars are inserted in concrete pillars during construction of large structures.

Figure 19.7 *Steel bars are used in construction because they are very stiff*

Elasticity

Elasticity is where a solid can be stretched and it returns to its original shape and size; for example, a rubber band. Solids are elastic because their particles are held together with stretchy bonds, so when you pull the material the bonds stretch but can then spring the particles back to their original position.

Figure 19.8 *Elastic bands can be stretched and then they return to their original size*

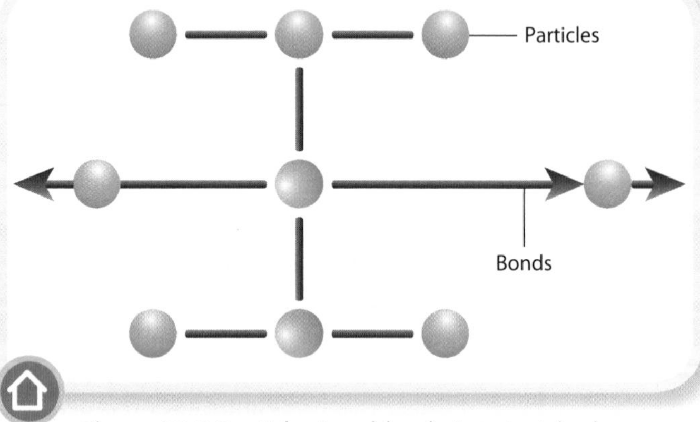

Figure 19.9 *Particles in rubber being stretched*

19.7 Each group of students must have a rubber band. Do the following:

(a) Make a sketch of how the particles are arranged in the unstretched rubber band.

(b) Predict what will happen to the **thickness** of the rubber band as it is stretched.

(c) Sketch a particle diagram of the stretched rubber band.

(d) What do you think will happen to the stretchy bonds between the particles if the rubber band is stretched too far?

Density

This is how much matter (mass) there is in a certain volume. Solids can be dense because their particles are packed closely together so there is a large mass in a small volume of material.

19.8 Some solids have a low density; for example, aluminium, which is used to make aircraft. Research the main properties of aluminium and why it is suitable for making aircraft.

Melting point

This is the temperature at which solid material turns to a liquid. Most materials that are pure chemicals have a unique melting point. Metals tend to have very high melting points, whereas plastics fall into two categories:

- Plastics that melt when heated and therefore can be formed into different shapes
- Other plastics that do not melt or soften when heated.

Figure 19.10 *This aircraft is made from aluminium because of its low density*

Ability to conduct heat and electricity

Metals are very good conductors of heat and electricity (see chapter 17). They are made up of atoms whose electrons can move easily, so heat and electricity can flow through.

Non-metals such as plastic are not good conductors as their atoms are not easily freed, preventing the flow of electrons, so heat and electricity cannot flow through easily. These are good insulators and are therefore used as covering on electrical wires.

Figure 19.11 *The saucepan is made of metal because it is a very good heat conductor; plastic is not a good electrical conductor and so it is very good as an insulator for electric cables*

19.9 Name eight different properties of materials.

19.10 What is meant by the melting point of a material?

CHEMICAL WORLD

How do we choose which material to use?

The possible use for a material depends on its properties. There are some key questions to answer when deciding which material would be the most suitable for a particular use:

(a) Will the material last?

(b) Will the material look good?

(c) Will the material be easy to process and use?

(d) What are the costs?

(e) What effect will this material have on the environment?

Developing new materials

Polymer scientists and chemical engineers develop new materials. These scientists study polymers and use their knowledge to develop new plastic and rubber products. They are made by:

- Chemical reactions (plastics, nylon and lycra are made by chemical reactions)
- Mixing two or more materials – the result is known as a **composite**.

Materials are produced with specific properties suitable for a specific job.

19.11 Scientists have developed many new materials and one of these is **Teflon**, which is now used as a non-stick coating on cookware. Find out:

(a) What Teflon is made from.

(b) The properties that make it suitable for its use.

Figure 19.12 *This frying pan has a Teflon coating*

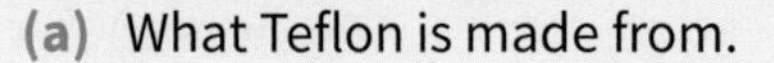

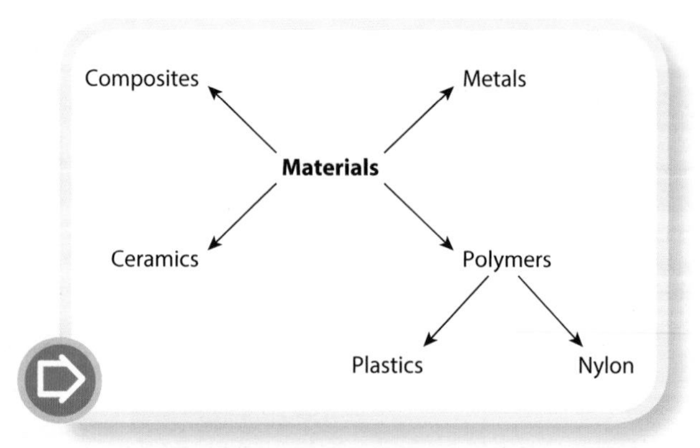

Figure 19.13 *Classification of materials*

Metals

Metals have some basic properties in common (see chapter 17). Their strength makes them good for making things like bridges and car bodies, and because they are good conductors of heat they are ideal for cookware. Their conductivity of electrical charge makes them great for making electrical wires.

Plastics

Plastics are synthetic materials. Most plastics are made from crude oil. The term 'plastic' is used to describe substances that soften when they are heated. Plastics have many uses. It is hard to believe they have been made on a large scale only since the 1930s.

The origins of plastics

Crude oil is a thick, black, foul-smelling liquid. Oil in this form is not of much use. The oil is a mixture of hydrocarbons (molecules made of hydrogen and carbon), which are separated in an oil refinery by fractional distillation. This is where crude oil is heated until it boils and the hydrocarbon gases are passed into the bottom of a fractionating column. The hydrocarbon gases condense back into liquids and these fractions are removed from the sides of the column. About 4% of all oil extracted is used to make plastics.

Figure 19.14 *Hydrocarbons are separated in a fractionating column at an oil refinery*

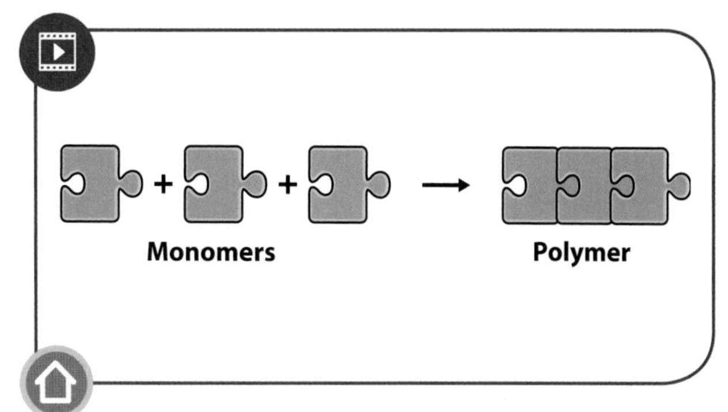

Figure 19.15 *A model of polymerisation*

Making plastics

The manufacture of plastics from crude oil involves two stages:

1. Simple hydrocarbons are separated from crude oil. They are known as **monomers** (*mono* means *one*, so monomers consist of only one molecule).
2. The monomers react together and form long chains called **polymers** (*poly* means *many*). All plastics are made up of repeating units (monomers) linked together to form polymers. This process is called **polymerisation**.

19.12 List three advantages of manufacturing items from plastic instead of traditional materials.

19.13 Briefly outline two environmental disadvantages of plastics.

19.14 Some plastics are non-biodegradable. What does this mean?

19.15 There are many different types of plastic products, as shown in Figure 19.16 overleaf. Each group should choose one product shown in the figure. List the properties of the plastic that the product is made from, and explain why this material is best suited to this product.

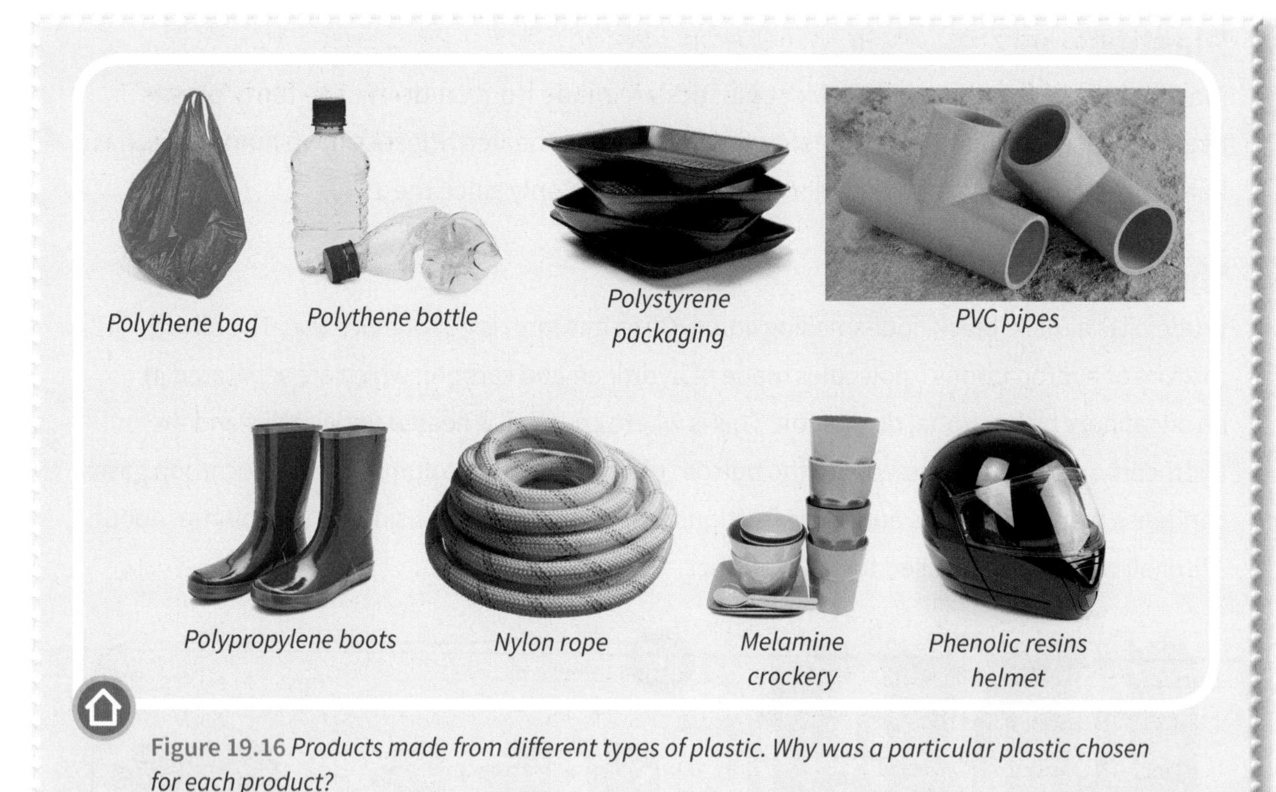

Figure 19.16 *Products made from different types of plastic. Why was a particular plastic chosen for each product?*

What is the environmental impact of plastics?

Plastic does not break down easily. It is not affected by air and water. It is not biodegradable – bacteria and fungi cannot break it down. The first ever plastic bag will still be in existence, unless it was burned. This is a major disadvantage of plastics. (See chapter 23.)

Landfill sites are full of plastic that will not break down and plastic pollution affects every waterway, sea and ocean in the world. Around 80% of marine litter originates from land and most of that is plastic. This has a severe impact on our environment. Seabirds, turtles, whales and other sealife are eating the plastic and are dying from choking and starvation. Also, toxic chemicals are released into the water; fish easily become contaminated and get ill. This has a knock-on effect further up the food chain, right up to humans, who may ingest the contaminated fish.

19.16 How can we prevent plastics pollution in our waterways?

Some plastics now contain an additive that promotes the breakdown of the plastic to water and carbon dioxide, but this can also affect our environment because carbon dioxide is one of the greenhouse gases that cause global warming. Despite the use of this additive in some plastic products, there is massive pollution from plastics and waste from plastics products.

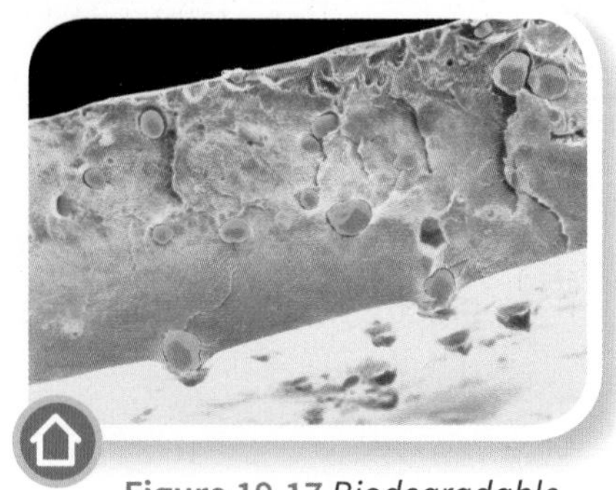

Figure 19.17 *Biodegradable plastic bag*

Many plastics are a fire risk. When they burn, poisonous fumes are created. PVC (polyvinylchloride), which is found in guttering pipes and raincoats, for example, releases poisonous hydrogen chloride gas as it burns. In house fires, many deaths are caused by poisonous fumes and smoke produced as plastics burn.

19.17 Plastic pollution involves the accumulation of plastic products in the environment. Find out what effect plastic pollution has on our lands, ocean, animals and humans.

Bioplastics

Bioplastics are biodegradable plastics made from renewable biological sources. For example, polylactide is made from sugarcane and is used in some packaging and disposable nappies. Making this new material requires a lot of energy – which produces carbon dioxide, which will add to the greenhouse effect – and uses up valuable resources.

Figure 19.18 *Cup made from bioplastic*

19.18 Some objects can be made of metal or plastic. Write down the advantages and disadvantages of metal or plastic for each of the following:

(a) Ruler
(b) Window frame
(c) Spoon
(d) Bucket.

19.19 Tony has a lump of black solid. It is light, breaks easily and does not conduct electricity. Is this a metal or non-metal?

What are composites?

A composite material is made up of at least two other materials. These materials may be layered or woven together. Composites are used when additional strength is needed. For example, plywood is made up of three or more thin layers of wood bonded with adhesive, concrete or cement – which is also a composite material, composed mainly of water, aggregates (rock, sand and gravel).

Figure 19.19 *Pressed wood is a composite – this makes it very strong*

CHEMICAL WORLD

What is ceramic?

Ceramic is a non-metallic synthetic mixture. Ceramics are:

- Cheap
- Hard
- Resistant to high temperatures
- Long-lasting
- Low density compared to metals
- Poor conductors of electricity.

Traditional ceramics include bricks and tiles, but new ceramics are used for space shuttle tiles and joint replacements.

Figure 19.20 *A traditional use for ceramics is in the making of roof tiles*

Figure 19.21 *Spacecraft have ceramic tiles on their exterior*

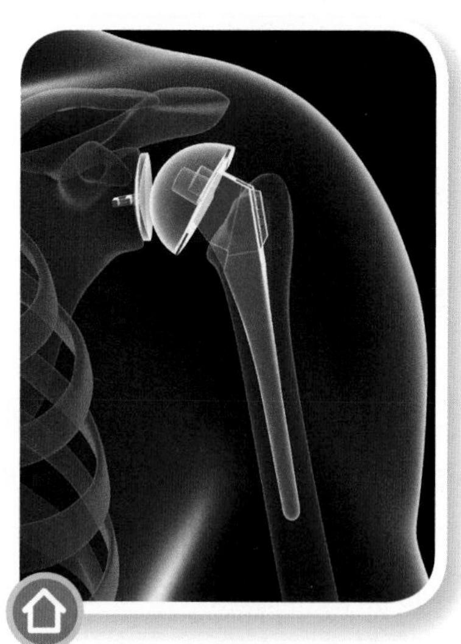

Figure 19.22 *Some joint replacements, like this shoulder replacement, are made from ceramic*

19.20 In your copy, copy and complete the table from your knowledge of materials.

Material	Properties	Uses
Metals		
Polymers		
Ceramics		
Composites		

19.21 Rubber is a strong but soft and flexible material. It is used to make car tyres. Research rubber to answer the following questions:

(a) Is rubber a natural or a synthetic material?

(b) Where does rubber come from?

(c) What are its properties?

Figure 19.23 *Rubber is used to make tyres*

What is nanotechnology?

Nanotechnology is the use of **nanoparticles**, which are tiny particles (atoms, molecules, ions). They are measured in **nanometres (nm)**. There are one million nanometres in a millimetre.

Nanoparticles have a variety of uses:

- Nanoparticles are used to create water-repellent clothing because nanoparticles can repel water and dirt.
- Nanoparticles are used in some medicines for cancer treatments because they are so small they will be absorbed very quickly into cancer cells.
- Nano-sized silver particles have an antibacterial agent and are added to food packaging so food will keep fresher for longer.

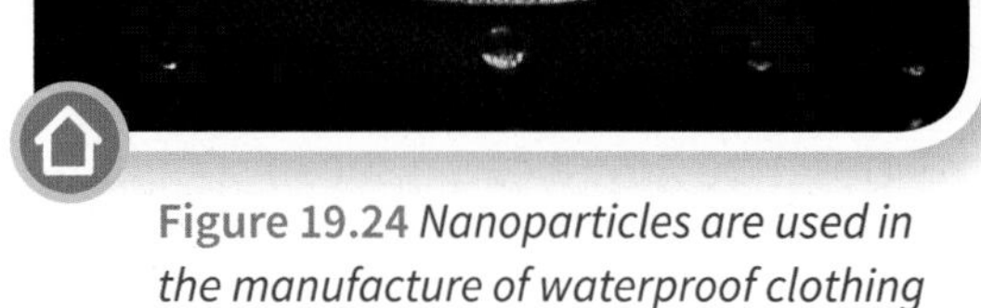

Figure 19.24 *Nanoparticles are used in the manufacture of waterproof clothing*

- UV protective nanoparticles are used in sunblocks.

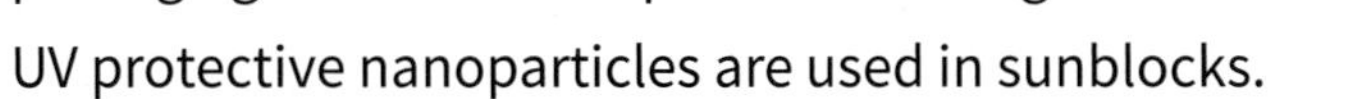

19.22 Explain how nanoparticles in sunblocks and medicine for cancer treatment could improve people's lives.

Environmental impact of nanotechnology

Nano-sized silver particles have the ability to kill harmful bacteria and several products containing these silver nanoparticles are already on the market, including:

- Socks, which contain silver nanoparticles to inhibit odour-causing bacteria
- Energy-efficient washing machines that disinfect clothes by generating silver nanoparticles.

Can these nanoparticles have a negative effect on our environment? There is an increased use of silver nanoparticles in consumer products and this material is being released into our sewage, wastewater treatment systems and eventually our rivers, lakes and oceans. Scientists have discovered that these nanoparticles are extremely toxic and are destroying the good bacteria which are needed for wastewater treatment.

19.23 Find out what other negative impacts the overuse of nanoparticles has on our environment.

CHAPTER 20 Rates of reactions

UNIT 3

Learning outcomes

At the end of this chapter you will be able to:

- Explain rate of reaction
- Investigate what factors affect the rate of a chemical reaction
- Describe how a catalyst can speed up a chemical reaction.

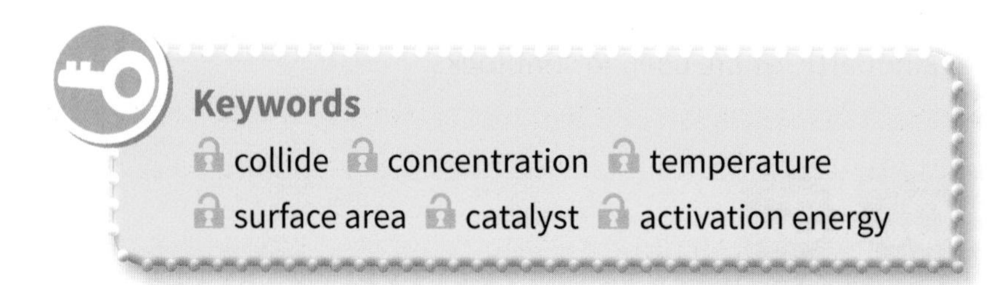

What is the 'rate of reaction'?

The rate of a chemical reaction tells us how quickly a chemical reaction happens. One of the slowest rates of reaction is the rusting of iron. A really fast reaction is an explosion, where it is all over in a fraction of a second.

Figure 20.1 *A nail rusting has a slow rate of reaction*

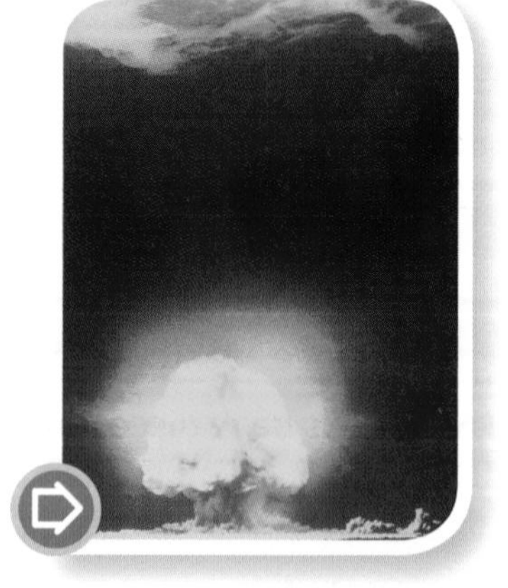

Figure 20.2 *An explosion has a very fast rate of reaction*

In industry it is very important to know how long it will take for a reaction to occur. Reactions can take varying amounts of time from start to finish, so chemists measure how much reactants are used up and how much product is formed in a certain time.

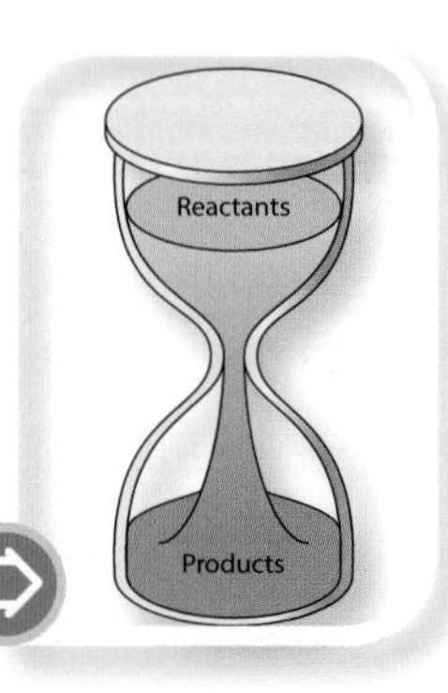

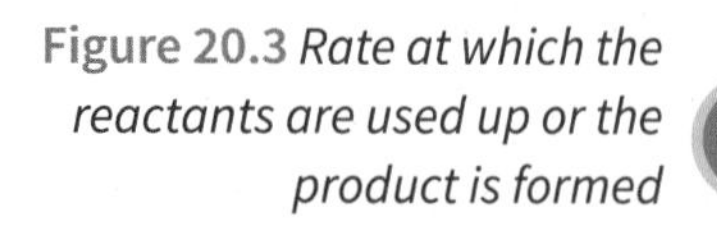

Figure 20.3 *Rate at which the reactants are used up or the product is formed*

What is particle theory?

During a chemical reaction the particles in the reactants are moving all the time. The rate of a reaction simply depends on how often and how hard the reacting particles **collide** with each other. For the particles to react they must collide with enough energy to break the bonds in the molecules. Once the bonds are broken the atoms can rearrange to make the products.

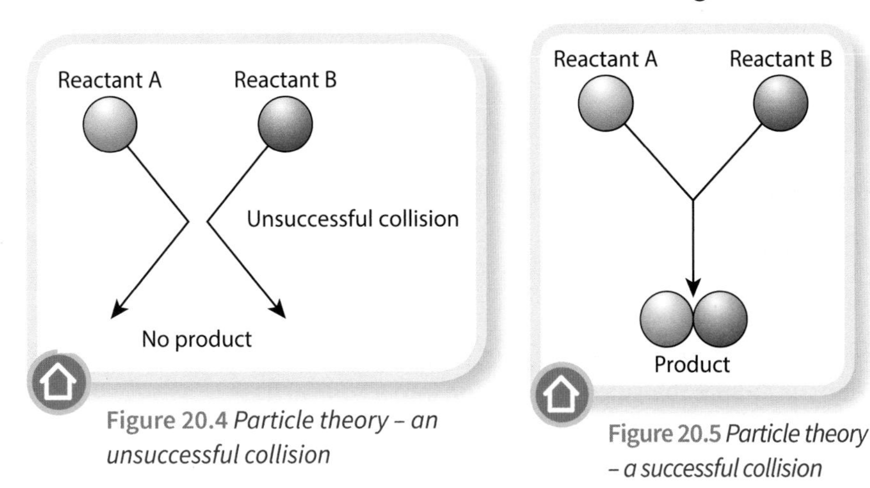

Figure 20.4 *Particle theory – an unsuccessful collision*

Figure 20.5 *Particle theory – a successful collision*

Increasing the rate of a reaction involves increasing the number of successful collisions between the reacting particles. There are a number of factors that will affect the behaviour of particles and will have an overall effect.

What is the effect of raising the temperature on the rate of a reaction?

If you change the temperature of the reaction, will this change the rate of reaction?

Investigating i2 Investigating i3 Investigating i4 Portfolio 146

Activity 20.1

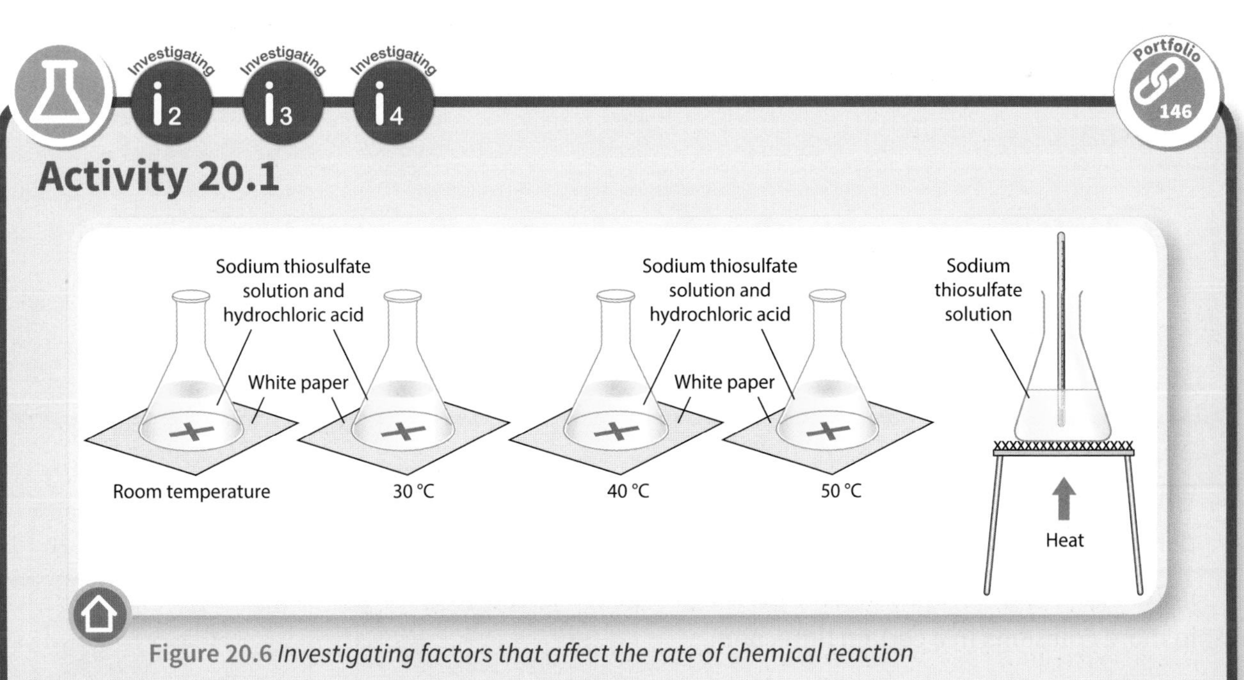

Figure 20.6 *Investigating factors that affect the rate of chemical reaction*

Question

What is the effect of temperature on rate of reaction?

We will be using a solution that turns cloudy with the addition of hydrochloric acid. We will test this at different temperatures by placing it in a flask over a piece of paper with a cross marked on it and seeing how long it is before we can't see the cross because of the cloudiness.

Equipment needed

- 4 conical flasks
- Tripod
- Bunsen burner
- Wire gauze
- Graduated cylinder
- Dilute hydrochloric acid (3 M)
- Sodium thiosulphate (0.05 M)
- Thermometer
- Paper
- Marker
- Stopwatch or timer
- Metal tongs

Safety

- Use metal tongs when removing the conical flask from the Bunsen burner.

Conducting the activity

1. Mark a cross on a piece of white paper.
2. Measure 50 cm³ of sodium thiosulphate solution into a conical flask.
3. Place the flask on a piece of white paper marked with a cross.
4. Record the temperature of the solution using the thermometer.
5. Add 5 cm³ of hydrochloric acid (3 M) and swirl. Start the timer.
6. Record the time it takes for the solution to obscure the cross.
7. Repeat steps 1 to 6 at 30°C, 40°C and 50°C, heating the sodium thiosulphate solution in the flask over a Bunsen burner. Record all your results in a table like the following and note any conclusions you make from the results.

Temp °C	Time taken for cross not to be seen (seconds)
Room temperature	
30	
40	
50	

20.1 What happens to the rate of reaction as you increase the temperature?

When you raise the temperature the particles have more energy so they move around more quickly. This results in more collisions in a certain time, and so reactions get faster as we raise the temperature.

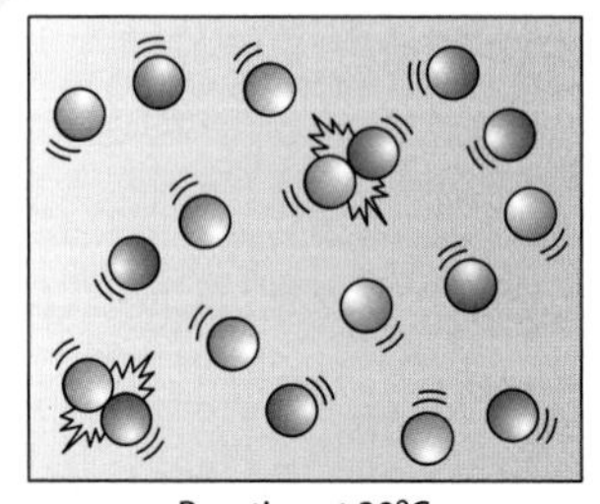

Figure 20.7 *As particles get more energy they move at a greater speed, and so there are more collisions and reactions get faster*

20.2 Have you ever tasted milk that has gone off? Some foods react when exposed to air, and turn into acids. Why do we store milk in a fridge, and why does refrigeration make it stay fresh for longer?

20.3 You are asked to make jelly for a party starting in three hours. What will you do to dissolve the jelly cubes in water as quickly as possible?

Did you know?

Light sticks produce light because of a chemical reaction. Dropping a light stick into hot water makes it glow more intensely, demonstrating that the reaction occurs faster at higher temperatures.

Figure 20.8 *A chemical reaction makes these light sticks glow*

CHEMICAL WORLD

20.4 Define rate of reaction.

20.5 Explain how a change in temperature can affect the rate of reaction.

20.6 Plot the data below on a graph, with time on the x-axis and temperature on the y-axis. Describe what effect an increase in temperature has on the volume of carbon dioxide produced.

Volume of CO_2 produced

Time (s)	20°C	30°C
0	0	0
20	7	9
40	14	16
60	18	19
80	21	24
100	25	25

What is the effect of concentration?

When a solution is more concentrated there are more reacting particles in the same volume. What effect will this have on the rate of reaction?

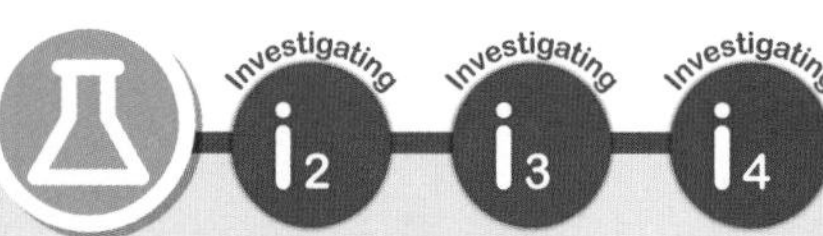

Portfolio 146

Activity 20.2

Question

What is the effect of concentration on rate of reaction?

Equipment needed

Conical flask	Basin	Water
Bung	Graduated cylinder	Marble chips
Glass tubing	Hydrochloric acid (0.1 M)	Stopwatch or timer

Conducting the activity

1. Set up the apparatus as shown in Figure 20.9.
2. Place 5 g of marble chips in the conical flask.
3. Add a solution containing 10 cm^3 of hydrochloric acid (0.1 M) and 40 cm^3 of water.
4. Start the timer as soon as you place the bung in the flask.
5. Time how long it takes to collect 20 cm^3 of gas.
6. Repeat steps 2 to 5 using different concentrations of acid as shown in the table.
7. Record all your results in the table.

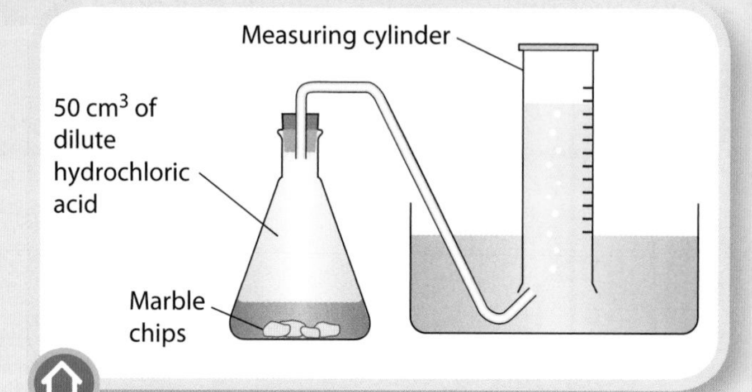

Figure 20.9

Acid (cm^3)	Water (cm^3)	Time to collect 20 cm^3 of carbon dioxide (s)
10	40	
20	30	
30	20	
40	10	
50	0	

20.7 What happens to the rate of reaction as you increase the concentration of the acid?

When you increase the concentration, you increase the number of particles, which results in more collisions in a certain time and so you get an increase in rate of reaction (that is, the reaction gets faster).

20.8 As you increase the concentration of acid there are more acid particles in the same volume. Use the particle theory and diagrams to explain why you think this may cause an overall increase in the rate of a reaction.

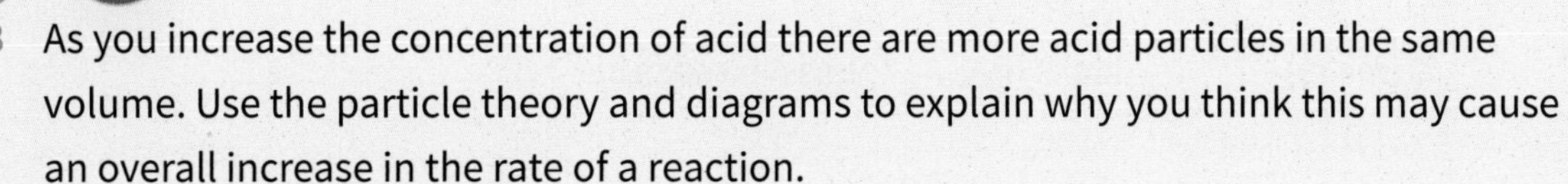

What is surface area?

Surface area is the measure of how much surface (of the reactants) is exposed. When a large piece of solid material is cut into smaller pieces its surface area is increased. What effect will an increase of surface area have on the rate of a chemical reaction?

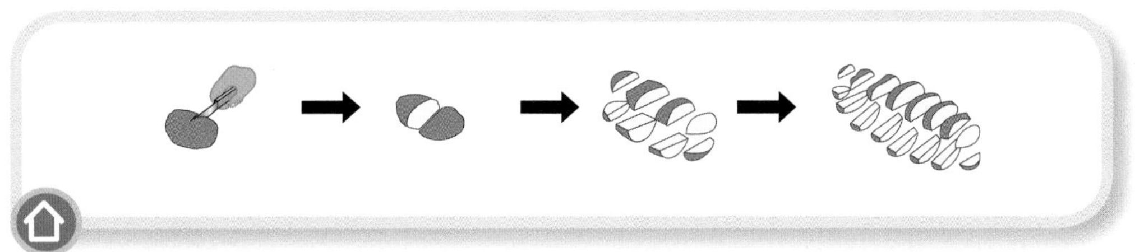

Figure 20.10 *You increase the surface area of the potato each time you cut it into smaller pieces*

Activity 20.3

Question

What is the effect of increasing surface area on the rate of a reaction?

Equipment needed

Conical flask
Electronic balance
Cotton wool
Dilute hydrochloric acid
Marble chips (5 mm)
Marble chips (10 mm)
Stopwatch or timer

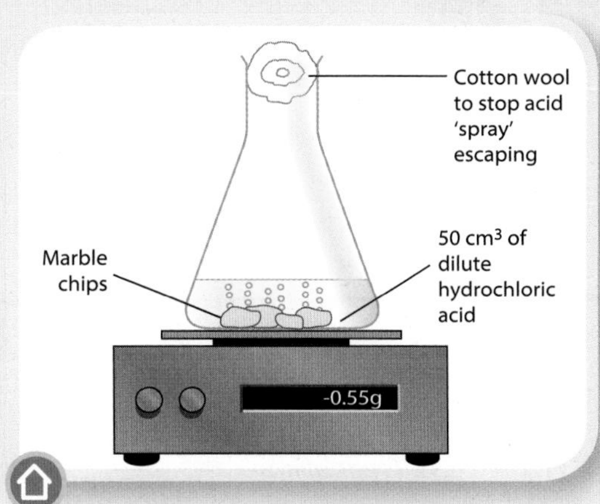

Figure 20.11 *Testing the effect of increasing the surface area on the rate of a reaction*

Conducting the activity

1. Set up the apparatus as shown in Figure 20.11.
2. Place 5 g of marble chips (5 mm) into a conical flask. Add 50 cm^3 of dilute hydrochloric acid.

3. Place cotton wool in the top of the flask.
4. Start the timer.
5. Record the loss in mass every 30 seconds.
6. Record your results in a table like the one below.
7. Repeat steps 2 to 6 using the larger marble chips (10 mm).

Time (s)	Mass (g)	Loss in mass
0		
30		
60		
90		
120		
150		
180		

20.9 Which marble chips have the larger surface area?

20.10 Why is it important to keep all other factors in the activity the same?

20.11 Plot both sets of results on a graph. Put loss of mass (mass of gas given off) on the y-axis and time on the x-axis.

20.12 Which size of marble chips reacts faster?

20.13 What happens to the rate of reaction as we increase the surface area?

The smaller the particle size of a solid, the greater the surface area on which the reaction can take place, and so the faster the reaction.

Iron nail

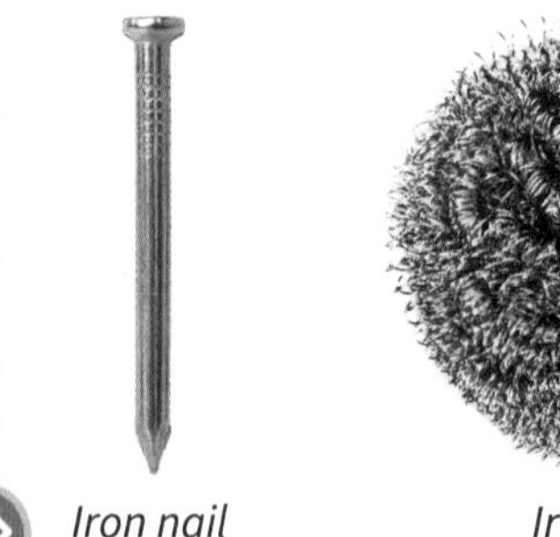

Iron wool

Iron filings

Figure 20.12 *Types of iron*

20.14 Place the three types of iron shown in Figure 20.12 in order of increasing surface area.

20.15 If each type of iron was heated over a Bunsen burner, which would show the greatest rate of reaction?

What is the effect of using a catalyst?

Transition metals lie in between group 2 and group 3 in the periodic table. Some well-known transition metals are iron, copper, chromium, nickel and gold. Transition metals and their compounds are important catalysts. (A catalyst makes something happen without being part of what happens.) How will a catalyst affect the rate of reaction?

Activity 20.4

Question

What is the effect of a catalyst on the rate of a chemical reaction?

Equipment needed

2 test tubes
Hydrogen peroxide (6%)
Manganese dioxide (catalyst)
Spatula
Wooden splints

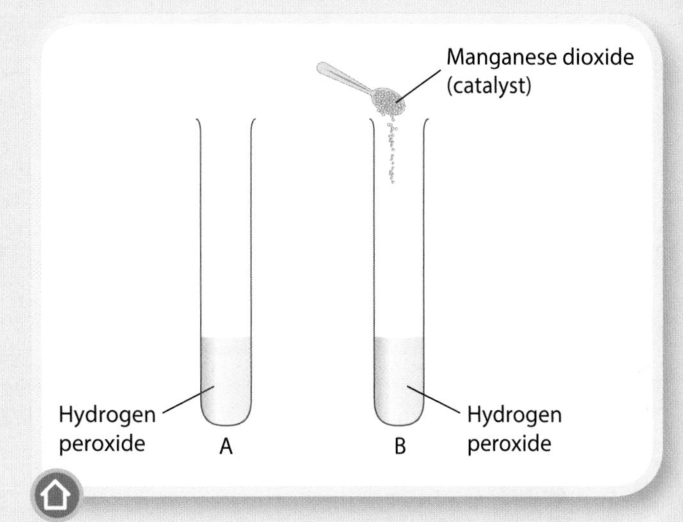

Figure 20.13 *Investigating the effect of a catalyst*

Safety

- Wear safety goggles and gloves at all times when using the hydrogen peroxide.

Conducting the activity

1. Place 5 cm^3 of hydrogen peroxide into each of test tubes A and B.
2. Add a little manganese dioxide to test tube B.
3. Test each test tube with a glowing splint.
4. Note your results.

Make sure that in your results you note answers to the following:

(a) Did bubbles form in test tube A?
(b) What happened as soon as you added the catalyst manganese dioxide?
(c) Did the glowing splint relight in each test tube?
(d) Which test tube showed the greater rate of reaction?
(e) How did you judge the rate of reaction?

20.16 The catalyst manganese dioxide speeds up the reaction in the previous activity without getting used up. How can you get the manganese dioxide back to be used again? (Hint: it is insoluble in water.)

CHEMICAL WORLD

How do catalysts increase the rate of a reaction?

Activation energy is the minimum amount of energy that reactant particles must have in order for them to react. When you add a catalyst it lowers the activation energy; this makes it easier for the particles to react, so there is an increase in the rate of reaction.

Did you know?

Enzymes are natural catalysts in the human body. Without the enzyme amylase in our saliva it would take starch several weeks to break down.

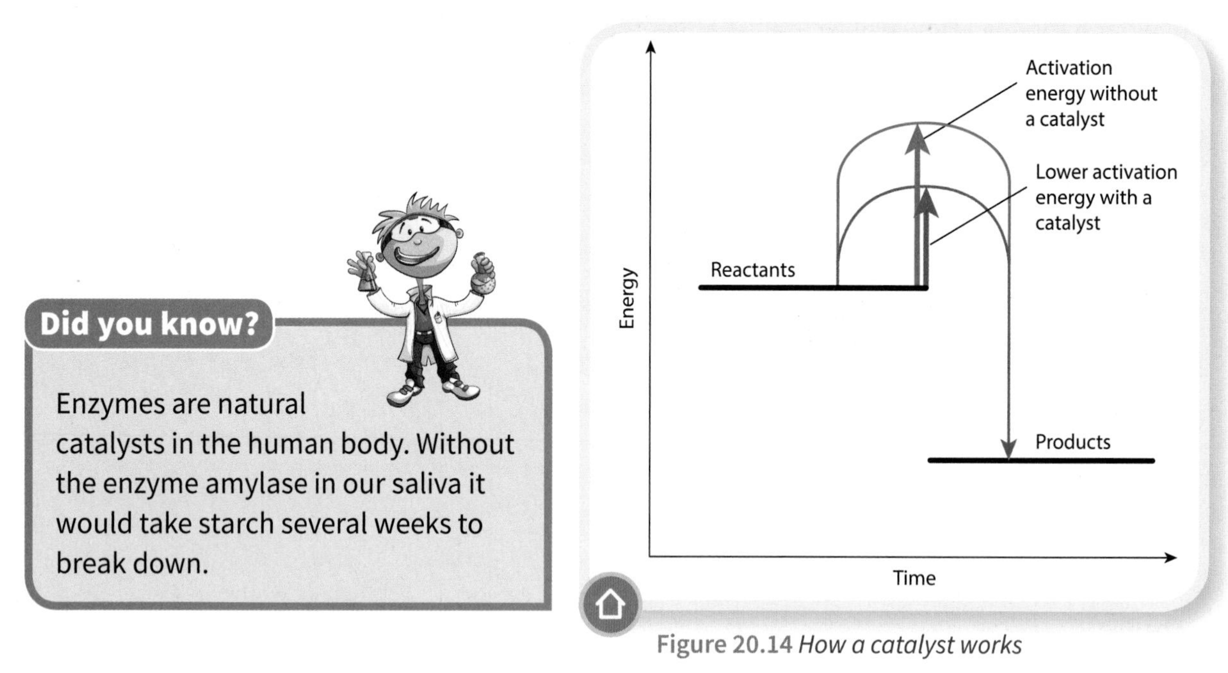

Figure 20.14 *How a catalyst works*

Investigating i5

20.17 What are catalysts?

20.18 Explain how catalysts increase the rate of a chemical reaction.

Investigating i5

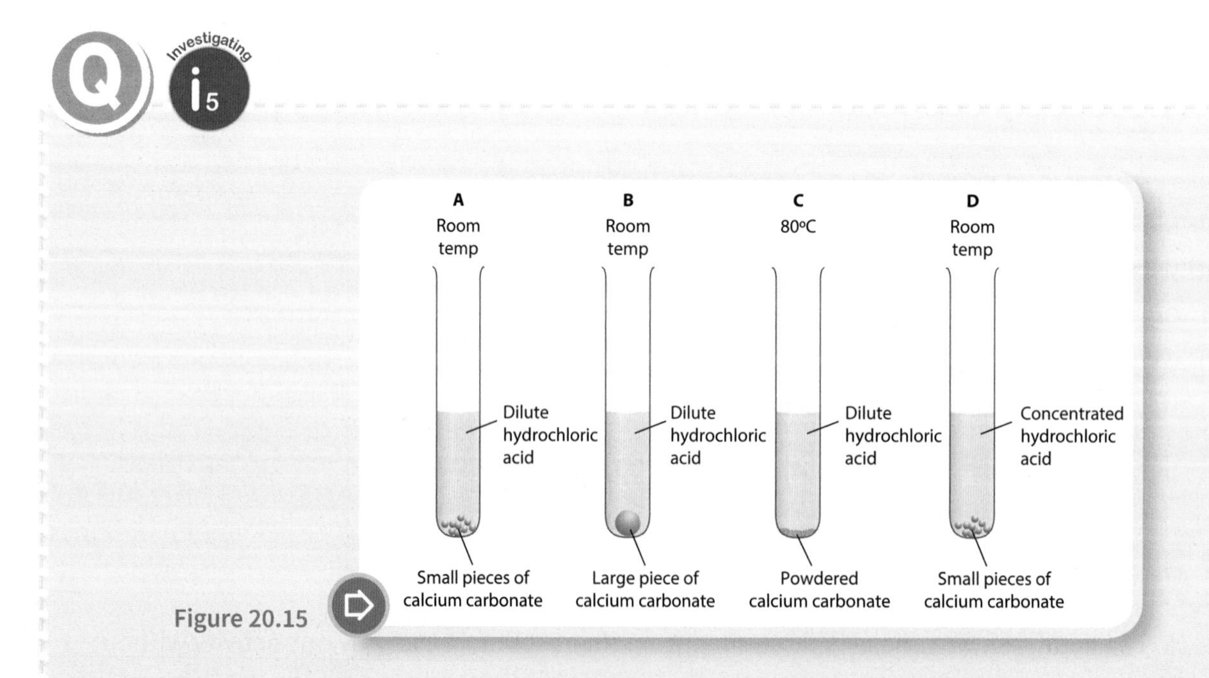

Figure 20.15

20.19 Place the reactions in Figure 20.15 in order of increasing rate of reaction.

CHAPTER 21

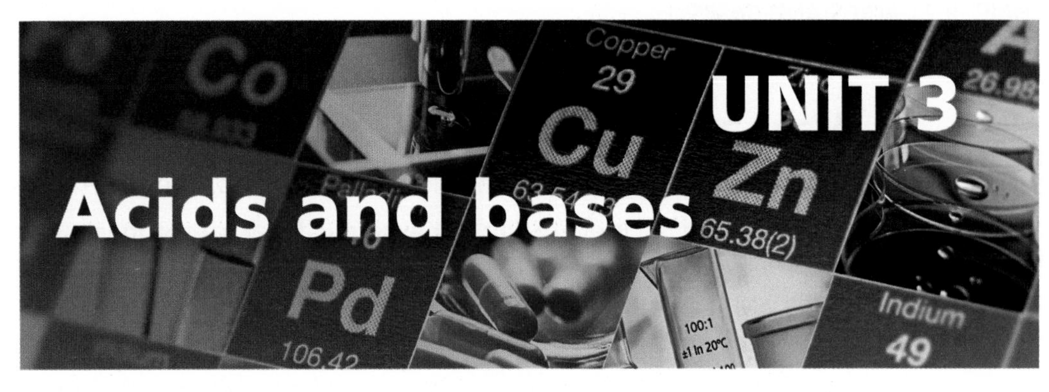

Acids and bases

Learning outcomes

At the end of this chapter you will be able to:

- Classify substances as acid, base or neutral
- Investigate reactions between acids and bases
- Use indicators and the pH scale.

Keywords

acid base alkali neutral litmus paper universal indicator pH scale titration neutralisation particle theory dissociate

What are acids?

What springs to mind when you hear the word 'acid'? Most people think of acids as dangerous, corrosive liquids. Not all acids are like this, however. For example:

- Lemon juice contains an acid called citric acid
- Vinegar is a dilute solution of ethanoic acid.

The word 'acid' comes from a Latin word meaning **sour**. The acids in food such as those listed above tend to have a sour, sharp taste. The acids you use in the laboratory are strong acids that are corrosive. So, be careful when using them! Table 21.1 shows some everyday acids and some laboratory acids.

A substance that is an acid is said to be **acidic**.

Table 21.1 **Some everyday acids and some laboratory acids**

Everyday acids	Laboratory acids
Lemon juice (citric acid)	Hydrochloric acid (HCl)
Rain water (carbonic acid)	Sulfuric acid (H_2SO_4)
Vinegar	

Figure 21.1 *Examples of acids*

What are bases?

There is another group of chemicals known as bases. They are the opposite of acids. Many bases are used by us every day. For example, bleach, toothpaste, oven cleaner and washing soda are all bases. Table 21.2 shows some everyday bases and some laboratory bases.

Many bases are as corrosive and dangerous as acids. For example, caustic soda, which is used to clear drains, is a corrosive base and must be handled with care (and gloves!).

Table 21.2 Some everyday bases and some laboratory bases

Everyday bases	Laboratory bases
Toothpaste	Sodium hydroxide (NaOH)
Bleach	Calcium carbonate ($CaCO_3$)
Indigestion tablets	Limewater $Ca(OH)_2$

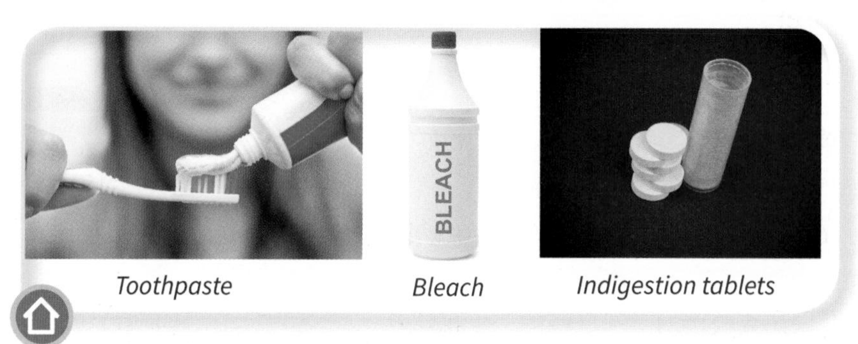

Figure 21.2 *A selection of household bases*

A substance that is a base is said to be **basic**.

Some bases will dissolve in water. They are known as **alkalis**. Drain cleaner (sodium hydroxide) is an example of an alkali. A substance that is an alkali is said to be **alkaline**.

There is another group of substances that are neither acid nor base. They are said to be **neutral**, such as water or a salt solution.

21.1 Name and give the formulas of two acids and two bases used in the lab.

21.2 What are alkalis?

21.3 We come across acids and bases every day and maybe don't realise it. The food industry uses acids in many products, such as fizzy drinks, and bases are used in many cleaning products.
Examine the labels on different food and cleaning products and see if you can identify any acids or bases.

How can you tell an acid from a base?

You cannot tell by looking at a substance whether it is an acid or a base or a neutral substance. You have to test them with an indicator.

What are indicators?

An indicator is a chemical that shows, by means of a colour change, whether a substance is an acid or a base. In the laboratory we use two types:

- Litmus indicator
- Universal indicator.

What is litmus indicator?

Litmus is paper that has been treated with a water-soluble mixture of different dyes from lichens, which grow on the bark of trees or on rocks.

Litmus indicator will change colour from blue to red in acids and from red to blue in bases (or alkalis).

Remember: *b* for *base*, *b* for *blue* litmus.

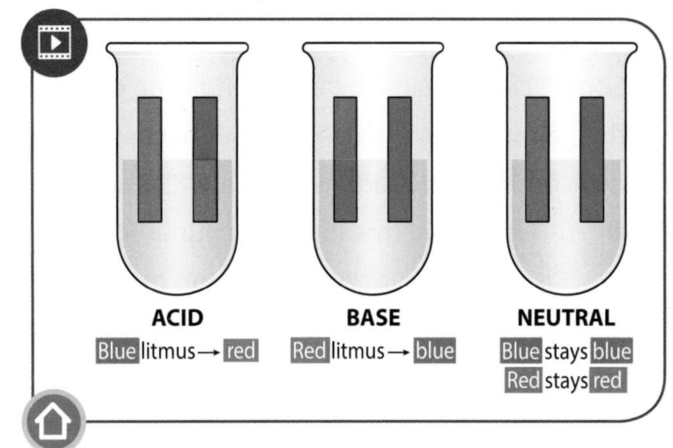

Figure 21.3 *Colour changes of litmus indicator*

Portfolio 151

Activity 21.1

Question

What household substances are acids, bases or neutral?

Equipment needed

Test tube rack — Litmus paper

Test tubes — Variety of household substances, laboratory chemicals and water

Conducting the activity

1. Place a selection of household and laboratory chemicals in different test tubes. If the substance is a solid, try dissolving a spatulaful of it in a small volume of water first.
2. Dip pieces of blue and red litmus papers into the liquid of each test tube.
3. Examine the papers and observe any colour changes.
4. Enter your results into a table like the one shown below.

Substances being tested	Acidic	Basic	Neutral
Vinegar	✓		
Water			✓

21.4 What effect do acids have on:

(a) Blue litmus paper?

(b) Red litmus paper?

What is universal indicator?

Universal indicator is a mixture of dyes that change to different colours according to how strong the acid or base is. Universal indicator gives a range of colours, as shown in Figure 21.4, which can be used to give a value on the pH scale, which we look at next.

What is the pH scale?

Some acids are safe to handle and even eat, whereas others such as car battery acid are very dangerous and corrosive. In order to compare the strengths of acids and bases chemists devised a scale called the pH scale. The scale is from 0 to 14:

- 0–7 is an acid (the lower the number, the more acidic it is)
- 7 is neutral (pure water has a pH at almost 7)
- 7–14 is an alkali (the higher the number, the greater the alkalinity).

The pH can be measured using a pH meter or universal indicator.

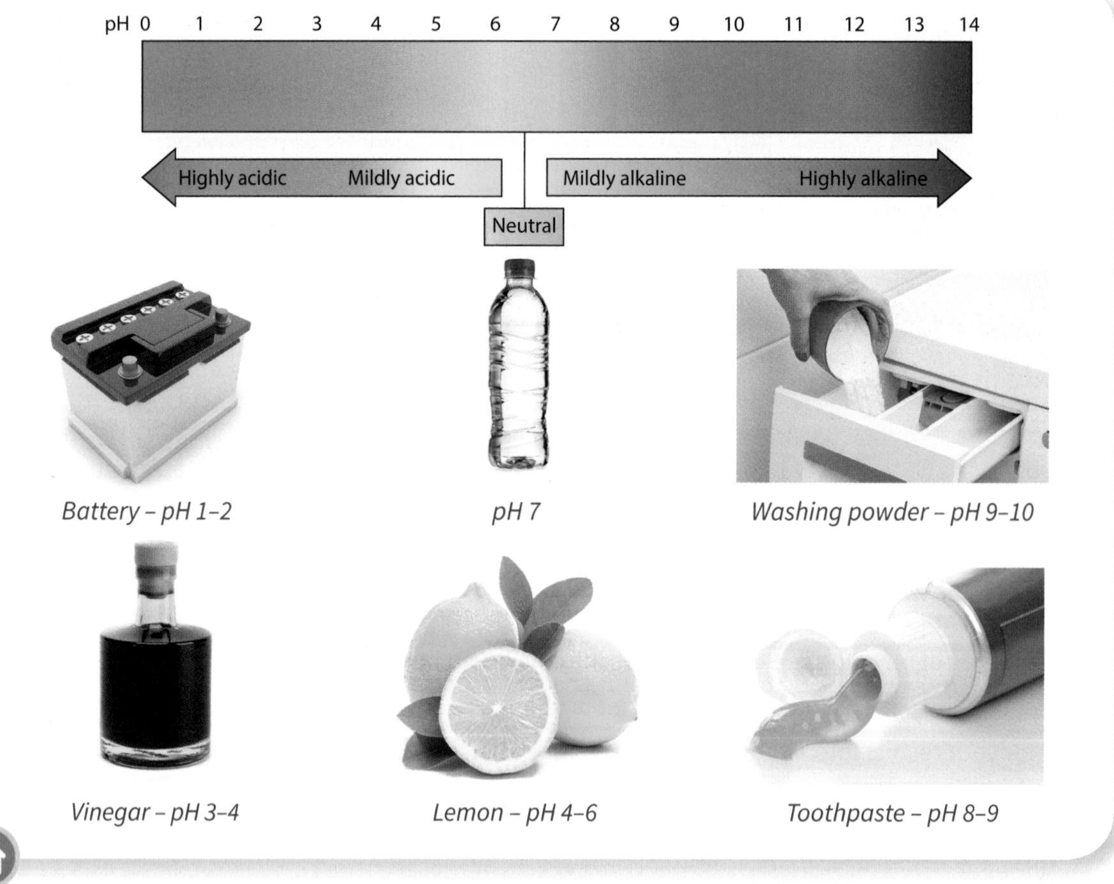

Figure 21.4 *A variety of household substances and their position on the pH scale*

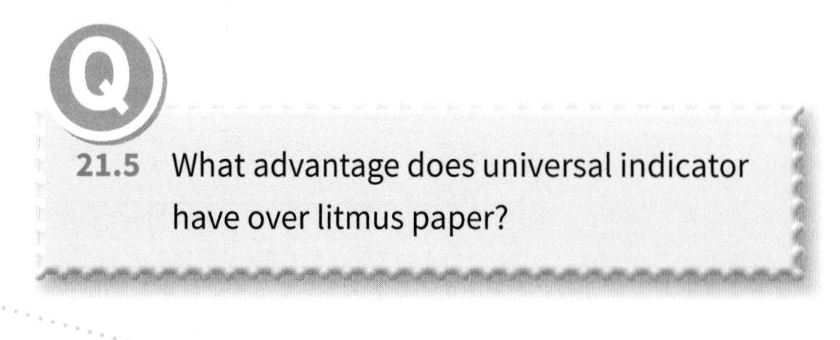

21.5 What advantage does universal indicator have over litmus paper?

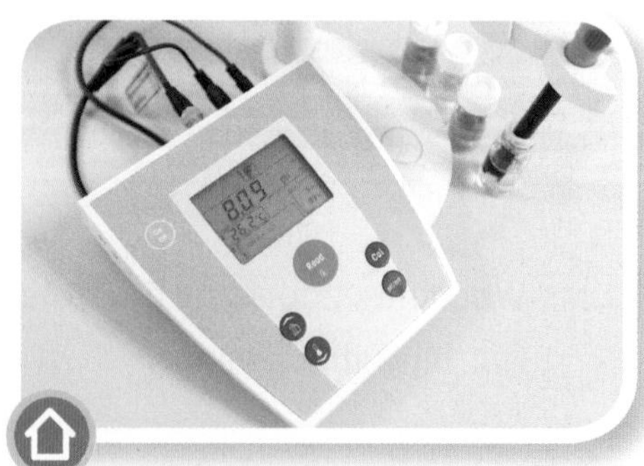

Figure 21.5 *A pH meter*

Activity 21.2

Question

What is the pH of a variety of household substances?

Equipment needed

Test tube rack
Test tubes
Universal indicator or pH meter
Variety of household substances

Conducting the activity

1. Place the substance being tested into a test tube. If the substance is solid, dissolve it in water first.
2. Place a piece of universal indicator paper into the liquid in the test tube.
3. Note the colour of the indicator and, using a colour chart, find its pH.
4. Draw a pH scale in your report by drawing a number line from 0 to 14.
5. On the pH scale, write the names of the substances tested and indicate their pHs as shown in Figure 21.7.

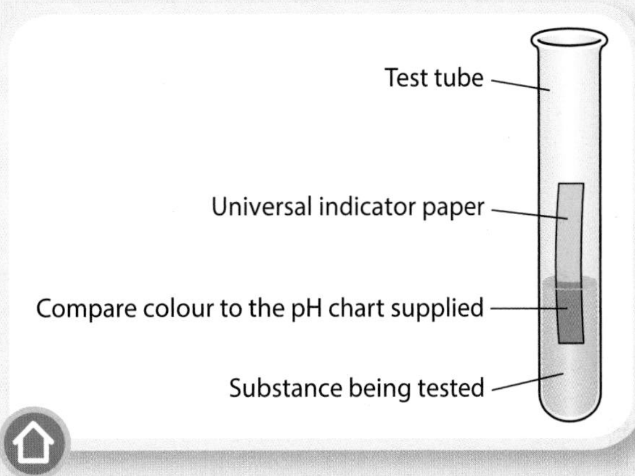

Figure 21.6 *Investigating the pH of a substance*

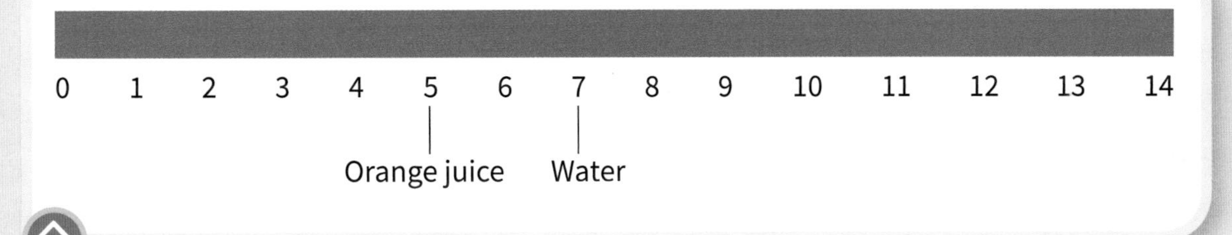

Figure 21.7 *A pH number line*

Did you know?

When you are stung by a nettle, hairs on the nettle leaf inject methanoic acid into your skin. A dock leaf contains chemicals that when rubbed over the sting neutralise this acid and cool down the skin.

CHEMICAL WORLD

21.6 What is the pH scale?

21.7 Name a substance that would have:

(a) A pH below 7

(b) A pH of 7

(c) A pH above 7.

Say which is acidic, basic or neutral.

21.8 Some people add lemon to tea instead of milk. When the lemon is added, the tea changes colour slightly. Why does this happen?

CHEMICAL WORLD

Making indicators

Activity 21.3

Portfolio 152

Question

How do you make your own indicator using red cabbage?

Equipment needed

Bunsen burner	Test tube rack
Tripod	Test tubes dropper
Wire gauze	Red cabbage
Beaker	Water
Glass rod	A range of acid, base and neutral substances

Conducting the activity

1. Tear up some red cabbage leaves and add them to a beaker containing approximately 100 cm^3 of water.
2. Heat the water to boiling and stir the leaves using a glass rod. The water turns purple as the indicator is extracted from the leaves.
3. Allow the solution to cool.
4. Add acidic, neutral and alkaline solutions to different test tubes.
5. Using a dropper add 5–6 drops of the red cabbage indicator to each test tube. Stopper the tubes and shake.

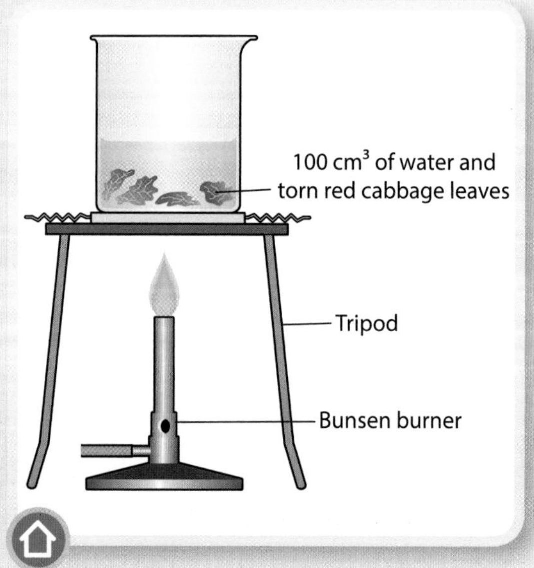

Figure 21.8 *Extracting the indicator from red cabbage*

6. Note the colour in each test tube and summarise your results in a table similar to the one below.

Substance tested	Indicator colour
Acidic substance	
Alkaline substance	
Neutral substance	

Note: If you store the red cabbage indicator in the fridge it will last longer.

21.9 State the colours of the red cabbage indicator in acid, base and neutral solutions.

Reactions of acids

Acids are part of our everyday life and we must understand their key reactions. Acids react with many substances but one product they all have in common is a **salt**.

Acid and metal

An acid always reacts with a metal to produce a salt and hydrogen gas. For example, the reaction between zinc and hydrochloric acid produces a salt and hydrogen gas.

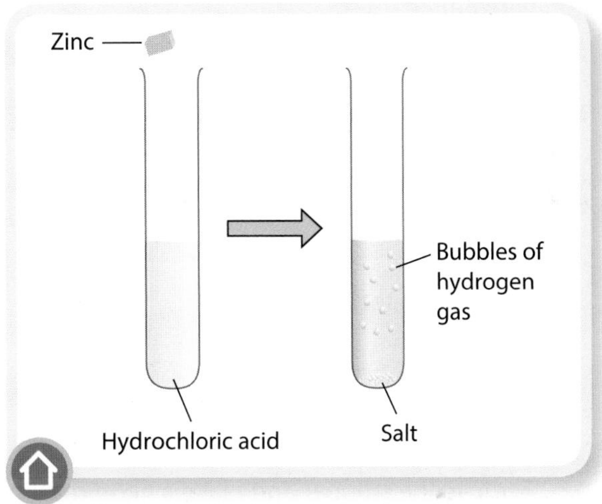

Figure 21.9 *Acid and metal*

Acids react with most metals and a salt is produced. But unlike the reaction between acids and bases we do not get water. Instead hydrogen gas is produced. The word equation for the reaction is:

metal + acid = salt + hydrogen

Note: When naming the salt the first part is the name of the metal (zinc) and the second is based on the acid used (hydrochloric acid). So:

- Zinc + hydrochloric acid = zinc chloride + hydrogen
- Zinc + nitric acid = zinc nitrate + hydrogen
- Zinc + sulfuric acid = zinc sulfate + hydrogen.

Test for hydrogen

To confirm the bubbles of gas are hydrogen you must place a lighted splint into the test tube. Hydrogen is easily ignited because it is flammable and you will hear a distinctive 'squeaky pop' sound if hydrogen is present.

Figure 21.10 *Testing for hydrogen*

Activity 21.4

Question

What happens when calcium reacts with hydrochloric acid?

Equipment needed

Hydrochloric acid (0.1 M)
Calcium
Cotton wool
Test tube
Test tube rack
Wooden splint

Safety

- Keep the test tube in the test tube rack at all times because it can become very hot.

Conducting the activity

1. Place 10 cm^3 of hydrochloric acid in the test tube.
2. Add a few granules of calcium.
3. Stopper the test tube with some cotton wool and allow gas to collect inside it for about 30 seconds.
4. Remove the stopper and place a lighted splint into the test tube. Record what happens.

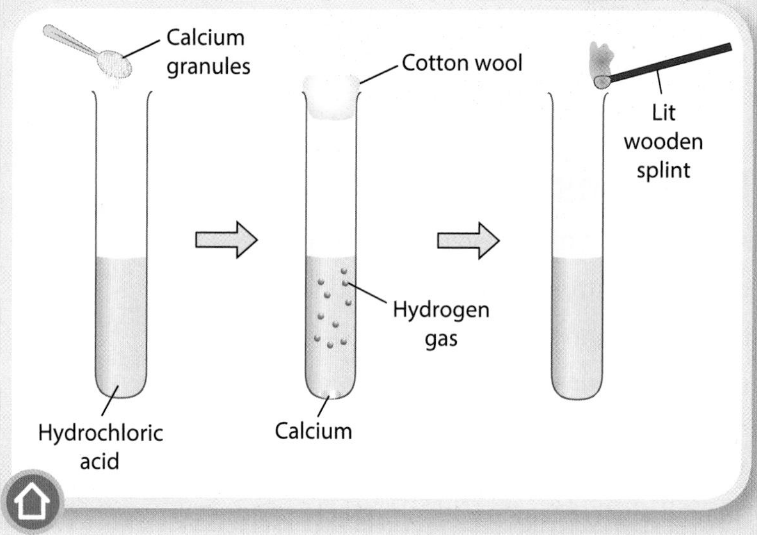

Figure 21.11 *Reacting calcium with hydrochloric acid*

21.10 What is the name of the salt formed?
21.11 Name the gas produced.
21.12 Outline what happened when you tested the gas with a lighted splint.

What is neutralisation?

We have already mentioned that an acid is the chemical opposite of a base. So, what would happen if an acid and a base were mixed together?

The answer is they react together and **neutralise** or cancel each other. They react and produce a salt and water. Both salt and water are neutral. These reactions are known as **neutralisation reactions.**

$$\text{an acid + a base} \longrightarrow \text{salt + water}$$

Neutralisation can be done in a very accurate way by **acid–base titration**. The acid is placed in a burette and the base and indictor are placed in a conical flask. The conical flask is placed under the burette and the acid is added slowly to the base until the indicator changes colour when the salt and water are formed (neutralisation).

Titrations allow you to find out exactly how much acid is needed to neutralise a base.

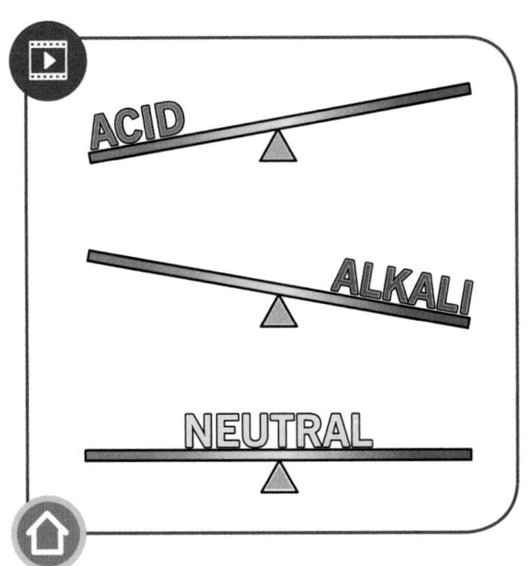

Figure 21.12 *Colour changes at different pHs*

Figure 21.13 *A student reading a burette*

Portfolio 154

Activity 21.5

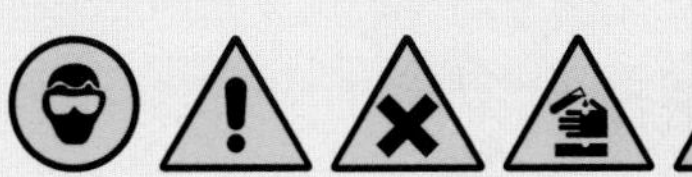

Question

How do you titrate hydrochloric acid (HCl) against sodium hydroxide (NaOH) and prepare a sample of sodium chloride (NaCl)?

Equipment needed

Burette	Evaporating dish	Dilute hydrochloric acid (0.1 M)
Pipette	Bunsen burner	Dilute sodium hydroxide (0.1 M)
Pipette filter	Tripod	An indicator
Conical flask	Wire gauze	Electronic balance
White tile	Beakers	
Retort stand	Funnel	

Conducting the activity

1. Using a pipette filter measure 25 cm^3 of dilute sodium hydroxide into a conical flask.
2. Add 3–4 drops of indicator, e.g. litmus, and place the flask on a white tile.
3. Using a funnel, fill the burette to the 0 cm^3 mark with the dilute hydrochloric acid.
4. Slowly and with continuous swirling of the conical flask add the acid from the burette until the indicator just changes colour. Note the volume of acid added.
5. Repeat the titration, taking care to add the acid drop by drop near the end point.
6. Calculate the average volume of acid from these two titrations.

CHEMICAL WORLD

7. Repeat the experiment without using any indicator and add the volume of acid calculated in step 6.
8. The conical flask contains a solution of sodium chloride in water.
9. Place a sample of the sodium chloride solution into an evaporating dish and evaporate off the water to leave the sodium chloride behind.
10. Use an electronic balance and find the mass of sodium chloride salt produced.

Remember: *A*cid is *a*bove in a burette. *B*ase is *b*elow in a flask.

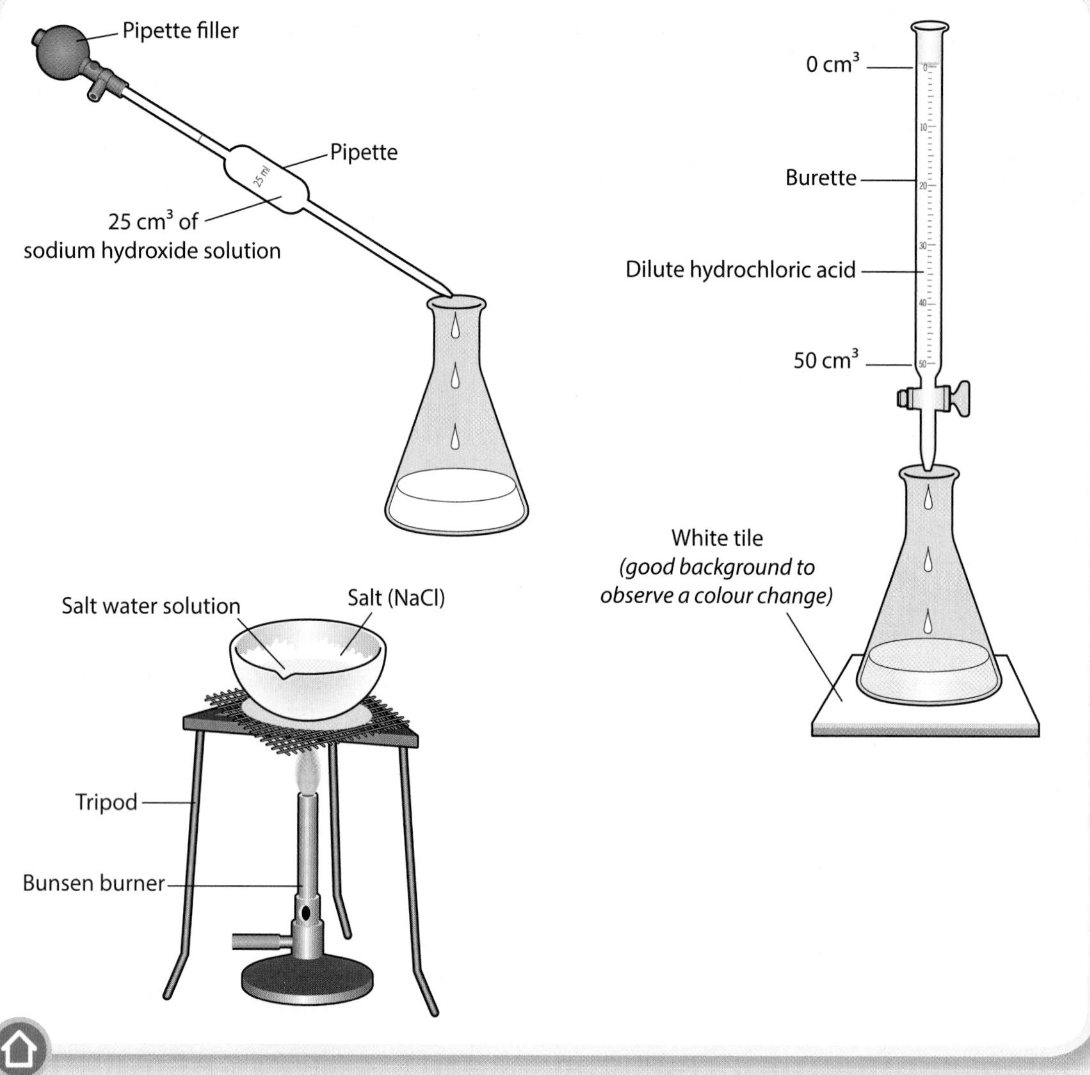

Figure 21.14 *Stages involved in a titration*

From the results of the titration, answer the following:

21.13 What was the colour of the indicator when you added it to sodium hydroxide in the conical flask?

21.14 What was the colour of the universal indicator at the end point?

21.15 What was the average volume of acid needed to neutralise the base?

21.16 What is the mass of the sodium chloride salt produced?

21.17 What is neutralisation?

21.18 Explain acid–base titration.

What is particle theory?

What happens during a neutralisation reaction is explained by particle theory (see chapter 13).

The common laboratory acids all have one atom in common: the hydrogen atom:

- Hydrochloric acid (HCl)
- Nitric acid (HNO_3)
- Sulfuric acid (H_2SO_4).

What happens to acids in water?

When laboratory acids are dissolved in water, the hydrogen atoms separate from the other atoms; it is these free hydrogen particles (**ions**) that make a solution acidic. The more hydrogen ions (H^+) there are, the lower the pH will be.

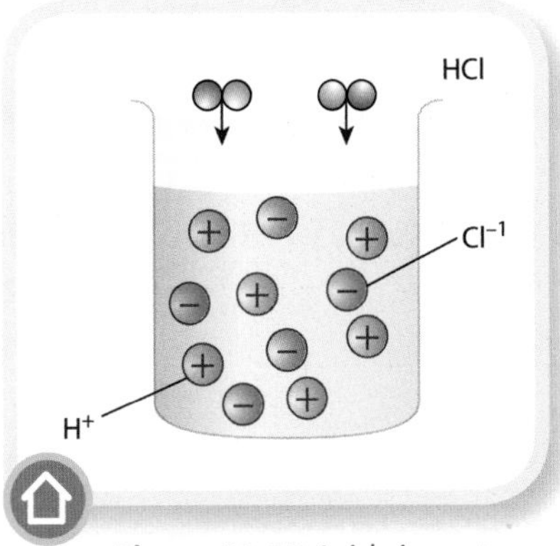

Figure 21.15 *Acids in water*

Acids are compounds that **dissociate** (break) into their ions when placed in water. The strong acid hydrogen chloride is one example – it breaks up into H^+ ions and Cl^- ions when placed in water:

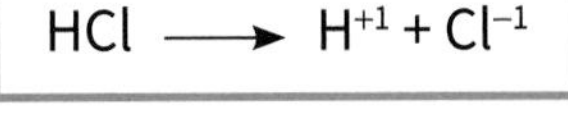
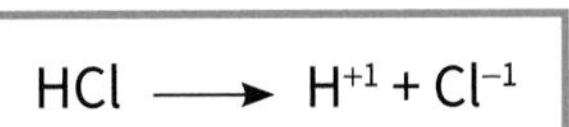

$$HCl \longrightarrow H^{+1} + Cl^{-1}$$

What happens to bases in water?

The common laboratory base sodium hydroxide (NaOH) will also dissociate when added to water.

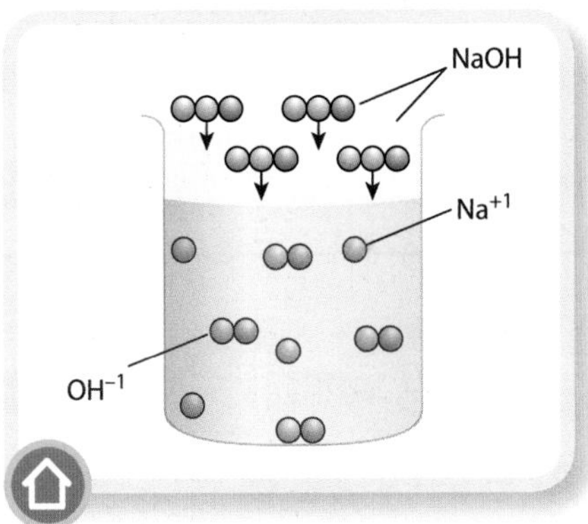

Figure 21.16 *Bases in water*

$$NaOH \longrightarrow Na^{+1} + OH^{-1}$$

Neutralisation

When you add an acid to a base they neutralise – all the ions will rearrange and the products salt and water are formed.

$$H^+ + OH^{-1} \longrightarrow H_2O$$

$$Na^{+1} + Cl^{-1} \longrightarrow NaCl$$

Did you know?

If soil is too acidic, most crops will not grow well. Farmers can spread powdered limestone or lime on the soil to neutralise it.

21.19 A bee sting is acidic and a wasp sting is alkaline. The bee sting can be neutralised by rubbing a mild base such as baking soda or toothpaste on it. How would you treat a wasp sting?

Acid and carbonate

Acids can also be neutralised by reacting them with carbonates (which are also bases). In this type of neutralisation, carbon dioxide gas is also produced.

an acid + a carbonate ⟶ salt + water + carbon dioxide

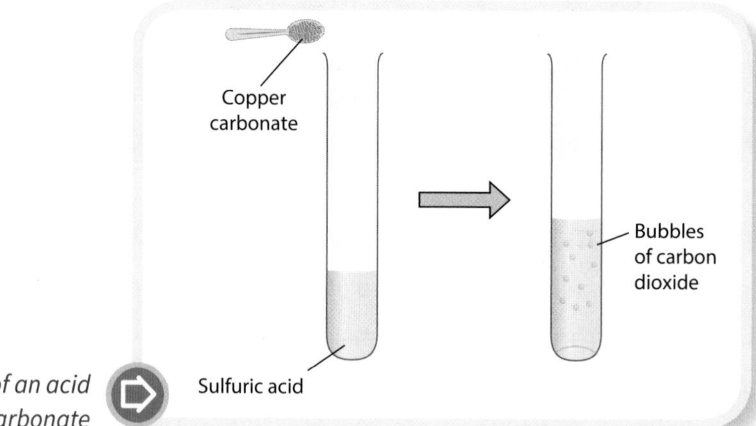

Figure 21.17 *The reaction of an acid and a carbonate*

Did you know?

Have you ever had indigestion? It is caused by too much hydrochloric acid in your stomach. The pain can be relieved by taking an antacid (anti-acid) chemical, which is a base.

Portfolio 155

Activity 21.6

Question

Which brand of indigestion tablet is the most effective at neutralising an acid?

Equipment needed

Conical flask	Mortar and pestle
Burette	De-ionised water (purified water with no dissolved salt ions)
White tile	Universal indicator
Retort stand	Two brands of indigestion tablets
Pipette	Hydrochloric acid (0.1 M)
2 beakers	

Conducting the activity

1. Grind to powder one tablet from the first brand using a mortar and pestle.
2. Place the powder into the conical flask. Wash out the mortar with de-ionised water and transfer the washings to the conical flask.

3. Add 25 cm^3 of de-ionised water to the conical flask and swirl to mix after adding a few drops of universal indicator with a pipette.
4. Fill a burette with dilute hydrochloric acid (0.1 M).
5. Place the conical flask on the white tile under the burette (the white tile makes it easier to see any colour changes). Add the hydrochloric acid from the burette into the conical flask slowly, until the indicator changes colour (end point).
6. Record the total volume of acid added.
7. Repeat steps 1 to 6 with a second tablet from the first brand.
8. Repeat steps 1 to 6 twice with the second brand of indigestion tablet.
9. Note your results in a table similar to the one below.
10. Draw a bar chart or line graph showing the results for each brand of tablet.

Brand	Volume of HCl neutralised by tablet (cm^3)		
	Try 1	Try 2	Average

21.20 Why do you think it is important to repeat each experiment twice for each brand of tablet?

21.21 Why did you place the conical flask on a white tile while carrying out titration?

21.22 From your observations during the activity:

(a) What colour was the universal indicator when added to the indigestion tablet solution?

(b) What was the colour change at the end point?

(c) Which brand of indigestion tablet was the most effective at neutralising the acid?

21.23 Petra has a solution that she thinks might be acidic. Describe three tests she could do to check whether or not it is acidic.

21.24 Thomas tested some solutions with universal indicator. He wrote down their pHs: 1, 5, 7 and 14.

But he forgot to write down the names of the solutions. Can you help him by matching the pHs to the correct solutions?

Solutions tested	pH (1, 5, 7, 14)
Distilled water	
Sulfuric acid	
Sodium hydroxide	
Vinegar	

CHAPTER 22

UNIT 3

Energy transfer in chemical reactions

Learning outcomes

At the end of this chapter you will be able to:

- Describe exothermic and endothermic reactions
- Explain activation energy
- Produce simple energy profile diagrams to illustrate energy changes.

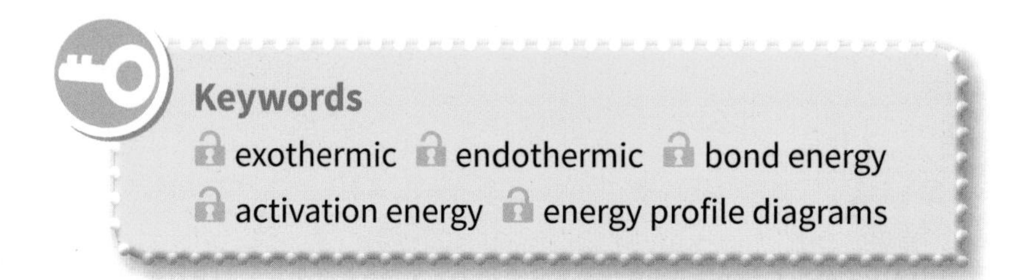

What energy changes occur during a chemical reaction?

One piece of evidence to show that a chemical change or reaction has taken place is to identify a change in temperature. In a chemical reaction, heat energy is usually released or taken from its surroundings.

What is an exothermic reaction?

An exothermic reaction is a reaction where energy is transferred from the chemicals to the surroundings. This is where the temperature of the reaction mixture usually rises. For example, combustion, such as the burning of fuels or fireworks is an exothermic reaction.

Figure 22.1 *An exothermic reaction is taking place on this barbeque*

Figure 22.2 *An exothermic reaction takes place when fireworks burn*

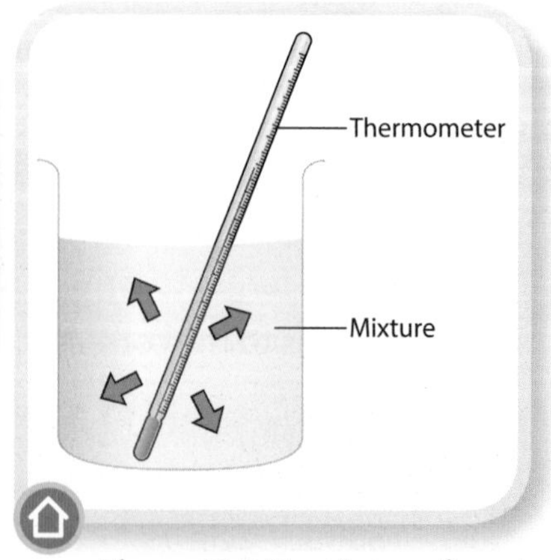

Figure 22.3 *Heat is transferred from the chemicals to the surroundings*

What is an endothermic reaction?

An endothermic reaction is where energy is absorbed by the chemicals from the surroundings in order for the reaction to take place. The reaction mixture usually shows a fall in temperature. For example, ammonium chloride dissolving in water is an endothermic reaction.

Figure 22.4 *Solid barium hydroxide and solid ammonium chloride in a flask on a damp piece of wood. As the two chemicals mix, an endothermic reaction occurs causing a drop in temperature which freezes the water between the conical flask and the block of wood*

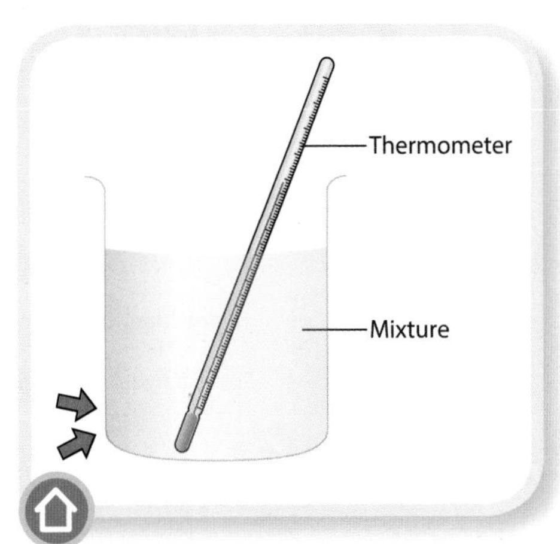

Figure 22.5 *Heat is absorbed by the chemicals from the surroundings*

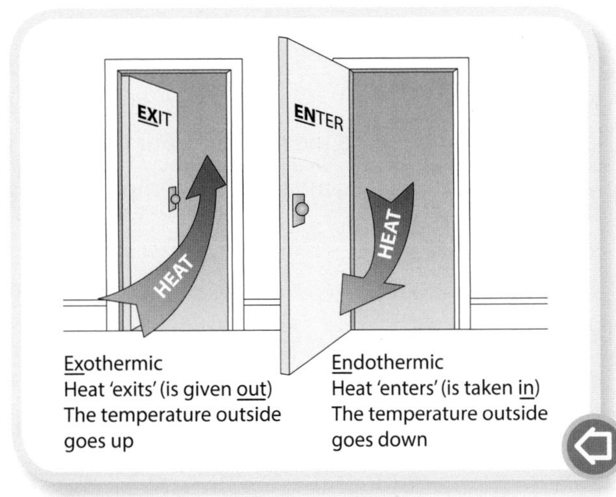

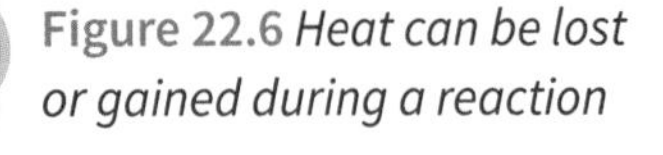

Figure 22.6 *Heat can be lost or gained during a reaction*

22.1 Distinguish between an exothermic reaction and an endothermic reaction.

Activity 22.1

Question

What energy changes are occurring in chemical reactions?

Equipment needed

- 4 polystyrene cups (labelled A–D)
- Graduated cylinder
- Thermometer
- Sodium hydroxide (0.1 M)
- Hydrochloric acid (0.1 M)
- Sodium hydrogen carbonate solution
- Citric acid
- Ammonium nitrate
- Water
- Dilute sulfuric acid (0.1 M)
- Magnesium ribbon

CHEMICAL WORLD

Conducting the activity

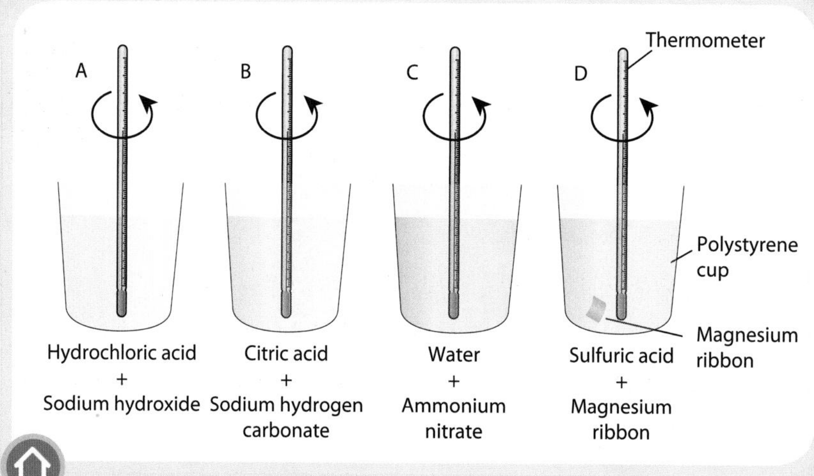

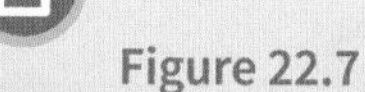

Figure 22.7

Reaction A

1. Measure 10 cm^3 of sodium hydroxide solution using a graduated cylinder and place it in polystyrene cup A.
2. Measure the temperature with the thermometer and record the result in your table (see below).
3. Add 10 cm^3 of hydrochloric acid. Stir with the thermometer; measure the temperature and record the result in your table.

Reaction B

4. Add 10 cm^3 of sodium hydrogen carbonate solution to polystyrene cup B. Measure the temperature and record the results in your table.
5. Add 10 cm^3 of citric acid. Stir with the thermometer; measure the temperature and record the result in your table.

Reaction C

6. Place 10 cm^3 of water in polystyrene cup C. Measure the temperature and record the result in your table.
7. Add 1 g of ammonium nitrate. Stir with the thermometer; measure the temperature and record the result in your table.

Reaction D

8. Add 10 cm^3 of sulfuric acid to polystyrene cup D. Measure the temperature and record the result in your table.
9. Add 1 g of magnesium ribbon. Stir with the thermometer; measure the temperature and record the result in your table.

Reaction	Initial temperature (°C)	Final temperature (°C)	Endothermic or exothermic
A			
B			
C			
D			

22.2 Did you find more exothermic or endothermic reactions?

22.3 The first reaction is between an acid and a base. What do you call this type of reaction?

22.4 What gas is produced in reaction B?

22.5 What gas is produced in reaction D?

22.6 Why did you use polystyrene cups and not glass beakers?

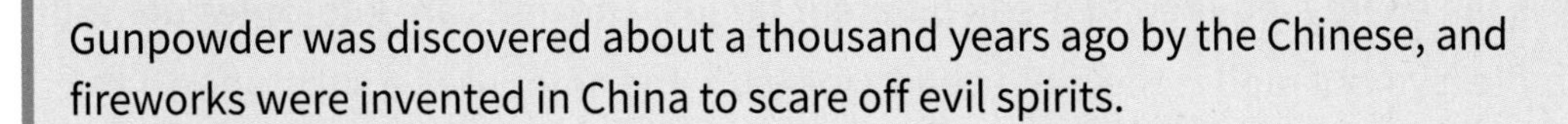

Did you know?

Gunpowder was discovered about a thousand years ago by the Chinese, and fireworks were invented in China to scare off evil spirits.

22.7 What is the clue in the terms 'exothermic' and 'endothermic' that indicates that they are linked to heat energy?

How are bonds made and broken?

During a chemical reaction, old bonds are broken (reactants) and new bonds are formed (products). Breaking bonds requires energy, so it is an endothermic process; but energy is released when new bonds are formed, so bond formation is an exothermic process.

Bond breaking – endothermic

Figures 22.8, 22.9 and 22.10 illustrate endothermic reactions.

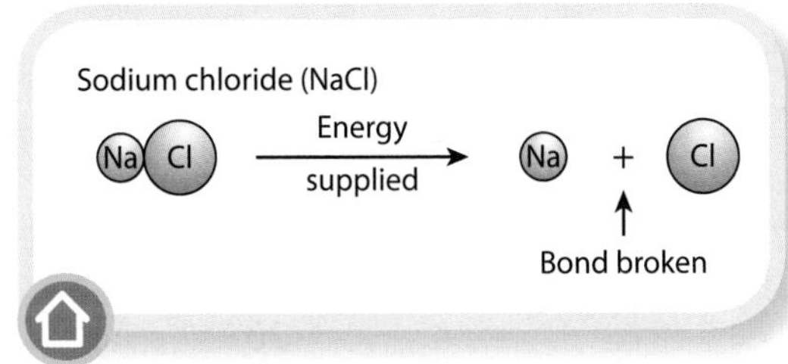

Figure 22.8 *The bonds in sodium chloride are broken*

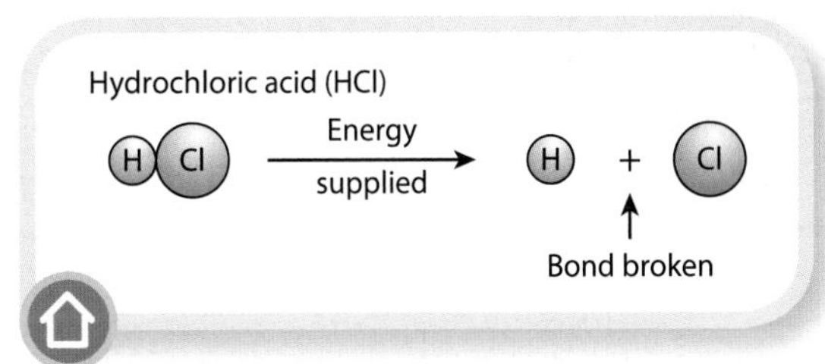

Figure 22.9 *The bonds in hydrochloric acid are broken*

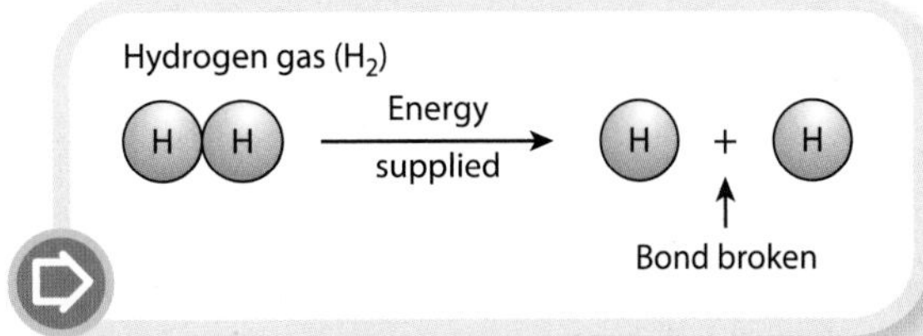

Figure 22.10 *The bonds in the hydrogen molecule are broken*

Bond formation – exothermic

Figure 22.11 and Figure 22.12 illustrate exothermic reactions.

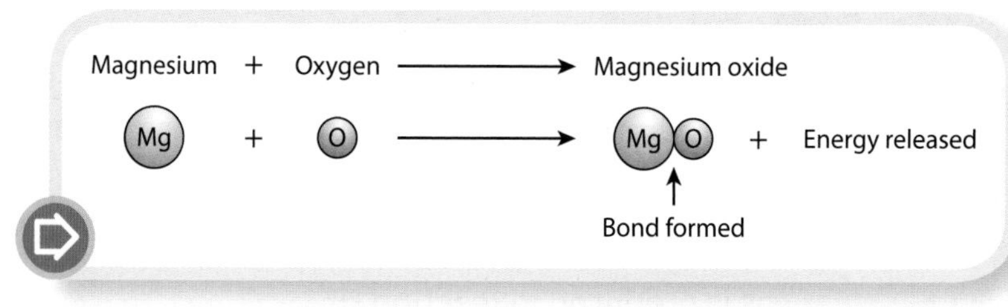

Figure 22.11 *The magnesium and oxygen atoms bond to form magnesium oxide and energy is released*

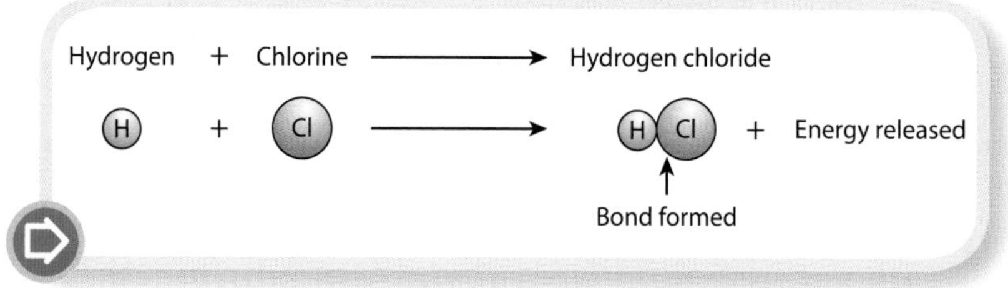

Figure 22.12 *The hydrogen and chlorine atoms bond to form hydrogen chloride and energy is released*

What is bond energy?

Bond energy is the energy required to break different bonds. The units are **kilojoules per mol** (**KJ/mol**). A mole (symbol **mol**) is the unit used to measure the amount of a substance. Table 22.1 shows the amount of energy required to break different bonds.

Table 22.1 **The amount of energy required to break different bonds**

Bond	Bond energy (KJ/mol)
H—H	436
Cl—Cl	242
H—Cl	431
C—H	413
C—C	347
C—O	335

22.8 Sodium reacts with water in an exothermic reaction. What does this suggest about the energy needed to break the bonds compared with the energy released when they are made?

22.9 Look at this table and answer the questions below.

Reaction	Starting temperature (°C)	Final temperature (°C)
A + B	19	27
C + D	20	25
E + F	19	17

(a) For each reaction say whether it is exothermic or endothermic. How can you tell?

(b) The volume of solution was the same in each reaction. Which had the largest energy change?

What are energy profile diagrams?

We can show the energy transfer in reactions on energy profile diagrams. The diagrams show us the energy stored in the reactants compared to the energy stored in the products, so they tell us if a reaction is exothermic or endothermic.

Activation energy, shown in energy profile diagrams, is the minimum energy that colliding particles must have for a reaction to occur.

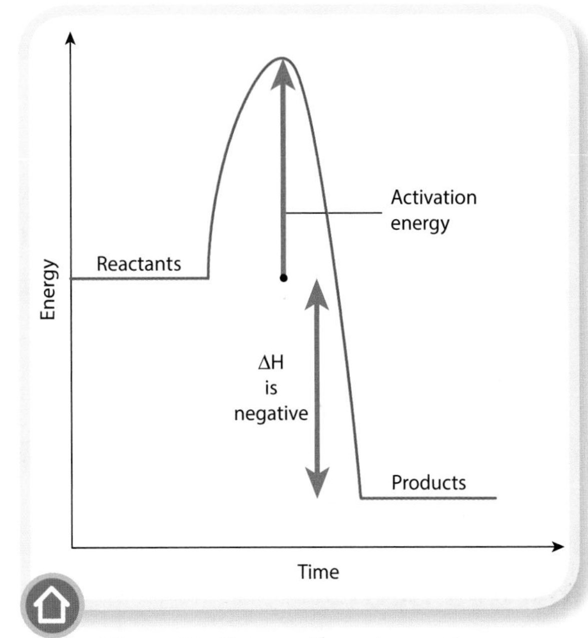

Figure 22.13 An exothermic reaction energy profile diagram

Energy profile diagram for an exothermic reaction

Figure 22.13 shows an exothermic reaction because the products are at a lower energy than the reactants so energy has been given out. The difference in height (ΔH) is the symbol for the 'change in energy' in a reaction. ΔH is negative for an exothermic reaction. The difference in energy is given out as heat, so the temperature of the surroundings rises.

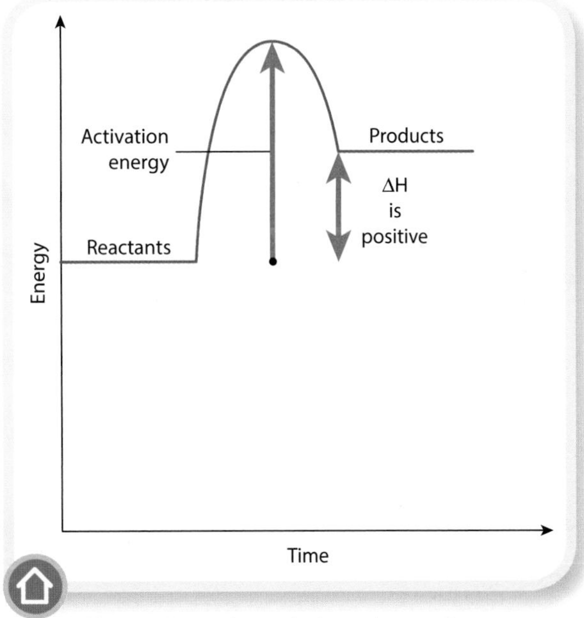

Figure 22.14 An endothermic reaction energy profile diagram

Energy profile diagram for an endothermic reaction

In Figure 22.14 the products are at a higher energy than the reactants so this shows an endothermic reaction. Extra energy was required to form the products, which was taken in from the surroundings; therefore, the temperature of the surroundings falls. ΔH (change in energy) is positive for endothermic reactions.

22.10 Draw energy profile diagrams for exothermic and endothermic reactions.

22.11 When hydrochloric acid and sodium hydroxide react in a beaker, the temperature rises:

$$HCl + NaOH \longrightarrow NaCl + H_2O \qquad \Delta H = -58\ KJ/mol$$

(a) Is this reaction exothermic or endothermic?

(b) Draw an energy profile diagram to show this change.

CHEMICAL WORLD

22.12 In your group, decide whether each of the following reactions are endothermic or exothermic and give reasons for your decision.

Reaction A Two chemicals are mixed together in a fume cupboard at room temperature. The reaction starts to fizz and a gas is produced, and the mixture soon catches fire with a purple flame.

Reaction B When two chemicals are combined in a beaker the outside of the beaker frosts up and it gets stuck to the desk due to the formation of ice.

Reaction C When a piece of sodium is added to chlorine gas in a flask a bright light is seen and a drop of water on the flask soon vaporises.

Reaction D Butane from the Bunsen burner is ignited to heat some water.

Is energy transfer always heat?

Energy transfer *is not* always heat. Photosynthesis, which is a reaction that takes place in plants, requires light energy (not heat energy). Photosynthesis is a process in which light energy from the Sun is converted to chemical energy (see chapter 10). The chemical energy is stored in the form of glucose (sugar).

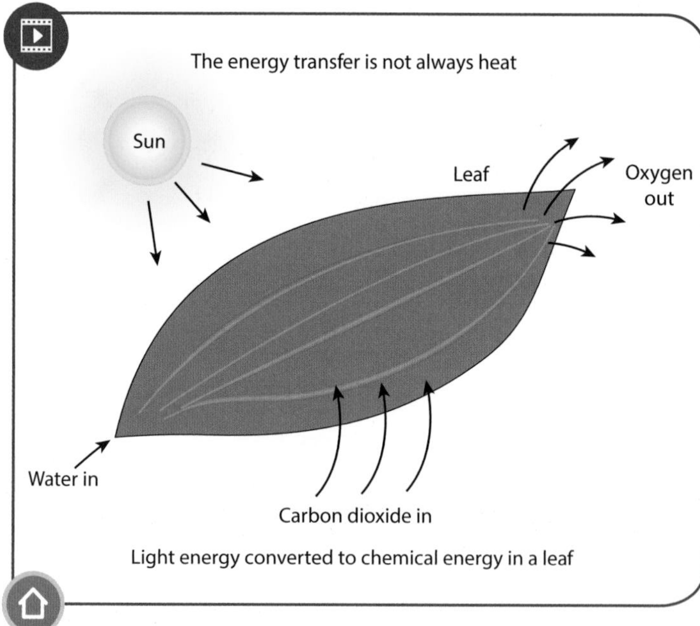

Figure 22.15 *Photosynthesis requires light energy*

22.13 What is a glow stick and how does it work?

Light sticks or glow sticks are used by campers, divers and trick-or-treaters. They are plastic tubes containing different chemicals. When a chemical reaction takes place it releases energy in the form of light – this is called **chemiluminescence**.

Research the names of the three chemicals found in glow sticks.

Figure 22.16 *Glow sticks*

CHAPTER 23

UNIT 3

Environmental impact of materials

Learning outcomes

At the end of this chapter you will be able to:

- Explain the complete life cycle of a material
- Describe sustainable development
- Research and present information on new materials and sources of energy.

Keywords

environment, extraction, transportation, manufacturing, raw materials, life cycle, sustainable development, electrolysis, distribution, recycling, composting, molten

What impact do materials have on the environment?

Materials can have an impact on the environment in a range of different ways and at different times during their life cycle. For example, extraction, transportation, manufacturing and uses of raw materials consume energy and produce carbon dioxide (which contributes to global warming). However, when a material is recycled or re-used the wider impact on the environment is much reduced.

Figure 23.1 *The greenhouse effect*

What is sustainable development?

Sustainable development is where demands on the environment by people can be met without harming the environment for future generations. The rules are simple:

- Leave the world better than you found it.
- Take no more than you need.
- Try not to harm the environment and make amends if you do.

23.1 Human activities have damaged the environment and this cannot easily be repaired. List five resources that you think will eventually run out.

What is the life cycle of a material?

Have you ever considered where the goods we use come from or where they go when you finish with them? Every product we use goes through a life cycle, and each stage of the life cycle has environmental impacts.

One impact is carbon dioxide. Any stage in a product's life that releases carbon dioxide into the atmosphere affects the environment and the total effect is calculated as the **carbon footprint** of the product (see chapter 41).

However, if we reduce the use of materials at each stage then this will lessen the impact on the environment.

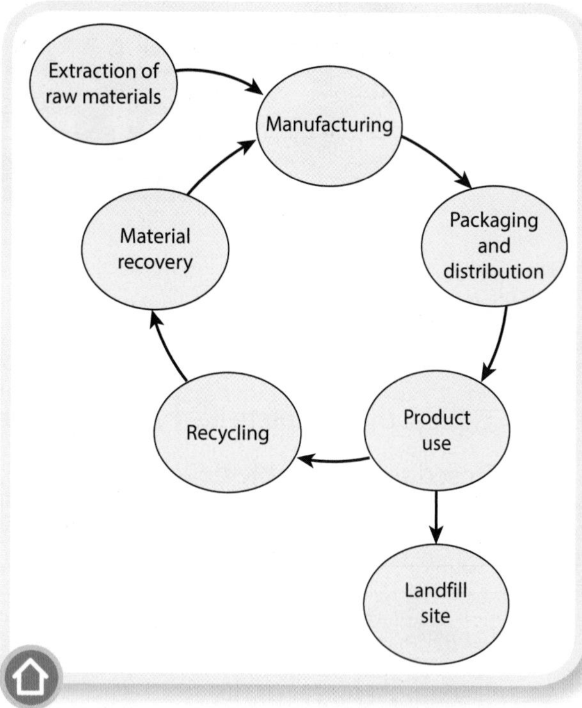

Figure 23.2 *The life cycle of a product*

23.2 Draw a diagram showing the stages in the life cycle of an aluminium (fizzy drink) can.

What are the stages in the life cycle of a material?

We will look at the individual stages in the life cycle of a material. They are:

- Stage 1 – extraction of the raw material
- Stage 2 – manufacturing
- Stage 3 – distribution
- Stage 4 – usage
- Stage 5 – disposal.

Stage 1 – extraction of the raw material

All products are made from materials found in or on Earth. Large machinery is used to dig rock out of large areas called quarries. The extraction of a raw material is the start of a product's **carbon footprint**.

Figure 23.3 *Gold*

A few unreactive metals, such as gold, are found as the metal itself rather than as a compound, but most metals are extracted from rocks (ores) using a chemical reaction. A metal **ore** is a naturally occurring solid material from which a metal can be extracted.

There are two ways of extracting metal from its ores:

- Chemical reduction using carbon
- Electrolysis.

We will look at both of these here. The position of the metal in the **reactivity series** determines which method is used. The reactivity series is shown in Table 23.1. It allows us to see how metals react. The most reactive metal is placed at the top of the table and the least reactive metal is placed at the bottom. The most reactive metals have a greater tendency to lose electrons and form ions.

Table 23.1 **The reactivity series**

Extraction	Element	Reactivity
Extraction using electrolysis	Potassium Sodium Calcium Magnesium Aluminium Carbon	Most
Extraction by reduction with carbon	Zinc Iron Tin Copper	↓ Least
Do not need extraction	Silver Gold	Found as the element

Reduction with carbon

A more reactive metal can displace a less reactive metal from its compound. This is what happens when carbon is reacted with the compounds formed by the metals below it in the reactivity series. For example:

copper oxide + carbon $\xrightarrow{\text{Heat}}$ carbon dioxide + copper

The copper oxide loses oxygen – it is **reduced**. The carbon gains oxygen – it is **oxidised**.

On an industrial scale this would happen in a blast furnace (at + 500°C). Coke, a pure sample of carbon, is used to extract copper or iron.

Figure 23.4 *Extracting iron from ore*

Activity 23.1

Question

Can you extract copper metal from copper oxide using carbon?

Equipment needed

Tripod	Bunsen burner
Metal tongs	Copper oxide
Crucible	Charcoal powder (carbon)
Pipe clay triangle	

Copper oxide covering charcoal powder
Lid
Crucible
Pipe clay triangle
Tripod
Bunsen burner

Figure 23.5 *Extracting copper metal from copper oxide using carbon*

Safety

- Make sure that the crucible has cooled down completely before you remove it from the tripod.

Conducting the activity

1. Transfer one spatula of copper oxide into a crucible.
2. Carefully add one spatula of charcoal powder on top of the copper oxide, completely covering it and without mixing it.
3. Strongly heat the crucible for five minutes with a Bunsen burner.
4. Allow the crucible to cool and then look closely at where the powders meet in the crucible.
5. Note any reaction that occurs and the colour of any metal produced.

Electrolysis – extracting with electricity

Metals that are higher than carbon in the reactivity series have to be extracted using electrolysis. When electric current is passed through a **molten** sample of a metal compound the compound will split up and release the metal.

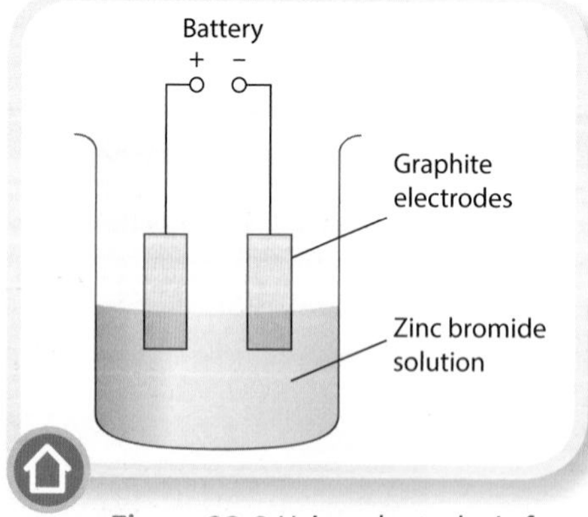

Figure 23.6 *Using electrolysis for extraction*

Did you know?

The covering of the Statue of Liberty in the United States is made of copper – about 80 tonnes of it in fact. Its surface reacts with gases in the air to form copper carbonate – which is why it is green.

Figure 23.7 *The Statue of Liberty has a covering of copper*

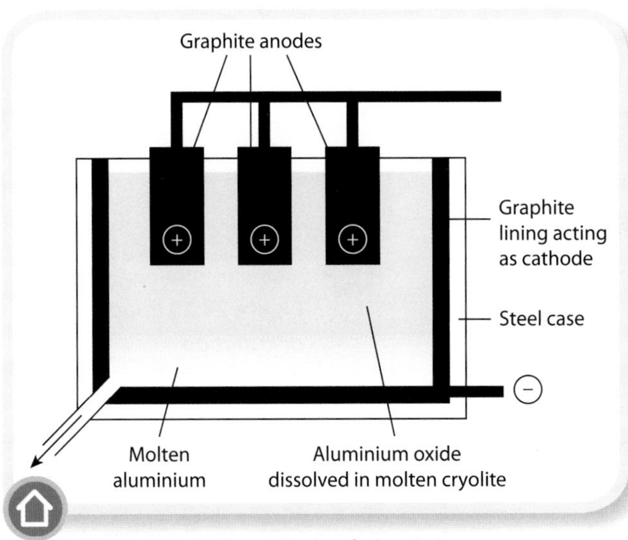

Figure 23.8 *Electrolysis of aluminium*

Electrolysis of aluminium

Aluminium oxide has a high melting point and to reduce costs it is dissolved in molten cryolite, an aluminium compound with a lower melting point. Even so, a high temperature is used and for safety the whole system is encased in steel.

There are several electrodes. These are conductors used to make electrical contact with some part of the circuit – the negative electrode is called a cathode, and the positive electrode is called the anode. They are made of graphite (a form of carbon) and are used to pass current through the molten aluminium oxide and cryolite.

Aluminium is separated out of the compound and falls to the bottom of the vessel from where it can be removed.

Impact of extraction on the environment

Extraction has some negative impacts on the environment. They are:

- The removal of rock from quarries causes scarring of the landscape.
- Transporting the ore to the factory results in carbon dioxide emissions from the fuel, as well as costing a lot of money.
- Electrolysis requires huge amounts of energy from electricity. As well as being very expensive, generating this electricity by burning fossil fuels produces greenhouse gases such as carbon dioxide, which contributes to the greenhouse effect and global warming.

23.3 Name two ways that metals can be extracted from its ores.

23.4 What is electrolysis?

23.5 The supply of copper-rich ores is limited. Scientists have discovered two ways for extracting copper from low-grade ores. These are called **bio-leaching** and **photomining**. Research what these terms mean and how copper is extracted by the two methods.

Stage 2 – manufacturing

Most production requires a great deal of energy, which results in greenhouse gas emissions. When companies plan new products they must consider their impact on the environment. When a product is made from recycled materials, less energy is needed to transport and process raw materials, which reduces manufacturing costs and makes it a more attractive option.

Figure 23.9 *A paper mill*

CHEMICAL WORLD

Stage 3 – distribution

Each stage of the life cycle of a material requires some form of transportation. The finished product needs to be transported from factories to warehouses then to stores and eventually your home. This transportation requires the use of fossil fuels for energy, which can contribute to global warming and climate change.

Figure 23.10 *Road freight distribution*

Everyone can do their small bit to help: it is important that we buy locally grown foods as this reduces energy use compared to buying food shipped or flown into the country. We can also plan ahead to reduce the number of times we drive to the shops as this will also reduce the use of fuel, which in turn will benefit the environment.

Stage 4 – usage

Using a product may require energy, so we need to purchase items that are energy efficient. Some consumable products such as detergents work well at low temperatures; this saves energy as there is no need to heat the water.

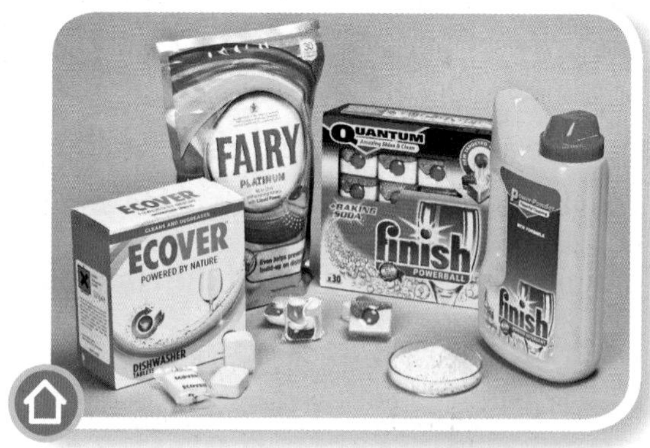

Figure 23.11 *Biological dishwasher detergents contain enzymes that help to break down particles of food on dishes in warm water instead of hot water, so the dishwasher is more energy efficient*

23.6 Biological washing powders contain enzymes that help to remove stains from clothes. These work best at moderate temperatures (40°C) and not at high temperatures. Find out the names of the enzymes found in the biological washing powders and why they work best at lower temperatures.

Stage 5 – disposal

How we manage our goods at the end of their current life, when they are no longer used, can make a big difference to our environmental footprint.

Landfill

When organic materials go to landfill (often called dumps) they decompose and form methane gas. This is a greenhouse gas that contributes towards global warming. Many landfill sites collect this gas and use it to generate electricity, or as a fuel for equipment such as a boiler.

Figure 23.12 *A landfill waste disposal site*

Reduce, reuse, recycle – the three Rs

Most of our rubbish is sent to the dump or landfill sites. This is not good for our environment. We can all contribute to improving this by following the three Rs – **reduce, reuse, recycle**.

Reduce

We need to reduce the amount of waste going to our landfill sites and we can do this in a number of ways, such as:

- Buy products that do not have a lot of packaging, or look for products that are packed in materials that can be recycled.
- Reduce waste of paper by reading newspapers and magazines online instead of buying the paper version.
- Carpool with friends, or walk or cycle to school as cars use a lot of energy and create a lot of pollution.

Reuse

This is where you do not throw things away but try and find ways to use them again. For example:

- Bring your own plastic bags to the shop instead of buying new ones.
- Bring your lunch to school in a lunch box or maybe plastic ice-cream containers.
- Use shoe boxes, coffee jars and other types of containers for storing things.
- Adapt clothes to make a different garment.
- Purchase second-hand items, such as books, clothes and furniture, which not only is good for the environment, but saves money as well.

Recycle

If a product ends up in a landfill site its atoms are no longer useful, but if it is recycled the atoms can remain useful for longer. Recycled items are put through a process that makes it possible to create new products out of the materials from the old one.

It is very important to recycle for the following reasons:

- **Less extraction of resources** Recycling reduces the need to extract raw materials. There is only a certain amount of materials – for example, metals and oil in Earth – so recycling helps to conserve these resources.
- **Less energy** Mining, extracting and manufacturing need lots of energy. For example, aluminium is extracted by electrolysis, which is very expensive as it requires a lot of energy. Recycling an aluminium can uses only 5% of the energy required to manufacture one from raw materials.
- **Less money** Energy is not cheap, so recycling saves money too.
- **Less rubbish** Recycling results in less rubbish in landfill sites, which means less environmental damage and less methane gas.

Figure 23.13 *Recycling saves resources and money*

23.7 List the five stages in the life cycle of a material.

23.8 Explain the 3Rs.

23.9 Think of ways in which you can apply the 3Rs. In other words, what would you reduce, reuse and recycle in your own home?

Table 23.2 **Recycling symbols you will see on products**

Recycling symbol	What it means
	Glass recycling – the glass can be recycled through a bottle bank. There will be no change in the material; used glass is collected and melted and used in the manufacture of glass bottles and glassware. There is a 14% saving in energy compared to the production from raw materials
	Green dot – some of the purchase price goes towards recycling of the product's packaging. *Note:* It does not mean the packaging is recyclable
alu	**Aluminium recycling**
	Steel recycling
	Mobius loop – the packaging can be recycled
NAPM RECYCLED 100% APPROVED	**Paper recycling** – the product *uses* a percentage of recycled materials
FSC	**Wood recycling** – the product contains wood from sustainably managed forests
	Tidyman – 'Do not litter'

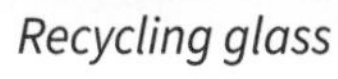
Recycling glass

Plastic recycling (the numbers show the grade of plastic and is used for sorting when recycling)

Figure 23.14 *Recycling saves resources and money*

Portfolio 166

Activity 23.2

Question

How can we make old paper into new, reusable paper?

Equipment needed

Newspaper	Tripod	Cornflour
2 beakers	Funnel	Decoration (dried flowers or glitter)
Glass rod	Filter paper	Aluminium foil
Bunsen burner	Water	Rolling pin

Safety

- The water will be boiling, so take care not to touch or tip the beaker.

Conducting the activity

1. Cut up four sheets of newspaper into small pieces and place them in a beaker.
2. Cover the paper with water and stir to a paste.
3. Place the beaker on the tripod and heat with a Bunsen burner until it starts to boil. Allow it to cool.

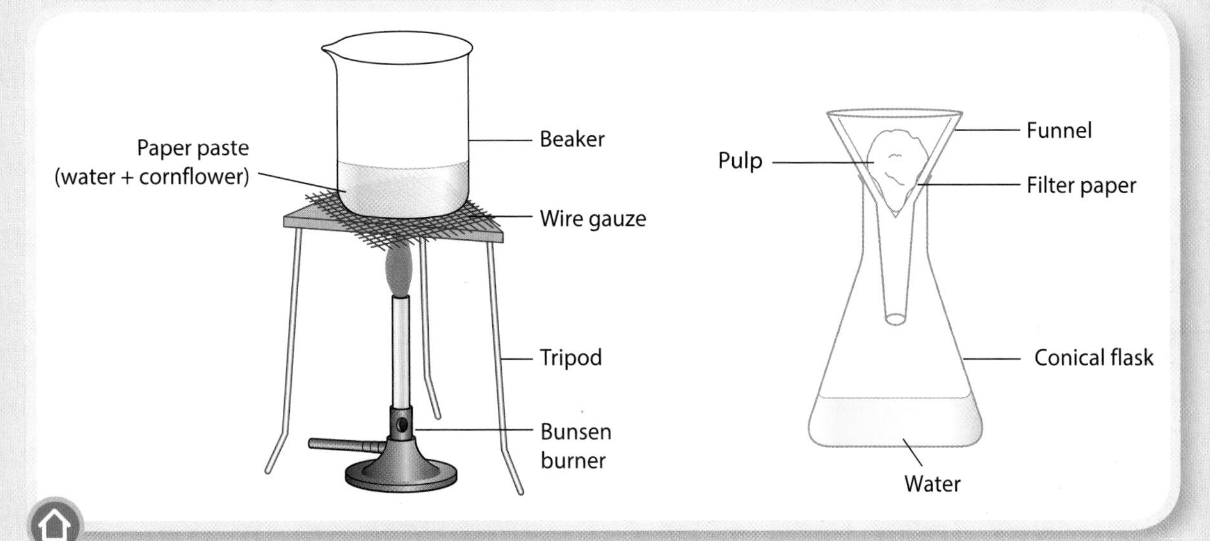

Figure 23.15 *Recycling of newspaper*

4. Add cornflour (5 g) and a little more water and stir the mixture (to form a pulp).
5. Heat the mixture again to boiling over the Bunsen burner.
6. Filter the pulp by filtration.
7. Spoon the pulp onto a sheet of aluminium foil and spread it out with a rolling pin. Add decorations if you wish.
8. Place a sheet of foil on top to cover and leave in a warm place to dry overnight.

You now have recycled paper.

CHEMICAL WORLD

What is composting?

Figure 23.16 *A composting recycling centre*

Composting keeps organic waste such as food scraps from landfill sites. When organic materials decompose in landfill they produce methane gas, which is a greenhouse gas twenty times more potent than carbon dioxide. But during composting the material decomposes in the presence of oxygen and so methane is not produced. You can have a compost bin in your own garden where you can dispose of certain types of food and plant materials. Over time these materials will break down through a natural process called decomposition (micro-organisms) resulting in compost, which supplies nutrients to the soil in your garden.

Energy recovery

This is the conversion of non-recyclable waste material into heat, electricity or fuel through combustion or landfill gas recovery.

Figure 23.17 *Generating electricity from a landfill site*

Figure 23.18 *A gas recovery well on a landfill site*

23.10 Does recycling have any impact on the environment? Explain your answer.

23.11 Find out what new products are produced from the recycled rubber of car tyres.

Figure 23.19 *A tyre recycling facility*

23.12 Divide into groups and create a promotional poster to encourage people to change their habits and save energy. Make the following points:

- Reduce, reuse and recycle waste at home
- Buy local goods
- Reduce energy use in the home.

23.13 Look up your city or county website and find out about recycling in your local area. Write a paragraph on what your local authority does to help recycling.

What are sustainable products?

Sustainable products are products that protect public health and the environment over their whole life cycle, from extraction of raw material until disposal. All of the materials from which they are made can be returned to the earth after composting, or they can be repeatedly recycled as raw materials. For example, some clothing companies have collections of products that are either recyclable or biodegradable. This includes T-shirts and sneakers that are fully compostable.

Cradle-to-cradle design

Cradle-to-cradle design shows how to design products that will not damage the environment. These are non-toxic, non-harmful materials that have no negative effects on the environment. They can be used over and over again instead of becoming waste in a landfill site (cradle-to-grave materials). In the cradle-to-cradle model all materials fall into one of two groups:

- **Technical materials** These are synthetic materials that will cause no harm to the environment because they can be used over and over again. For example, the metals aluminium and steel can be recycled repeatedly; this explains why drink cans are a truly renewable material because they can be recycled and the can retains the same characteristics as the original material. Polystyrene (plastic) is another example of a completely recyclable material which after collection is sorted from other plastics for recycling. It can be used many times without loss of quality and stay in a continuous cycle.
- **Biological** This is organic material that once used can be disposed of in any natural environment. It provides food for bacteria and microbiological life and it decomposes into soil causing no harm to the environment. Examples of these materials include: clay, cork, bamboo, hay and straw. Buildings and structures can be made from these materials.

Figure 23.20 *These plastic bottles will be recycled and used to make swimming pools*

Figure 23.21 *This house has been insulated with straw*

Figure 23.22 *Organic cotton fabric is a cradle-to-cradle material because it can be disposed of in any natural environment and decomposes into soil*

23.14 Explain how sustainable products are good for the environment.

23.15 What is meant by cradle-to-cradle design?

Packaging

In our modern society we have become more dependent on packaging as households have become increasingly busy and convenience has become an important factor in purchases. While packaging does improve safety and convenience and reduces theft, it also has a number of disadvantages.

It can be expensive and can cause damage to our environment because most of the waste produced by packaging ends up in landfill. For example, some meat products are packed in polyethylene, which is a petroleum-based plastic and therefore cannot be recycled.

Sustainable packaging is very important so that we can reduce the waste in our landfill sites. Some examples are:

- Many food processors have reduced their packaging by offering reusable and refillable containers. For example, branded coffee where the refill packaging is manufactured from cardboard or paper which can be recycled and composted.
- Supermarkets are buying products from suppliers that use recyclable material in their packaging. Polyethylene terephthalate (PET) is 100% recyclable, making it ideal for packaging. It is light and easily crushed and so is easy to transport to the recycling plant.
- The biodegradable plastic polylactide (PLA) is processed from the starch of plants such as corn or sugarcane and is ideal for shopping bags because it is a compostable material.

The key factors when choosing a sustainable material is that it is from easily grown materials, is recyclable and is locally available.

23.16 A company called Ecolean has developed ecologically sustainable food packaging that is not a fossil fuel-based material, but is made with the natural material chalk (limestone).

Research answers to the following questions:

(a) Where is limestone formed in nature?

(b) What is the name of this new packaging material?

(c) Explain why this new material has less impact on our environment.

(d) What products is this new sustainable packaging material used for?

(e) How many countries does Ecolean sell its products in?

UNIT 4

PHYSICAL WORLD

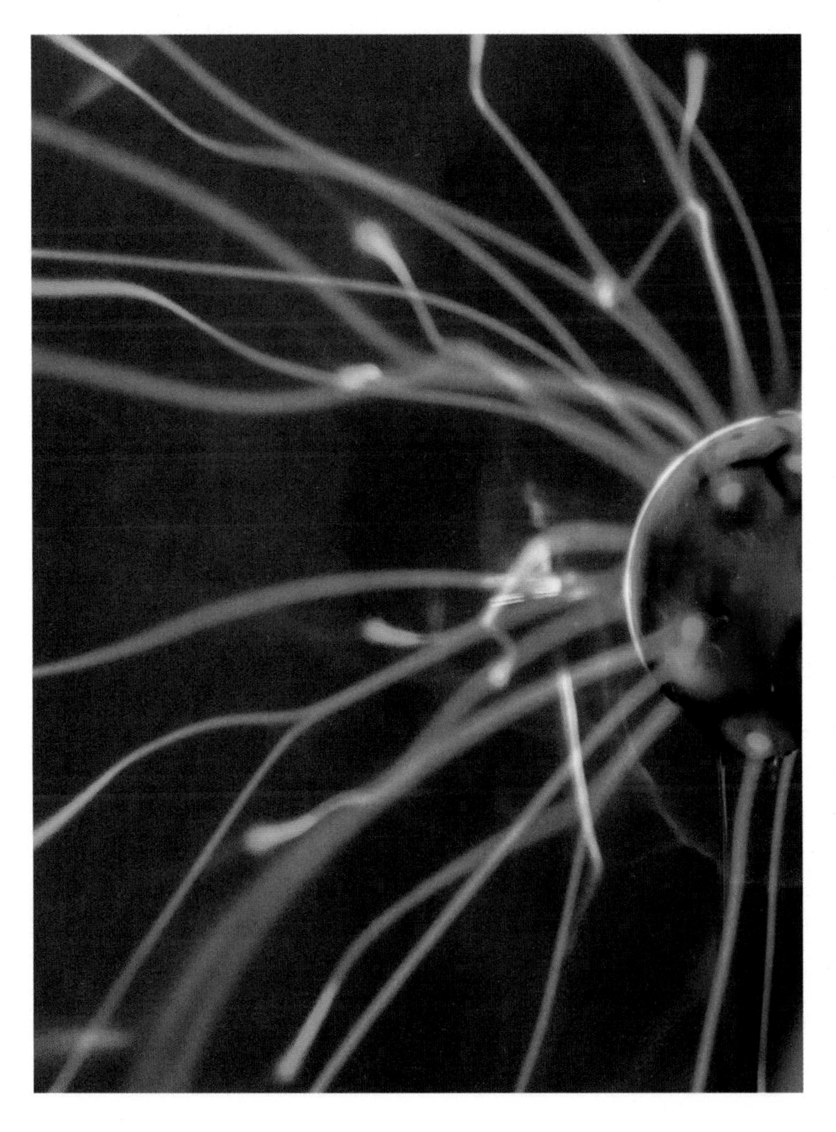

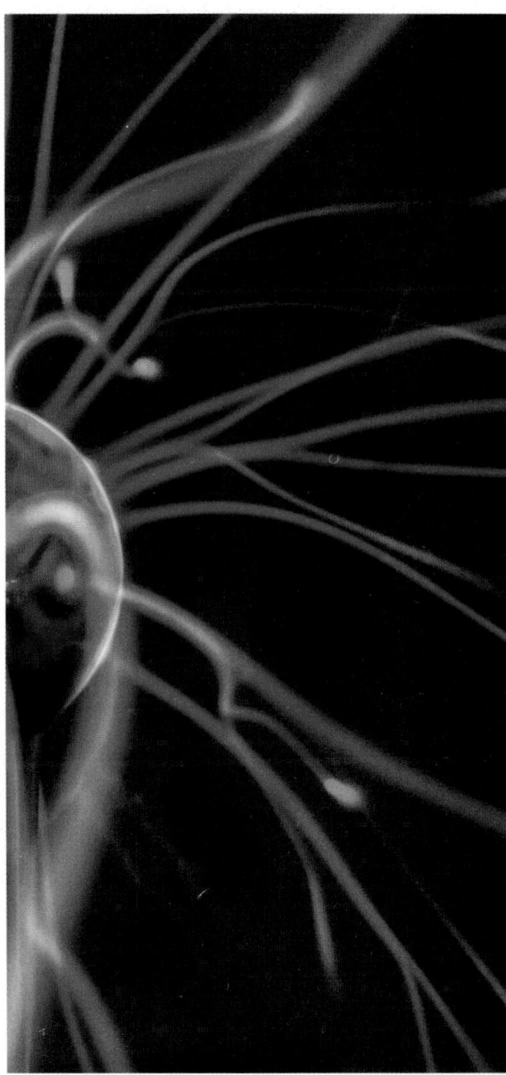

UNIT 4

Making accurate measurements

Learning outcomes

At the end of this chapter you will be able to:

- Make measurements of length, mass, time, area and volume
- Work with units relevant to your measurements
- List examples of where measurements are made in everyday life.

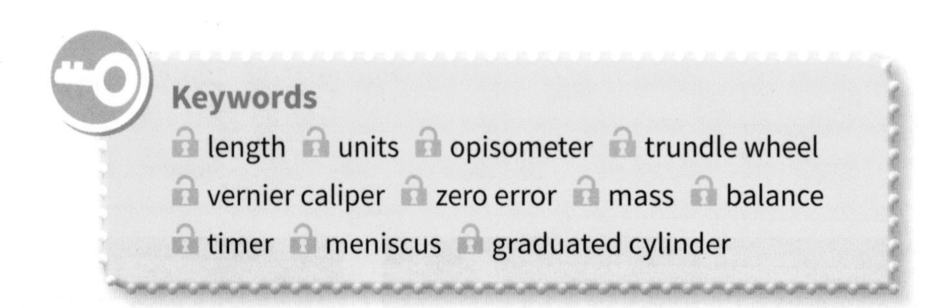

Keywords

length, units, opisometer, trundle wheel, vernier caliper, zero error, mass, balance, timer, meniscus, graduated cylinder

Measurement

24.1 Spend five minutes making a list of where measurements are used in everyday life. Then one member of your group will read out your list to the rest of the class.

There are certain skills you need in order to be good at physics. Measuring is most definitely one of these skills. Some of the quantities you will measure are:

- Length
- Mass
- Time
- Area
- Volume.

It is very important that your measurements are **accurate** and that your measurements are given in **units** that can be understood internationally.

Why is it important to be accurate?

Some measurements need to be more accurate than others. Some measurements have to be spot-on accurate. For example, if you have to replace a broken window pane the new piece of glass has to be the right size. If it is too small it will fall out, and if it is too big it will not fit into the window. To get the right size you have to make accurate measurements.

All sorts of things have to be measured with accuracy. A DVD has to be the right size to fit into the drive. Pieces of Lego are manufactured to a high degree of accuracy so they fit together. Accuracy is extremely important with things like medicines; for example, the amount of insulin taken by a person with diabetes must be just right to maintain a correct blood sugar level.

24.2 List three everyday things that are manufactured using accurate measurements.

Why do we need units?

It would be unhelpful to be asked to fetch 'a long piece of wood'. Nor would it be helpful to be asked to fetch 'a piece of wood of length 3'. Three what? Centimetres? Metres? Can you guess how long 3 metres is?

We use a system of **SI** units. The name comes from the French *Système Internationale d'Unités* – the International System of Units. By using an international system of units, scientists, engineers, manufacturers, office workers and everybody else from every country in the world can understand each other.

24.3 **The problem:** You are shopping online and you see a shirt that you really like. The shirt is made in France, which uses a different measurement for clothes sizes.

The task: Go online to find a chart that will allow you to compare clothes sizes in Ireland and France. Print or copy this out. Now make a list of five items of your own clothes and give their Irish sizes and their French sizes.

Instruments for measurement

In this chapter we will look at different instruments that are used to make measurements.

24.4 We mentioned that we may need to measure quantities like length, mass, time, area and volume. Research answers to the following questions for each quantity:

(a) What are the instruments that could be used for the measurements?

(b) Can some of the quantities be measured with different instruments?

(c) How old are these measuring instruments? Were they in use one hundred years ago?

(d) Would these instruments be expensive to buy?

(e) How many of these instruments do you already have in your school laboratory?

Present your findings in the form of a reference sheet.

As you read on further compare your answers with the measuring instruments we suggest.

Measuring length

Length is measured in:

- Millimetres (mm)
- Centimetres (cm)
- Metres (m)
- Kilometres (km).

Remember:

10 mm	is the same as	1 cm
100 cm	is the same as	1 m
1000 m	is the same as	1 km

Measuring items

Case 1:

To measure the length of a copy book you would use a **ruler** or a **metre stick**. The most suitable units would be **centimetres**.

24.5 Why do you think that the metre or the millimetre would not be suitable for measuring your copy book?

Figure 24.1 *Measuring the length of a copybook with a ruler*

Note: Be careful not to confuse the end of a ruler and the zero mark on the ruler. Sometimes the zero mark is exactly at the end of the ruler, but not always. Make sure the zero mark is at one edge of the copy book and then note the position on the ruler corresponding to the other end. This gives the length of the copy book.

Did you know?

If you make the mistake of including the space between the end of the ruler and the zero mark in your measurement, you will have made a **zero error**.

Case 2:

To measure the length of a curve you would use an **opisometer**.

Start with the wheel of the opisometer at the left side. Move the wheel along the curve until you come to the end of the curve. Now place the wheel on the zero mark of a metre stick and roll the wheel along the metre stick until the wheel stops at the left side. The position on the metre stick where the wheel stops corresponds to the length of the curve.

Case 3:

Large curved lengths are often measured with a **trundle wheel**.

Case 4:

To measure the diameter of a coin you would use a **vernier caliper**.

Figure 24.2 *An opisometer*

Figure 24.3 *A trundle wheel*

Figure 24.4 *Vernier caliper*

Portfolio 172

Activity 24.1

Question

How can we measure without measuring instruments?

Equipment needed

String, about 2 metres long

Lunch box

Goal posts

Bicycle

Safety

- Take care not to get in the way of others as you move around the school.

Conducting the activity

The problem: In groups, you will need to measure some items around the school but the measuring instruments must remain in the science room. You may use a piece of string about 2 metres long, which you can then take back to the science room.

The task: Measure the following:

(a) Measure the perimeter of a lunch box.

(b) Measure the distance between the uprights of a goalpost.

(c) Measure the diameter of the handlebar of a bicycle.

(d) Compare your measurements with the other groups.

24.6 Why might the measurements of all the groups be slightly different?

Sample calculation 1

Convert 8.6 cm to millimetres.

Answer:

1 cm ⟶ 10 mm

8.6 cm ⟶ $10 \times 8.6 = 86$ mm

Sample calculation 2

Convert 67 mm to cm.

Answer:

10 mm ⟶ 1 cm

1 mm ⟶ $\frac{1}{10}$ cm

67 mm ⟶ $\frac{1 \times 67}{10} = 6.7$ cm

Sample calculation 3

Convert 7.2 km to metres.

Answer:

1 km ⟶ 1000 m

7.2 km ⟶ $1000 \times 7.2 = 7200$ m

24.7 Name three different units that can be used to measure length.

24.8 A scientist is unlikely to measure a length in inches today. Why do you think this is so?

24.9 Name two instruments that could be used to measure a curved length.

24.10 What would be the difference in the use of the two instruments you named in question 24.9?

24.11 Name the instrument used to measure the diameter of a coin.

What is mass?

The mass of an object is the amount of matter in the object.

Mass is measured in **grams** (g) or **kilograms** (kg). Smaller quantities, such as the mass of a chemical you would use in a classroom experiment, would usually be measured in grams. The kilogram is more suitable for the mass of a person or the mass of a large bag of potatoes.

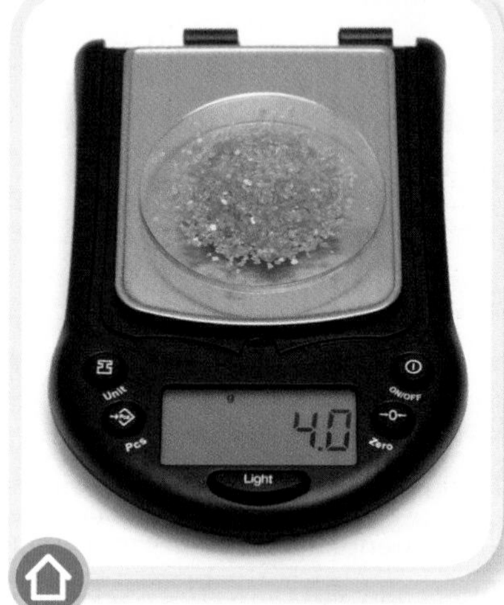

Figure 24.5 *A balance*

1 kilogram is the same as 1000 grams.

The instrument used to measure the mass of an object is called a **balance**.

Most food items that you buy in a supermarket come in packaging with the value of the mass written on it. For example, a box of breakfast cereal (not including the packaging) might have a mass of 500 g. This allows you to know exactly how much you are getting for your money.

Did you know?

In science the words 'mass' and 'weight' do not have the same meaning. Later in the book we will look at the word weight and learn its exact meaning. The problem for many people is that in everyday language we use weight and mass as if they were the same. But in science you have to be more precise with your choice of words.

PHYSICAL WORLD

24.12 Name two units that could be used to measure mass.

24.13 What unit would be most suitable to measure the mass of the quantity of a chemical in a class experiment?

Measuring time

Time can be measured in many units. Examples are: second, minute, hour, day, week.

In science we use the **second** and the symbol for the second is **s**. The instrument we would use is a stopwatch or an electronic timer.

Figure 24.6 *A stopwatch is used for measuring time*

Sample calculation 4

How many seconds are there in a week?

Answer:

There are 7 days in a week, therefore	1 week $\longrightarrow$ 7 days
There are 24 hours in a day, therefore	1 week $\longrightarrow$ $7 \times 24 = 168$ hours
There are 60 minutes in an hour, therefore	1 week $\longrightarrow$ $168 \times 60 = 10\,080$ minutes
There are 60 seconds in a minute, therefore	1 week $\longrightarrow$ $10\,080 \times 60 = 604\,800$ seconds

That is a lot of seconds!

24.14 What is your age at midday today in seconds?
(A little help! Assume that you were born at exactly midday on your birthday.)

24.15 Convert the following times to seconds:
(a) 6 minutes **(b)** 12 hours **(c)** 2 days **(d)** 4 weeks.

Measuring area

24.16 Measuring area is studied in maths classes and is something we do quite often in a science course. Working in small groups, discuss the following and then design a reference sheet to refer to in your work:

(a) What geometrical shapes do you meet most often in maths classes? (The formulae and tables booklet might help you here.)

(b) What formulae could you find to calculate the area of the various shapes from part (a)?

(c) Could you use any of these formulae to calculate the area of a leaf? Briefly explain your answer.

(d) What unit would you use for area?

(e) If you find more than one unit, give examples of where each unit would be used.

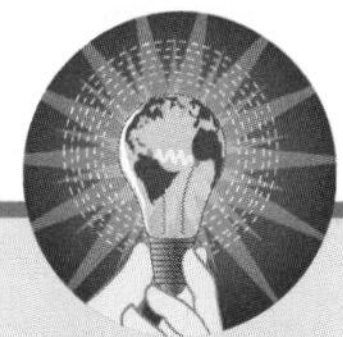

Did you know?

The price of a house or an apartment for sale depends on many factors. One of these is the total area of the floors. The scientific system for measuring floor space is the metre squared (m^2). Most countries around the world use this system.

PHYSICAL WORLD

Measuring volume

The volume of an object is the amount of space an object takes up.

The unit for volume is the **centimetre cubed** (cm^3) or the **metre cubed** (m^3).

In your maths class you will learn how to calculate the volume of regular shapes like a rectangular box. In science we will have to be able to calculate the volume of *irregular shapes* like a small stone you would find on a beach.

Measuring the volume of a regular shape

The volume of this box $= 10\text{ cm} \times 8\text{ cm} \times 5\text{ cm}$

$= 400\text{ cm}^3$

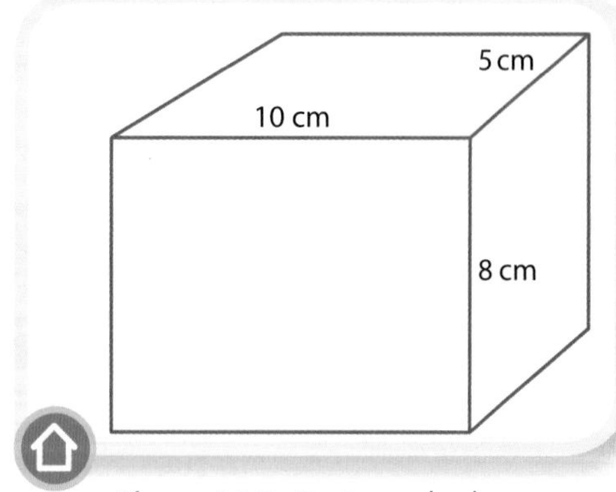

Figure 24.7 *Rectangular box*

24.17 What is the word formula for the calculation used for the volume of the box?

24.18 Could your formula work for calculating the volume of a small stone? Explain your answer.

Sample calculation 5

Calculate the volume of a rectangular box of length 1 m, width 70 cm and height 12 cm.

Answer:

volume of box = length × width × height

$= 100 \times 70 \times 12$

$= 84\,000\ \text{cm}^3$

Note: Be careful with the trick in this question. You must change the 1 m to cm. Make sure that all the units are the same.

Sample calculation 6

Calculate the volume of a cube with a side of length 15 cm.

Answer:

In a cube, length = width = height

Therefore volume $= 15 \times 15 \times 15 = 3375\ \text{cm}^3$

Measuring the volume of an irregular shape

Portfolio 173

Activity 24.2

Question

How can we measure the volume of an irregular shape?

Equipment needed

Water | Graduated cylinder
Overflow can | A stone

Safety

- Be careful not to spill water on the floor to avoid the danger of somebody slipping.

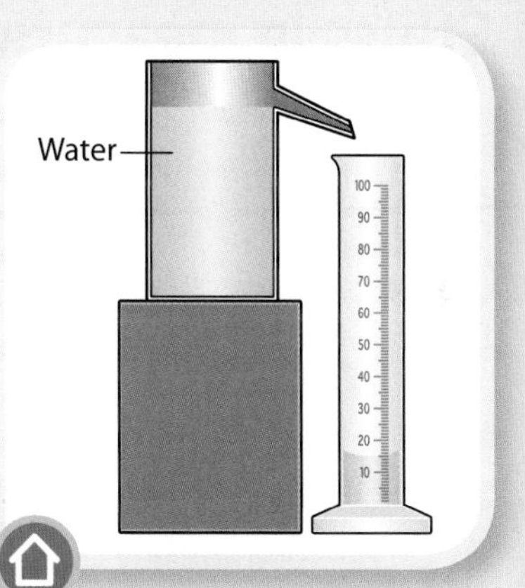

Figure 24.8 *Overflow can and graduated cylinder*

Conducting the activity

1. Pour water into the overflow can until some spills out into the graduated cylinder.
2. When the water stops spilling out you know that the level of the water is exactly at the level of the spout.
3. Carefully read the level of the water in the graduated cylinder and write down the value.
4. Place the stone into the overflow can and allow it to sink to the bottom. Take care not to splash water.
5. Carefully read the new level of the water in the graduated cylinder and write down the value.
6. Subtract the first value from the second to get the volume of the stone.

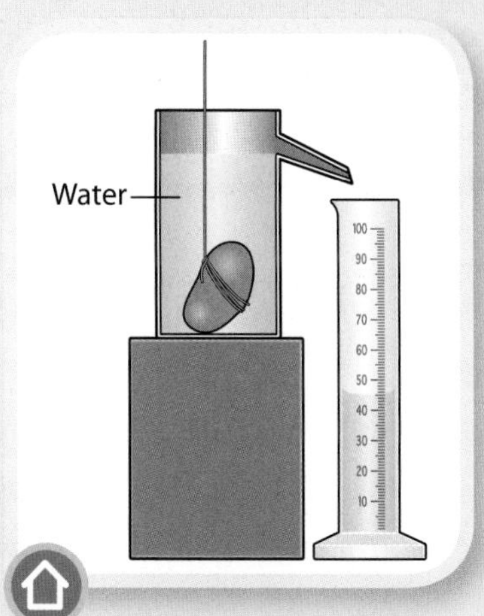

Figure 24.9 *Graduated cylinder showing meniscus*

Meniscus

The top surface of water in a graduated cylinder is curved a little, as you can see in Figure 24.9. This is called the **meniscus**.

When reading a graduated cylinder you must allow for the meniscus. Always take a reading corresponding to the *bottom* of the meniscus to get the correct water level.

24.19 Measuring the volume of a small object.
Look at Figure 24.10 and answer the questions below.

(a) What is the volume of liquid in the graduated cylinder on the left of the diagram?

(b) Take the reading of the level of the liquid in the graduated cylinder on the right of the diagram.

(c) Calculate the volume of the irregular object that was placed in the graduated cylinder.

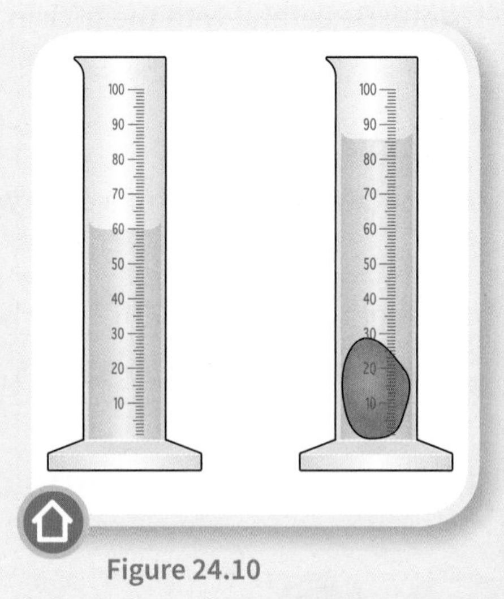

Figure 24.10

Ethics in measurement

When you buy petrol or diesel for a car the amount you pay depends on the volume of fuel you put into the car. If the pump is faulty the amount you pay for is not the amount you put into the car.

24.20 Discuss the problems that arise when a customer is overcharged for the petrol or diesel that they bought.

24.21 Discuss the problems that arise when a customer is undercharged for the petrol or diesel that they bought.

24.22 List five other examples of where faulty measuring machines could lead to problems in shops.

24.23 Research the organisation in Ireland responsible for checking that petrol pumps and weighing scales in shops etc. are working correctly. Make a note of how this organisation can be contacted if someone needed to make a complaint.

CHAPTER 25

UNIT 4

What is density and why do some things float?

Learning outcomes

At the end of this chapter you will be able to:

- Explain density
- Use the correct units when measuring density
- Calculate values of density using a mathematical formula
- Carry out activities to measure densities of solids
- Explain flotation.

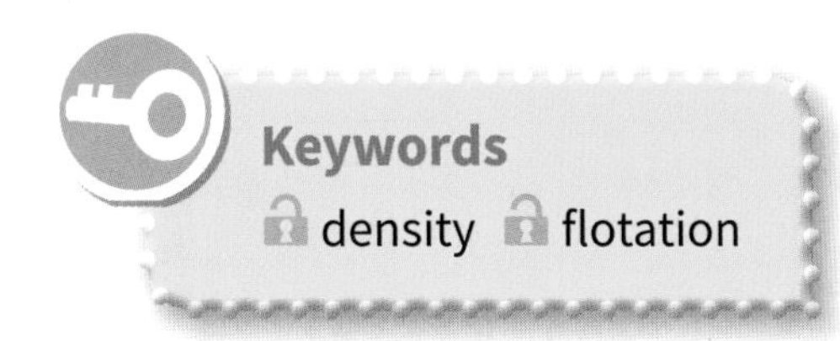

Density

When you go shopping for a new school bag you will often see several bags on display. To give the customer an idea of the size of the bag the shopkeeper might stuff the bag full of crumpled-up tissue paper. This helps you to visualise the size of bag you want. The bag looks full but feels very light when stuffed with the tissue paper. But when this bag is full of books, it is so much heavier.

Figure 25.1 *A full school bag – if there is tissue paper in it, it will be light; if there are books in it, it will be heavy*

Portfolio 178

Activity 25.1

Question

What is the relationship between mass and volume?

Equipment needed

Set of brass weights
Water
Overflow can
Graduated cylinder

Safety

- Be careful not to spill water on the floor to avoid the danger of somebody slipping.

Figure 25.2

Conducting the activity

1. Choose five different size brass weights: 25 g, 50 g, 100 g, 200 g and 500 g. Record their mass values.
2. Using the method for measuring the volume of irregular objects in activity 24.2 on page 245, you should measure and record the volume of the five weights.

25.1 Do you notice any pattern between the values of the mass and the values of the volumes?

25.2 Take each pair of values and see what happens when you: (a) add, (b) subtract, (c) multiply and (d) divide the values.

25.3 Draw a graph with the mass values on the y-axis and the volume values on the x-axis. What do you notice about your graph?

3. Repeat the activity, only this time use five small objects that are made of different materials – wood, metal, plastic, etc.

25.4 Do you notice any pattern between the mass values and the volume values of these new objects?

The paper in books is more tightly packed than the paper in the crumpled up pieces of tissue. In a bag full of books there is more paper in the same size or volume of bag. The mass of the books is greater than the mass of the tissue paper, even though the volumes are the same. We would say that the **density** of the books is greater than the density of the tissue paper.

Density of a substance tells you how much mass is packed into a particular volume.

Experience will tell you that a bag full of books will be heavier than a bag of crumpled tissue paper. A mathematical formula explains it, and can be used in other situations:

$$\text{density} = \frac{\text{mass}}{\text{volume}} \text{ (Density is the mass divided by the volume.)}$$

Units for density

There are two sets of units that can be used for density:

First,

$$\text{Since density} = \frac{\text{mass}}{\text{volume}}, \text{ units of density} = \frac{\text{units of mass}}{\text{units of volume}} = \frac{\text{gram}}{\text{cm}^3}$$

In science we write this as **gram cm^{-3}** or simply **g cm^{-3}**.

PHYSICAL WORLD

The minus sign in front of the number 3 is to remind you that the cm^3 are below the line in the formula.

Second,

$$\text{Again density} = \frac{\text{mass}}{\text{volume}}, \text{ units of density} = \frac{\text{units of mass}}{\text{units of volume}}$$
$$= \frac{\text{kilogram}}{m^3}$$

In science we write this as **kilogram m^{-3}** or simply **kg m^{-3}**.

Helpful hint: Look at the following triangle:

$$\frac{\text{mass}}{\text{density} \times \text{volume}} \quad \textit{or} \quad \frac{M}{D \times V}$$

In a calculation you may be asked to find:

- The value of density
- The value of mass
- The value of volume.

Place your finger over the quantity you are measuring in the triangle above and the instruction for your calculation is right in front of you. This is what you get:

- To calculate the value of density: $\text{density} = \frac{\text{mass}}{\text{volume}}$
- To calculate the value of mass: $\text{mass} = \text{density} \times \text{volume}$
- To calculate the value of volume: $\text{volume} = \frac{\text{mass}}{\text{density}}$

Sample calculation 1

Brian noted that 100 cm^3 of a liquid had a mass of 80 g. Calculate the density of this liquid.

Answer:

$$\text{Density} = \frac{\text{mass}}{\text{volume}} = \frac{80}{100}$$
$$= 0.8 \text{ g cm}^{-3}$$

Sample calculation 2

The rectangular block in Figure 25.3 has a length of 5 m, a width of 3 m and a height of 2 m. The mass of the block is 21 000 kg. Calculate the density of the block.

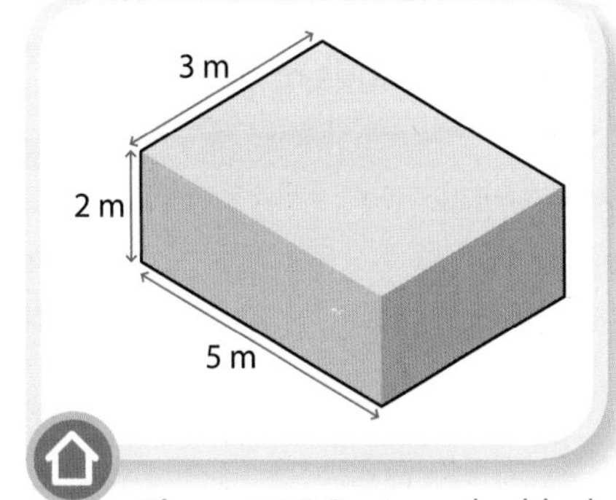

Figure 25.3 *Rectangular block*

Answer:

First you have to calculate the volume of the block:

$\text{Volume} = \text{length} \times \text{width} \times \text{height}$

$\text{Volume} = 5 \times 3 \times 2$

$\text{Volume} = 30 \text{ m}^3$

continued

Then use your answer in the formula:

$$\text{Density} = \frac{\text{mass}}{\text{volume}} = \frac{21\,000}{30} = 700 \text{ kg m}^{-3}$$

Sample calculation 3

A substance has a density of 19 g cm^{-3}. Calculate the mass of 8 cm^3 of this substance.

Answer:

Mass = density × volume

Mass = 19 × 8

Mass = 152 g

Sample calculation 4

The density of a stone is 5 g cm^{-3}. Calculate the volume of this stone if it has a mass of 17 g.

Answer:

$$\text{Volume} = \frac{\text{mass}}{\text{density}} = \frac{17}{5} = 3.4 \text{ cm}^3$$

By now you have noticed that there is a relationship between the mass and the volume of objects made of the same material, for example the brass weights.

This relationship leads to the idea of density. You have also seen some maths calculations based on the density formula.

25.5 In your group discuss the practical difficulties of measuring the density of each of the following. Then each take one of the list to tell the rest of the class what the difficulties are.

(a) A sponge
(b) An inflated balloon
(c) A sample of soil
(d) An ice cream.

Now that you have discussed the above, do you better understand the need for very clear instructions before doing an activity?

Values of density

Table 25.1 gives some values of density for a range of materials.

Table 25.1 Values of density

Material	Density (kg m^{-3})	Density (g cm^{-3})
Polystyrene	20	0.02
Cork	200	0.2
Paraffin oil	800	0.8
Ice	900	0.9
Water	1 000	1
Aluminium	2 700	2.7
Mercury	13 600	13.6
Gold	19 300	19.3
Osmium	22 600	22.6

Be careful with the units for density. The table shows how the numerical value of density depends on the units you choose. For water the density is 1 if you use g cm^{-3} and the density is 1000 if you use kg m^{-3}.

Did you know?

Different numbers can have the same value depending on the units used. For example, a person's height of 5 feet and 5 inches is the same as 165 cm.

The **density of water** is exactly 1 g cm^{-3}. This is not a coincidence. This value was used many years ago when scientists were deciding on an exact meaning for the kilogram.

Did you know?

Water is at its most dense at a temperature of 4° Celsius. If you heat water above this temperature it will become less dense. If you cool water below this temperature it will also become less dense.

25.6 What is the most dense material and what is the least dense material to be found on Earth?

25.7 Name a material in space that might be more dense than a material you will find on Earth.

25.8 Why is a bag full of books heavier than a bag stuffed with tissue paper?

25.9 What is the mathematical way to explain the meaning of density?

25.10 What are the two sets of units that can be used to measure density?

25.11 Write down the value of the density of water in the two different units for density.

25.12 An object has a mass of 48 g and a volume of 6 cm^3. Calculate the density of this object.

25.13 A rectangular block has a length of 8 cm, a width of 5 cm and a height of 3 cm. It has a mass of 1440 g. Find:

(a) The volume of the block

(b) The density of the block.

25.14 A liquid has a density of 1.2 g cm^{-3} and the volume of this liquid is 20 cm^3. Calculate the mass of this liquid.

25.15 Calculate the volume of an object if it has a mass of 96 g and a density of 12 g cm^{-3}.

25.16 To measure the density of a rectangular block:

(a) What four measurements do you need to make?

(b) How do you calculate the volume of the rectangular block using these measurements?

(c) How do you calculate the density of the rectangular block using your measurements?

PHYSICAL WORLD

25.17 In an activity to measure the density of an irregular solid, Ciara noted the following measurements:

- The mass of a small stone was 27 g.
- The reading of the level of water in the graduated cylinder was 10 cm^3 before the stone was placed into the overflow can.
- The reading of the level of water was 19 cm^3 after the stone was placed into the overflow can.

Answer the following:

(a) Calculate the volume of the stone. **(b)** Calculate the density of the stone.

PHYSICAL WORLD

Flotation

We observe many examples of floating objects in our everyday lives. Boats float in the sea, twigs float in rivers, and we know that icebergs are huge floating blocks of ice.

Why do some objects float and other objects sink? The answer to this question lies in knowing about the density of the objects.

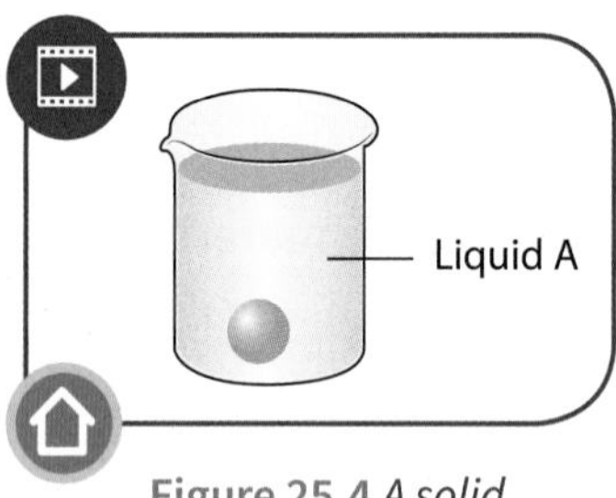

Figure 25.4 *A solid sinks in liquid A*

Figure 25.5 *A solid floats in liquid B*

Portfolio 180

Activity 25.2

Question

Why do some objects float and other objects sink?

Equipment needed

Water	Cork
Paraffin oil	Brass weight
Ice cubes	3 plastic beakers

Safety

- Be careful not to spill the water or the oil on the floor to avoid somebody slipping.

Conducting the activity

1. Half fill one beaker with water and half fill the other with paraffin oil.
2. Place the cork, the ice cube and the brass weight on the surface of the water. Which objects remain floating? Record your observations.
3. Place the cork, the ice cube and the brass weight on the surface of the oil. Which objects remain floating? Record your observations.
4. Pour some of the oil into a third beaker and then pour some water on top of the oil. Record your observations.

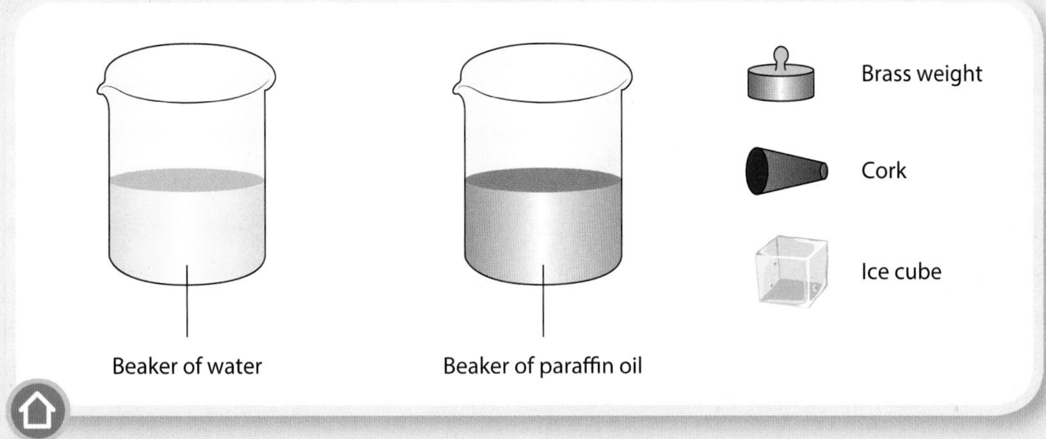

Figure 25.6

25.18 Using the information in Table 25.1 about ice, water, cork and paraffin oil, when will an object float and when will an object sink?

25.19 Brass is not included in Table 25.1. Based on your activity, what can you say about the density of brass?

25.20 How does the information in Table 25.1 about oil and water help to explain your observation in the last part of your activity?

Figure 25.7 shows three different liquids, each with different densities. The liquid on the top has the smallest value of density while the liquid on the bottom has the greatest value of density.

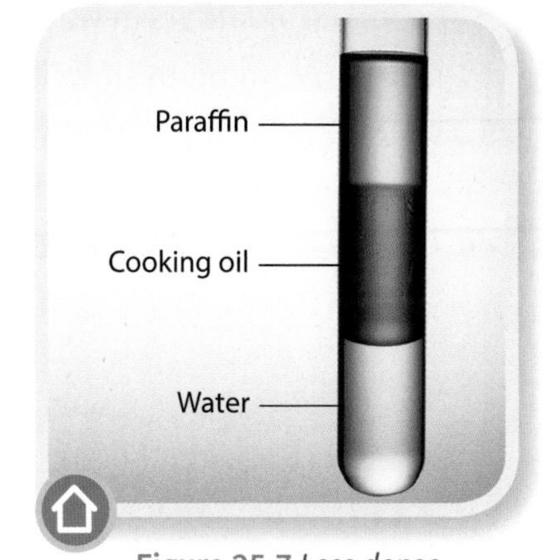

Figure 25.7 *Less dense liquids can float on top of more dense liquids*

How can seemingly heavy objects float?

Have you ever wondered why a ship that is made of a metal is able to float in water? If the metal is more dense than the water you might expect the ship to sink. However, the ship is hollow and the inside of the ship is filled with air. The **average density** of the ship and the air in it is less than the density of the water. The ship is therefore able to float.

Figure 25.8 *A laden cargo ship can float in water*

Did you know?

The average density of the human body is 0.985 g cm^{-3}. As this is less dense than water we are able to float in water.

25.21 How might you be able to change the average density of your body?

25.22 What is the condition needed for a solid to float in a liquid?

25.23 What is the condition needed for one liquid to float on top of another liquid?

25.24 State which of the following are true and which are false:

- **(i)** Ice floats in water
- **(ii)** Ice floats in paraffin oil
- **(iii)** Cork floats in paraffin oil
- **(iv)** Water can float on top of paraffin oil
- **(v)** Mercury floats on top of water
- **(vi)** Water floats on top of mercury
- **(vii)** Gold floats in water
- **(viii)** Aluminium sinks in water

25.25 How can a ship that is made of a metal float in water when the metal is more dense than water?

Measuring speed and acceleration

Learning outcomes

At the end of this chapter you will be able to:

- Measure and calculate values of speed
- Measure and calculate values of velocity
- Measure and calculate values of acceleration.

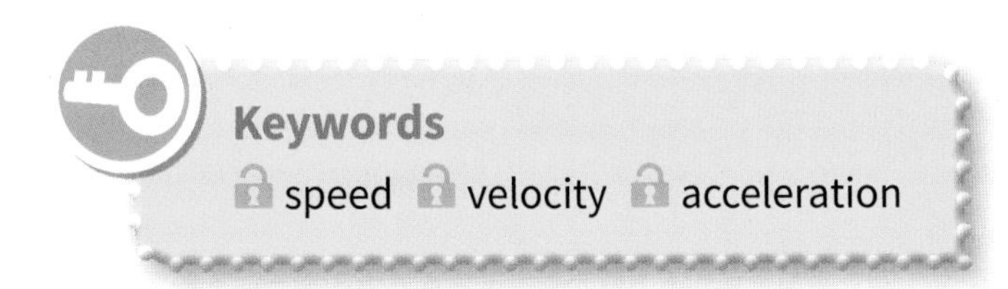

Motion

Motion, or movement, is happening around us every day. You arrived in school today as a result of motion – by bus, by car, by bicycle or by walking. There are many different methods of transportation, some being faster than others. There are also many different types of motion. For example:

- A DVD spins in a **circular** manner quite fast.
- A guitar string moves when you pluck it – we say that it **vibrates**.
- A car or train moves in **linear** motion.

Figure 26.1 *A DVD player*

Figure 26.2 *A moving train*

Activity 26.1

Question

What is the relationship between distance and time?

Equipment needed

Trundle wheel

Chalk

Stopwatch or timer

Safety

- The exercise should be carried out in a safe environment where the person walking or running cannot trip or come to harm.
- The person running or walking should wear appropriate footwear and be in good general health.

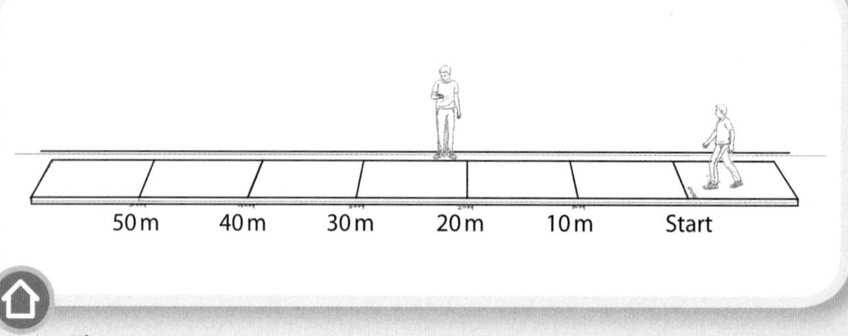

Figure 26.3

Conducting the activity

1. Outside if possible, mark a starting place with chalk.
2. Using the trundle wheel measure and mark distances of 10 m, 20 m, 30 m, 40 m and 50 m from the starting place.
3. As a student walks quickly from the starting place measure and record the time on the stopwatch when they pass each of the five marks.
4. Repeat the procedure for a student who sprints the same 50 m.

26.1 Do you notice any pattern between the values of distance and the values of time for the student walking or for the student running?

26.2 Take each pair of values and: (a) add, (b) subtract, (c) multiply and (d) divide the values. Do this separately for the walker and the runner.

26.3 Draw a graph with distance values on the y-axis and time values on the x-axis for both the runner and the walker. What do you notice about the graph?

5. Repeat the procedure for a student who changes from walking to running and running to walking as they get to each mark.

26.4 Do you notice any pattern for this student?

PHYSICAL WORLD

Objects moving in a straight line

While there are many types of motion, in this chapter we examine one type: objects moving in a straight line. We use certain words to describe motion, such as:

- Speed
- Velocity
- Acceleration.

We will look at what these mean in the following sections.

We have to be very careful with the units for motion because not everyone uses the SI units, although that is what we will use here.

Speed

In activity 26.1 you noticed a pattern between the distance travelled by a person and the time to travel this distance.

In the language of mathematics we say: $\text{speed} = \frac{\text{distance}}{\text{time}}$

Units for speed

Since $\text{speed} = \frac{\text{distance}}{\text{time}}$, units are $\frac{\text{unit of distance}}{\text{unit of time}} = \frac{\text{metre}}{\text{second}} = \frac{\text{m}}{\text{s}}$

Instead of writing $\frac{\text{m}}{\text{s}}$ we usually use **m/s** or **ms^{-1}**.

Note: When you are answering a mathematical question about speed you might be given the distance in centimetres (cm) or in kilometres (km). You must always **change the distance value to metres.**

Remember:

100 cm	is the same as	1 m
70 cm	is the same as	0.7 m
16 cm	is the same as	0.16 m
1 km	is the same as	1000 m
4 km	is the same as	4000 m
7.5 km	is the same as	7500 m

In mathematical questions in physics we always use seconds for values of time. If the value for time is in minutes or hours then **change the time value to seconds.**

Remember:

1 minute	is the same as	60 s
5 minutes	is the same as	$60 \times 5 = 300$ s
1 hour	is the same as	$60 \times 60 = 3600$ s

Did you know?

- In science we measure speed in metres per second (ms^{-1}).
- Most European countries measure the speed of cars in kilometres per hour (kph).
- In the United Kingdom the speed of cars is measured in miles per hour (mph).
- Scientist Albert Einstein said that nothing can travel faster than the speed of light.

26.5 What is the meaning of speed?

26.6 What units are used for speed?

26.7 Convert the following to metres:

(a) 17 cm (b) 9 cm (c) 4 km (d) 7.2 km

26.8 Convert the following to seconds:

(a) 6 minutes (b) 4 hours (c) 1 day

Calculating speed

Helpful hint: look at the triangle:

Where D = distance

S = speed

T = time

$$\frac{D}{S \times T}$$

Place your finger over the quantity you are measuring in the triangle above and the instruction for your calculation is right in front of you.

- To calculate speed: $\text{speed} = \frac{\text{distance}}{\text{time}}$
- To calculate time: $\text{time} = \frac{\text{distance}}{\text{speed}}$
- To calculate distance: $\text{distance} = \text{speed} \times \text{time}$

Sample calculation 1

Calculate the speed of a car that travels 400 m in a time of 10 s.

Answer:

$$\text{speed} = \frac{\text{distance}}{\text{time}} = \frac{400\text{ m}}{10\text{ s}} = 40\text{ ms}^{-1}$$

Sample calculation 2

Calculate the speed of a train that travels a distance of 1.8 km in a time of 1 minute.

Answer:

$$\text{speed} = \frac{\text{distance}}{\text{time}} = \frac{1.8\text{ km}}{1\text{ min}} = \frac{1800\text{ m}}{60\text{ s}} = 30\text{ ms}^{-1}$$

Sample calculation 3

How long does it take a car travelling at a speed of 40 ms^{-1} to travel a distance of 720 m?

Answer:

Be careful with a question that starts with the words ‘how long’ because the word ‘long’ can refer to both distance and time. In this question you are being asked about time.

$$\text{time} = \frac{\text{distance}}{\text{speed}} = \frac{720\text{ m}}{40\text{ ms}^{-1}} = 18\text{ s}$$

Sample calculation 4

Calculate the distance travelled by a person running at a speed of 5 ms^{-1} for 2 hours.

Answer:

$$\text{distance} = \text{speed} \times \text{time}$$
$$= 5 \times 2 \times 60 \times 60$$
$$= 36\,000 \text{ m}$$

26.9 Calculate the speed of a car that travels a distance of 450 m in a time of 90 s.

26.10 Calculate the speed of a car that travels a distance of 2.4 km in 2 minutes.

26.11 Calculate the time taken for a car to travel 50 m if the speed of the car is 20 ms^{-1}.

26.12 Calculate the distance travelled by a train in 50 s if it has a speed of 70 ms^{-1}.

Did you know?

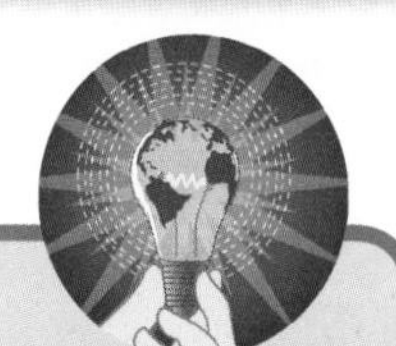

Words don't always mean the same in science as they do in general conversation. When talking normally with friends we often use words that can have more than one meaning. For example, the word 'cool' does not always refer to the fact that something is cold. But in science we need to be very precise with the meaning of words.

Velocity

The words **speed** and **velocity** have similar meanings but there is a very important difference between them.

The velocity of an object tells you the **speed** at which it is travelling *and* the **direction** in which it is travelling.

The **direction** of a moving object is usually given using points of the compass, for example: north, south, east or west.

Figure 26.4 *Skydivers – after falling for a short time skydivers reach a 'terminal velocity'*

26.13 Using the internet research the term 'terminal velocity' as it applies to:

(a) rain drops **(b)** hailstones.

Present your findings to the class as a brief PowerPoint presentation.

Unit for velocity

The **unit** we use for velocity is the same as the unit we use for speed: **m/s** or **ms^{-1}**.

Acceleration

In normal conversation many people would use the word acceleration to refer to an object that is increasing its speed, i.e. going faster. In science this is not fully correct.

Acceleration is about the rate of **change in velocity**. Remember that a change can be an increase or a decrease. Acceleration could refer to a car slowing down. In this case we would have a negative acceleration or a deceleration.

Portfolio 188

Activity 26.2

Question

How can you identify acceleration?

Equipment needed

Laptop with data logging software installed
Printer
Speed sensor
Trolley
Motion track
Protractor
Set of books

Safety

- The laptop and printer are electrical devices that may be plugged into a socket. Take care when working with electrical appliances.
- Take care not to drop heavy equipment such as the trolley and the track.

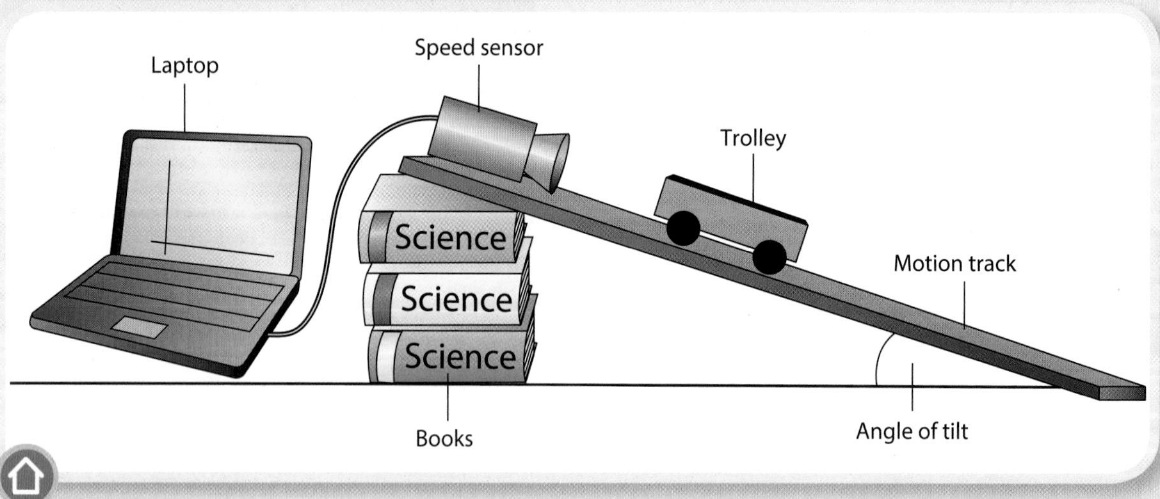

Figure 26.5

Conducting the activity

1. Arrange the motion track so it is tilted at an angle of 10° above the horizontal. Books can be used to tilt the track.
2. Release the trolley from rest at the top of the track.
3. Using the speed sensor connected to the laptop, record the speed of the trolley as it rolls down the tilted track.
4. On the laptop display a graph of speed on the y-axis and time on the x-axis.

5. Print a copy of this graph. Write on it what angle of tilt was used.
6. Repeat the above steps for different angles of tilt, 20°, 30° and 40°.

26.14 Compare the four graphs. Have they the same shape. How do they differ?

26.15 From doing the activity, which angle of tilt caused the greatest acceleration?

You will need to know this formula for acceleration:

$$\text{acceleration} = \frac{\text{final speed} - \text{first speed}}{\text{time taken for the change in speed}}$$

Unit for acceleration

The unit we use for acceleration is ms^{-1} divided by the second.

This can be written two ways: **m/s^2** or **ms^{-2}**.

Sample calculation 5

A car is moving at a speed of 4 ms^{-1}. After 12 s it is moving at a speed of 28 ms^{-1}. Calculate the acceleration of the car.

Answer:

$$\text{acceleration} = \frac{\text{final speed} - \text{first speed}}{\text{time taken for the change in speed}}$$
$$= \frac{28 - 4}{12}$$
$$= \frac{24}{12}$$
$$= 2\ ms^{-2}$$

Figure 26.6 *A moving car*

Sample calculation 6

A train starts from rest in a station and after 2 minutes it is moving at a speed of 90 ms^{-1}. Calculate the acceleration of this train.

Answer:

The words 'from rest' mean that the first speed of the train was zero.

Remember to change the minutes to seconds.

$$\text{acceleration} = \frac{\text{final speed} - \text{first speed}}{\text{time taken for the change in speed}}$$
$$= \frac{90 - 0}{2 \times 60}$$
$$= \frac{90}{120}$$
$$= 0.75\ ms^{-2}$$

PHYSICAL WORLD

Sample calculation 7

A car was travelling at a speed of 50 ms^{-1}. After a time of 14 seconds the speed of the car had changed to 8 ms^{-1}. Calculate the acceleration.

Answer:

$$\text{acceleration} = \frac{\text{final speed} - \text{first speed}}{\text{time taken for the change in speed}}$$

$$= \frac{8 - 50}{14}$$

$$= \frac{-42}{14}$$

$$= -3\ ms^{-2}$$

This could be considered as a deceleration.

26.16 When a car is first observed it has a speed of 20 ms^{-1}. After a time of 10 s it is observed that the speed is 50 ms^{-1}. Calculate the acceleration of this car.

26.17 A car starts from rest and after a time of 20 s it has a speed of 40 ms^{-1}. Calculate the acceleration of this car.

26.18 When a car is first observed it has a speed of 30 ms^{-1}. After a time of 6 s the speed has been reduced to 12 ms^{-1}. Calculate the value of the deceleration.

Ethics

26.19 Split into small groups and discuss the following. When the discussion is finished, select one person from your group to present the ideas from the discussion to the whole class.

(a) Reducing the speed limits on roads is the most effective way of avoiding accidents.

(b) Reducing speed limits on motorways near large cities reduces carbon dioxide emissions from cars.

(c) In the last thirty years the demand for cheap air travel is greater than the demand for faster air travel.

PHYSICAL WORLD

CHAPTER 27

UNIT 4

Force, work, power and pressure

Learning outcomes

At the end of this chapter you will be able to:

- Explain force
- List some examples of forces
- Explain the relationship between the force you put on a spring and the extension of the spring caused by the force
- Explain a moment of a force
- Explain levers and what they are used for
- Explain the words 'work', 'power' and 'pressure'
- Carry out simple calculations for work, power and pressure.

Keywords

force · moment of a force · lever · work · pressure · power · extension

27.1 **What is the meaning of force?** Split into groups and take five minutes to agree on the meaning of the word force.

What is force?

Remember our need to be very precise with the meaning of words. A famous scientist, Isaac Newton (1642–1727), wrote a very exact meaning of force. If we take Newton's ideas and use simple and modern English we could say:

- A force can cause a stationary object to move.
- A force can cause a moving object to move more quickly, to move more slowly or to change the direction in which it is moving.

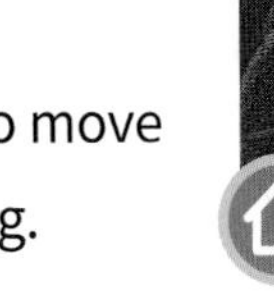

Figure 27.1 *Isaac Newton (1642–1727)*

Animated Scientist Biography

Watch an *Exploring Science* animation to find out more about Newton and his ideas.

Unit of force

The unit used to measure force is the **newton** and the symbol is **N**.

Different types of force and their effects

27.2 Use the internet to research different types of forces. Present your findings in the form of a poster.

In particular pay attention to:

(a) The force of gravity: its value on different planets, its role in the formation of the early universe.

(b) Magnetic force: its everyday uses and some possible uses in the area of medicine.

(c) Electric force: clothes sticking together in a tumble dryer, and lightning.

(d) Force of friction: the benefits of friction and friction as a nuisance.

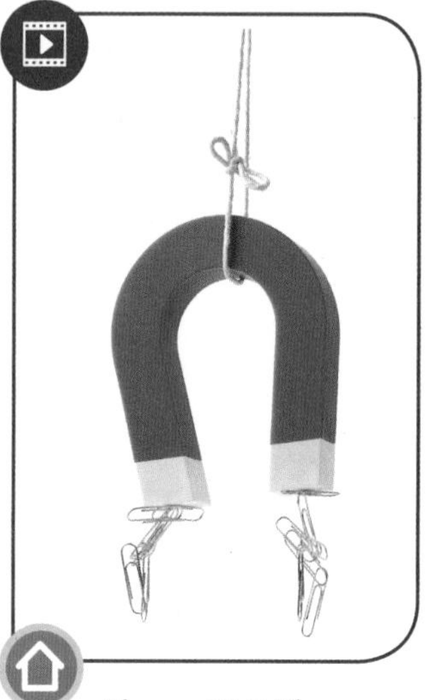

Figure 27.2 *The magnetic force attracts the iron paper clips*

Figure 27.3 *There is friction between a car's tyres and the road – this is what stops the car from skidding and helps the car to stop when brakes are applied*

Did you know?

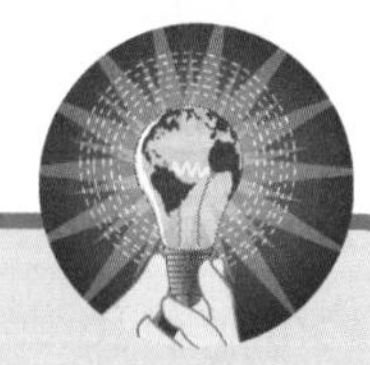

The force of gravity always attracts objects towards Earth while magnetic force can attract or repel.

27.3 What are three things that a force can do?
27.4 What is the unit of force?
27.5 What are four different types of force?
27.6 Give a practical use of each of the four different forces that you named in question 27.5.
27.7 What causes friction between two surfaces?
27.8 How could you reduce the friction between two surfaces?
27.9 List three examples of where friction is a useful force in everyday life.
27.10 List three examples of where friction is a nuisance in everyday life.
27.11 Lubricants are used to reduce friction. Give three examples of the use of lubricants.

Weight and mass

In the physical world the words weight and mass have very different meanings. These are summarised in Table 27.1.

Table 27.1 The differences between weight and mass

Weight	Mass
The weight of an object is the force pulling an object towards the centre of the earth. Weight is a force	The mass of an object is the amount of matter in it
Measured in the newton	Measured in the gram or the kilogram
Has a direction, i.e. a force that acts towards Earth	Does not have a direction
The weight of an object can change. Weight gets smaller as you rise upwards from ground level	The mass of an object remains constant

Converting mass to weight

Portfolio 192

Activity 27.1

Question

How can we see the relationship between weight and mass?

Equipment needed

Balance to measure mass

Set of five different brass weights where the weights are given in newtons

Graph paper

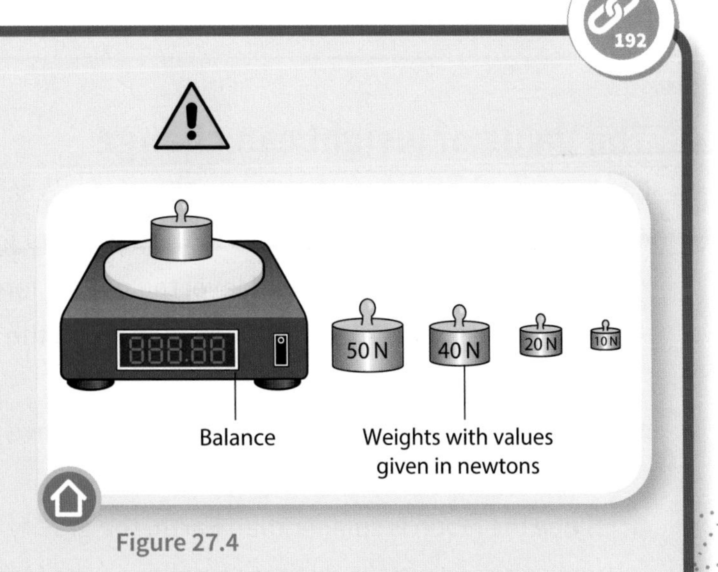

Figure 27.4

PHYSICAL WORLD

PHYSICAL WORLD

Safety

- Take care not to drop the weights on the floor as they could cause injury or result in someone tripping.

Conducting the activity

1. Write down the weights given in newtons of the five different brass weights.
2. For each one find the mass and record the mass value beside the weight value.

27.12 What pattern do you notice between the two sets of values?

27.13 Draw a graph with the weight values on the y-axis and the mass values on the x-axis. What is the shape of your graph?

27.14 Did you measure the mass in grams or in kilograms? Did it make any difference to the relationship between weight and mass?

There is a very simple formula to convert mass to weight:

$$\text{weight (in newtons)} = \text{mass (in kilograms)} \times 10$$

Sample calculation 1

What is the weight of an object of mass 6.5 kg?

Answer:

$$\text{weight} = \text{mass} \times 10$$
$$\text{weight} = 6.5 \times 10$$
$$\text{weight} = 65 \text{ N}$$

Sample calculation 2

Calculate the weight of an object of mass 200 g.

Answer:

Remember to change the unit of mass to the kilogram.

$$200 \text{ g} = 0.2 \text{ kg}$$
$$\text{weight} = \text{mass} \times 10$$
$$\text{weight} = 0.2 \times 10$$
$$\text{weight} = 2 \text{ N}$$

The value of weight can change

Earth pulls objects towards it. This pulling force is called weight. The size of the pulling force depends on how near the object is to the surface of Earth at sea level:

- As objects rise above ground level the pulling force of Earth decreases. The weight of the object decreases. The weight of an object on the top of Mount Everest is smaller than the weight at sea level.
- The International Space Station is 400 km above the surface of Earth. Objects would have a smaller weight at this height.
- Since the Moon is smaller than Earth, the gravity force is smaller on the Moon. An object would have a weight six times smaller on the Moon compared to Earth.

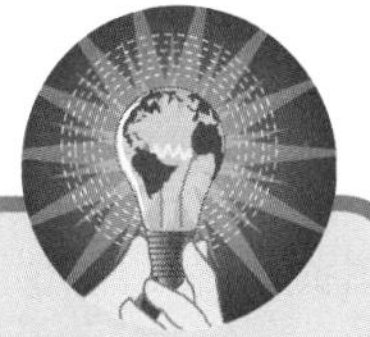

Did you know?

In pictures of astronauts in the International Space Station you will see them floating around. You might think that they have no weight at all. However, there is a gravity force at 400 km above Earth.

The International Space Station moves in such a way that it creates a situation of zero gravity. Carry on to do Leaving Certificate physics and you will find out why!

Figure 27.5 *Astronaut floating inside the international Space Station*

PHYSICAL WORLD

27.15 Explain the difference between mass and weight.

27.16 What is the unit for weight?

27.17 What is the unit for mass?

27.18 Convert the following mass values to weight:

(a) 4.5 kg (b) 900 g (c) 70 g

27.19 Convert the following to mass values:

(a) 270 N (b) 16 N

27.20 A block has a weight of 12 N. Explain how the value of this weight could change even though the mass would remain the same.

27.21 Explain why the force of gravity is smaller on the Moon than on Earth.

Portfolio 194

Activity 27.2

Question

What is the relationship between the extension of a spring and the applied force?

Equipment needed

Spring

Light holder for weights

Weights measured in newtons

Metre stick

Safety

- Take care handling the weights so that you don't drop them.

Conducting the activity

1. Hang a spring from a clamp connected to a retort stand as shown in Figure 27.6.
2. Connect a light holder for weights to the end of the spring. The holder should have a pointer on one side.

3. Arrange a metre stick so that the pointer is directly opposite the zero on the metre stick.
4. Place a known weight on the holder.
5. Note and record both the value of the weight and the extension of the spring.

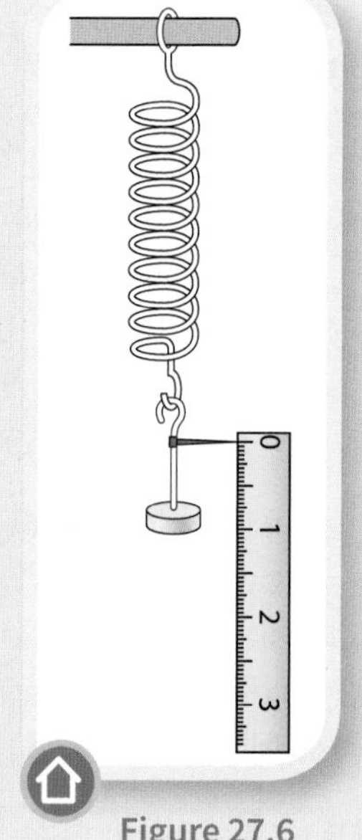

Figure 27.6

Measure and note how far the pointer moved along the metre stick. This is the value of the extension. For example, when the first weight was added to the holder the pointer might move to the 4 cm mark: then the extension is 4 cm.

6. Place another weight on the holder with the first.
7. Note and record the value of the two weights and the extension of the spring.
8. Continue this procedure for several weights. Each time note and record the total weight and the extension.

The pattern and relationship

Draw a graph to illustrate your result:

- Using the data you recorded, plot a graph with weight on the x-axis. Remember that weight is a force and is measured in newtons.
- The values of extension are plotted on the y-axis. Extension is measured in centimetres.
- Examine the plotted points on the graph paper. You will notice that they form a **straight line passing through the origin.**

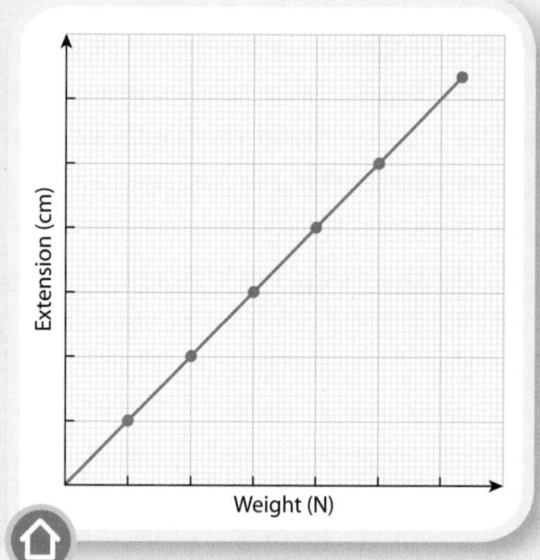

Figure 27.7 *Extension plotted against weight*

Because the points gave a straight line through the origin it can be concluded that:

The extension of an elastic body (a spring) is directly proportional to the force causing the extension.

27.22 Find out what connection the scientist Robert Hooke (1635–1703) has to activity 27.2.

Sample calculation 3

David performed an experiment to investigate the relationship between the extension of a spring and the force (weight) that caused the extension. He recorded the following data:

Force (N)	3	6	9	12	15	18
Extension (cm)	2	4	6	8	10	10.2

Plot a graph on graph paper with force (weight) on the x-axis and extension on the y-axis. From the graph:

(a) Calculate the extension that a force of 4 N would cause.

(b) Calculate the force needed to cause an extension of 7 cm.

Answer:

Graph:

(a) Go to 4 N on the x-axis. Draw a line vertically upwards from 4 N to the graph. Now move across horizontally to the y-axis. The extension value is approximately 2.6 cm.

(b) Go to 7 cm on the y-axis. Draw a line horizontally across to the graph. Now draw a line vertically down to the x-axis. The force value is approximately 10.5 N.

In this sample calculation the graph is not straight at the top. The spring has been stretched too far. This is because the spring has gone beyond its **elastic limit**.

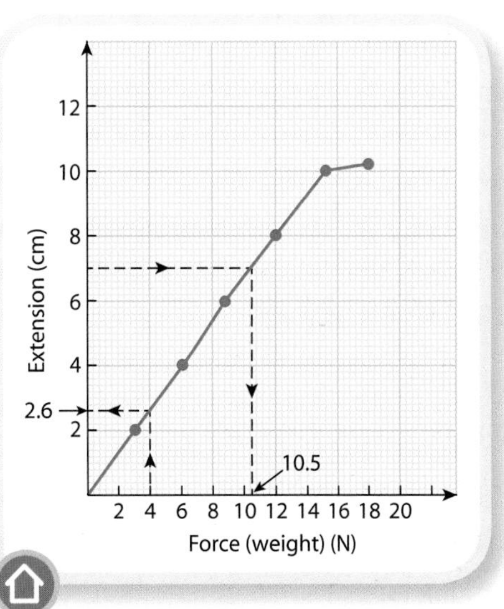

Figure 27.8 *Extension plotted against force*

27.23 Erin performed an experiment to investigate the relationship between the extension of a spring and the force that caused the extension. She recorded the following data:

Force (N)	2	4	6	8	10	12
Extension (cm)	1.5	3	4.5	6	7.5	9

Plot a graph on graph paper with force on the x-axis and extension on the y-axis. From the graph:

(a) Calculate the extension that a force of 7 N would cause.

(b) Calculate the force needed to cause an extension of 4 cm.

What is the moment of a force?

Think of the last time you saw a footballer take a free kick. This is a good example of a force causing an object to move. The force was supplied by the footballer and the ball moved.

However, a good footballer can also make the ball spin as it moves through the air. Sometimes when a force is applied to an object the object will move in a circular manner. In Figure 27.10 a force is applied to a child's windmill. Force will make the plastic windmill spin around in a circular manner.

Figure 27.9 *Kicking a football may cause the ball to move forward and to spin*

Figure 27.10 *The blades on a child's windmill spin round*

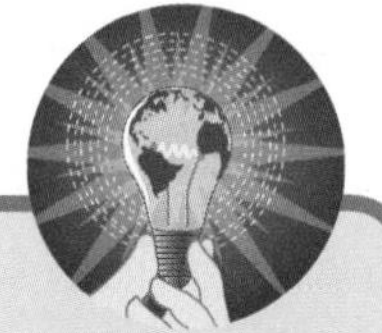

Did you know?

The moment of a force tells us how much spin or circular motion a force can cause.

PHYSICAL WORLD

If the force caused the blades to spin around several times, we would say that the force had a large **turning effect**. The turning effect is the spinning of the blades of the windmill. In scientific language we would say that the force had a **large moment**, so moment of a force simply refers to a force causing something to spin.

Activity 27.3

Question

How can we demonstrate the moment of a force?

Equipment needed

An open classroom or cupboard door

Masking tape or some other removable marker

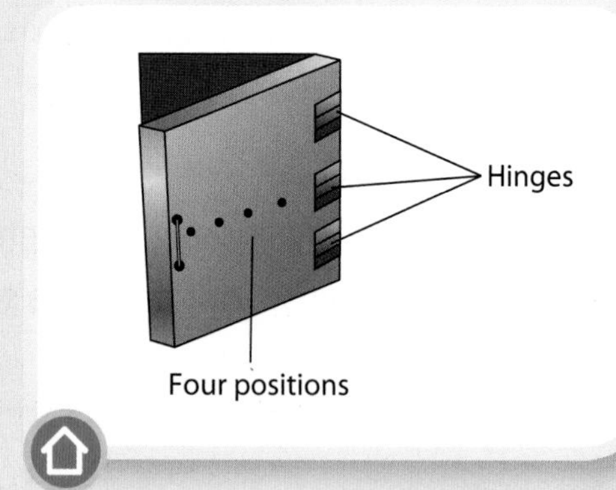

Figure 27.11

Safety

- As you may be standing around the classroom pay attention to your teacher's instructions to avoid bumping into somebody or tripping over school bags.
- Avoid an excessive force when pushing the door with your finger.
- Keep fingers away from the frame of the door in case the door slams shut causing injury to you or others.

Conducting the activity

1. Using masking tape, mark positions 20 cm, 40 cm, 60 cm and 80 cm away from the hinge on the door.
2. With the door open push it at the 20 cm position using your finger. You are trying to close the door.
3. Repeat this step using the same finger at the other three positions you marked.
4. Record in words what force you think you needed to use to close the door.

27.24 Explain the difference in the force needed to close the door in each of the four cases?

27.25 Outline the relationship between the force needed and the distance from the hinge?

27.26 Where on a door do you normally find the handle? Explain why.

27.27 Why did you use the same finger each time you pushed the door?

27.28 How could you measure the value of the force? (Hint: pull the door open with a newton balance.)

Levers

One of the main reasons that we study the moment of a force is to help us understand the lever. A lever is any rigid body that is free to move about a fixed point (in Figure 27.12 the fixed point is shown by the yellow triangle and the lever is the plank of wood). We'll start by looking at what levers can do.

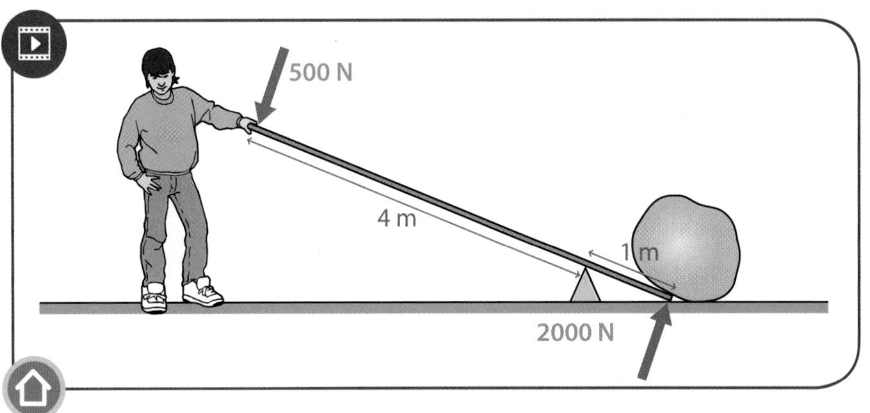

Figure 27.12 *The student can increase his strength by a factor of four*

In Figure 27.12 the student pushes down on the bar with a force of 500 N. However, the force on the large rock is 2000 N (see the explanation below). The student's force of 500 N on the 4 m length of bar is the same as the upward force of 2000 N on the rock. What happened here was:

smaller force × larger distance = larger force × smaller distance
500 N × 4 m = 2000 N × 1 m
2000 Nm = 2000 Nm

The student used his intelligence and knowledge to increase the effectiveness of his strength.

Figure 27.13 *A heavy car can easily be raised using a lever*

Very few people could lift a car 15 cm off the ground to change a wheel if one of the tyres is flat. However, with the correct lever, called a jack, this can easily be done.

What we see here is the application of a law of physics to assist people in everyday life.

You could consider a lever as a device to increase the effectiveness of a force. In many ways it is like a force amplifier.

27.29 Use the internet to find six examples of the use of levers.

27.30 Within your group take ten minutes to decide on the meaning of the words pressure, work and power. Make a note of your answers and see how they compare to the information that follows in this chapter.

PHYSICAL WORLD

What does pressure mean?

Figure 27.14 *The weight of a brick will cause a force*

Pressure is a word that you meet regularly in normal conversation. You may be under pressure to finish homework. In sport you may decide to put more pressure on the opposing team. However, in science we are looking for the exact scientific meaning of pressure.

If you place a solid brick on a table the brick will put a force on the table. The weight of the brick is causing the force. The brick is also exerting a pressure on the part of the table it is touching. So how do we calculate this pressure?

Calculating pressure

27.31 In your group, take ten minutes to read and discuss the following.

A group of students was testing a new machine for measuring pressure. Five bricks of different weights were placed on a horizontal surface. The areas of contact between the bricks and the horizontal surface were recorded. The following table has the data gathered. The students did not know the units for pressure.

Weight of brick (N)	Area of contact (cm^3)	Pressure
25	50	0.5
30	60	0.5
35	70	0.5
40	80	0.5
45	90	0.7

(a) What pattern do you notice in the data above?

(b) What might be the cause of any break in the pattern?

(c) From the data, work out a mathematical rule that would allow you to calculate the pressure value.

Does your mathematical rule agree with the following formula for calculating pressure?

$$\text{pressure} = \frac{\text{force}}{\text{area}}$$

Use the formula in this way:

1. First calculate the force that the brick puts on the table.
2. Then calculate the area of the brick in contact with the table.
3. Now divide the force by the area to find the pressure.

Units for pressure

Any of the following units may be used to measure pressure:

- N/cm^2 or $N\ cm^{-2}$
- N/m^2 or $N\ m^{-2}$
- Pascal (Pa), which is another way of saying N/m^2.

The unit you choose for measuring the pressure will depend on the information given.

Sample calculation 4

A force of 200 N acts on an area of 25 m^2. Calculate the pressure.

Answer:

$$\text{pressure} = \frac{\text{force}}{\text{area}} = \frac{200\text{ N}}{25\text{ m}^2} = 8\text{ N m}^{-2}$$

Sample calculation 5

(a) Calculate the pressure on the ground due to a person of weight 500 N if they can balance themselves on the heel of a stiletto shoe. The area of the heel of the shoe is 1 cm^2.

(b) Calculate the pressure on the ground due to an elephant of weight 50 000 N . The elephant is balanced on one foot. The area of the elephant's foot is 400 cm^2.

Figure 27.15 *How much pressure is there on a stiletto heel?*

Answer:

(a) $$\text{pressure} = \frac{\text{force}}{\text{area}} = \frac{500\text{ N}}{1\text{ cm}^2} = 500\text{ N/cm}^2$$

(b) $$\text{pressure} = \frac{\text{force}}{\text{area}} = \frac{50\,000\text{ N}}{400\text{ cm}^2} = 125\text{ N/cm}^2$$

It may seem strange that the pressure of the person is four times greater than the pressure of the elephant. However, this is due to the very small area of the stiletto heel.

Did you know?

Stiletto heels can put dents in wooden floors, much to the annoyance of homeowners.

Changing pressure and the importance of understanding pressure

27.32 Use the internet to research pressure using the following pointers. Present your findings as a PowerPoint presentation. Find out:

(a) How to increase and decrease values of pressure.

(b) How pressure changes as you go deeper in water and how this affects the design of a dam.

(c) Why an airplane is pressurised when flying at a high altitude.

(d) About values of pressure in space and the design of spacesuits.

27.33 What is pressure?

27.34 Give three different units for pressure.

27.35 Calculate the pressure when a force of 400 N acts on an area of 8 m^2.

27.36 An elephant can walk on a sandy beach quite easily. A cyclist would find it difficult to cycle on a sandy beach. Explain why.

27.37 Describe briefly how you would show that pressure increases with depth in a liquid.

What is the meaning of work?

27.38 In your group take ten minutes to read and discuss the following.

The data in the table below is part of a report prepared by a group of students.

Force (N)	Distance (m)	Work (J)
20	5	100
17.5	10	175
12	4	48
25	5	125
11	2.4	26.4

(a) What pattern do you notice in the data above?

(b) From the data, work out a mathematical rule that would allow you to calculate the work value.

Does your mathematical rule agree with the following formula for calculating work?

$$\text{work} = \text{force} \times \text{distance}$$

So work is done if a force results in an object moving a particular distance. If you apply a force to an object and there is no movement, no work is done. If you push the wall of a house, the wall will not move. Therefore, your pushing force did no work on the wall of the house.

Figure 27.16 *The pushing force on a trolley is doing work*

Figure 27.17 *No work is done when pushing against a wall*

PHYSICAL WORLD

Unit of work

The unit we use to measure work is the **joule** and the symbol is J.

Earlier in the chapter we saw that force is measured in newtons. You will remember that distance is measured in metres. Using the above meaning of work you could say that:

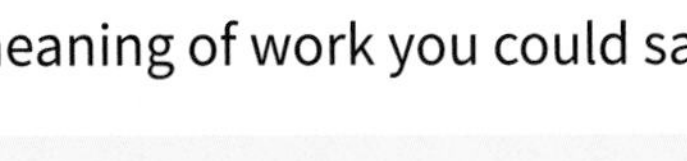

$$1 \text{ joule} = 1 \text{ newton} \times 1 \text{ metre}$$
$$1\text{ J} = 1\text{ N} \times 1\text{ m}$$

Animated Scientist Biography

Watch an *Exploring Science* animation to find out more about the scientist James Prescott Joule and his experiments.

Sample calculation 6

A force of 10 N is being used to move an object a distance of 20 m. Calculate the work done.

Answer:

$$\begin{aligned} \text{work} &= \text{force} \times \text{distance} \\ &= 10\text{ N} \times 20\text{ m} \\ &= 200\text{ J} \end{aligned}$$

Sample calculation 7

Calculate the work done when a force of 15 N moves an object a distance of 40 cm.

Answer:

When calculating the work done it is important that the distance is measured in metres. In this question we change 40 cm to 0.4 m.

$$\begin{aligned} \text{work} &= \text{force} \times \text{distance} \\ &= 15\text{ N} \times 0.4\text{ m} \\ &= 6\text{ J} \end{aligned}$$

27.39 Explain how we calculate the value of work done.
27.40 What is the unit for work?
27.41 Calculate the work done when a force of 15 N moves an object 12 m.
27.42 Calculate the work done when a force of 90 N moves an object 80 cm.

What is the meaning of power?

When work is being done we often need to know how fast this happens. This is the idea of power.

Power is the rate at which work is done. The amount of work done in one second is the power.

27.43 In your group take ten minutes to read and discuss the following.

A student was sitting an exam and was presented with the following table of data.

Work done (J)	Time taken (s)	Power (W)
100	5	20
450	9	50
1000	125	8
625	25	25
196	10	19.6

(a) What pattern do you notice in the data above?

(b) What might be the cause of any break in the pattern?

(c) From the data, work out a mathematical rule that would allow you to calculate the power value.

Does your mathematical rule agree with the following formula for calculating power?

$$\text{power} = \frac{\text{work done}}{\text{time taken}}$$

Unit for power

The unit we use to measure power is the **watt** and the symbol is **W**.

Earlier in the chapter we saw that work is measured in joules. You will remember that time is measured in seconds. Using the above meaning of power you could say that:

$$1\text{ watt} = \frac{1\text{ joule}}{1\text{ second}}$$

You will often see the unit kilowatt: 1 kW = 1000 W.

Sample calculation 8

A force of 10 N is being used to move an object a distance of 20 m in a time of 5 seconds. Calculate:

(a) The work done.

(b) The value of average power.

Answer:

(a) work done = force × distance
= 10 N × 20 m
= 200 J

(b) $\text{power} = \frac{\text{work}}{\text{time}} = \frac{200\text{ J}}{5\text{ s}}$ = 40 watt

27.44 What is the unit for power?

27.45 Calculate the power when a force of 50 N moves an object 5 m in 10 seconds.

PHYSICAL WORLD

CHAPTER 28

Learning outcomes

At the end of this chapter you will be able to:

- Explain the word 'energy'
- List the many different forms of energy
- Explain that energy can change from one form to another
- Explain why we must reduce the waste of useful energy and learn to conserve energy
- Use the term 'energy dissipation' when talking about energy changing from useful forms to non-useful forms
- Design, build and test a device that transforms energy from one form to another to perform a function
- Improve the efficiency when changing energy from one form to another.

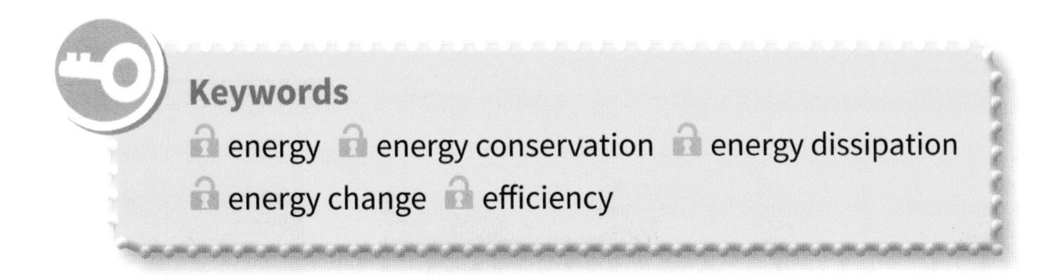

What does energy mean in science?

'Energy' is a word you probably use quite often in your everyday conversation. In science, it has a precise meaning, and that is:

Energy is the ability to do work.

Unit used for energy

The unit we use to measure energy is the **joule** (J), the same unit as used for work.

Work involves moving an object. Since energy is the ability to do work, then energy is the ability to make things move.

Forms of energy

There are many different forms of energy. These include:

- Kinetic energy
- Potential energy
- Sound energy
- Heat energy
- Chemical energy
- Electrical energy
- Solar energy
- Nuclear energy.

28.1 By researching on the internet, prepare a short PowerPoint presentation on six different forms of energy. Your presentation might include:

- A photograph (be guided by some of the following photographs).
- A sentence that will explain what each form of energy is.
- Two examples of each form of energy.

Sample presentation:

Both the wave and the surfer have kinetic energy

Kinetic energy:
Moving objects have kinetic energy

Examples:
- A car travelling along a road has kinetic energy.
- Waves crashing onto a beach have kinetic energy.

Figure 28.1 *Sample presentation*

Figure 28.2 *Energy in a spring*

Figure 28.3 *A vibrating guitar string*

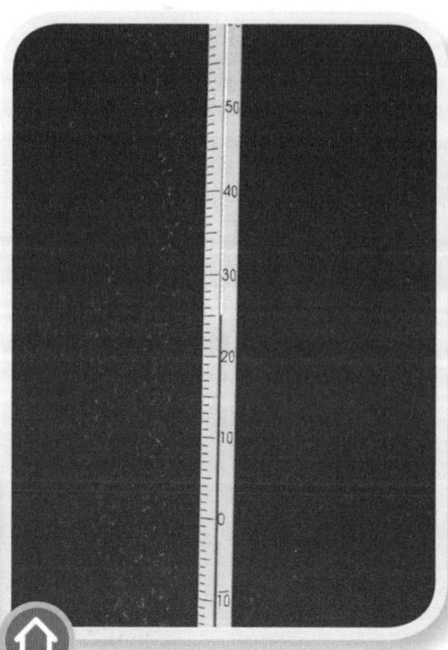

Figure 28.4 *Heat energy, which can be measured by an alcohol thermometer*

Figure 28.5 *Batteries store energy*

Figure 28.6 *An electric car uses electrical energy to make it run*

28.2 Outline the benefits and disadvantages of getting energy from:
(a) Nuclear fission
(b) Nuclear fusion.

Figure 28.7 *A nuclear power station*

28.3 Explain the term 'energy'.
28.4 Name eight different forms of energy.
28.5 For each of the eight forms of energy you named in the previous question give an example of how the energy can cause motion.
28.6 The Sun is often regarded as the primary source of energy. What does this mean?

The principle of conservation of energy

The amazing thing about energy is that it never goes away. Energy does not get used up. Energy changes from one form to another form. For example:

- The chemical energy stored in a battery can change to the sound energy you hear from your mobile phone.
- The chemical energy in the food that we eat can change to kinetic energy when we move.
- Nuclear energy can change to electrical energy. This electrical energy can change to sound energy, heat energy or kinetic energy in our homes.

The fact that energy never gets used up leads to a famous principle in physics. This principle is called the principle of conservation of energy:

Energy is neither created nor destroyed but can be converted from one form to another.

Wasted energy – a challenge to us all

We must reduce the waste of energy. While it is true that energy never gets used up, energy changes from useful forms to not so useful forms, so there is a very great need to avoid wasting useful forms of energy. This is what we mean when we talk about **energy conservation**.

What is the meaning of dissipation of energy?

Dissipation of energy is when energy changes from a useful form to a not so useful form.

For example, the food we eat provides the chemical energy we need to walk. When walking, our bodies produce heat energy, some of which passes into the air around us; we have no way of making use of this. Some of the original chemical energy has been **dissipated**.

In a very simple way you could refer to energy dissipation as a waste of useful energy.

28.7 Describe how energy is wasted in:

(a) A car engine **(b)** A TV **(c)** A central heating boiler.

28.8 Create a poster to present to the class on one of the following:

(a) Renewable forms of energy.

(b) Non-renewable forms of energy.

(c) How to improve the heat insulation in a house or apartment.

(d) How to reduce the energy needed for a public transport system.

(e) Reasons for and against a nuclear power station.

When you have all presented your posters, vote for the best three to display.

Examples of energy changes

We'll look at some examples of energy changes and consider how much energy is dissipated.

Solar water heater

The energy from the Sun is referred to as solar energy. Solar energy can be used to heat water in specially designed glass pipes. This hot water is stored in a tank and can be used for baths, showers, washing clothes, etc., so you will use less electricity or natural gas to heat your water.

- The energy change that occurs is from solar energy to heat energy.
- A large amount of the solar energy is dissipated. However, with improvements in design more and more of the solar energy is changed to useful heat energy.

Figure 28.8 *A solar panel connected to a hot-water system*

Figure 28.9 *A solar panel*

The bicycle dynamo

A dynamo is a device for converting mechanical energy into electrical energy.

Here is a story about converting energy:

- You get out of bed nice and early on a day that you plan to cycle to school.
- You eat a very good breakfast, or we could say you consume a lot of **chemical energy**.
- Some of this chemical energy will be changed to **kinetic energy** as you cycle. A certain amount of the chemical energy will be **dissipated** into the air as heat energy from your body.
- As the bicycle is moving, some of the kinetic energy will be changed to **electrical energy** by the dynamo. A certain amount of the kinetic energy will be **dissipated** as you try to cycle against the breeze.
- Some of the electrical energy will be converted into **light energy** in the bulb connected to the dynamo. A certain amount of the electrical energy will be **dissipated** as heat energy into the air as the bulb heats up.

chemical energy ⟶ kinetic energy ⟶ electrical energy ⟶ light energy

Figure 28.10 *A bicycle dynamo*

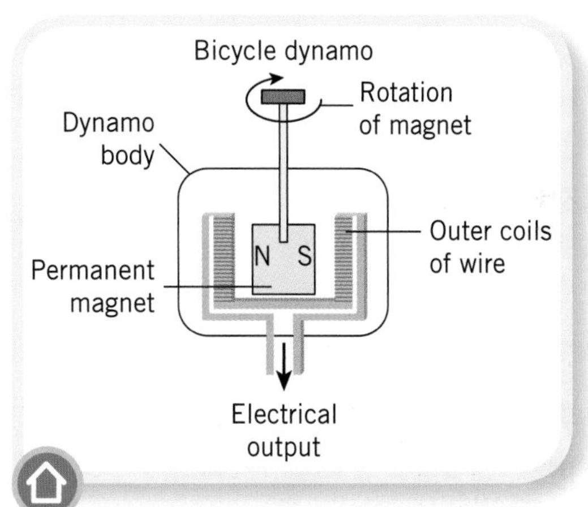

Figure 28.11 *Inside a bicycle dynamo*

How sound travels

Picture two students at opposite ends of a classroom: Emma is talking and Naomi is listening. How exactly does the sound travel?

This is what happens:

- Emma's vocal cords will vibrate, which is **kinetic energy**.
- The air molecules in Emma's mouth will vibrate.
- When Emma opens her mouth the vibration energy is passed on to the air molecules in the room. The air molecules in the room are now vibrating.
- The air molecules in Naomi's ear canal will vibrate and knock against her ear drum.
- The energy falling on Naomi's ear drum generates vibrations that allow her to hear Emma's voice.

Figure 28.12 *Sound travels across a classroom*

In this example the energy started as a vibrating vocal cord, which is an example of kinetic energy. The energy stays in the form of kinetic energy but transfers like this:

the vocal cords → the air in Emma's mouth → the air in the room → the air in Naomi's ear → the vibrating ear drum

You might ask: 'How did Emma's vocal cords produce so much energy to vibrate all the air in the room?' In actual fact, Emma's vocal cords produced very little energy. Only a tiny fraction of this energy reached Naomi's ear, but she still hears the sound. You could say that a large amount of the sound energy was **dissipated** into the air.

Did you know?

The human ear is an amazing device. We can detect sounds of extremely small energy. In science we say that the ear is very **sensitive to energy**.

Sound energy travels quite fast. It can travel about 340 metres in one second through air. We can write this speed as 340 ms^{-1}.

28.9 Is there sound in space? Explain your answer.

28.10 Would solar water heaters work better in Ireland or in Spain? Give two reasons in support of your answer.

28.11 Why are solar water heaters usually placed only on one side of the roof of a house?

28.12 What problem might arise with solar water heaters in extremely cold weather?

28.13 We get chemical energy when we eat food. What kinds of food give more energy?

28.14 Describe the kind of weather that would cause a lot of heat energy to leave your body as you cycle.

28.15 What kind of light bulbs heat up only a little when they light up?

Activity 28.1

Question

Can we design a device to transform energy from one form to another?

A challenge! On a warm day an electric fan would help cool people indoors. How could we use solar energy to make the electricity operate the fan? The Sun, which is causing the room to be too warm, can be used to solve the problem. We will demonstrate this using a lamp.

Equipment needed

Several solar cells

Small electric motor with a fan attached

A study lamp

Safety

- Take care when handling the lamp as the bulb may get hot and should not be touched.
- The lamp will be plugged into a socket and great care must be taken with all electrical devices.

The idea is that the light energy (similar to solar energy) will fall onto the solar cells and change to electrical energy. The electrical energy will operate the motor which rotates the fan.

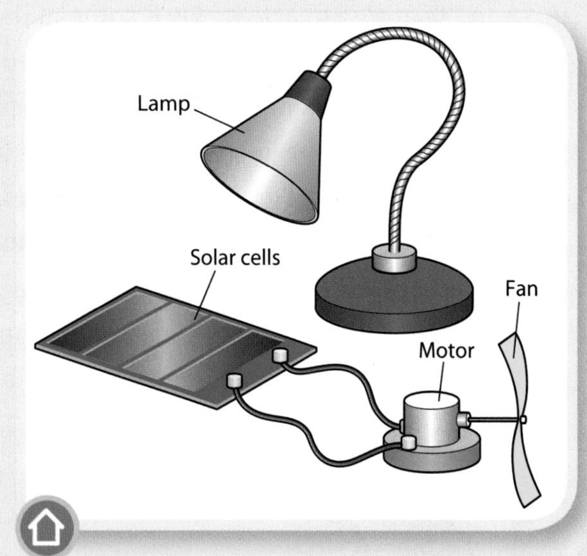

Figure 28.13 *Changing light to electrical to kinetic energy*

The design

Arrange the apparatus as indicated in Figure 28.13 with the solar cells connected to the electric motor, which is connected to a fan.

When the lamp is switched on you will observe the fan moving.

Energy transfer

The **light energy** from the lamp was converted to **electrical energy** in the solar cells, which was converted to **kinetic energy** in the moving fan.

28.16 In activity 28.1 what would you think happens to the rotation of the fan when:

(a) The lamp is moved closer to the solar cells?

(b) The lamp is moved away from the solar cells?

(c) A lamp with a brighter bulb is used?

(d) A lamp with a less bright bulb is used?

(e) The angle of the lamp is changed?

(f) There is dust on the panel?

28.17 Declan decided to do activity 28.1 outdoors using sunlight instead of the study lamp. What would you think happens to the rotation of the fan when:

(a) There is bright sunlight?

(b) A dark cloud blocks the sunlight for a few minutes?

(c) Declan is standing in the shade of a tall building?

(d) Declan tries the activity at night time when it is dark?

28.18 In the design of activity 28.1, some of the original light energy is dissipated. If we can reduce the amount of energy dissipated or lost we would improve the **efficiency** of our design. By working in small groups discuss the following:

(a) Not all of the light energy from the lamp falls on the solar cells. How might you get more of the light energy to shine on the solar cells?

(b) Solar cells can be joined together to make a cell with a bigger surface area. Is there any practical limit to how large the solar cell should be?

(c) What material might you use for the blades of the fan? Would you suggest a strong metal blade or a blade made from a light plastic?

28.19 In your group take ten minutes to examine the photograph in Figure 28.14, read the caption and discuss the following. Then present a short report to the class.

(a) Describe the transformations that would occur in the situation depicted in the photograph.

(b) Could the idea shown by the photograph be extended to include all gyms?

(c) Would you consider it ethical that residents of a homeless shelter should be encouraged to generate electricity in this manner?

Figure 28.14 *Workers generating electricity using stationary exercise bikes in a gym at a homeless shelter. These bikes generate electricity when they are used by residents, staff and volunteers, which is then put back into the power grid*

28.20 Ethics

Split into groups and prepare the following topics for a class discussion.

(a) Why should we try to conserve energy?

(b) Give examples of where people have wasted energy in the past.

(c) 'Ireland should have many more wind generators for electricity so that we can export electrical energy to other countries.' Do you agree with this statement? Give reasons to support your opinion.

Chapter 29 Heat

Learning outcomes

At the end of this chapter you will be able to:

- Explain why heat is a form of energy
- Use a thermometer to measure temperature, i.e. the hotness of a body
- Show by suitable activities that solids, liquids and gases expand when heated and contract when cooled
- Explain how heat sometimes changes a state instead of changing a temperature.

Keywords

heat · temperature · thermometer · expansion · contraction · latent heat

How can we say that heat is a form of energy?

The evidence that heat is a form of energy is that heat can cause movement. Think of:

- Steam engines pulling trains
- Curtains moving when they are over a hot radiator.

As heat is a form of energy it can be converted into other forms. For example, in power stations oil and gas are burned to produce heat energy. This heat produces steam, which turns the blades of a turbine — kinetic energy. This turning of the blades produces electrical energy.

Figure 29.1 *A steam engine is an example of heat energy causing motion*

29.1 List everyday examples of heat being converted into other forms of energy.

29.2 Electricity power stations burn oil and gas to produce heat to generate the electricity. What other fuels can also be used?

29.3 In what way is heat energy beneficial to animals?

29.4 What forms of transport besides trains used steam engines in the past?

How do we measure the hotness of a substance?

We measure hotness using a **thermometer**.

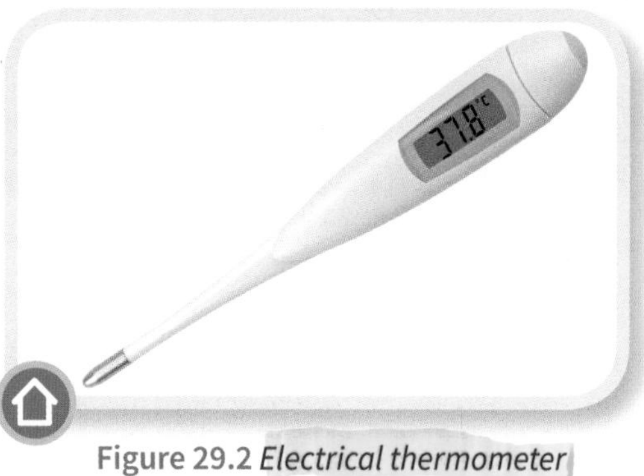

Figure 29.2 *Electrical thermometer*

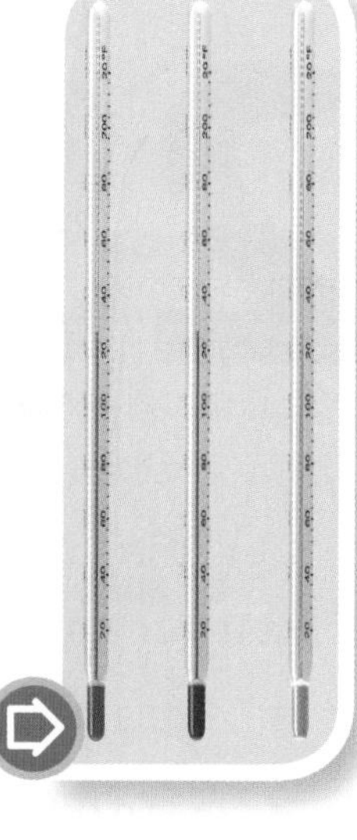

Figure 29.3 *Laboratory thermometers*

29.5 Use the internet to research and then prepare a poster on a comparison between two different types of thermometers. Be guided by the following suggestions:

- Examples of types of thermometer: liquid in a glass thermometer, an electrical thermometer, a liquid crystal thermometer
- Include pictures of your choices of thermometers
- State the scientific principle on which the thermometer is based (for example, in a liquid in a glass thermometer the liquid expands when it gets hotter and it then rises up the glass tube)
- State where the thermometer would be used
- Is the thermometer used in many situations or does it have a limited use?
- Is the thermometer expensive to buy?
- State how the thermometer is used to measure temperature
- State the units used to measure temperature.

29.6 Name two liquids suitable for laboratory thermometers.

29.7 Explain the benefit of using a dye to colour the liquid in a thermometer.

29.8 Give one reason for using an electrical thermometer rather than a glass thermometer with liquid in it.

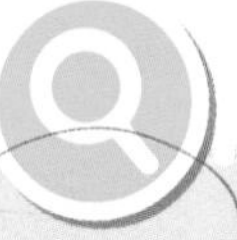

29.9 Research on the internet and prepare a short presentation on the following:

(a) The Celsius temperature scale.

(b) The Fahrenheit temperature scale.

(c) Any easy method to change a temperature value from one scale to the other scale.

(d) Why alcohol is safer to use than mercury.

Activity 29.1

Question

What are the temperatures of everyday items?

Equipment needed

Laboratory thermometer	Cold tap water	Water that has been stored in a fridge
Ice from a freezer	Warm tap water	

Safety

- Be careful not to spill water or ice on the floor to avoid the danger of somebody slipping.

Conducting the activity

1. Measure and make a note of the temperature in degrees Celsius of each of the following:
    - Air temperature
    - Cold tap water
    - Ice from a freezer
    - Warm tap water
    - Cold water from a fridge
2. Compare your results with those of another student in your class.

29.10 Do your and your classmates' results differ?

29.11 What might the reason be for any differences?

29.12 What is the normal range for human body temperature?

What is meant by expanding and contracting?

Heat can cause things to expand (get bigger) and cooling causes things to contract (get smaller).

Activity 29.2

Question

How does heating and cooling of solids affect their expansion and contraction?

Equipment needed

Retort stand	Bunsen burner	Tongs
Metal ball and ring apparatus	Stopwatch or timer	

Safety

- Make sure you are aware of and follow all the recommended precautions when working with a Bunsen burner.
- Do not touch the metal ball after heating as it can get quite hot.

Conducting the activity

1. Test to see that the metal ball fits through the ring at room temperature.
2. Using tongs to hold the metal ball, heat it over a Bunsen flame for 4 minutes.
3. Try to fit the metal ball through the ring now that it is heated.
4. Allow the metal ball to cool for about 10 minutes.
5. See if the metal ball fits through the ring now that it has cooled.
6. Record your results.

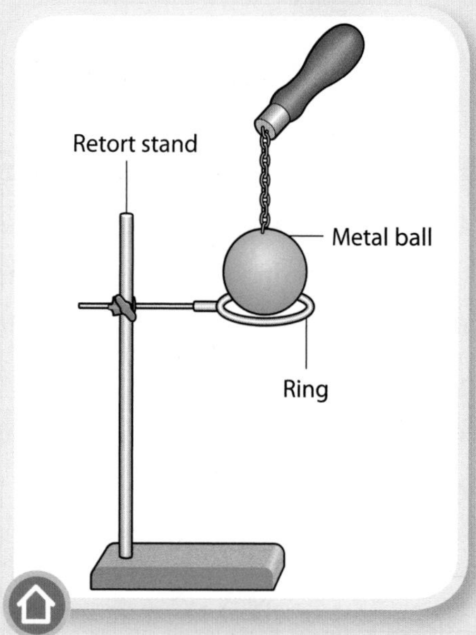

Figure 29.4 *Solids expand when heated and contract when cooled*

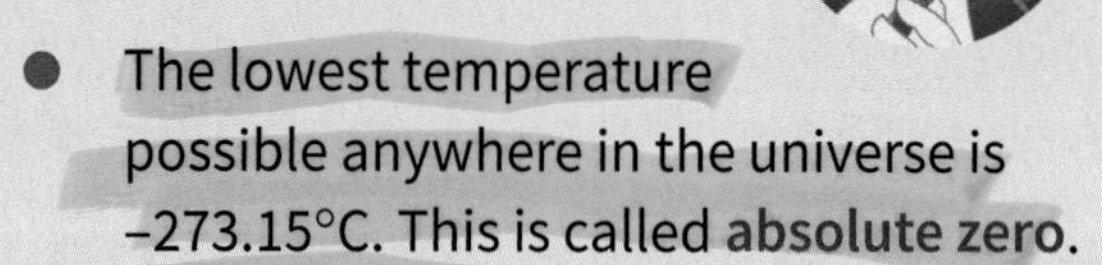

Did you know?

- The lowest temperature possible anywhere in the universe is –273.15°C. This is called **absolute zero**.
- –40° Celsius is the same temperature as –40° Fahrenheit.

29.13 Explain why water is not suitable for use in a thermometer.

Investigating i3 Investigating i4

Portfolio 210

Activity 29.3

Question

How does heating and cooling of liquids affect their expansion and contraction?

Equipment needed

Retort stand
Round-bottomed flask
Glass tube
Water
Food dye
Bunsen burner
Stopwatch or timer

Safety

- Make sure you are aware of and follow all the recommended precautions when working with a Bunsen burner.
- Do not touch the round-bottomed flask after heating as it can get quite hot.

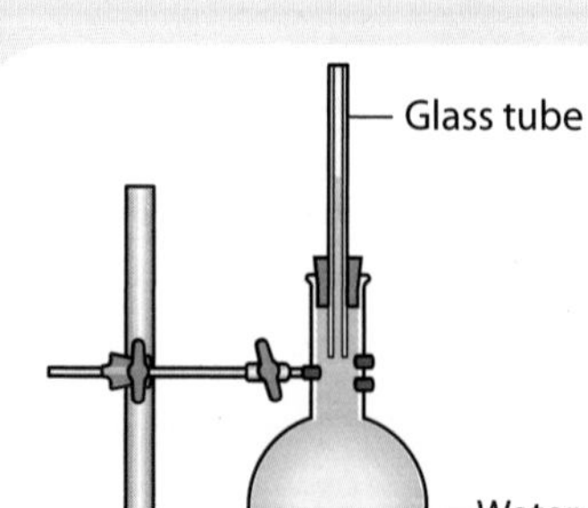
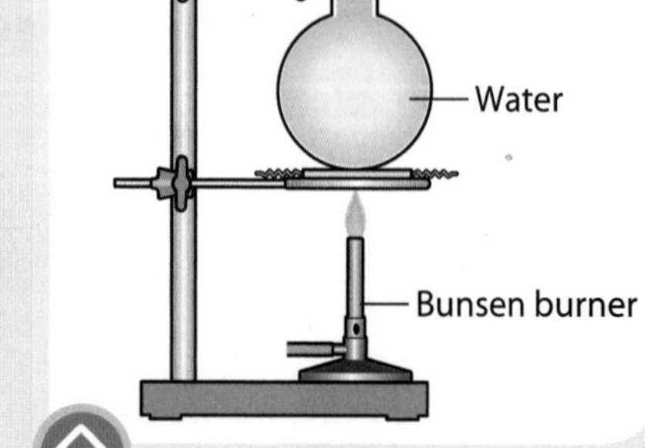

Figure 29.5 *The effect of heat on the volume of a liquid*

Conducting the activity

1. Totally fill a round-bottomed flask with water and add a few drops of food dye.
2. Insert a stopper with a glass tube into the top of the flask.
3. Hold the flask in place with clamps as shown in Figure 29.5.
4. Heat the flask with the Bunsen burner for a few minutes.
5. Watch the level of the coloured water in the glass tube as the water heats.
6. Turn off the Bunsen burner from under the flask.
7. Observe the level of water in the glass tube over the next 10 minutes.
8. Record your results.

Note The food dye does not affect the expansion or contraction. The purpose of the dye is to make it easier to see the water in the narrow glass tube.

Portfolio 211

Activity 29.4

Question

How does heating and cooling of gases affect their expansion and contraction?

Equipment needed

Retort stand	Water	Beaker
Round-bottomed flask	Bunsen burner	
Glass tube	Stopwatch or timer	

Safety

- Make sure you are aware of and follow all the recommended precautions when working with a Bunsen burner.
- Do not touch the round-bottomed flask after heating as it can get quite hot.

Conducting the activity

1. Insert a stopper with a glass tube into the top of the flask.
2. With a retort stand and a clamp, set up the arrangement as shown in Figure 29.6.
3. Make sure one end of the glass tube is below the level of the water in the beaker.
4. Gently heat the round-bottomed flask. This will also heat the air in the flask.
5. Observe the glass tube in the beaker.
6. Turn off the Bunsen burner and move it away from the apparatus.
7. Observe the glass tube and make a note of what you see.

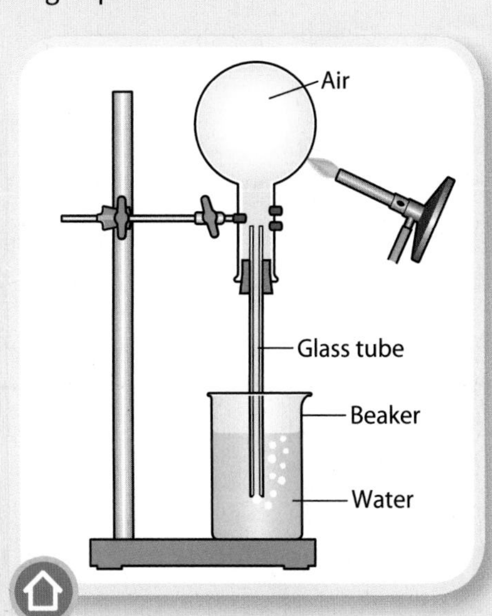

Figure 29.6 *The effect of heat on the volume of a gas*

Did you know?

- The Golden Gate Bridge in San Francisco changes length by over 1 m between winter and summer due to expansion and contraction.
- The Eiffel Tower in Paris is 300 m high and is made of iron. Between summer and winter its height changes by as much as 7.5 cm.
- Sealed bottles or cans explode in fires.
- If you take an empty cold glass bottle and put a coin over the open neck and then wrap your hands around the bottle, after a while the coin will pop up.

Figure 29.7 *The Golden Gate Bridge in San Francisco changes length depending on whether it is summer or winter*

Figure 29.8 *The Eiffel Tower in Paris changes height depending on whether it is summer or winter*

29.14 Explain why a metal ball was used in activity 29.2 instead of a wooden ball.

29.15 What was the benefit of using a dye to colour the water in activity 29.3?

29.16 In activity 29.4 the water passes up into the glass tube when the air is cooled. Explain why this happens.

29.17 Use the internet to research the unusual behaviour of water as it cools to just below 4°C and as it heats to just above 4°C.

29.18 Can you now explain why icebergs float on water?

29.19 Can you now explain why water pipes sometimes burst in very cold weather?

What do we mean by latent heat?

When you heat an object you expect the temperature of the object to rise. However, this does not always happen. Look at the situation in Figure 29.9.

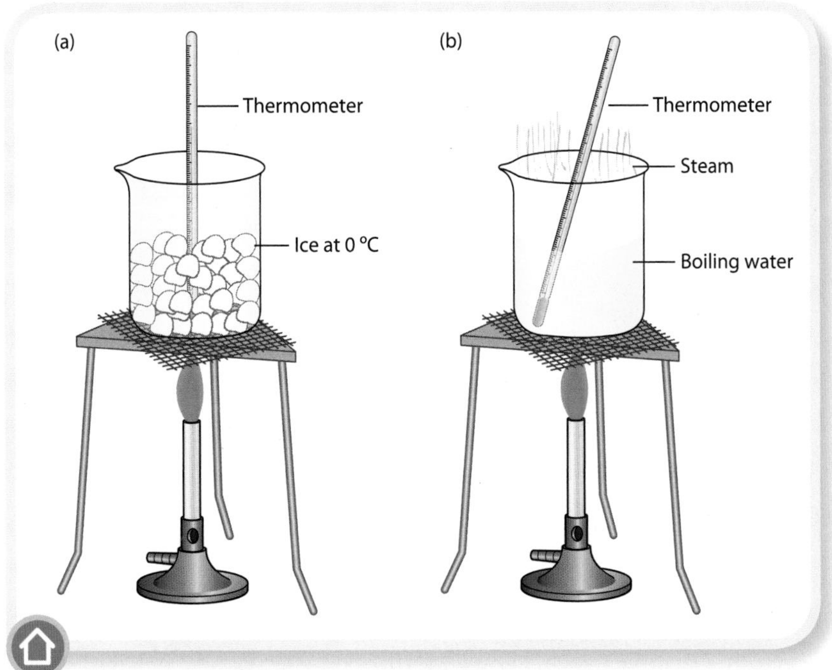

Figure 29.9 *(a) When you heat a beaker of ice, the temperature does not rise until all the ice has melted; (b) When you heat a beaker of boiling water, the temperature does not change*

When you slowly heat a beaker of ice you will notice that the temperature does not rise at first. The temperature remains at 0°C for several minutes until the last piece of ice has melted.

When you heat a beaker of boiling water you will notice that the temperature does not rise. The temperature remains at 100°C.

What happens to the heat energy? Heat energy cannot just disappear! In the situations shown in Figure 29.9 the heat changes the state of the ice and of the boiling water. When heat changes a state instead of the temperature we call it **latent heat**.

Did you know?

When we exercise vigorously we perspire or sweat. This causes small droplets of liquid to form on our skin. Heat then leaves the body to evaporate this liquid, or to change its state to a gas. Perspiration is the body's natural way to cool down.

Unlike a human perspiration system, a dog's body cools itself mainly through an evaporation system that involves the dog's tongue. Although a dog's body does have sweat glands located on the pads on its feet and ears, the dog's body is cooled off mainly through its tongue. Because of dogs' inability to sweat, they must never be left in a car on sunny days, because they can die very, very quickly from overheating.

PHYSICAL WORLD

Portfolio 213

Activity 29.5

Question

How can we show that heating something may not change the temperature?

Equipment needed

12-V power supply	Stirrer
Electrical leads	Beaker
Thermometer	Ice cubes
Heating coil	Joulemeter

Safety

- The power supply unit may be plugged into a socket. Take care with all electrical appliances.

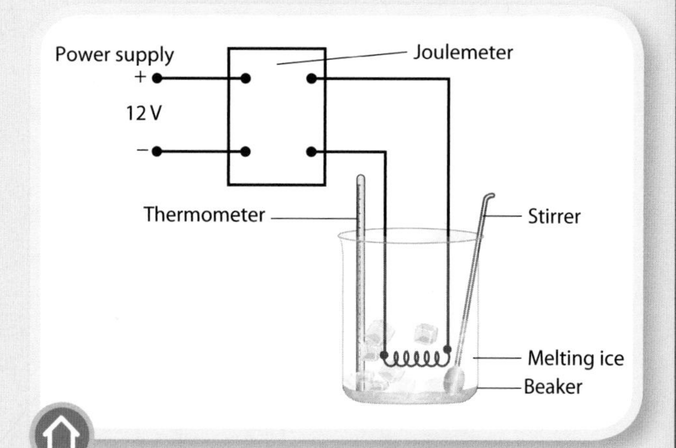

Figure 29.10

Conducting the activity

1. Set up the apparatus as indicated in Figure 29.10.
2. Note the temperature on the thermometer as the ice starts to melt.
3. Turn on the electricity and the joulemeter will indicate how much electrical energy is being supplied to the melting ice.
4. What do you notice about the temperature reading on the thermometer as the electrical energy is being supplied?
5. Record your results.

Electricity – current electricity

Learning outcomes

At the end of this chapter you will be able to:

- Correctly use the terms current, potential difference and resistance when talking about electricity
- Measure current, potential difference and resistance
- Describe the relationship between the current and potential difference for electricity flowing in a circuit
- Recognise the symbols used for various objects that are commonly used in the study of electricity
- Do simple calculations involving current, potential difference and resistance.

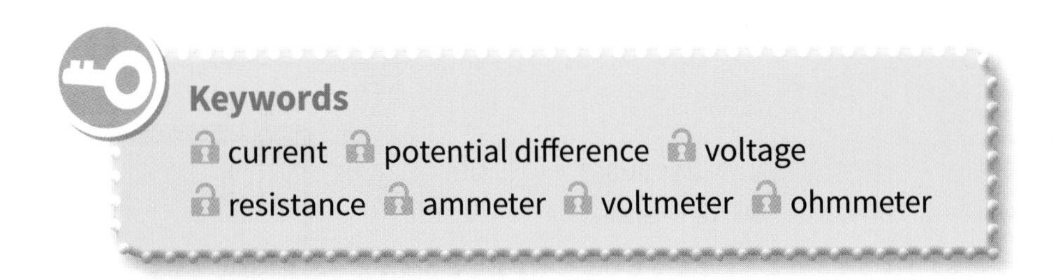

What is electrical current?

The wire in Figure 30.1 is made of a metal such as copper. In this piece of copper wire each atom has one or more loosely held electrons that are free to move within the wire. If you connect a battery across the ends of the wire these free electrons move along the wire.

The electrons move from the negative terminal of the battery towards the positive terminal of the battery. This movement of electrons is called current.

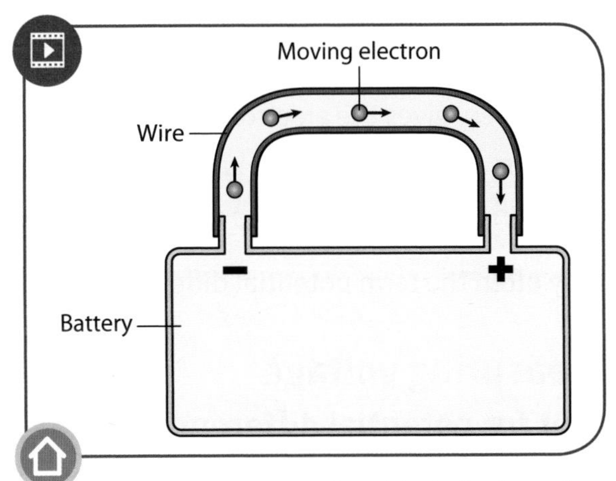

Figure 30.1 *Current electricity is the flow of electrons along a wire*

Electricity was discovered before the electron was discovered. In the early days when scientists first studied electricity they agreed that current was the flow of positive charge from the positive terminal of a battery to the negative terminal of the battery. Today this is called **conventional current**.

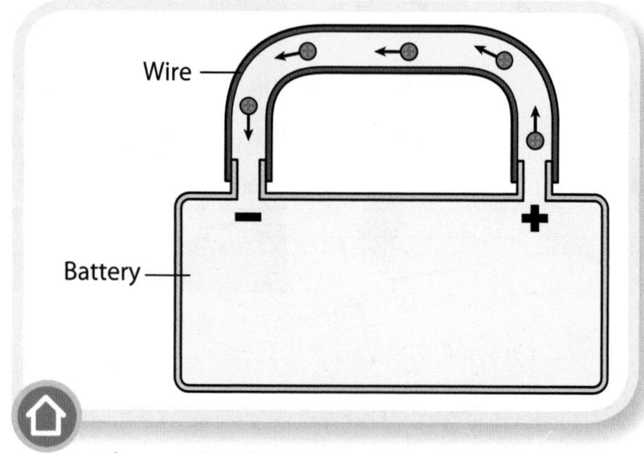

Figure 30.2 *Conventional current in a circuit*

Although there is some historical confusion, just try to remember this:

- Current electricity is actually the flow of negative electrons from the negative terminal to the positive terminal of a battery.
- However, because of a historical agreement, we say that current flows from the positive terminal to the negative terminal of a battery.

Measuring current

Unit for current

Current is measured in the **ampere** (A). This is often called the **amp**.

Current is measured with an **ammeter**.

What is potential difference (voltage)?

A chemical reaction happens inside a battery. The result of this reaction is that excess electrons build up on the negative terminal of the battery. The reaction also causes a loss of electrons at the positive terminal of the battery.

When you join a conducting wire (a wire through which an electric current can pass) from one terminal to the other, the excess electrons flow from the negative terminal to the positive terminal.

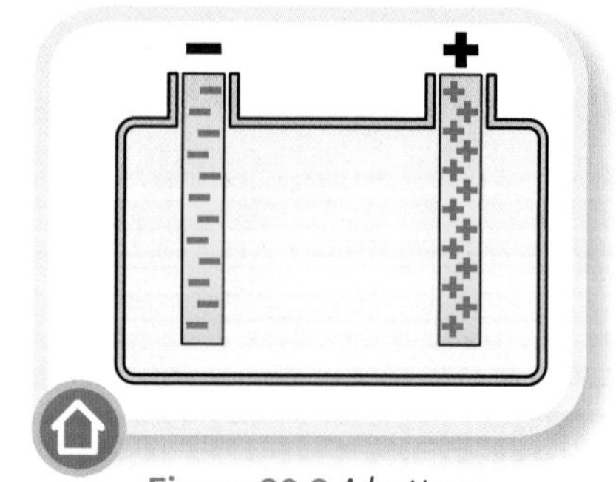

Figure 30.3 *A battery showing excess electrons at the negative terminal*

The battery gives the electrons the ability to move. Another word for ability is potential. We therefore say that the battery has a **potential difference** between the positive and the negative terminals.

Very often the term potential difference is called **voltage**.

Measuring voltage

Unit for potential difference (voltage)

Voltage is measured in the **volt** (V).

Potential difference is measured with a **voltmeter**.

To help you remember ...

Figure 30.4 shows a positive charge leaving the battery with a box full of voltage. He uses up a little bit of this voltage to get to the lamp. He uses up most of the voltage to light the lamp. He has just enough voltage left to get back to the battery. At the battery he fills up his box with voltage again.

Notice that in the diagram we let the current flow in the direction agreed by the early scientists.

Just remember:

- Whatever current leaves the battery, the same current returns to the battery.
- Voltage gets used up as the current flows around the circuit.

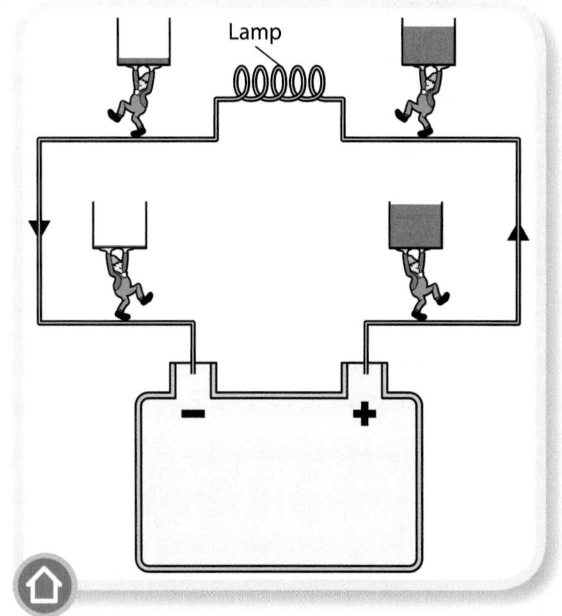

Figure 30.4 *Charge moving around a circuit*

What is the difference between current and voltage?

- **Current** is a measure of the number of electrons flowing along the wire.
- **Voltage** is a measure of the ability of the electrons to do a particular task.

To help you remember ...

You have organised a football match between five players from sixth year and forty players from junior infants:

- The sixth years have a small number of players but are individually very capable at football. Their team would be small current but high voltage.
- The junior infant team has a large number of players but individually they would not be very capable. Their team would be high current but low voltage.

What is resistance?

Electrons find it easier to flow along some conducting materials than others. We say that some materials are better conductors than others. However, all conductors try to oppose the moving electrons. The opposition to the flow of electrons is called **resistance**.

Metals such as silver and copper are **good conductors** of electricity and have a **low resistance**.

Carbon is **not as good a conductor** and we say that carbon has a **higher resistance**.

Measuring resistance

Unit for resistance

Resistance is measured in the **ohm**. The symbol for the ohm is a Greek letter called 'omega' (Ω).

Resistance is measured with an **ohmmeter**.

PHYSICAL WORLD

Portfolio 219

Activity 30.1

Question

How can we demonstrate an electrical circuit?

Equipment needed

Electrical lead for each student
Low voltage battery
Bulb
Clips

Safety

- As the whole class has to stand around the room, follow the teacher's instructions to avoid bumping into other students or tripping over school bags.

Conducting the activity

1. Each student has an electrical lead.
2. Join your lead to the leads of the students on either side of you, so that when everyone does this the leads are joined all around the class.
3. The student with the battery unclips the lead from his or her neighbour's lead and joins it instead to the positive terminal of the battery.
4. The student whose lead is not now joined to another lead on one side attaches the loose end to the negative terminal of the battery.
5. The two students with the bulb unclip their leads and one student attaches the loose end to one of the terminals on the bulb and the second student attaches the loose end of their lead to the other terminal of the bulb.

The bulb should light up as long as all the other leads are attached to each other and there is no break in the circuit.

What symbols are used in electricity?

When you perform activities to do with electricity you use objects such as batteries, bulbs, switches and resistors. Diagrams of equipment used normally have a symbol for those objects rather than of the object itself. Figure 30.5 shows the symbols you are most likely to come across.

All the symbols in Figure 30.5 are in the formulae and tables booklet used in all state exams.

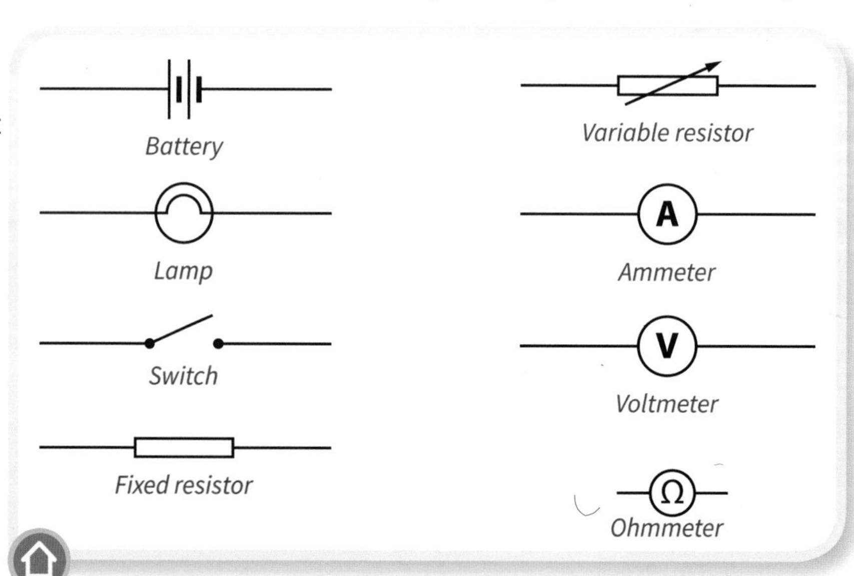

Figure 30.5 *Symbols used in electricity*

How do we measure current and potential difference?

Figure 30.6 shows an ammeter, which is used to measure current. When it is connected into a circuit the needle moves on the scale for you to read the amount of current.

Figure 30.7 shows a voltmeter, which is used to measure potential difference. When it is connected into a circuit the needle moves on the scale for you to read the amount of potential difference.

Figure 30.8 shows a multimeter. This is a digital meter and does not have a moving needle. By adjusting the settings it can be used to measure current, potential difference and resistance. It is really a combination of an ammeter, a voltmeter and an ohmmeter.

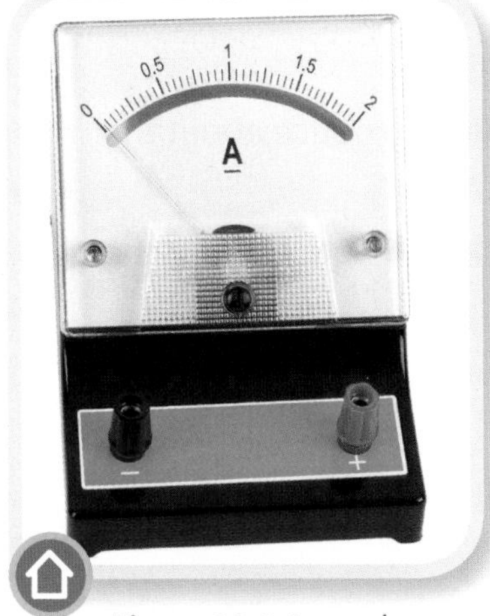

Figure 30.6 *An analog ammeter*

Figure 30.7 *An analog voltmeter*

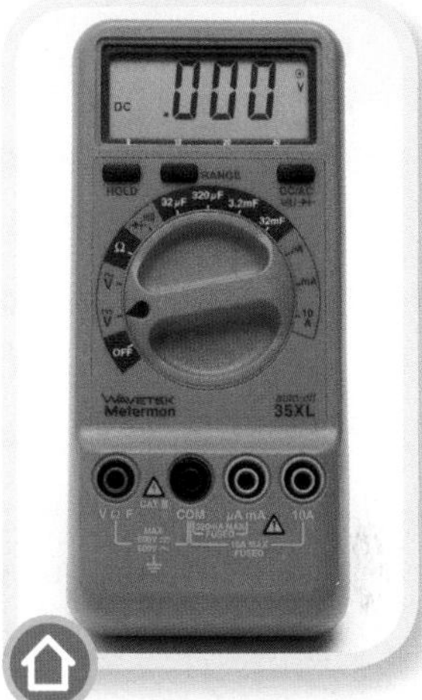

Figure 30.8 *A digital multimeter*

30.1 Use the internet to research the difference between analog instruments and digital instruments. Present your findings in the form of a poster. Pay particular attention to:

- Which type of instrument was used first.
- Which type of instrument might be more expensive to buy.

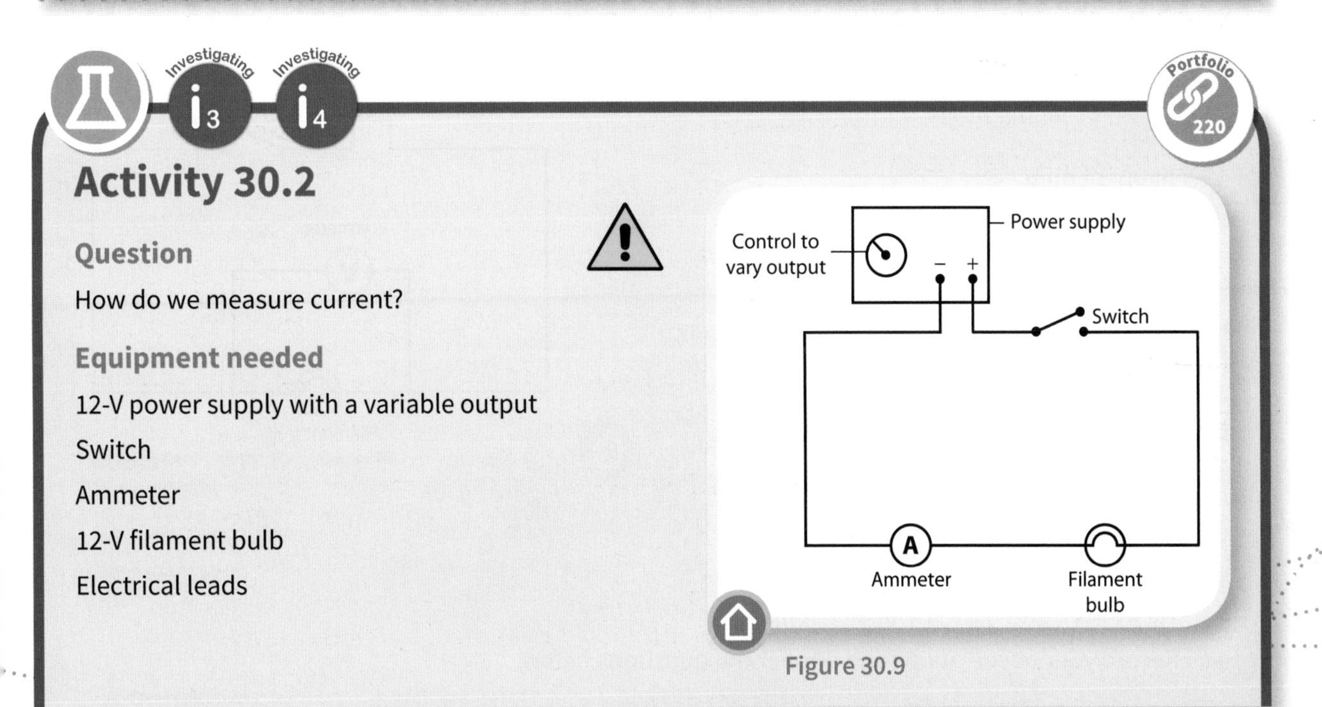

Activity 30.2

Question

How do we measure current?

Equipment needed

12-V power supply with a variable output

Switch

Ammeter

12-V filament bulb

Electrical leads

Figure 30.9

Safety

- Take care not to drop the ammeter as it may break leaving the parts with sharp edges.

Conducting the activity

1. Set up the equipment as indicated in Figure 30.9.
2. Close the switch.
3. Vary the output from the power supply.
4. Record your observations and answer the questions below.

30.2 As you varied the output from the power supply what did you notice about the bulb?

30.3 As you varied the output from the power supply what did you notice about the reading on the ammeter?

30.4 Did you notice any pattern about the reading on the ammeter and the brightness of the bulb?

30.5 Would it make any difference if you put the ammeter on the other side of the filament bulb?

PHYSICAL WORLD

Activity 30.3

Question

How do we measure voltage?

Equipment needed

12-V power supply with a variable output
Switch
Voltmeter
12-V filament bulb
Electrical leads

Safety

- Take care not to drop the voltmeter as it may break leaving the parts with sharp edges.

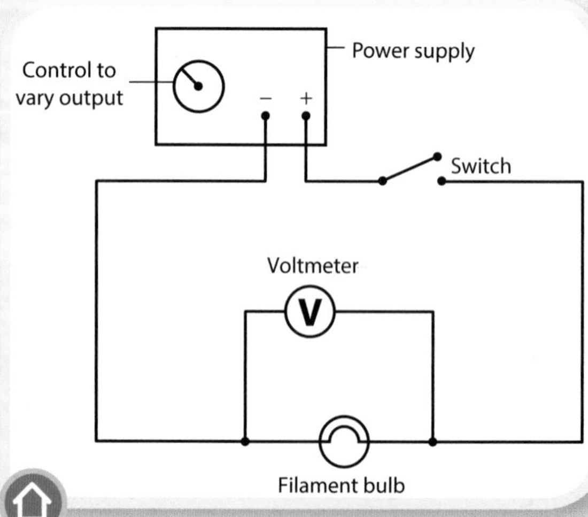

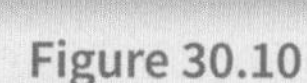
Figure 30.10

Conducting the activity

1. Set up the apparatus as indicated in Figure 30.10.
2. Close the switch.
3. Vary the output from the power supply.
4. Record your observations and answer the questions below.

30.6 As you varied the output from the power supply what did you notice about the bulb?

30.7 As you varied the output from the power supply what did you notice about the reading on the voltmeter?

30.8 Did you notice any pattern about the reading on the voltmeter and the brightness of the bulb?

30.9 Would it make any difference if you put the voltmeter on the side of the filament bulb where you put the ammeter in activity 30.2?

30.10 Find out the terms used for the difference in how the ammeter is connected in Figure 30.9 and how the voltmeter is connected in the circuit in Figure 30.10.

Portfolio 224

Activity 30.4

Question

How can we see the relationship between current and potential difference?

Equipment needed

6-V battery
Switch
Ammeter
Voltmeter
Resistor
Variable resistor
Connecting wires
Graph paper

Safety

- Take care not to drop the ammeter or voltmeter as they may break leaving the parts with sharp edges.

Conducting the activity

1. Set up the circuit as illustrated in Figure 30.11. Take great care that the ammeter and voltmeter are in the correct positions.
2. Allow the current to flow by closing the switch to complete the circuit.
3. Adjust the variable resistor until the voltmeter reads 1 volt. Now record the current reading on the ammeter.
4. Adjust the variable resistor until the voltmeter reads 2 volts. Now record the current reading on the ammeter.

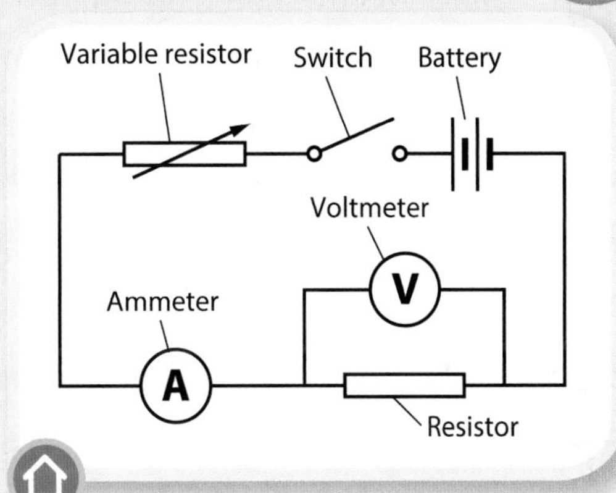

Figure 30.11 Circuit diagram to show the relationship between current and potential difference

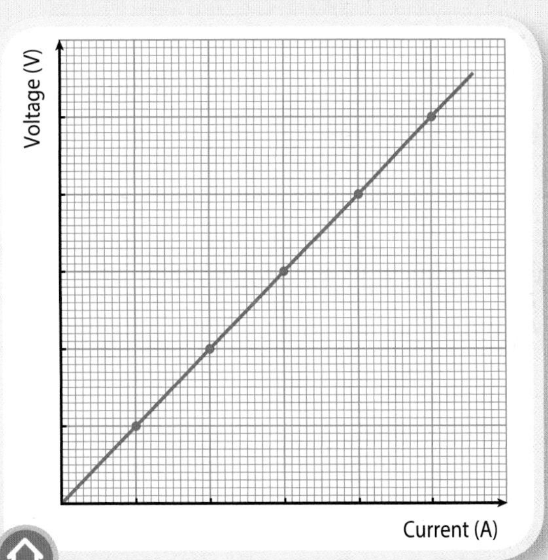

Figure 30.12 A graph to show potential difference plotted against current

5. Repeat this procedure for 3 volts, 4 volts, 5 volts and 6 volts.
6. Record your results in a table similar to this:

Voltage (V)	1	2	3	4	5	6
Current (A)						

7. Draw a graph of the data collected with potential difference (voltage) on the y-axis and current on the x-axis.

Result

The graph will be a straight line passing through the origin as shown in Figure 30.12.

Conclusion

Because the graph is a straight line through the origin we conclude that the **potential difference (voltage) is directly proportional to the current.**

30.11 Research Georg Ohm on the internet and prepare a short biography of him. Present your work in the form of a poster.

Did you know?

The scientist Georg Simon Ohm discovered the relationship between the current and the potential difference.

Note The resistor used in activity 30.4 usually has a low resistance, i.e. it is quite a good conductor. *The temperature of this resistor should stay constant.* For this reason the resistor is sometimes placed in a liquid to prevent it from getting hot. A loosely coiled piece of nichrome wire (this wire resists the flow of electricity, which causes the electrical energy to be converted into heat) works well here as the resistor. The wire is coiled to keep it compact, as shown in Figure 30.13.

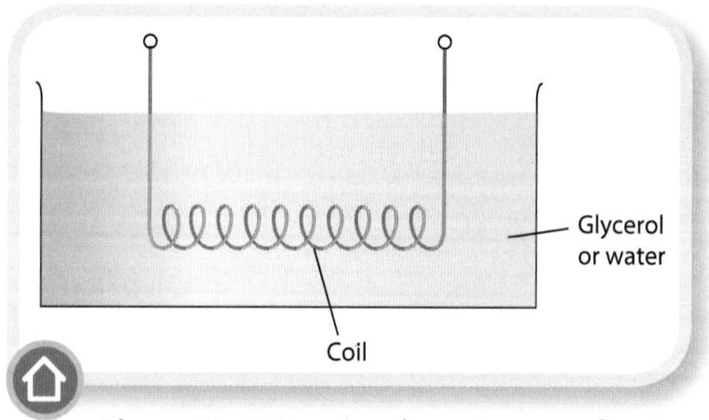

Figure 30.13 *Keeping the resistor at a fixed temperature*

Calculations

From activity 30.4 we found that voltage is directly proportional to current. However, when we write this law as a mathematical equation we get:

$$\frac{V}{I} = R$$

where:

V = potential difference (voltage)
I = current
R = resistance

A triangle makes this equation easy for us:

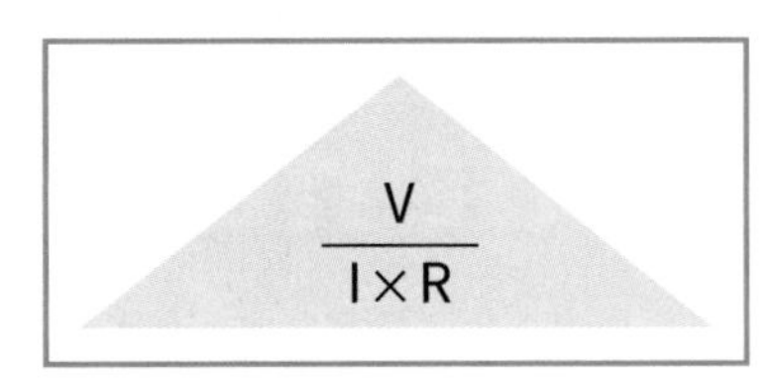

- To calculate the value of **potential difference**, put your finger over V. This will show you that you have to multiply I and R ($V = I \times R$).
- To calculate the value of **current**, put your finger over I. This will show you that you have to divide V by R $\left(I = \frac{V}{R}\right)$.
- To calculate the value of **resistance**, put your finger over R. This will show you that you have to divide V by I $\left(R = \frac{V}{I}\right)$.

Sample calculation 1

Calculate the potential difference (voltage) across a resistor of resistance 10 Ω if the current flowing through it is 2 amperes.

Answer: $V = I \times R$ $V = 2 \times 10$ $V = 20$ volts

Sample calculation 2

Calculate the current flowing through a resistor of 20 Ω when the potential difference (voltage) across it is 6 volts.

Answer: $I = \frac{V}{R}$ $I = \frac{6}{20}$ $I = 0.3$ amperes

Sample calculation 3

Calculate the resistance of a resistor when a potential difference (voltage) of 12 volts causes a current of 0.2 amperes to flow.

Answer: $R = \frac{V}{I}$ $R = \frac{12}{0.2}$ $R = 60$ ohms

30.12 Calculate the potential difference (voltage) across a resistor of resistance 5 Ω if the current flowing through it is 3 amperes.

30.13 Calculate the potential difference (voltage) across a resistance of 240 Ω if the current flowing through it is 0.05 amperes.

30.14 Calculate the current flowing through a resistor of 30 Ω when the potential difference (voltage) across it is 12 volts.

30.15 Calculate the current flowing through a resistor of 2000 Ω when the potential difference (voltage) across it is 12 volts.

30.16 Calculate the resistance of a resistor when a potential difference (voltage) of 6 volts causes a current of 2 amperes to flow.

30.17 Calculate the resistance of a resistor when a potential difference (voltage) of 240 volts causes a current of 0.2 amperes to flow.

CHAPTER 31

UNIT 4

Issues that arise from generation and use of electricity

Learning outcomes

At the end of this chapter you will be able to:

- Identify the different ways of generating electrical energy
- List the good points and bad points about the different ways of generating electrical energy
- Do simple calculations on electrical power
- Understand the unit of energy that is used for electricity in the home
- Research and discuss issues about how we use electrical energy and how our actions today may affect future generations.

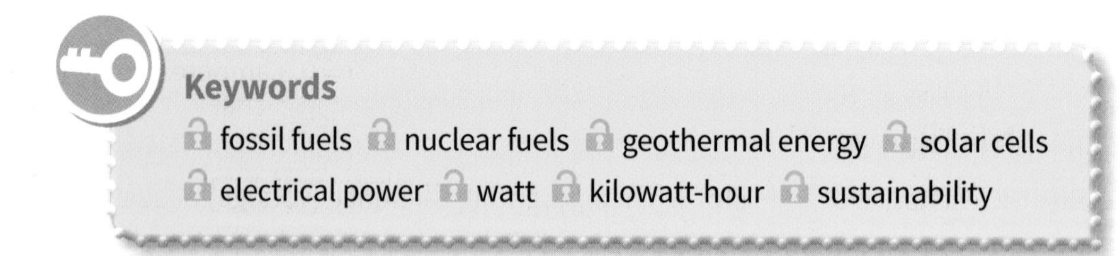

Keywords

fossil fuels, nuclear fuels, geothermal energy, solar cells, electrical power, watt, kilowatt-hour, sustainability

How is electricity generated?

Activity 31.1

Question

How can we generate electricity?

Equipment needed

About 1 metre of insulated copper wire

Pencil

Different types of magnet

Digital multimeter

Safety

- Take care not to drop the magnets as they can be quite heavy or trip someone.

Conducting the activity

1. Wrap the wire around the pencil and leave about 10 cm of the wire unwrapped at both ends. You now have a copper wire coil.
2. Connect the two free ends of the wire to the terminals of the multimeter.
3. Turn the dial of the multimeter so that it will read millivolts.
4. Move one of the magnets back and forth near the wire wrapped around the pencil.
5. Note what you observe from the multimeter.
6. Repeat steps 4 and 5 using different magnets.

Figure 31.1 *Copper wire coil*

Figure 31.2 *Magnets*

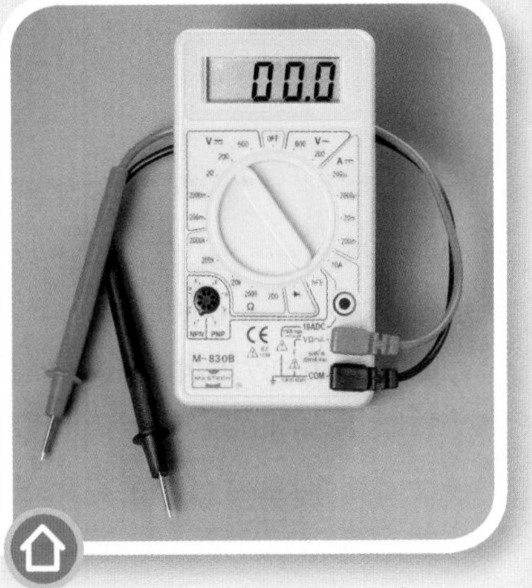

Figure 31.3 *Digital multimeter*

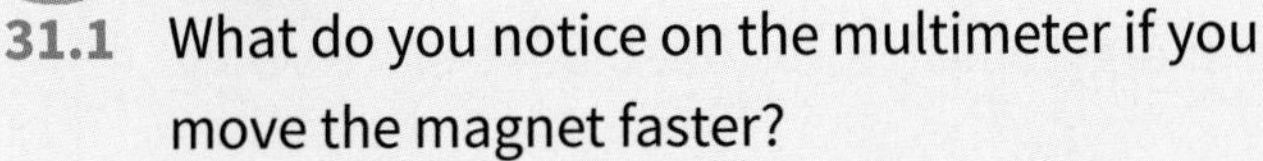

31.1 What do you notice on the multimeter if you move the magnet faster?

31.2 What do you notice on the multimeter if you use a stronger magnet?

31.3 Does using a magnet of a different shape make any difference?

31.4 Would using a longer piece of wire make any difference?

31.5 What do you notice if you move the wire instead of the magnet?

31.6 The insulation used for copper wire may be varnish, which is a type of clear paint. Why do you think this type of wire would be helpful in the above experiment?

Generating electricity

Some of the ways that electricity is generated in the world today are from:

- Fossil fuels
- Nuclear fuels
- Wind
- Moving water
- Geothermal
- Solar.

Energy from fossil fuels

The main fossil fuels used are:

- Coal
- Oil
- Natural gas.

They are **fuels** because they release heat energy when they are burned.

They are **fossil fuels** because they were formed from the remains of organisms living millions of years ago.

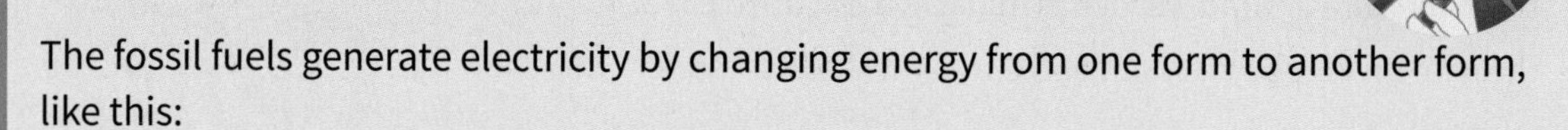

The fossil fuels generate electricity by changing energy from one form to another form, like this:

Coal, oil and gas are stores of chemical energy.

↓

When burned they release heat energy.

↓

The heat energy boils water to make steam.

↓

The moving steam has kinetic energy, which turns the blades of a turbine.

↓

The turbine spins the magnet near the coil of wire in the generator, which makes the electrical energy.

Points to note about fossil fuels:

- At present most of the world's electricity is generated using fossil fuels.
- Their supply is limited and they will eventually run out.
- Fossil fuels release carbon dioxide when they burn, which adds to the greenhouse effect and increases global warming (see chapter 41).
- Coal and oil release sulfur dioxide gas when they burn, which causes breathing problems for living creatures and contributes to acid rain.

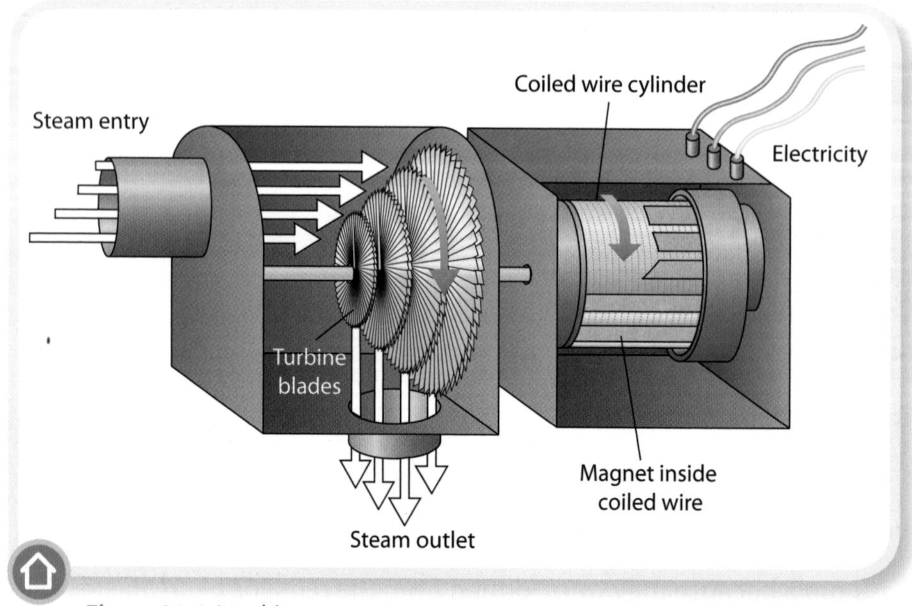

Figure 31.4 *A turbine generator*

31.7 Using the internet for research, prepare a short PowerPoint presentation on four of the different ways that electricity is generated. Your presentation might include:

- A photograph.
- A brief explanation as to how the electrical energy is generated.
- Two points to note about that particular method of generating electricity.

(**Hint:** read about how electricity is generated from fossil fuels before you start your presentation.)

Activity 31.2

Question

How can we generate electricity from solar cells?

Equipment needed

Solar cells
Study lamp
Multimeter

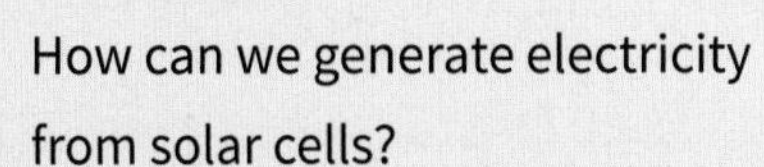

Safety

- Take care when handling the lamp as the bulb may get hot and should not be touched.
- The lamp will be plugged into a socket and great care must be taken with all electrical devices.

Figure 31.5 *Generating electricity from solar cells*

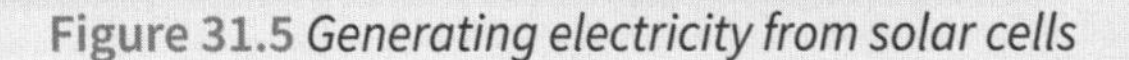

Conducting the activity

1. Set up the equipment as shown in Figure 31.5.
2. Switch on the lamp and allow the light to fall onto the solar cells.
3. Turn the dial of the multimeter so that it reads millivolts.
4. Note and record the reading on the multimeter.
5. Move the lamp nearer the solar cells.
6. Note any differences to the reading on the multimeter.
7. Cover some of the solar cells with a piece of paper. You have now reduced the area of the solar cells that is exposed to the light.
8. Note the reading on the multimeter.

PHYSICAL WORLD

Use the internet to find out:

31.8 What percentage of electrical energy is generated in Ireland by each of the individual methods discussed (fossil fuels, nuclear fuels, wind, moving water, geothermal, solar).

31.9 What percentage of electrical energy is generated in the world by each of the individual methods discussed above.

31.10 Write a brief account of how you think each of the individual methods of generating electricity will be used in twenty years' time. Which methods do you think will be more popular and which will be less popular?

What is electrical power?

As with other words we have looked at, **power** has a very precise meaning in the physical world. Note the following:

- Electrical power is the amount of electrical energy changed to other forms of energy in one second.
- The unit for electrical power is the **watt** (W).
- Sometimes you see the **kilowatt** (kW), which is 1000 watts.

31.11 Read the following and then answer the questions below.

A research scientist was investigating the performance of electric kettles by connecting them to power supplies of different voltage values. In each trial he noticed the value of the voltage and the value of the current flowing through the kettle. He also recorded the power rating of each kettle.

The following is the data he recorded.

Power rating (W)	Voltage (V)	Current (A)
1200	120	10
1500	150	10
1800	180	10
2000	250	8
2200	110	20
2500	125	20

(a) Do you notice any pattern in the data the scientist recorded?

(b) From the data, work out a mathematical rule that would allow you to calculate the power rating.

Does your mathematical rule agree with the following formula for calculating a power rating?

PHYSICAL WORLD

power = potential difference × current

We can write this formula as:

$$P = V \times I$$

Where:

P = power
V = potential difference (voltage)
I = current.

We can rewrite this as a triangle to help solve other calculations:

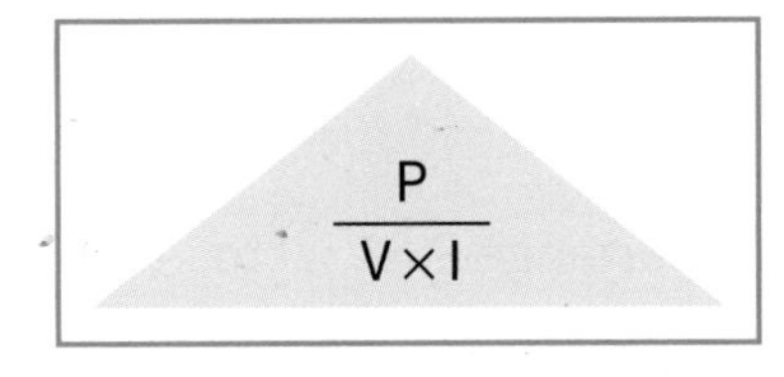

Note: This maths formula is used only for questions on electricity. Try not to confuse this with the formula for power, on page 276.

31.12 When you buy an electrical appliance the power is usually written on it. How do the following values compare to what you have at home:

(a) An 11 watt energy saving bulb?
(b) A 900 watt microwave oven?
(c) A 2500 watt electric kettle?
(d) A 110 watt flat-screen TV?

What do you notice about the heat output of appliances that have a higher power rating?

Note: Be very careful with electrical appliances at home. Examine them only when they are **plugged out** from the socket. Hot appliances should be allowed to cool before being examined.

Sample calculation 1

Calculate the power used by an electrical appliance that consumes 2 amperes of current when connected to a 230 volt supply.

Answer:

$$P = V \times I$$
$$P = 230 \times 2$$
$$P = 460 \text{ watts}$$

PHYSICAL WORLD

Sample calculation 2

Calculate the current used by an electric kettle rated 2300 watts when it is plugged into the socket at home, which gives 230 volts.

Answer:

$$\text{Rearrange } P = V \times I \text{ to get } I = \frac{P}{V}$$

$$\text{Therefore } I = \frac{2300}{230}$$

$$I = 10 \text{ amperes}$$

Sample calculation 3

Calculate the potential difference applied when a 24 watt car bulb uses a current of 2 amperes.

Answer:

$$\text{Rearrange } P = V \times I \text{ to get } V = \frac{P}{I}$$

$$\text{Therefore } V = \frac{24}{2}$$

$$V = 12 \text{ volts}$$

31.13 Calculate the power used by an electrical appliance that consumes 10 amperes of current when connected to a 230 volt supply.

31.14 Calculate the power used by an electrical appliance that consumes 0.25 amperes of current when connected to a 230 volt supply.

31.15 Calculate the current used by an electric kettle rated 2760 watts when it is plugged into the socket at home, which gives 230 volts.

31.16 Calculate the current used by an electric kettle rated 1840 watts when it is plugged into the socket at home which gives 230 volts.

31.17 Calculate the potential difference applied when an 18 watt car bulb uses a current of 1.5 amperes.

31.18 Calculate the potential difference applied when a 14 watt living-room bulb uses a current of 0.06 amperes.

What is the unit of electrical energy?

We saw in previous chapters that the unit of energy is the joule. This unit would not be very suitable for calculating the electrical energy used in our homes as the joule is a very small amount of energy. So electricity supply companies use a different unit for energy: the **kilowatt-hour** (kWh).

The kilowatt-hour is the energy used when 1 kilowatt of power is used for 1 hour.

Note: The kilowatt-hour is often called the **unit of electricity**.

The price of 1 kWh can vary just like the price of most items. However, an average price would be about 18 cent for 1 kWh.

Power rating of electrical appliances

Most electrical appliances will have their power rating written on them. The power rating can be given in watts or in kilowatts. When you want to calculate the cost of using an appliance you must **always work with kilowatts.**

To help you convert to kilowatts remember to divide the power in watts by 1000.

$$500 \text{ watts} = \frac{500}{1000} = 0.5 \text{ kW}$$

$$75 \text{ watts} = \frac{75}{1000} = 0.075 \text{ kW}$$

Sample calculation 4

An electrical kettle has a power rating of 2 kW. The kettle is used to boil water for a total of 2 hours each day for a full week. Calculate:

(a) The number of units of electricity used in the week.

(b) The total cost if 1 kWh costs 18 cent.

Answer:

(a) number of units = number of kW × total number of hours

$= 2 \times (2 \times 7)$

$= 28$ kWh

(b) cost = number of kWh × cost per unit

$= 28 \times 18$ cent

$= 504$ cent

$= €5.04$

Sample calculation 5

A family goes away on holiday for exactly 2 weeks. An 11 W bulb is left on for the full 2 weeks. Calculate:

(a) The number of units of electricity used in the 2 weeks.

(b) The total cost if 1 kWh costs 18 cent.

Answer:

(a) Remember: $11 \text{ W} = \frac{11}{1000} \text{ kW} = 0.011 \text{ kW}$

number of units = number of kW × total number of hours

$= 0.011 \times (24 \times 14)$

$= 3.696$ kWh

(b) cost = number of kWh × cost per unit

$= 3.696 \times 18$

$= 66.528$ cent

$= 67$ cent (rounded to the nearest cent)

Were you surprised by the cost of lighting the bulb for a full fortnight?

Portfolio 234

Activity 31.3

Question

How can we estimate the cost of electricity in our homes for a week?

Equipment needed

Various electrical appliances in your home

A recent electricity bill from your home (don't bring this into class as it is private to your family)

Safety

- Unplug any appliance before you examine it.
- Allow any hot appliance to cool down before you examine it.

Conducting the activity

Using a table similar to the one below:

1. Make a list of ten electrical appliances you have at home.
2. Beside each appliance on your list write down the power rating, taking care to unplug any appliance before you examine it. (The power rating will be written on the appliance.) **Let any hot appliance cool before you examine it.**
3. Make an estimate of the number of hours that each appliance is used in a week.
4. Calculate the total number of kilowatt-hours for all these appliances for the week.
5. Find out the cost of one kilowatt-hour (one unit) from a recent electricity bill in your home.
6. Calculate the total cost of using all these appliances for the week.

	Appliance	Power rating (kW)	Number of hours	Number of kWh
1				
2				
3				
4				
5				
6				
7				
8				
9				
10				
Total number of kilowatt-hours				
Cost per unit				
Total cost				

31.19 How does your estimated cost compare with your bill?

31.20 How much time is covered by your bill at home? Was it one week, one month or longer?

31.21 Give some reasons why your estimated bill and your actual bill might be quite different.

31.22 An electrical kettle has a power rating of 2500 W. The kettle is used to boil water for a total of 3 hours each day for a full week. Calculate:
- **(a)** The number of units of electricity used in the week.
- **(b)** The total cost if 1 kWh costs 18 cent.

31.23 A flat-screen TV has a power rating of 120 W. The TV is on for a total of 8 hours each day for a full week. Calculate:
- **(a)** The number of units of electricity used in the week.
- **(b)** The total cost if 1 kWh costs 18 cent.

31.24 A family goes away on holiday for exactly 2 weeks. A 500 W garden security light bulb is left on for the full 2 weeks. Calculate:
- **(a)** The number of units of electricity used in the 2 weeks.
- **(b)** The total cost if 1 kWh costs 18 cent.

How can we reduce consumption of electrical energy?

Many people in the world benefit from electrical energy. In some cases this benefit is very obvious. However, in order to conserve energy and keep costs down, we need to know how much electrical energy is used in the world and what it is used for.

31.25 Use the internet to find out factual information on the following:
- **(a)** Which household appliances in the home use most electrical energy.
- **(b)** How much electrical energy different industries use.
- **(c)** How much electrical energy has been used in Ireland in different periods in the last fifty years.
- **(d)** How much electrical energy is used in different countries.

Ethical issues and sustainability

'Sustainable development is development that meets the needs of the present without compromising the ability of future generations to meet their own needs.'

31.26 By working in small groups, discuss the following issues:
- **(a)** What can we do in school to be responsible with our use of electrical energy?
- **(b)** What can we do at home to be responsible with our use of electrical energy?
- **(c)** What can the people of Ireland do to be responsible with their use of electrical energy?
- **(d)** What steps do world leaders need to take to help future generations meet their energy needs?

CHAPTER 32

Learning outcomes

At the end of this chapter you will be able to:

- Identify the symbols for a buzzer, a diode, a light-emitting diode (LED) and a light-dependent resistor (LDR)
- Explain that when a diode is forward biased it can conduct electricity
- Explain that when a diode is reverse biased it cannot conduct electricity
- Explain that LEDs can emit light when a current flows through them
- Explain that an LDR can have its resistance changed simply by shining light on it
- Investigate how diodes, LEDs and LDRs work.

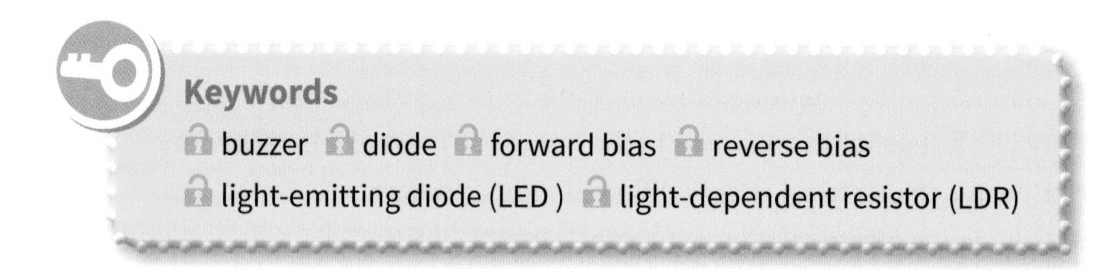

Circuits

An **electrical circuit** will mainly change electrical energy into other forms of energy, usually heat, light or movement. An **electronic circuit** can process information and make a decision.

In a washing machine the electrical circuit will heat the water and rotate the clothes. The control panel is an electronic circuit, used to select and control temperature and time settings and it turns on an indicator light when the clothes are washed.

32.1 Make a list of five electrical appliances you have at home that contain both electrical and electronic circuits. For each appliance give one example of what the electrical circuit is used for and one example of what the electronic circuit is used for. Present your findings in the form of a poster.

What electronic components will we use?

You will remember that we listed the devices that are used in electrical circuits in chapter 30. The list comprised: battery, filament lamp, switch, resistor, variable resistor, ammeter, voltmeter and ohmmeter. Here, we will look at some electronic devices, namely:

- Buzzer
- Diode
- Light-emitting diode (LED)
- Light-dependent resistor (LDR).

What is a buzzer?

A device that converts electrical energy to sound energy. It makes a buzzing sound when an electric current passes through it. Its symbol is shown in Figure 32.1.

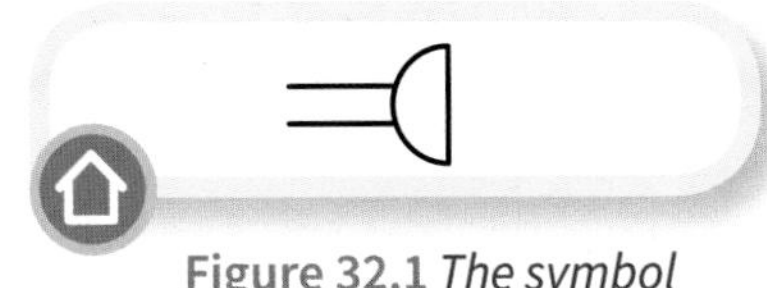

Figure 32.1 *The symbol used for a buzzer*

What is a diode?

A diode is a device that allows an electric current to flow in one direction only. The symbol used for the diode is shown in Figure 32.2.

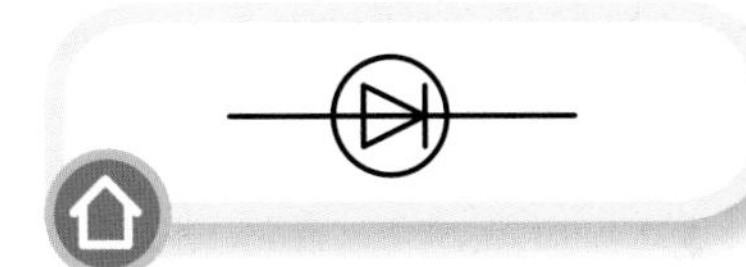

Figure 32.2 *The symbol used for a diode*

32.2 By comparing the symbol in Figure 32.2 and the photograph of the diode in Figure 32.3, can you tell if the right-hand side of the diode in the photograph corresponds to the right-hand side of the diode symbol?

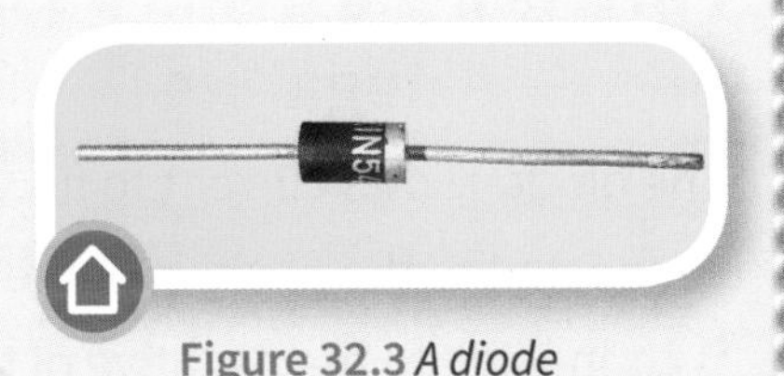

Figure 32.3 *A diode*

Activity 32.1

Question

What happens when a diode and a bulb are connected to a battery?

Equipment needed

1.5-V battery	Diode
Small bulb	Connecting wires

Safety

- Take care not to let the bulb fall as it could break into very sharp pieces.

Conducting the activity

1. Connect the diode and the bulb to the battery as shown in Figure 32.4.
2. Note what happens to the bulb.
3. Disconnect the diode, turn it around the other way and connect it in the circuit again.
4. Record what happens to the bulb.

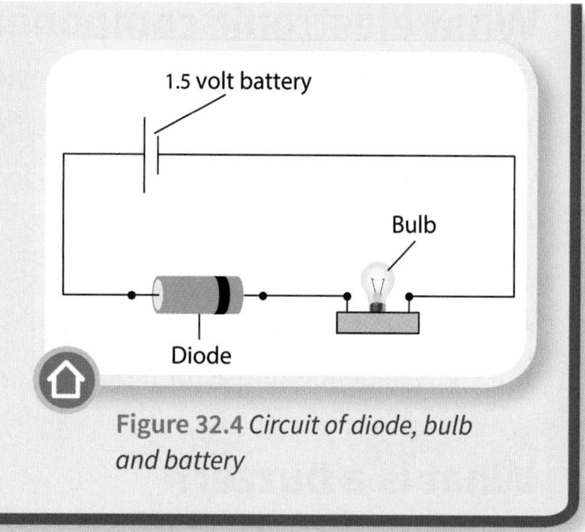

Figure 32.4 *Circuit of diode, bulb and battery*

To help you remember ...

If you look at the symbol for the diode it looks like parts of the letters P (for positive) and N (for negative) have been squashed together:

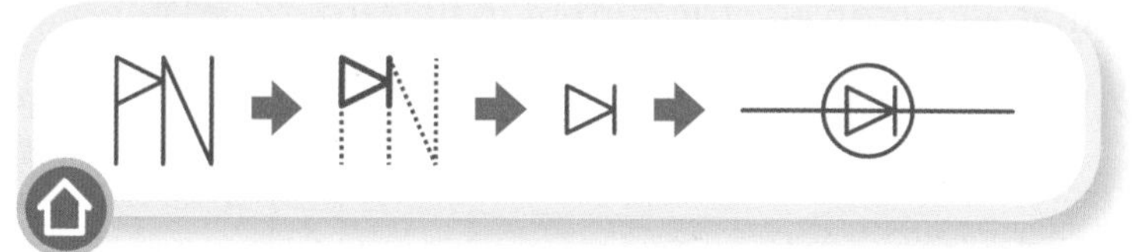

Figure 32.5 *The symbol for a diode*

Forward bias: P is positive and N is negative

The diode allows current to flow if the P terminal is connected to the positive of the battery and the N terminal is connected to the negative of the battery.

When the diode allows current to flow we say that the diode **conducts**. We also say that the diode is in **forward bias**.

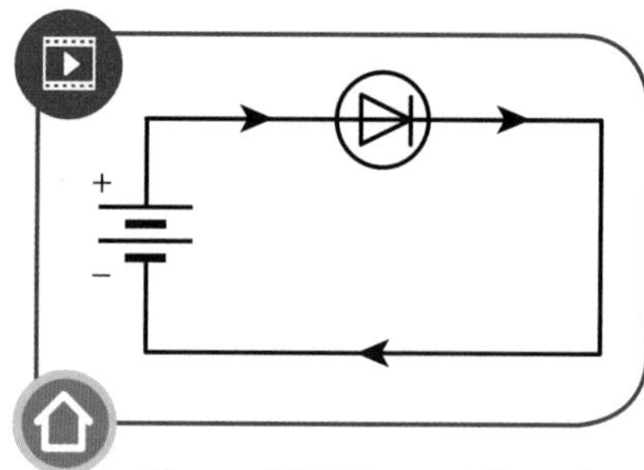

Figure 32.6 *Current flows in the circuit (forward bias)*

Reverse bias: N is positive and P is negative

The diode will not allow current to flow if the P terminal is connected to the negative of the battery and the N terminal is connected to the positive of the battery.

When the diode does not allow current to flow we say that the diode does **not conduct**. We also say that the diode is in **reverse bias**.

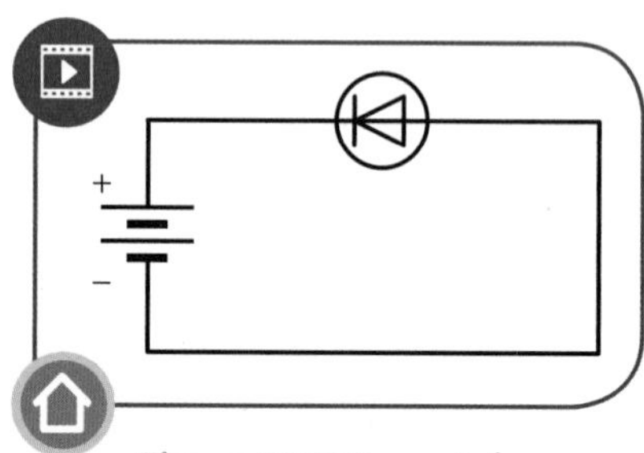

Figure 32.7 *Current does not flow (reverse bias)*

Did you know?

Diodes can change between being forward biased and reverse biased many millions of times each second. This is the basic idea behind modern digital electronics.

What is a light-emitting diode (LED)?

Some diodes can give out light when current flows through them. They are called light-emitting diodes and the abbreviation used is LED. The symbol for the LED is shown in Figure 32.8.

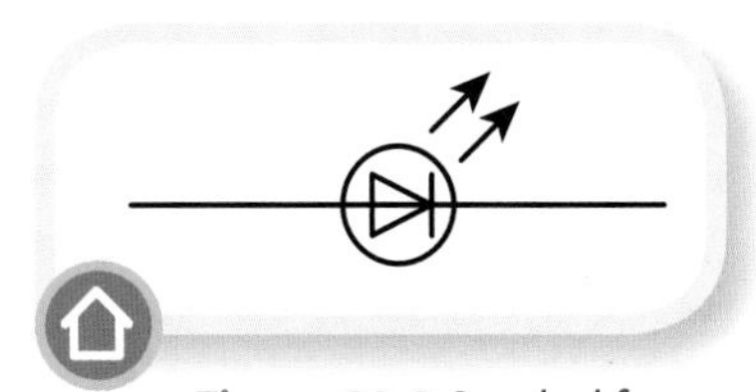

Figure 32.8 *Symbol for the LED*

Portfolio 240

Activity 32.2

Question

When does an LED emit light?

Equipment needed

An LED

1.5-V battery

A resistor

Electrical leads

Conducting the activity

1. Connect the LED, the resistor and the battery as indicated in part (a) of Figure 32.9.
2. Record your observations.
3. Now connect the LED, the resistor and the battery as indicated in part (b) of Figure 32.9.
4. Record your observations and answer the questions below.

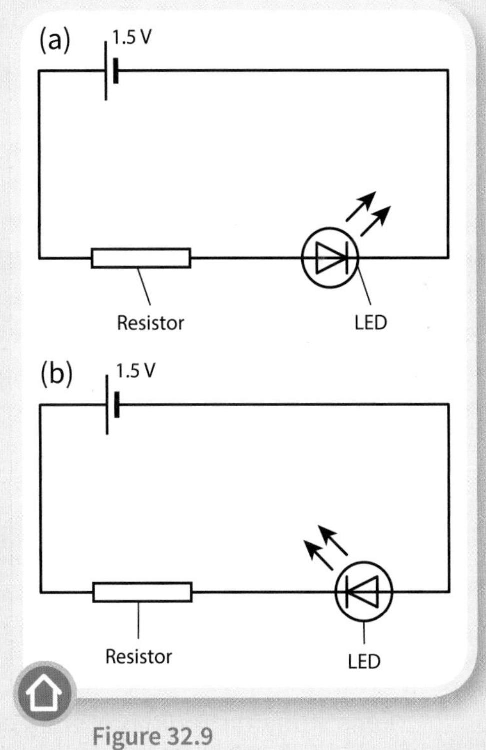

Figure 32.9

32.3 Under what condition will the LED emit light?

32.4 Under what condition will the LED not emit light?

32.5 What are the terms used for when an LED will emit light and when it will not emit light?

Why does an LED need a resistor?

An LED uses only a very small current when it is emitting light. In fact the **LED uses much less current than a bulb**.

If a large current flows through an LED it will most likely burn out. The LED will no longer work. To prevent damage to the LED we always have a resistor connected in series to limit the current, as you can see from Figure 32.10.

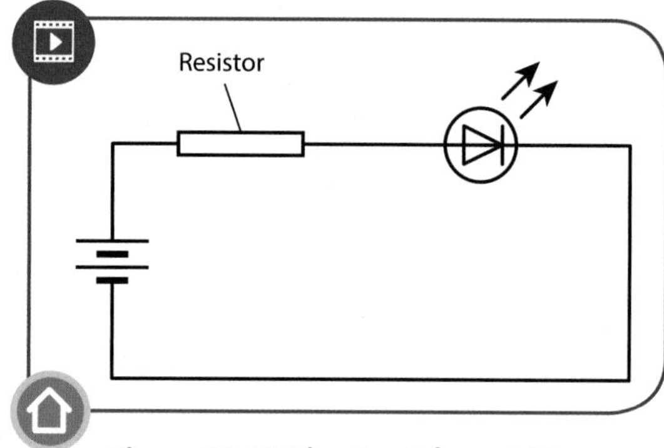

Figure 32.10 *The circuit for an LED, including a resistor to limit the current*

32.6 (a) Individually, on a sheet of paper draw circuit diagrams including a battery, a resistor and an LED to show:

(i) An LED that is lighting

(ii) An LED that is not lighting.

(b) Give a brief explanation of why the LED does or does not light.

(c) In pairs compare your answer to that of your fellow student.

Did you know?

The Nobel Prize in Physics 2014 was awarded jointly to Isamu Akasaki, Hiroshi Amano and Shuji Nakamura 'for the invention of efficient blue light-emitting diodes which has enabled bright and energy-saving white light sources'.

32.7 Each person from a group of four should select one of the following topics for internet research.

Each student should present a poster project to the class.

(a) The history of the diode before 1960.

(b) The history of the diode after 1960.

(c) The history of the LED and examples of where LEDs are used in the home.

(d) The reason for awarding the 2014 Nobel Prize in Physics to Isamu Akasaki, Hiroshi Amano and Shuji Nakamura.

What is a light-dependent resistor (LDR)?

Figure 32.12 *A light-dependent resistor*

The light-dependent resistor (LDR) is a resistor whose value of resistance can change. The value of the resistance will change as the intensity or brightness of the light falling on it changes.

Using an LDR you can arrange for an electrical appliance to be controlled by light. In fact some appliances can be switched on or switched off simply by shining light on the LDR connected to them.

The symbol for the LDR is shown in Figure 32.11.

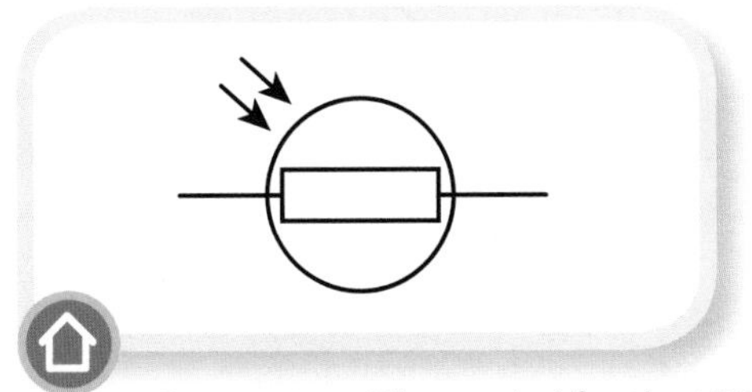

Figure 32.11 *The symbol for the LDR*

Portfolio 241

Activity 32.3

Question

What factor controls the resistance of an LDR and the current flowing through it?

Equipment needed

An LDR	Digital ohmmeter (multimeter)
6-V battery	Filament bulb
Electrical leads	Switch

Safety

- Take care not to drop the 6-V battery as it is quite heavy.
- Take care not to let the bulb fall as it could break into very sharp pieces.

Conducting the activity

1. Connect the 6-V battery, the LDR, the switch and the filament bulb as indicated in part (a) of Figure 32.13.
2. Close the switch and record your observations.

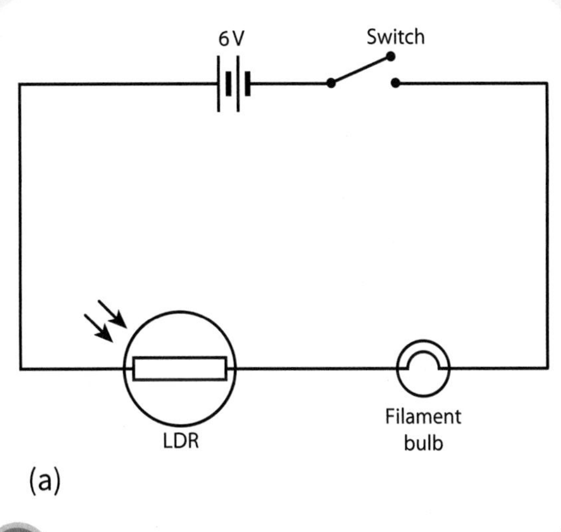

Figure 32.13

3. Now cover the LDR with your hand. Record your observations.
4. Now connect the LDR directly to the digital ohmmeter as indicated in part (b) of Figure 32.13.
5. Record the value of the resistance.
6. Now cover the LDR with your hand. Record the value of the resistance.

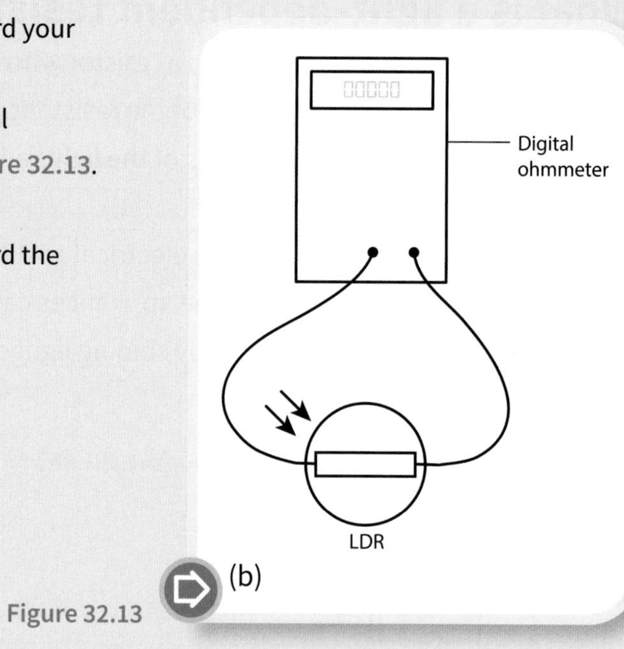

Figure 32.13

32.8 What happened to the light from the filament bulb when you covered the LDR with your hand?

32.9 What can you conclude about the current flowing through an LDR when it is covered from the light in the room?

32.10 What was the difference in the resistance of the LDR when it was covered and when it was not covered?

32.11 Use the internet to find three examples of where LDRs are used in everyday situations.

Activity 32.4

Question

How can we set up a circuit to choose between a high-frequency buzzer and a low-frequency buzzer?

Equipment needed

- 6-V battery
- Resistor
- 2 diodes
- Low-frequency buzzer
- High-frequency buzzer
- Connecting wires

Safety

- Take care not to drop the 6-V battery as it is quite heavy.

Conducting the activity

1. Connect the terminals of the battery so that A is connected to the positive terminal and B to the negative terminal, as shown in Figure 32.14.
2. The high-frequency buzzer will sound. Explain why.
3. The low-frequency buzzer is silent. Explain why.
4. Now connect the terminals of the battery so that A is connected to the negative terminal and B to the positive terminal.
5. The low-frequency buzzer will sound. Explain why.
6. The high-frequency buzzer is silent. Explain why.

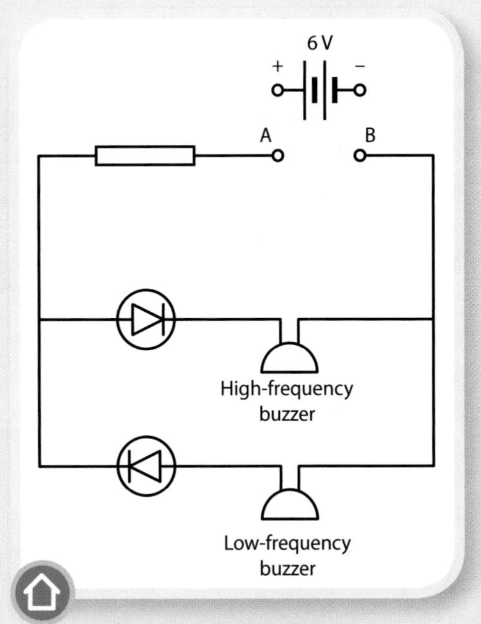

Figure 32.14 *High-frequency and low-frequency buzzers*

Portfolio 243

Activity 32.5

Question

How can we choose which LED will emit light?

Equipment needed

6-V battery
2 switches
2 resistors
LED emitting green light
LED emitting red light
Connecting wires

Safety

- Take care not to drop the 6-V battery as it is quite heavy.

Figure 32.15 *Changing from a red light to a green light*

Conducting the activity

1. Set up one circuit as shown in Figure 32.15.
2. Close switch A and keep switch B open. Write down your observations and explain why this happened.
3. Close switch B and keep switch A open. Write down your observations and explain why this happened.
4. Close both switches. Write down your observations and explain why this happened.

Did you know?

By using three different LEDs, the first could emit red light, the second green light and the third blue light. You can then combine the three colours to get the type of light we get from ordinary bulbs. We call this light **white light**. This idea gives us bulbs that use very little energy and won the Nobel Prize in Physics for the three scientists mentioned earlier.

Portfolio 245

Activity 32.6

Question

How can we activate a buzzer by switching on a light?

Equipment needed

6-V battery

LDR

Buzzer

Study lamp

Connecting wires

Safety

- Take care not to drop the 6-V battery as it is quite heavy.
- The bulb may get hot and should not be touched.
- The lamp will be plugged into a socket and great care must be taken with all electrical devices.

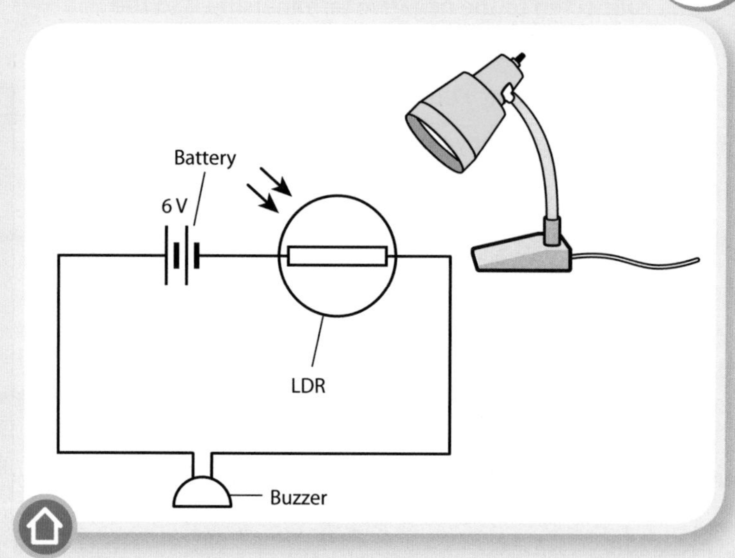

Figure 32.16 *Activating a buzzer by switching on a light*

Conducting the activity

1. Turn off the lights in the laboratory so the room is quite dim.
2. The resistance of the LDR is high because of the dim light and only a very small current flows through the buzzer. There is no sound from the buzzer.
3. Switch on the study lamp so that bright light shines on the LDR.
4. The resistance of the LDR is now low, allowing a greater current to flow through the buzzer.
5. You can now hear sound from the buzzer.

CHAPTER 33 UNIT 4 Impact of modern physics on society

Learning outcomes

At the end of this chapter you will be able to:

- Explain the impact that digital electronics has had on the world
- Examine the impact that modern telecommunications has had on society
- Examine how the internet has affected our daily lives.

Keywords
digital electronics telecommunications internet

What is digital electronics

We saw in chapter 32 that a diode could control the direction in which a current could flow. Based on this idea many other digital electronic devices were developed in the second half of the last century. Indeed, in the last twenty-five years huge improvements have been made in the performance of these devices.

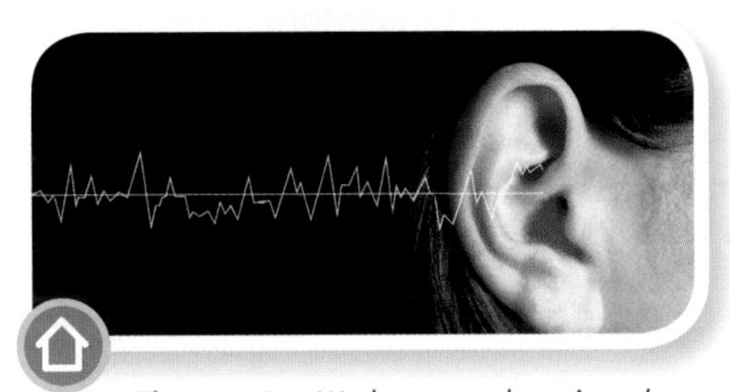

Figure 33.1 *We hear analog signals*

Sounds entering our ears can be represented by a wave, as shown in Figure 33.1. This type of wave is an **analog signal**, represented in the diagram in Figure 33.2. A digital signal is different, as you can see in Figure 33.3.

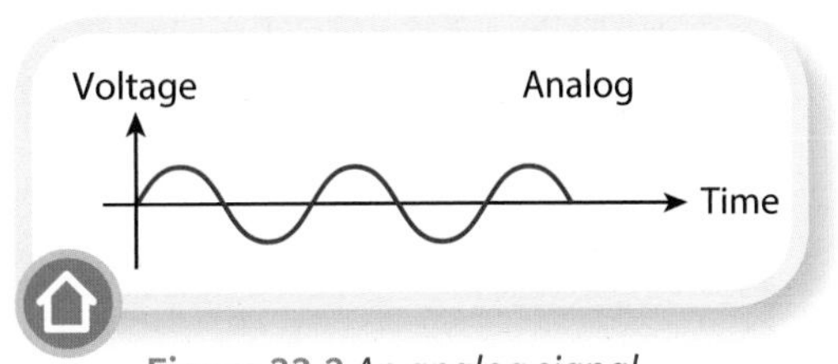

Figure 33.2 *An analog signal*

Digital signals, as you can see from the figures, are not smooth like analog signals. Digital signals are simple 'true-false' or 'on-off' statements to represent information. Because digital devices

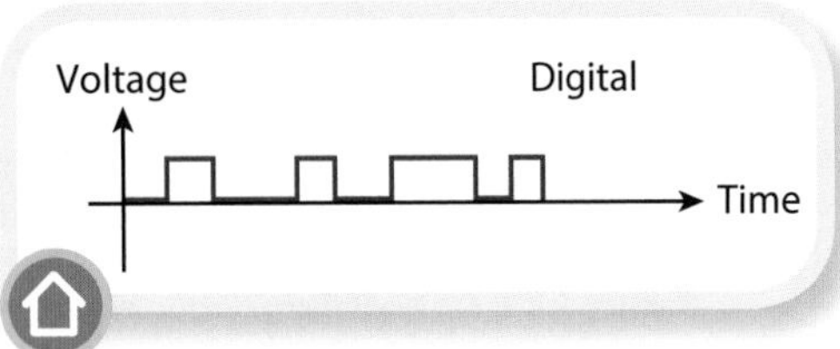

Figure 33.3 *A digital signal*

recognise only one of two possible signals, they are less affected by unwanted electronic signals.

The mathematics for digital electronics is based on the work of George Boole, who was the first professor of mathematics in Cork University, from 1849 to 1864.

Digital electronics has had a great impact on society. You might call it an electronics revolution.

To help us to discuss and research how digital electronics has affected the world, we will examine the technology associated with telecommunications and the internet. We will look at how science, the environment and society in general have been affected by these technologies.

33.1 By using the internet, research the life and work of George Boole. Present your findings in the form of a poster.

What is meant by telecommunications?

Keeping in touch by telephone has become easier, cheaper and more reliable in recent years. We will consider some short statements on how the following have been affected by new forms of communication:

- Science
- Environment
- Society.

Once you have looked at these topics, you will get into groups to research and discuss issues relating to them.

Figure 33.4 *Optical fibres have replaced old cables for phones and are much more efficient*

Figure 33.5 *Antique telephones*

Science

The popularity of mobile phones has resulted in a greater need for people to be skilled in electronics and computing. Many courses in electronics are offered by universities and third-level colleges. More people today understand and appreciate the wonders of this area of science.

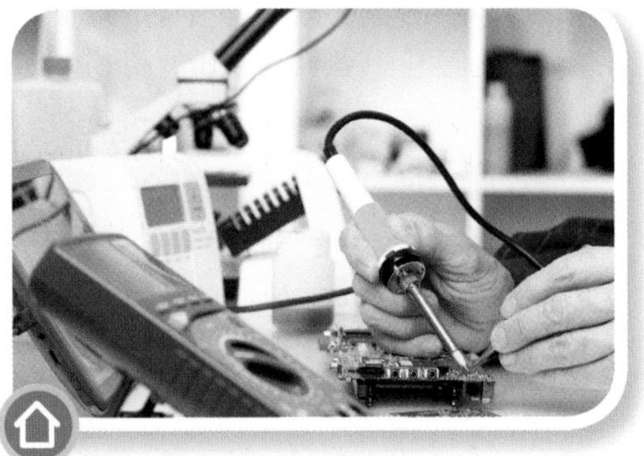

Figure 33.6 *Soldering equipment and electronic parts*

Environment

Many modern electronic devices become outdated very quickly. Outdated devices are dumped or recycled and newer devices are manufactured. Earth's natural resources are being used up in the manufacturing process. The problem has also led to a greater awareness of the need to recycle. The copper in old wiring is very often recycled.

Society

Instead of walking or cycling to a friend's house, people today choose to text from the comfort of a couch at home. Are people becoming lazier? How will this lack of exercise affect a person's health as they get older?

Many young adults move to foreign countries after they finish their education. With the improvement in telephones they can keep in contact with their parents and friends back home on a regular basis. This is very comforting to the young person abroad and to the family at home.

Figure 33.7 *Much material is recycled, like these speakers*

Figure 33.8 *Is the ease with which we can keep in touch with people making us lazy?*

Topics for discussion and research

33.2 **(a)** In your group, discuss the following topics (i)–(ix). One person from each group should record and present the group's views to the rest of the class.

(b) At home do some research on the same nine topics. Back in class, discuss these same topics again. This time you will have the benefit of having done some research. Is there a difference in the views of the groups on the various topics?

i Third-level colleges provide many courses on digital electronics and computer-related studies. Is this having a negative impact on more traditional areas of study such as languages, history, geography, and so on?

ii Will the study of digital electronics have a negative impact on the study of the biological sciences?
iii Is the education system producing too many people interested in electronics and computer studies?
iv People spend more time indoors talking and texting on their phones than in previous years. Has this made people less aware of their natural environment?
v Is the electronics industry a major cause of pollution in the environment?
vi What parts of an out-of-date mobile phone can be recycled?
vii Parents can keep in contact with their children so easily by using mobile phones. Is this good for the children? Are children safer today because of mobile phones? Have children today lost the ability to think for themselves?
viii How are parents affected when their adult children move abroad to work? Has the improvement in telephone technology made things easier for the parents?
ix Modern technology has enabled us to get information so quickly. Have people lost the patience to wait for things? Do we really need instant access to information?

What is the internet?

The internet is a vast, world-wide network of computers all connected together.

33.3 Explain the difference between the internet and the world wide web.

A quick look at Table 33.1 will show how the internet has influenced the lives of people.

Table 33.1 Numbers of people using the internet

At the end of the year	Number of people using the internet
1995	16 million
1999	248 million
2003	719 million
2006	1093 million
2009	1802 million
2012	2497 million
Present year	?

33.4 What do you predict will be the figure in the last row of the table?
33.5 Research the number of people using the internet worldwide this year. How close was your estimate?

Consider the following short statements on how the internet has affected each of the following:

- Science
- Environment
- Society.

Once you have looked at these, you will get into groups to research and discuss topics on them.

Figure 33.9 *The internet is like an infinite library*

Science

The internet is an amazing library, with an almost endless supply of information. The study of science has been greatly facilitated by the internet: you can find information from others and share information with others so easily. You can study the historical development of science as well as keeping up to date with recent discoveries.

Environment

The internet has made it very easy to learn about what is happening all around the world. An example of a benefit of this is the idea of renting bicycles to travel around a city: one city started this, and in a short time cities all around the world were copying this clever idea after having read about it on the internet. People are healthier for cycling and cities are less polluted.

Society

Life has been easier for many people because of the internet. You can book a holiday, order a book and buy clothes on the internet. However, the people who worked for the holiday company, the book shop and the clothes shop may have lost their jobs. Has the internet been good for society?

Figure 33.10 *Dublin bikes*

Figure 33.11 *Internet shopping affects bricks-and-mortar shops and livelihoods*

Topics for discussion and research

33.6 **(a)** In your group, discuss the following topics (i)–(x). One person from each group should record and present the group's views to the rest of the class.

(b) At home do some research on the same ten topics. Back in class, discuss these same topics again. This time you will have the benefit of having done some research. Is there a difference in the views of the groups on the various topics?

i Has the internet helped students to be skilled at research on a computer but less capable at performing activities in a laboratory with their own hands?

ii What do you use the internet for? What is the most common use of the internet among students in your class?

iii The internet has allowed students from some poorer countries to compete with students from wealthier countries because of equal access to the internet. How does this benefit poorer countries?

iv New discoveries are being made at a very rapid rate. Will these new ideas make the science you learn in school totally out of date?

v In the past people lived in cities to find a good job. However, with the internet you can live far away from a city and work online. Will this be good for the environment?

vi When you use the internet a certain amount of electrical energy is needed to power this. Is the energy consumption of the internet a cause of concern for the environment?

vii Has the internet made people more aware of the need to protect our environment for future generations?

viii What kinds of jobs have people lost because of the internet?

ix Because of the internet people work less hard than before. People have more free time to relax. Is this good for society?

x Internet bullying (often referred to as cyber bullying) is a major problem all around the world. What can be done to help prevent this bullying?

33.7 Class discussion:

You have now discussed several topics based on how the internet has affected our lives. For this you used the internet itself as a source of information.

(a) How reliable is the information on the internet?

(b) Is it possible to tell if the information is biased?

(c) Could the information be out of date?

(d) Who is responsible for keeping information up to date?

UNIT 5

EARTH & SPACE

CHAPTER 34

UNIT 5

The big bang – how our universe began

Learning outcomes

At the end of this chapter you will be able to:

- Outline the big bang theory
- Explain the term 'singularity'.

Keywords

solar system · singularity · expanding universe · galaxies · astronomer · gravity

What is in the universe?

Our universe is a vast area of space within which we find all the galaxies, stars and solar systems that make up the universe as we know it.

34.1 Find a simple explanation of 'a galaxy'. Write your answer in your copy, together with a note of the source of your answer.

34.2 Name three stars that you know of.

34.3 What is a solar system?

Was there a beginning to the universe?

How did our universe begin? Where did it all start? What was there at the very beginning? These are some of the questions that humans have asked in their desire to discover the origins of the universe.

Animated Scientist Biography

Watch an *Exploring Science* animation to find out more about Stephen Hawking and his theories about the beginning of the universe.

People have always had more questions than answers on this subject. The limits of our technology meant there was a complete lack of evidence for scientists to work with. These questions about the creation of the universe remained unanswered until discoveries in astronomy and physics led scientists to determine that there was a beginning to our universe.

34.4 Find out and write a paragraph explaining what is meant by:

(a) The study of astronomy

(b) The study of physics.

Figure 34.1 *The beginning of the universe*

Figure 34.2 *The expanding universe*

In 1929 the American **astronomer** Edwin Hubble discovered that the universe is **expanding**. This means that all objects in the universe are moving away from each other.

Trying to imagine something on this scale is a very difficult concept for people to grasp. Here is a simple task that may demonstrate how the universe is expanding.

Portfolio 255

Activity 34.1

Question

How can we visualise how the universe is expanding?

Equipment needed

White (or pale) balloons | Ruler

Black marker pen | Length of string

Safety

- Take care when blowing up the balloons that they do not burst.

Conducting the activity

1. Blow up your balloon to a small size – no more than half of its maximum size.
2. Randomly mark about ten dots on your balloon with the marker pen. These represent galaxies. Give them numbers so you can identify them for the next part of the activity.
3. Let about half the air out of your balloon.
4. Use the ruler to measure how far apart the galaxies (the dots), are from each other and record this.
5. Blow up your balloon as large as you can without bursting it.
6. Look at where the dots representing your galaxies are now located.

7. Use a piece of string to measure how far apart the galaxies now are from each other. You will do this by holding the string on one dot and stretching it to the next dot, holding the length or marking the string with a pen, and then measuring the length of string you used with a ruler. Use one galaxy as a starting point for your measurement.
8. Record your results.
9. Repeat the measurements between several of the dots to record how each dot has moved away from others.

34.5 In activity 34.1, why did you use a ruler for your first measurements (at step 4) and a piece of string for your second measurement (at step 7)?

Hubble noted that not only was the universe expanding, it was expanding at a great rate. Hubble's discovery became known as **Hubble's Law**.

Hubble's Law: Galaxies are moving away from each other. The farther away a galaxy is, the faster the galaxy is moving away from us.

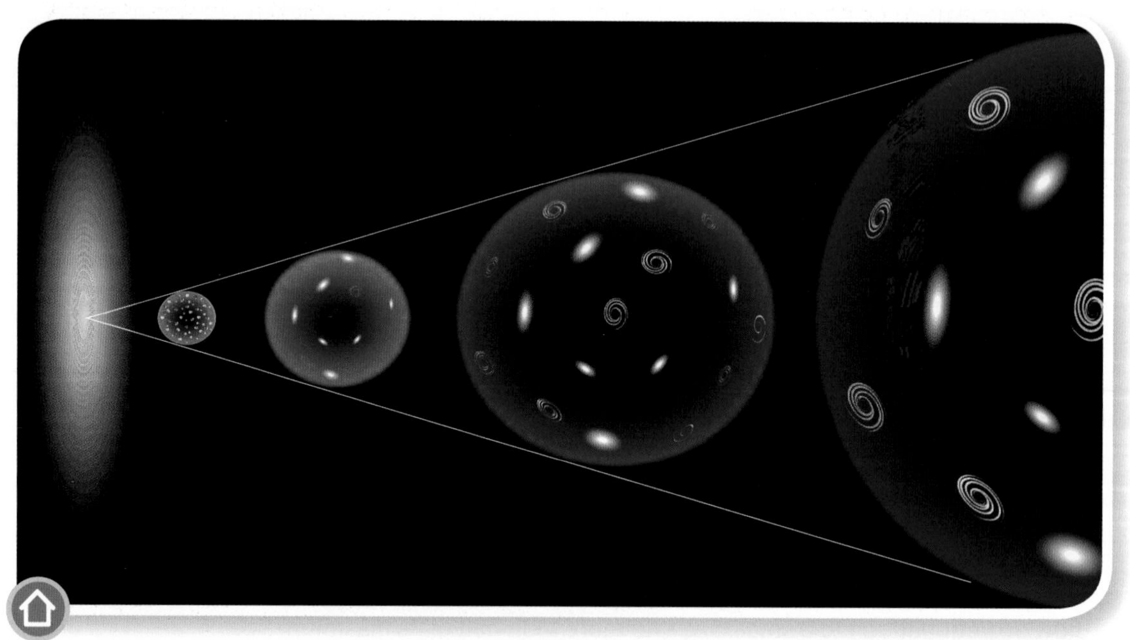

Figure 34.3 *The universe expanding ever since the big bang*

Figure 34.4 *Edwin Hubble, US astronomer*

Figure 34.5 *The Hubble Space Telescope*

Why is the Hubble Space Telescope so important?

The Hubble Space Telescope, which was launched by NASA in 1990, is named after Edwin Hubble. The Hubble Space Telescope is extremely important for furthering our knowledge of space. Normally when we look into space we are looking through telescopes that are located on Earth. The images that we see are distorted or changed by Earth's atmosphere. This can affect what we see.

The Hubble Space Telescope is out in space, orbiting at a height of 569 km above Earth. Therefore, Earth's atmosphere does not affect the images the telescope receives from space.

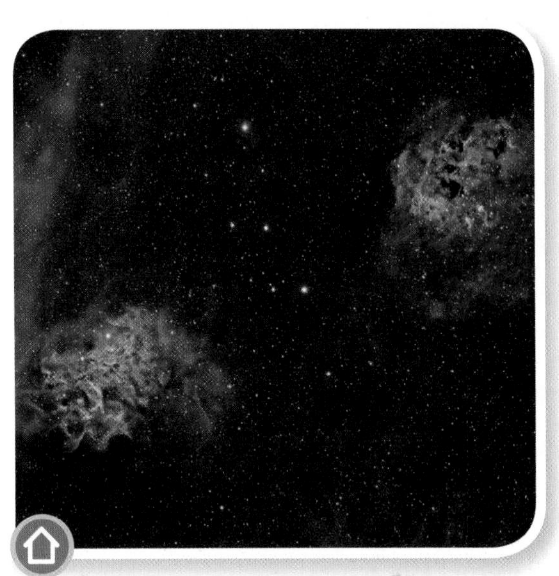

Figure 34.6 *An image taken from the Hubble Space Telescope*

34.6 Research the main discoveries that scientists have made about the universe using information provided by the Hubble Space Telescope.

In your research identify four key discoveries that have been made with the help of the Hubble Space Telescope in relation to any object, planet or galaxy that is located in our universe.

Animated Scientist Biography

Watch an *Exploring Science* animation to find out more about Edwin Hubble and his work.

Was there really a big bang?

The term 'bang' suggests that there was an explosion of some form. But this is not actually what happened at the start of the universe.

EARTH & SPACE

A starting point

Edwin Hubble concluded that there must have been a **single moment** when the entire universe was held within a **single zone**. This was the beginning of the universe, which Hubble's observations put at around **13.8 billion years ago**. Scientists call this single zone in a single moment the **singularity**. It was very, very small; very, very dense and very, very hot.

BIG BANG THEORY

4 ~9 BILLION YEARS LATER FORMATION OF THE SOLAR SYSTEM AND EARTH

3 ~300 MILLION YEARS LATER BEGINNING FORMATION OF THE STARS AND GALAXIES

2 ~380 000 YEARS LATER ELECTRONS AND NUCLEI COMBINED INTO ATOMS

1 FIRST SECONDS AFTER BIG BANG BIRTH OF SUBATOMIC PARTICLES

~13,8 BILLION YEARS AGO BIG BANG

EXPANDING AND COOLING UNIVERSE

Figure 34.7 *Evolution of the universe*

The big bang

The singularity was a region so intensely hot that the normal particles of matter – particles that occur in atoms – did not exist. Within a single moment (some scientists believe this time frame to be as short as one second) this intensely hot singularity **expanded**. This is what we term **the big bang**.

In the first few moments after the big bang the universe was so hot that we cannot imagine a level of temperature that great.

Did you know?

Where did this singularity, this point in space, actually come from? What was this singularity? Did this singularity actually appear out of nowhere? Scientists do not know!

After the big bang

As the universe continued to expand it began to cool. The cooler temperature allowed particles to exist. It was now also cool enough for light to begin to travel through the universe.

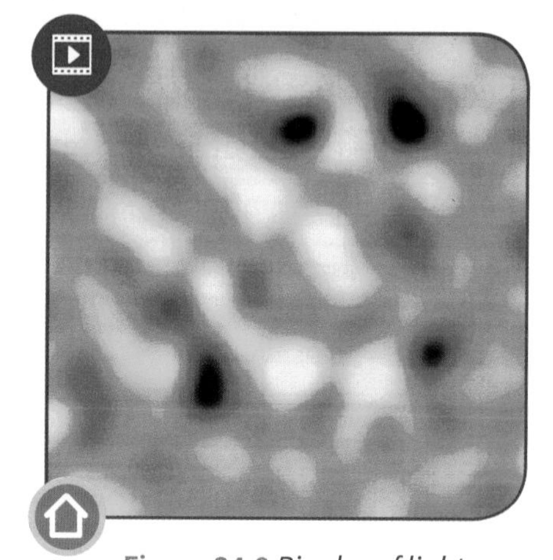

Figure 34.8 *Ripples of light radiation from the big bang*

How did matter form?

Gravity is a force that pulls particles together. This force of gravity, which was originally present within the singularity, allowed the particles to form matter.

This matter came together and formed into the stars, the planets and all other known structures in the universe. We will be looking at all of these structures in the following chapters.

Therefore, gravity formed all the structures within the universe. The combination of matter and gravity formed an estimated 100 octillion (100 000 000 000 000 000 000 000 000 000) stars. That's hard to picture, so imagine the universe represented by a sandy beach and a single star being equal to one grain of sand on the entire beach.

Large groups of stars formed into the galaxies and our universe came into existence.

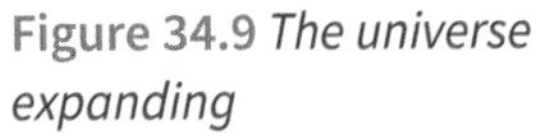
Figure 34.9 *The universe expanding*

Figure 34.10 *The Milky Way, the galaxy within which Earth is found*

The big bang theory is only one of the explanations for the formation of the universe. It is how scientists have tried to explain how the universe developed from a single moment.

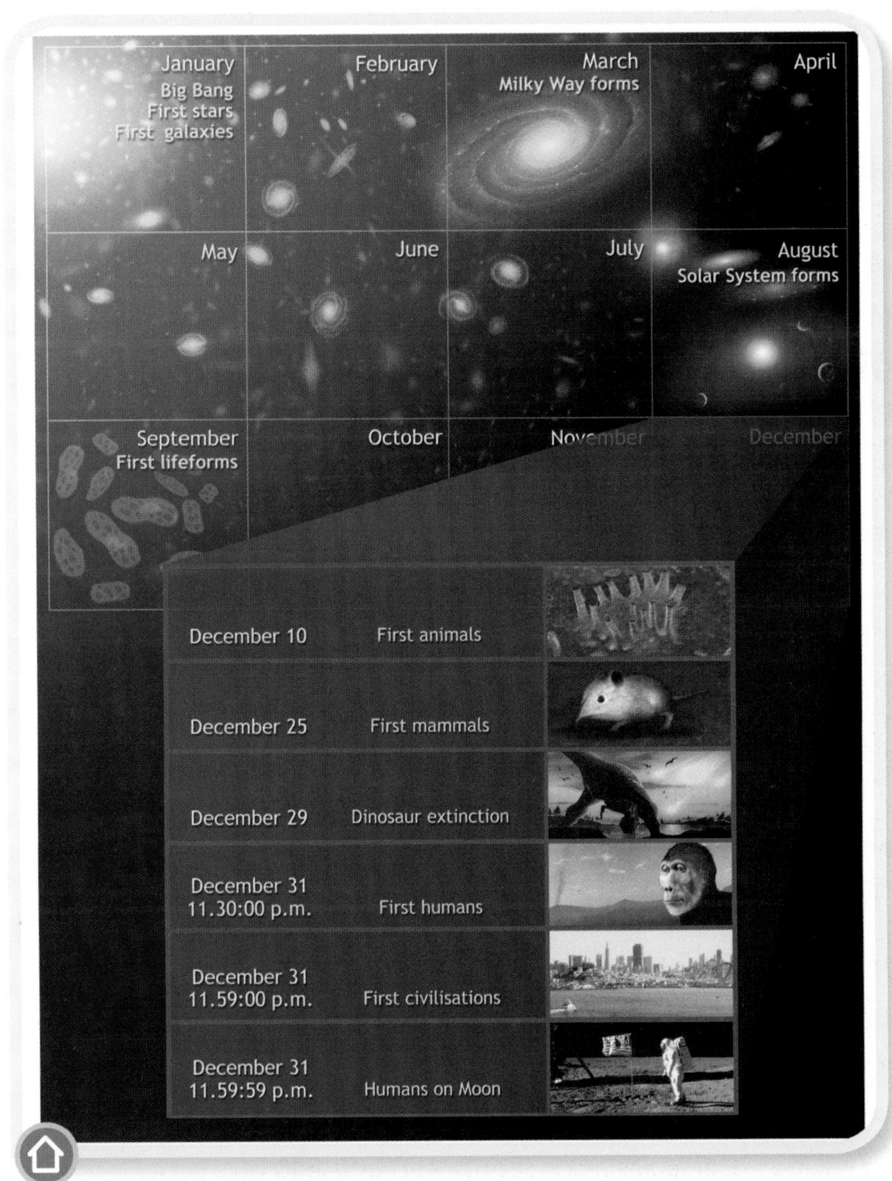

Figure 34.11 *Calendar of the universe represented by a yearly calendar*

It is amazing to think that we are living on a planet that is orbiting a dazzling star. This star, the Sun, is one of billions of other stars that are part of our galaxy. Our galaxy is also one of many other galaxies that make up the universe.

The exact answer to how our universe began is still unknown. Scientists continue to look for an explanation for the origin of our universe.

UNIT 5

CHAPTER 35 Galaxies, stars and the Solar System

Learning outcomes

At the end of this chapter you will be able to:

- Identify the type of reactions that take place in a star
- Describe the life cycle of a star
- Describe the shape of the Milky Way galaxy
- Classify the objects that are located within the Solar System
- Distinguish between the planets in the Solar System in terms of size, atmosphere, gravity and proximity to the Sun.

Keywords

star · nuclear fusion · red giant · nebula · white dwarf · luminous · terrestrial

What are stars?

When you look up at the sky on a clear night, are you amazed by the stars that exist there, shining brightly? Do you ever wonder what a star is and how it was formed?

A star is a luminous object made up of gas that can produce its own light and heat by nuclear reactions.

35.1 (a) From the statement above, what do you think the term 'luminous' means?
(b) Identify another everyday luminous object.
(c) Name a non-luminous object that exists in space.

What are nuclear reactions?

Nuclear reactions that take place in a star occur between two hydrogen atoms. The nucleus of one hydrogen atom fuses with the nucleus of another hydrogen atom, forming a completely new element called **helium**.

It is the conversion of hydrogen to helium that releases the heat and light that causes our stars to shine. The heat and light released are forms of energy.

Figure 35.1 *Nuclear fusion reactions*

Figure 35.2 *Light energy from the Sun*

35.2 How do we know that nuclear reactions are still taking place in the Sun?

Does a star last forever?

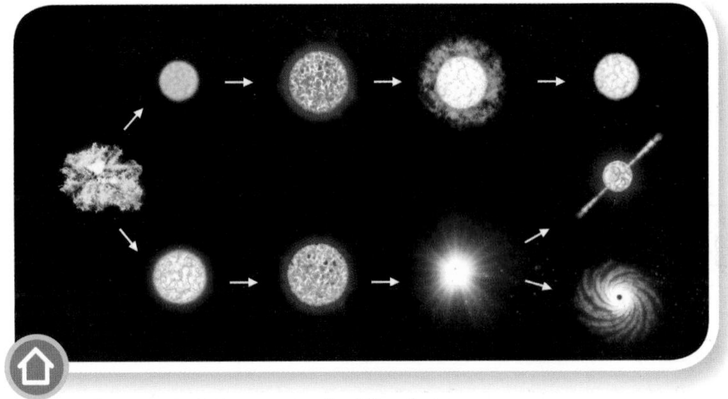

Figure 35.3 *Stages in the life of a star*

Some stars have only a small amount of matter; some stars have a large amount of matter. Every star is different and every star is at a different stage in its life cycle. A life cycle is a series of changes that an object goes through in its life.

Figure 35.4 *Formation of a new star*

Some stars have already died. Some stars explode during the process of dying, dramatically releasing a dazzling amount of light that may be seen throughout the universe in what is called a **supernova**.

Some stars appear small and they are called **dwarfs**. A small star may be around 200,000 km across – about the same size as the planet Jupiter.

The life cycle of a star has four phases:

- Phase 1 – formation
- Phase 2 – the stable period
- Phase 3 – the red giant
- Phase 4 – the white dwarf.

EARTH & SPACE

Phase 1: formation

There are large gas clouds in space, called **nebulae**. The attractive forces of gravity of the gas particles cause these gases to collapse and come together.

As temperature and pressure within the cloud increase, the gases begin to spin rapidly, which causes the nuclei of elements to join together (i.e. nuclear fusion reactions take place) and a star is born!

Phase 2: the stable period

Figure 35.5 *A main sequence star*

Over billions of years the star becomes stable. We call such a star a **main sequence star**.

A star spends the majority of its life as a main sequence star. It is in this phase that the star is using up all its available resource of hydrogen in nuclear reactions to emit heat and light energy.

A main sequence star balances between:

- Its own gravity trying to shrink it, and
- The heat energy that it is producing trying to make it expand.

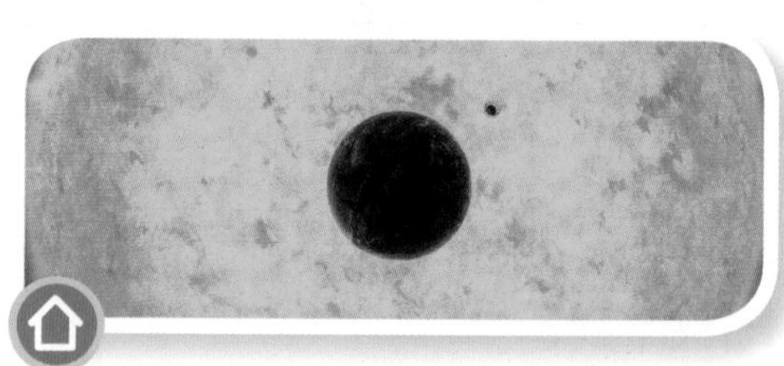

Figure 35.6 *A red giant*

The star in this form will continue to glow for billions of years. Our own sun is in this phase of its life.

Phase 3: the red giant

When the star has used up all its supplies of hydrogen in its core, it begins burning helium on its outer parts. This causes the star to release more heat. As a result the outer part of the star expands.

The star now becomes a huge structure, and is known as a **red giant**.

When the Sun becomes a red giant it will engulf and destroy Earth. Scientists believe this will take place, but not until around five billion years from now.

Phase 4: the white dwarf

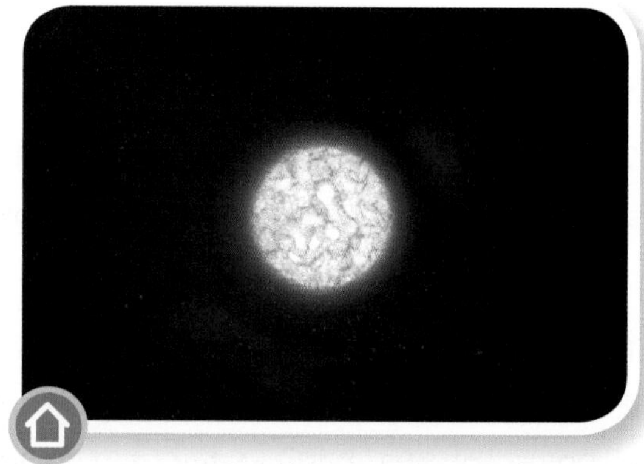

Figure 35.7 *A white dwarf*

Once the red giant has turned all the hydrogen that it contains to helium – this may take from five to ten billion years, depending on the size of the star – it condenses and collapses in on itself, forming a tiny, but very dense, star called a **white dwarf**. A white dwarf has only about one-quarter of its original mass left. The white dwarf will produce less and less light until eventually it produces no more light.

Is that a star I see?

Stars emit light. That light takes time to travel through the vacuum of space to Earth until we can see it. So as we look at the night sky we are in reality looking back in time – possibly millions of years. When we see a star in the sky, the light that we see coming from that star is light from the past that has travelled through space to where we can see it now.

Figure 35.8 *Hubble Space Telescope in orbit – the stars it is photographing may not actually exist any more!*

Figure 35.9 *Stargazing*

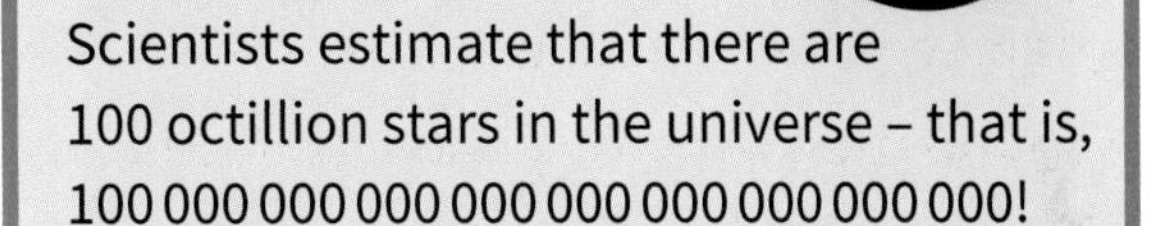

Did you know?

Scientists estimate that there are 100 octillion stars in the universe – that is, 100 000 000 000 000 000 000 000 000 000!

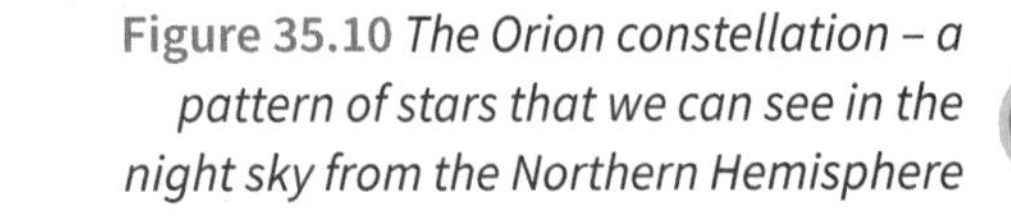

Did you know?

The 'twinkle' from the stars is a result of turbulence in Earth's atmosphere.

Figure 35.10 *The Orion constellation – a pattern of stars that we can see in the night sky from the Northern Hemisphere*

Now that we know how stars are formed we will look at their role within the universe.

What is in the universe?

It is mind-boggling to think about how many galaxies are in the universe, and how many stars are in each galaxy. It is fascinating to wonder whether there is life in other galaxies. Many science-fiction stories have been written imagining what those life forms would be like!

We'll start with our own tiny spot in the universe.

Galaxies

A galaxy is a collection of millions or billions of stars, along with gas and dust, all held together by gravitational forces.

There are billions of galaxies in the universe. Some galaxies are small, with only a few million stars. Other galaxies have 400 billion stars, or more.

Galaxies are constantly moving away from each other.

Earth is in the Milky Way galaxy. This galaxy is spiral-shaped, which is the most common galaxy shape in the universe.

Figure 35.11 *The Milky Way – Earth's galaxy*

Figure 35.12 *A spiral galaxy*

35.3 Research a galaxy in the universe that is not our own. Find answers to the following questions:

(a) What is the name of the galaxy?

(b) What shape is the galaxy?

(c) Are there any similarities in the shape of the Milky Way and the galaxy you are studying?

(d) Identify the name of the galaxy closest to our own galaxy and find out what distance away that galaxy is from the Milky Way.

Our solar system

Our solar system is made up of the Sun and the planets (including Earth) that orbit around it. The Sun (which is a star) is one of billions of stars that make up the Milky Way galaxy.

Did you know?

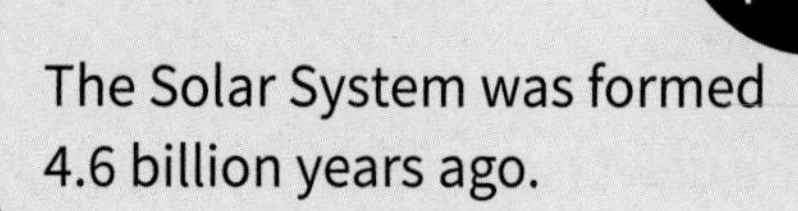

The Solar System was formed 4.6 billion years ago.

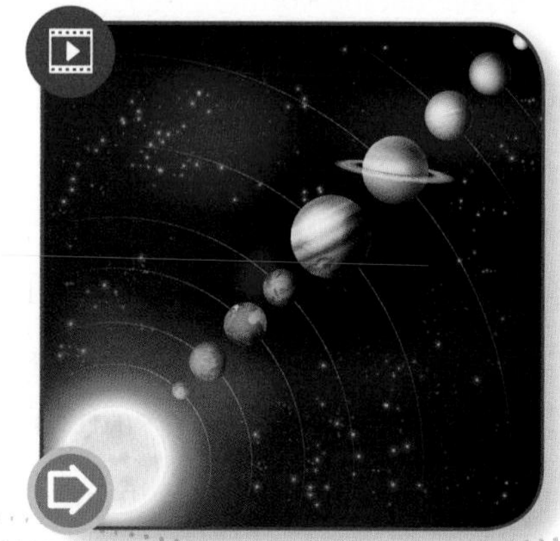

Figure 35.13 *Our solar system*

Did you know?

The outer part of the Sun reaches temperatures of 5 500°C. The Sun's core (the inner part) reaches temperatures of a whopping 15 000 000°C!

35.4 Without looking it up, how would you explain the term 'planet'?

Planets

To be called a 'planet' three conditions must be met:

1. The object must orbit a sun.
2. The object must be big enough to allow its own gravity to pull it inwards to make it look like a sphere (rounded).
3. The object must be big enough for its own gravity to move other objects around the same size out of its way in its orbit around the sun.

Within our solar system there are three types of planets:

- Terrestrial planets
- Jovian planets
- Dwarf planets or planetoids.

We will look at these types of planets in relation to the Solar System, although there are many other planets in the universe.

Terrestrial planets

Our solar system's terrestrial (or rocky) planets are:

- Mercury
- Venus
- Earth
- Mars.

These orbit closest to the Sun and are known as the **inner planets**. They are composed mainly of rock and metal.

Figure 35.14 *Venus*

Figure 35.15 *Mercury*

EARTH & SPACE

Figure 35.16 *Earth*

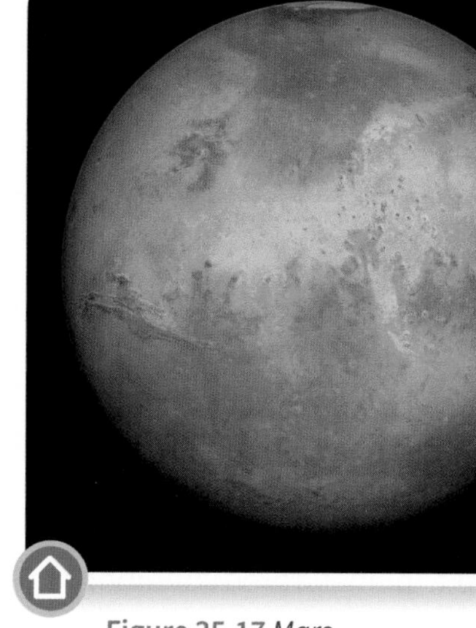
Figure 35.17 *Mars*

Jovian planets

'Jovian' means 'Jupiter like'. The Jovian planets in our Solar System are:

- Jupiter
- Saturn
- Uranus
- Neptune.

These planets are mostly composed of helium and hydrogen. They are very large and have rings around them.

Figure 35.18 *Jupiter*

Figure 35.19 *Saturn*

Figure 35.20 *Uranus, taken from the Hubble Space Telescope*

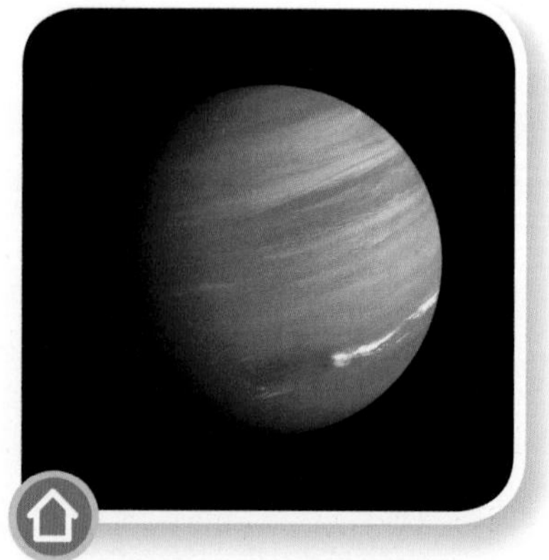
Figure 35.21 *Neptune*

Did you know?

Jupiter has the biggest ocean of any planet. It is 40 000 km deep. That is as deep as Earth is round! (The circumference of Earth is 40 075 km.)

Planetoids

A planetoid is a 'dwarf' planet. These are objects that are:

- Too large to be asteroids (which are rocky bodies located in our Solar System)
- Too small to be called planets.

Our solar system has one planetoid: Pluto.

Figure 35.22 *Pluto*

35.5 We used to regard Pluto as a planet. Now we call it a planetoid. Find out why we no longer think of it as a planet and when it got 'demoted'.

Did you know?

Leading astronomers want to reinstate Pluto's status to 'planet' in the near future.

Did you know?

Amazing facts about each planet

Earth is the only planet in the Solar System that is not named after a mythical god.

Mercury's day is equivalent to fifty-eight Earth days.

Venus is the hottest planet in the Solar System, with a temperature of 477°C. This is because its atmosphere is composed of carbon dioxide gas (an extreme version of the greenhouse effect).

Mars appears red as it is mostly covered in iron oxide (rust).

Jupiter is so big that if all the planets in the Solar System were put together they would make a structure that would be the same size as Jupiter.

Saturn has such low density it could float on water.

Uranus seasons can last for up to 20 years.

Neptune has the strongest winds in the Solar System, with speeds of up to 2100 kph.

Pluto's surface area is smaller than the surface area of North America.

How do planets orbit?

The planets orbit around the Sun. That is why we have a 'solar system'.

The Sun is a very large object and as a result has a very large gravity.

The Sun's gravity 'pulls' planets towards it. At the same time the planets are always trying to pull away from the Sun out into space. But the Sun's gravity keeps each of the planets in a curved orbit.

Figure 35.23 *The gravitational pull of the Sun on the planets*

35.6 **(a)** Within groups or pairs, select a planet and prepare a presentation for the class, making sure you include answers to the following:

- **(i)** How does the gravitational force of the planet you have chosen compare to Earth's gravity?
- **(ii)** How many moons are orbiting your chosen planet?
- **(iii)** Where is your planet located in the Solar System (in terms of distance from the Sun)?
- **(iv)** What is the length of time it takes for your planet to orbit the Sun?
- **(v)** What is the surface temperature of your planet?
- **(vi)** Has your planet an atmosphere? If so, what is the composition of that atmosphere?

(b) Compare Earth, using the above questions as a guide, to your chosen planet within the Solar System.

(c) Present your group's findings to the class, being as informative as you can be.

Is there more than one moon?

Moons are objects that are found revolving around planets in our solar system. Some planets, such as Earth, have one moon. Other planets have more than one moon – Jupiter, for example, has at least sixty-three moons! We will be looking at our moon and other moons in more detail in a later chapter.

What else is in our universe?

In space, there are other components that make up our known universe:

- **Regular matter** Matter is anything that takes up space and has a mass. For example, your chair, your school bag and your book are all regular matter. Even humans are made of regular matter.

- **Dark matter** Dark matter controls how all matter comes together to form stars, moons, galaxies and everything in the universe, including you. It is called 'dark' because this type of matter does not produce or absorb any light. Scientists have not yet seen or observed dark matter. They are confident though that it exists because they have studied how galaxies come together.
- **Dark energy** This is a very mysterious energy that scientists know very little about, even though we do know that it makes up 73% of the universe. We also know that it is this energy that is causing the galaxies to keep moving apart from each other at ever-increasing speeds.

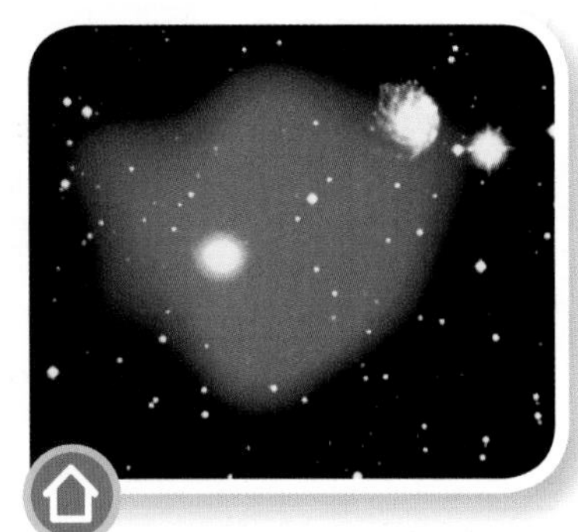

Figure 35.24 *An artist's impression of dark matter in space*

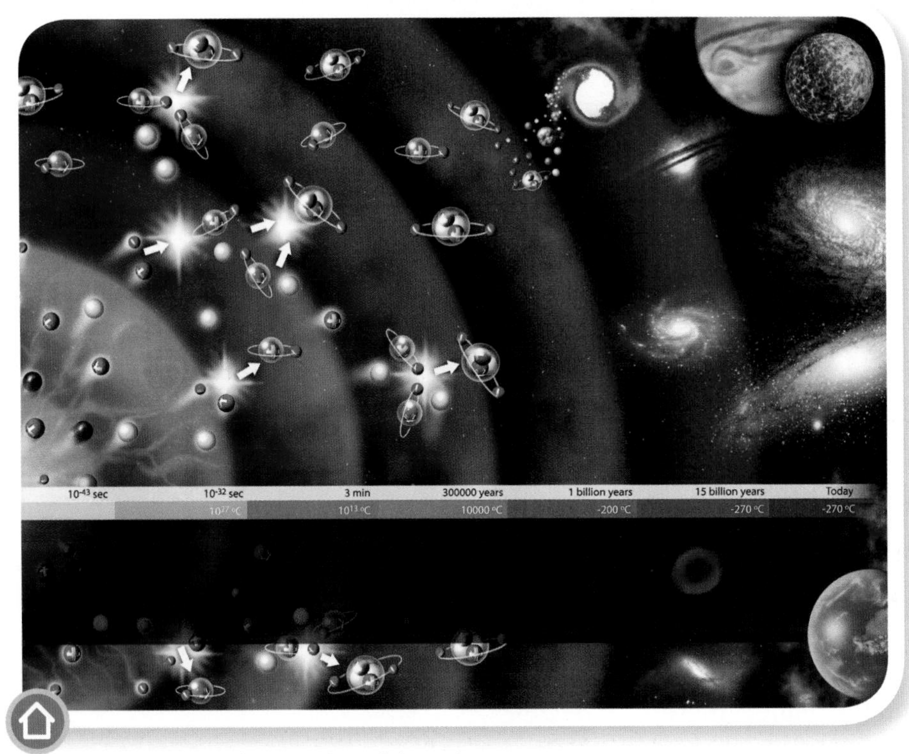

Figure 35.25 *The creation of the universe*

Are there other life forms in the Solar System?

Earth is unique within the Solar System as it has been able to sustain life. Earth has a suitable temperature, gravity and an atmosphere containing the correct gases that allow all living organisms to exist.

Class discussion:

35.7 **(a)** Do you think life forms exist on other planets?

(b) What are the features of planets that have prevented life from being created there?

35.8 Name the stages in the life cycle of a star.

35.9 What is a galaxy?

35.10 What are the types of planet in our solar system?

CHAPTER 36

UNIT 5

Comets, asteroids and meteors

Learning outcomes

At the end of this chapter you will be able to:

- Explain how a comet is formed
- Distinguish between the terms meteoroid, meteor and a meteorite
- Explain the difference(s) between a comet, an asteroid and a meteor
- Identify the locations of comets and asteroids within the Solar System.

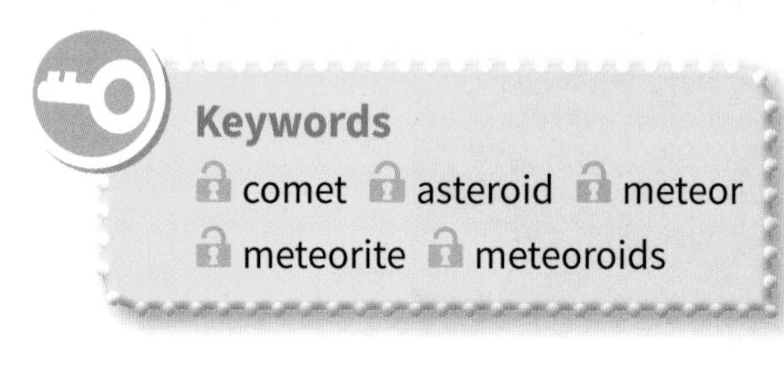

Keywords

comet asteroid meteor meteorite meteoroids

What other small objects are in our sky?

Apart from the Sun and the planets there are many other objects within our solar system.

We can look in the night sky and observe a vast array of spectacular cosmic structures. People used to consider them 'mythical' objects, but what exactly are they and where in space do they come from?

Figure 36.1 *The Great Comet of 1811*

What are comets?

Comets are probably the most ancient objects within our solar system and may hold the key to how our solar system was formed 4.6 billion years ago.

Comets are termed by scientists as **giant dirty snowballs**. They are composed of frozen gases, rocks and dust. Comets have an icy existence as they were formed and continue to be located a great distance from the heat energy of the Sun.

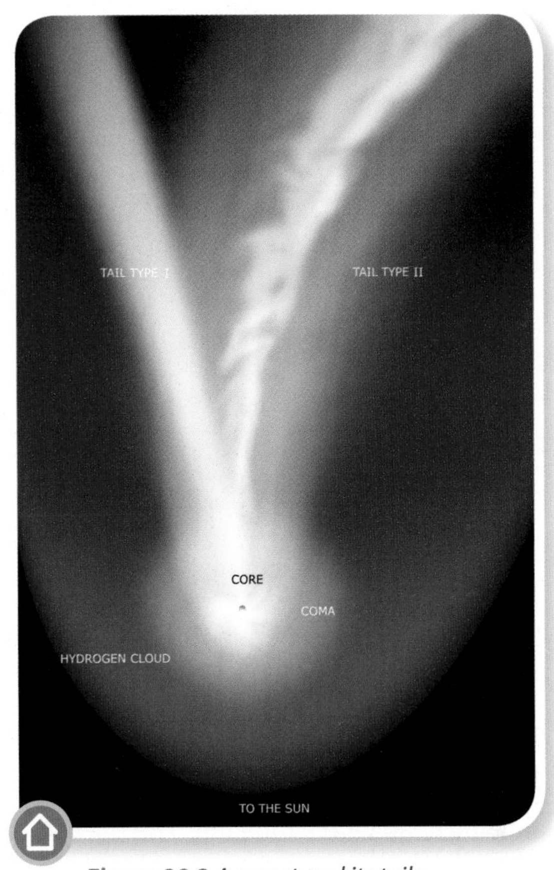

Figure 36.2 *A comet and its tails*

Comets originate from two areas of our solar system:

- **The Kuiper Belt** The region containing the belt is beyond the orbit of the planet Neptune. Comets that originated here are termed **short-period comets**. This is because their orbit around the Sun takes around 200 years or less.
- **The Oort Cloud** This 'cloud' surrounds the outer limits of the Solar System and it contains trillions of comets. Comets that are located here are termed **long-period comets**, as their orbit around the Sun can take from 200 years to 30 million years!

Figure 36.3 *Kuiper Belt objects*

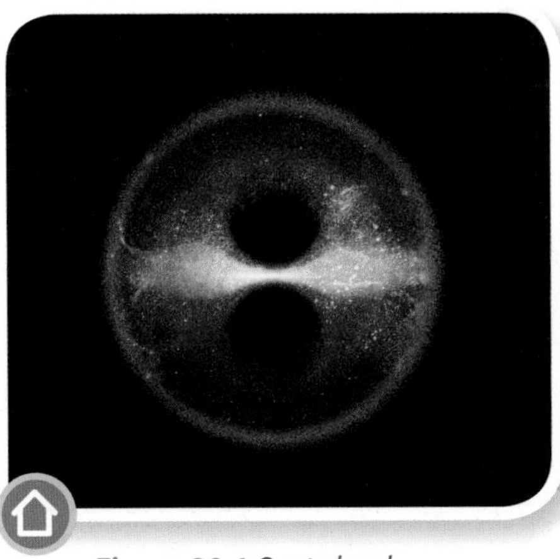

Figure 36.4 *Oort cloud*

Did you know?

The Roman emperor Nero thought a comet was the gods' sign for his possible assassination and to avoid this event he had all of his living successors killed.

EARTH & SPACE

Figure 36.5 *A comet*

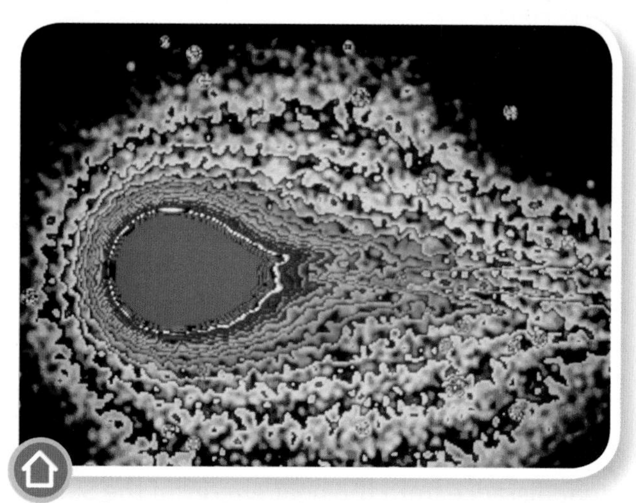

Figure 36.6 *Comet de Vico – this is an example of what a comet looks like*

Comets look like solid objects until their orbit brings them close to the Sun. Then the Sun's heat energy evaporates the comet's ice. This sends dust and gases out into space, which forms into a giant glowing head with a long tail. The tail can stretch out for millions of miles behind the comet.

Figure 36.7 *Comet Ikeya-Seki orbiting the Sun showing the tails of the comet stretching away from its head*

There can be two tails behind a comet: one composed of rocks and dust, the other composed of gas. The tails of a comet always stretch away from the Sun.

Comets do not support life. It is possible that they brought water and other compounds to Earth.

Did you know?

Comet dust particles fall continuously to Earth at a rate of one billion dust particles per second. We cannot see this comet dust; however, scientists have found the dust preserved in the ice and snow in Antarctica.

36.1 What are the differences between a comet and a planet?

The **great comets** are so called because they produce spectacular tails. They are very rare in our solar system, with some passing by Earth about once every one hundred years. Other comets can take over 200 hundred years to be visible again from Earth.

Did you know?

History was made on 12 November 2014 when the Rosetta mission, a joint mission between the European Space Agency (ESA) and NASA, landed the Philae space probe on a moving comet. The Rosetta spacecraft travelled 6.4 billion km to land on the comet 67P/Churyumov-Gerasimenko, which was travelling at a speed of 135 000 km an hour. Data was sent back to Earth that will help us understand more about comets.

Figure 36.8 *Rosetta space probe*

Unfortunately Philae landed 1 km away from its target landing spot. Its energy-generating solar panels were in the shade and so Philae had to use up its batteries to complete its mission. ESA powered down the probe with the final tweet from Philae saying: 'I'm feeling a bit tired, did you get all my data? I might take a nap'.

ESA are hoping that as the comet continues its orbit around the Sun that light may again fall on Philae's solar panels allowing the probe to continue with its mission. The Rosetta spacecraft is still orbiting the comet.

36.2 In groups research, using the internet or books from your school library, one of the 'great' comets. Present your findings in a report format. Here are some topics to assist your research:

(a) Define the word 'comet'.

(b) Name three famous 'great' comets that have been seen from Earth.

(c) Note for each of the three comets you have listed in (b) above:

- **(i)** The person, or persons, who discovered it.
- **(ii)** The year that each comet was discovered.
- **(iii)** The time span for its orbit around the Sun.
- **(iv)** The last appearance of the comet as seen from Earth.
- **(v)** The year of its predicted reappearance.

(d) Briefly outline why scientists have linked the extinction of the dinosaurs with a collision by a comet.

What are asteroids?

Apart from comets there are other small objects that exist within our solar system. These objects are termed **asteroids**.

Asteroids are small, rocky structures that have no air and no atmosphere. They are located in the Solar System's asteroid belt, which lies between Mars and Jupiter.

Asteroids can often collide with each other, which can knock them out of their asteroid belt and send them off on a different journey within the Solar System. This different journey can sometimes bring them close to Earth.

Even though scientists believe that there are millions of asteroids within the asteroid belt, their total mass is less than the mass of Earth's moon!

Scientists are trying to learn more about asteroids. If there was an asteroid collision with Earth – which is a very rare event – it could bring about global destruction. Scientists believe that it was either a comet or an asteroid collision with Earth that caused the extinction of dinosaurs.

Figure 36.9 *A large asteroid near Earth*

Figure 36.10 *Scientists think it is likely that it was an asteroid or a comet colliding with Earth that killed the dinosaurs*

Figure 36.11 *The impact of an asteroid on Earth*

36.3 Investigate the possible explanation that scientists have given for the formation of the asteroid belt.

Asteroids vary greatly in size:

- Some are small at about 10 m in diameter. These are known as **meteors.**
- Some are large at about 100 km wide. These are known as **planetoids.**

Figure 36.12 *Asteroid Ida and its companion moon*

Asteroids are divided into three classes.

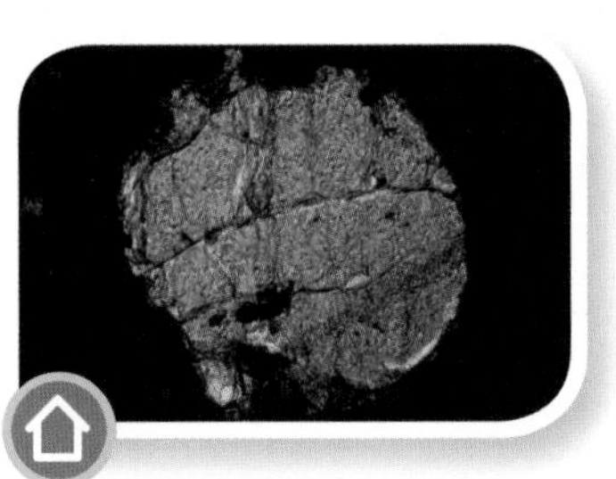

Figure 36.13 *C-type asteroid*

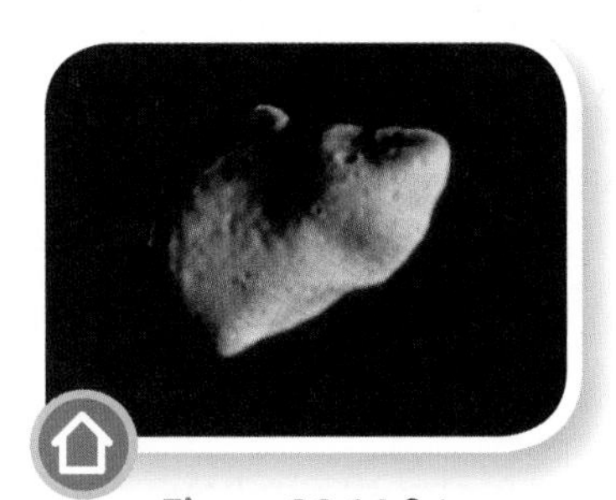

Figure 36.14 *S-type asteroid Gaspra*

Figure 36.15 *M-type asteroid Calypso*

C-types

These are the most common asteroids. They are carbon-based and are located in the outer limits of the asteroid belt.

S-types

These asteroids are silicon based and exist in vast numbers in the inner region of the belt.

M-types

These are metallic asteroids that occupy the middle region of the belt.

Did you know?

The space station that orbits Earth is protected from meteor collisions. One example of the protection is that the windows are made of a specially reinforced glass.

Asteroids may appear to be small bodies but they have been and continue to be very dangerous structures that can do untold damage to Earth.

36.4 In groups or pairs, research the following topics from the internet and your school library and present your findings to the class as a PowerPoint presentation.

(a) The most recent asteroid collision with Earth (remembering the term you learned for small asteroids).

(b) The events that occurred in 1908 in Siberia when an 'object' impacted that area.

In your research identify:

- When and where the event took place
- What actually occurred to the surrounding area when there was a collision with Earth
- What scientists studying these events have learned about the asteroids.

EARTH & SPACE

Asteroids can be assigned other names depending on where they are in the sky and whether or not they impact Earth. Use the following task to identify these other names for asteroids and clearly identify the difference between them.

36.5 What do the following terms mean? Clearly distinguish between each of these words.
- **(a)** Meteoroid
- **(b)** Meteor
- **(c)** Meteorite.

36.6 What was the largest known meteorite to have been found on Earth? State the location of the meteorite's impact and its composition.

Scientists from NASA are currently studying the two largest asteroids within the asteroid belt, Ceres and Vesta. They are trying to gain a better understanding of these rocky worlds and hopefully find clues to the formation of the early Solar System. NASA's project is called the Dawn Mission; the space probe was launched on 27 September 2007.

Figure 36.16 *NASA's Dawn Mission*

Figure 36.17 *Dawn Mission spacecraft within the asteroid belt*

Asteroid Ceres

Ceres is the largest asteroid in the belt. It is a massive 950 km in diameter. On 22 January 2014 the European Space Agency announced that Ceres contained water. This is evident from the water vapour that was erupting into space from the asteroid.

NASA's Dawn Mission will begin its study of Ceres when it arrives at the asteroid in April 2015.

Figure 36.18 *Asteroid Ceres*

Figure 36.19 *A comparison of cores (in the centre) to Earth (left) and the Moon (right)*

EARTH & SPACE

Asteroid Vesta

Vesta is the second-largest asteroid. It is a mere 530 km in diameter and has a surface three times more reflective than our own moon, and is the only asteroid visible from Earth with the naked eye.

36.7 What does 'reflective' mean?

Figure 36.20 *Asteroid Vesta*

Figure 36.21 *Ceres and Vesta in comparison to Europe*

The Dawn Mission studied Vesta from July 2011 to September 2012.

Did you know?

Ceres and Vesta each occupy more than one-third of the total mass of the asteroid belt.

36.8 Name two places in the Solar System where comets come from.

36.9 Describe an asteroid.

CHAPTER 37

To the Moon and beyond

Learning outcomes

At the end of this chapter you will be able to:

- Explain the effect the Moon has on Earth
- Provide key data about the Moon
- Compare Earth to moons within the Solar System.

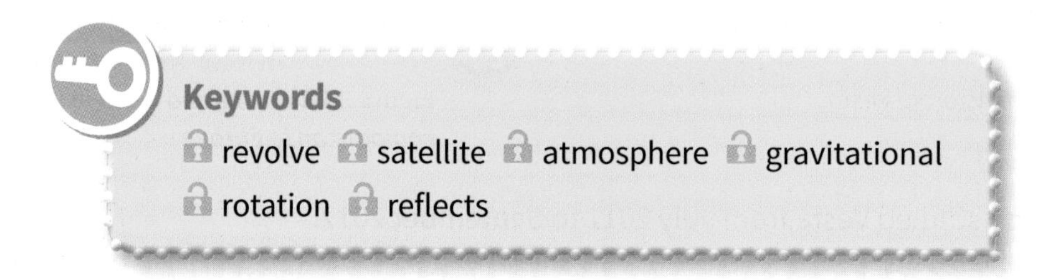

Keywords

revolve satellite atmosphere gravitational rotation reflects

What is Earth's relationship with the Moon?

The Moon is our nearest neighbour in space. It is a constant in our everyday lives – it is always there and we are used to seeing it (unless it is very cloudy). The Moon affects a lot of what happens on Earth every day.

The Moon is the second brightest object in our sky after the Sun.

Figure 37.1 *The full moon in the night sky*

Figure 37.2 *Earth, Sun and Moon*

Figure 37.3 *Earth and the Moon*

Figure 37.4 *Earth rising, from Apollo 8*

Scientists believe that it is the Moon that has made our planet stable. This has occurred due to the Moon's own gravitational forces which, through time, slowed down the rotation of Earth.

This 'slowing down' allowed Earth to rotate on an even axis – imagine a ball turning or rotating the same way and at the same speed all of the time.

Did you know?

The continuing slowing down of Earth adds up to 1.5 to 2 milliseconds on to the length of the day every century. A millisecond is one thousandth of a second.

The energy that Earth has lost in being slowed down has been picked up by the Moon. This allows the Moon to propel itself away from Earth by 3.8 cm a year. Earth has lost this energy to the Moon by the gravitational interactions between the Moon and Earth.

37.1 What are some possible effects for us of the Moon moving away from Earth?

But what exactly are moons? And more importantly, what effect do they have on a planet around which they revolve?

In terms of space:

- Any object that orbits a sun is called a planet.
- Any object that orbits another world, apart from the Sun, is termed a moon.

The Moon is also known as a **satellite** of Earth.

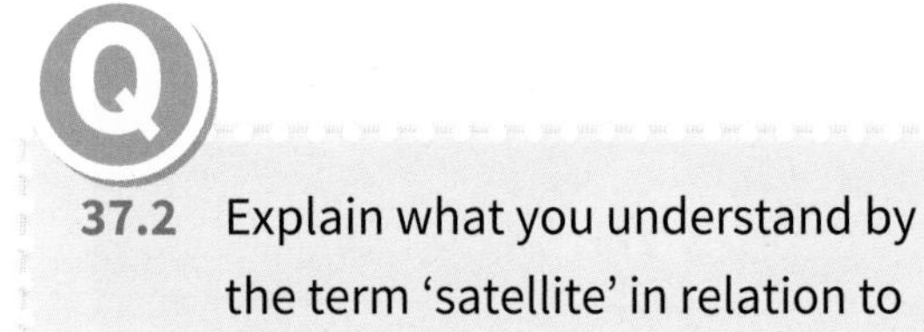

37.2 Explain what you understand by the term 'satellite' in relation to the Moon.

Figure 37.5 *The Moon's surface*

How the Moon was formed?

The Moon was probably formed when a large object, about the size of the planet Mars, collided with Earth. This impact ejected material from Earth into orbit; this material fused together and so formed the Moon. The formation of the Moon took place at approximately the same time as the Solar System was formed: around 4.6 billion years ago.

Figure 37.6 *Formation of the Moon*

Can we see the far side of the Moon?

From Earth we can observe only one side of the Moon.

It takes the Moon approximately twenty-eight days to **revolve** around Earth. During this time the Moon is **rotating** on its own axis. This means that the Moon is turning around on itself in one complete circle at the same time as going completely around Earth once.

As both of these movements by the Moon – the rotating and the revolving – are synchronised (that is, they are taking place at the same time) we see only one side of the Moon. This means that the time taken for the Moon to rotate on its own axis once is the same as the time it takes to revolve around Earth once.

In fact, because of movements of the Moon we can sometimes see as much as 59% of its surface.

Figure 37.7 *The far side of the Moon*

Activity 37.1

Question

How can we demonstrate that we see only one side of the Moon?

Equipment needed

Small ball about the size of a tennis ball

Larger ball, the size of a football or a basketball

Black marker

Safety

- Take care always when moving around the science room.

Conducting the activity

1. Take the small ball and place a black dot or mark on its surface. This ball represents the Moon.
2. Now take the larger ball to represent Earth.
3. Begin moving the tennis ball around the larger ball. As you do this you must ensure that the black dot on the smaller ball is facing the larger ball *at all times*.
4. Do step 3 again to make sure you see what is happening.

Figure 37.8 *Orbits of Earth and Moon around the Sun*

37.3 As you were turning the ball around what did you notice was happening to it?

37.4 Did you have to change your grip of the small ball in any way?

37.5 The side of the Moon that we do not see used to be called the 'dark' side of the Moon. The correct word is the 'far' side of the Moon. Why do you think scientists changed the wording for this side of the Moon?

The distance from Earth to the Moon is 384 400 km.

The Moon has no atmosphere and its force of gravity is about one-sixth of that of Earth.

Did you know?

Only twelve people have walked on the Moon and all of them have been American.

EARTH & SPACE

Figure 37.9 *A man's footprint on the Moon*

Figure 37.10 *Astronaut Buzz Aldrin on the Moon, Apollo 11*

37.6 How have scientists been able to measure so accurately the distance from Earth to the Moon?

The Moon cannot produce its own light. It reflects the light from the Sun that falls on it.

Figure 37.11 *The Moon reflecting light off its surface*

37.7 What term best describes this reflective property of the Moon?

37.8 There are other 'types' of moon that have come into our everyday language. The two that are most common are:

(a) The harvest moon

(b) A blue moon.

Work with a partner. Take one of the above moons each and find out the following about it:

(a) How that moon came to be given its name.

(b) When during the year that moon is seen in the night sky.

Present your findings to your partner.

Figure 37.12 *The harvest moon*

Figure 37.13 *A blue moon*

37.9 Name some famous landmarks on Earth's moon.

Are there other moons in the Solar System?

We will look at the following five moons in the Solar System:

- Titan
- Europa
- Ganymede
- Io
- Phobos.

Did you know?

There are 170 moons within the Solar System. Each of these moons orbits (rotates around) a planet within the Solar System.

EARTH & SPACE

Titan

Titan orbits Saturn. It is the only moon within the Solar System to have an atmosphere almost fully made up of nitrogen gas (98.4%). Titan's atmosphere is so thick that telescopes cannot see the surface when they are looking at it. Special telescopes and cameras had to be developed to see through Titan's thick atmosphere.

If Earth had the same circumference as a 50 cent coin, Titan would be the size of a pea.

NASA has discovered that Titan looks more like Earth than any other structure we know about. It has geological features of lakes and valleys. The big difference is that all flowing liquids on Titan's surface are composed of toxic methane.

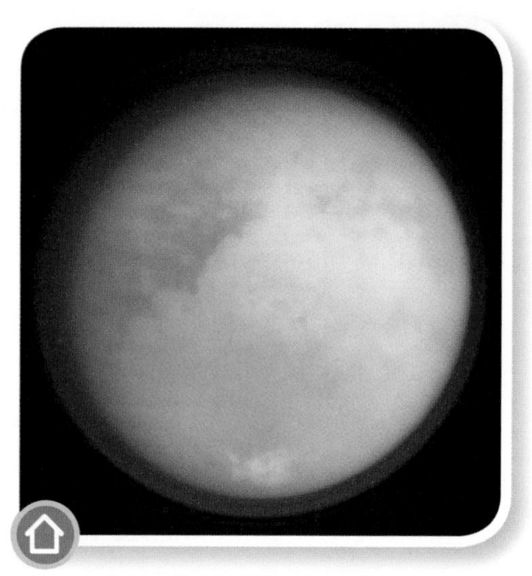

Figure 37.14 *Titan and its atmosphere*

Europa

Europa orbits Jupiter. It is a frozen moon with its surface covered by ice 62 km deep. Scientists believe that there may be liquid oceans underneath Europa's icy exterior. This may be due to its core being warmed by changing gravitational pull from Jupiter. Europa is smaller than our moon.

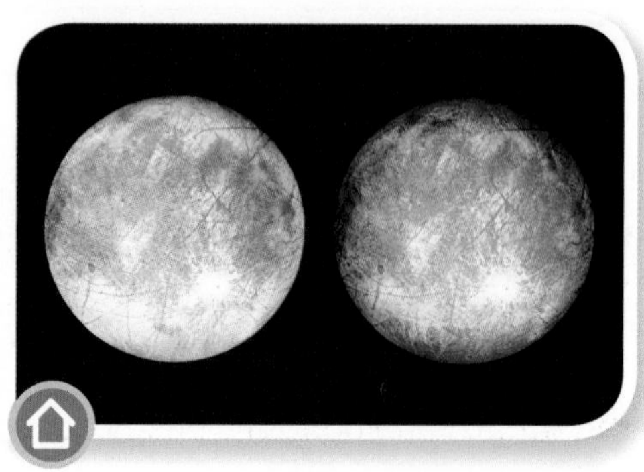

Figure 37.15 *Europa, taken from the Galileo global navigation satellite system*

Ganymede

Ganymede orbits Jupiter. It is the largest moon in the Solar System and is larger than the planet Mercury, which is the smallest planet in the Solar System.

Ganymede is the only moon to have a magnetic field. It has this because it has a molten iron core.

In 1996 the Hubble Space Telescope found a thin atmosphere of oxygen around Ganymede. However, it is considered too thin to support any life.

Figure 37.16 *Ganymede, taken from the Voyager 1 space probe*

Io

Io orbits Jupiter. It is similar in size to our own moon. However, Io is the most violently volcanic moon in the Solar System, with over 400 active volcanoes on its surface.

Figure 37.17 *Io, one of Jupiter's moons*

Phobos

Phobos, which is one of the two moons that orbit Mars, is a very lumpy and dark moon. Even though Phobos is only 18 km wide it suffers extreme ranges of temperature, ranging from –4°C on its sunlit side to –112°C on the side facing away from the Sun. This is because the surface on Phobos is mostly dust, which cannot retain the heat that it receives from the Sun.

Figure 37.18 *Phobos (on the right) orbits Mars*

37.10 Using the internet and/or books from your school library compare the above named moons, or any other moons you may choose, to Earth in terms of their mass, gravity, size, what the moon is made from and what the moon's atmosphere is made of.

37.11 Describe the movement of the Moon around Earth.

37.12 Name two moons in the Solar System.

EARTH & SPACE

CHAPTER 38

UNIT 5

Earth, Sun and Moon – it's all relative

Learning outcomes

At the end of this chapter you will be able to:

- Explain the lunar phases of the Moon
- Illustrate how the relative positions of the Sun, Earth and the Moon result in the phases of the Moon as seen from Earth
- Describe how the occurrence of the seasons is directly related to the tilted revolution of Earth
- Outline how the changing elevation of the Sun in the sky directly affects the day length and the changing of the seasons
- Examine how the processes of a lunar eclipse and a solar eclipse occur.

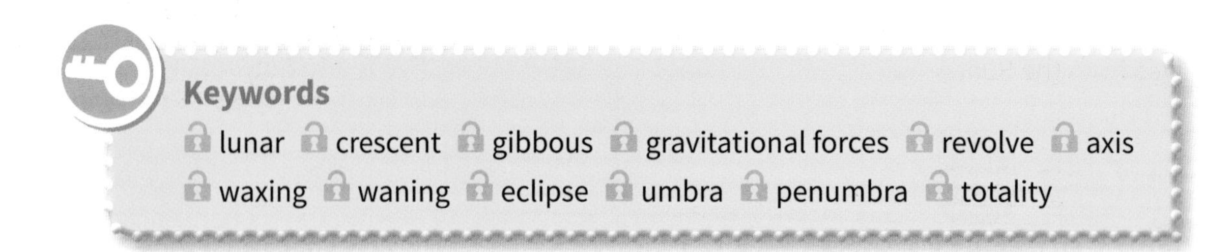

Keywords

lunar crescent gibbous gravitational forces revolve axis waxing waning eclipse umbra penumbra totality

What is the relationship between bodies found within the Solar System?

The Sun, Earth and the Moon are all bodies that exist within the Solar System.

Each of these bodies is a different structure.

- The Sun is a star.
- Earth is a planet.
- The Moon is a satellite of Earth.

They are quite different in terms of their structures. In this chapter we will be looking at their relationship with each other and what results from that relationship.

Figure 38.1 *The relative orbits of Earth, the Sun and the Moon*

The relationship between Earth, the Sun and the Moon is based on their positions relative to one another.

What is the lunar cycle?

We will look first at changes in the appearance of the Moon in our night sky. This cycle is called the lunar cycle. *Luna* is the Latin term for the Moon.

Did you know?

The word *lunatic* is from the Latin term for 'moonstruck'. People used to believe that if the moonlight struck them when they were asleep they became mad (i.e. a 'lunatic')! Some houses had roofs that came over the windows to prevent the moon from shining in.

When we view the Moon from Earth it seems to change its shape and appearance from night to night. These changes in the Moon's appearance are called the **phases** of the Moon.

Figure 38.2 *The new moon*

The phases of the Moon

Each phase relates to the point that the Moon is in relation to Earth and how much sunlight is being reflected off the Moon at that particular time.

Phase 1: the new moon

Earth, the Sun and the Moon are approximately in a straight line with each other. The Moon at this phase is between Earth and the Sun.

38.1 During a new moon the Moon can seem to disappear. Why do you think this happens?

Phase 2: the waxing crescent

The term **waxing** means **growing**. This phase is due to the 'growing' or increased levels of light both from the Sun falling onto the Moon and being reflected off its surface.

As a result we can now see more of the Moon. But only a portion, which is called a **crescent**. At this time we are seeing less than half of the Moon.

Figure 38.3 *The first quarter Moon*

Phase 3: the first quarter

On day 7 of the lunar cycle the Moon has revolved a quarter of the way around Earth and is at a 90° angle to the Sun and Earth.

At this phase we can see exactly half of one side of the Moon, i.e. a quarter; the other half is still in shadow.

EARTH & SPACE

38.2 What is the difference between the words 'revolving' and 'rotating'?

Phase 4: the waxing gibbous

More of the surface of the Moon becomes visible as more and more light from the Sun strikes it.

The term **gibbous** means that it is more than half illuminated, but less than fully.

Phase 5: the full moon

On day 14 of the lunar cycle Earth, the Sun and the Moon are again in an approximate line. But now the Moon is on the opposite side of Earth.

One side of the Moon is now completely sunlit due to the Sun's light rays being fully reflected off it. This means that we can now see a fully illuminated side of the Moon.

Figure 38.4 *The full moon*

Phase 6: the waning gibbous

A complete moon is no longer visible due to decreased levels of light from the Sun now striking it. The term **waning** means **shrinking** or getting smaller.

Phase 7: the third and last quarters

On day 21 of the lunar cycle, the Moon is at the same 90° angle that it was for the first quarter.

Phase 8: the waning crescent

Sometimes this is referred to as the 'old moon'. At this stage the Moon has completed its orbit around Earth. We can see only part of the Moon – a crescent.

This phase occurs just before another new moon and the whole cycle starts again.

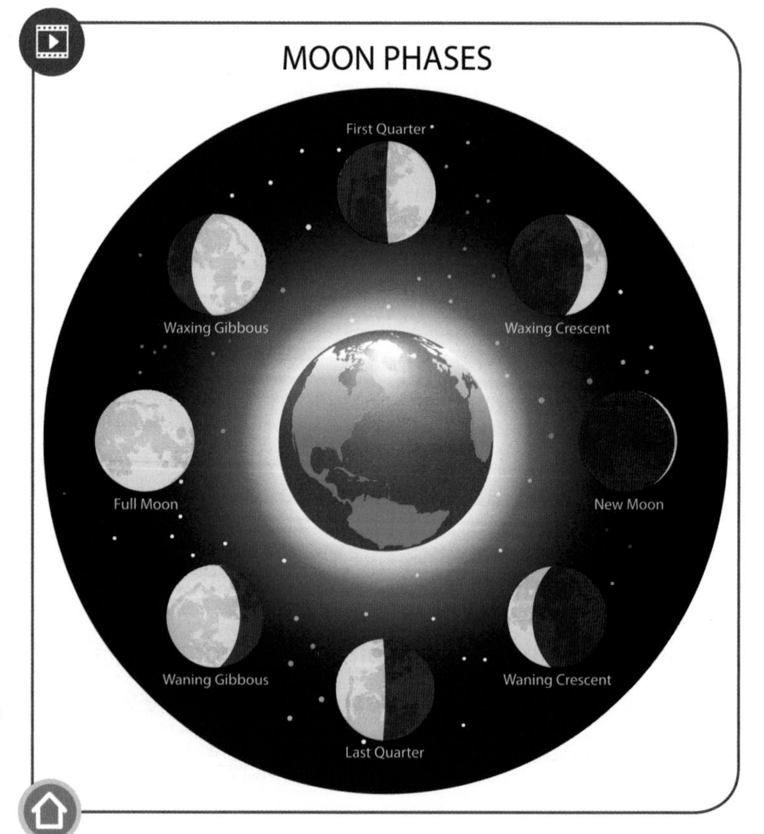

Figure 38.5 *The lunar cycle*

38.3 Looking at the illustrations of the phases of the Moon (Figure 38.5), do you think that the full moon can be seen in the daytime?

38.4 Why do you think the Moon does not shine as brightly in the daytime as it does during the night? Discuss this with a classmate.

38.5 Can everybody on Earth see the same phase of the Moon at the same time? Give a reason for your answer.

Portfolio 275

Activity 38.1

Question

Can we create our own lunar guides for a month?

Conducting the activity

1. Use the grid provided in your portfolio book, or make a grid in your copy containing a box for each day of the month you are studying.
2. For each night for one month observe and draw the Moon phase in the night sky for that particular date.
3. Sketch a diagram of what you have seen into the box in the grid that corresponds to that date in the month.
4. If you are unable to see the Moon due to weather conditions, check the internet, the daily paper or Met Éireann to find the phase of the Moon for that date.

What are the seasons?

There are other events that occur as a direct result of Earth revolving through space. The seasons that we experience during a calendar year are directly linked to the movement of Earth around the Sun. Seasons are times in the year when we experience changes in our weather.

The seasons result in our environment experiencing warmer or cooler temperatures and also affects the amount of daylight hours that we experience.

Figure 38.6 *The seasons on a tree*

38.6 Do you think other planets in the Solar System have seasons? Based on what you learned about planets, predict which planets may, or may not, have seasons.

Investigate, using the internet, to see if your predictions are correct.

EARTH & SPACE

Many people think that we experience summer because we are closer to the heat energy of the Sun and winter because we are farther away from the Sun's energy. This is completely inaccurate.

In fact we are closest to the Sun during winter and farthest away during summer.

38.7 Investigate the actual distance that Earth is from the Sun in winter and in summer.

So if it is not Earth's proximity or closeness to the Sun that cause our seasons, what is the factor that determines them?

38.8 Examine Figure 38.8 and Figure 38.9 and explain why when it is winter in Ireland it is summer in Australia.

How does Earth rotate?

Earth rotates on an **axis**. The axis is an imaginary line that goes directly down the middle of Earth. Earth spins around this axis.

It is the rotation of Earth on its axis that allows us to experience day and night.

But not only does Earth rotate on its axis, it actually rotates on a **tilted** axis of **23.5°**.

As Earth completes its revolution around the Sun, the part of Earth that is tilted towards the Sun will experience summer and the part of Earth tilted away from the Sun will experience winter.

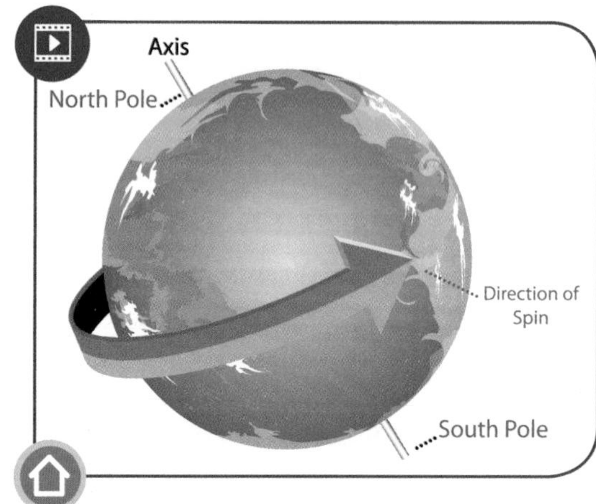

Figure 38.7 *Earth spins around an axis*

Figure 38.8 *NASA image of winter in the northern hemisphere due to Earth's axial tilt*

Figure 38.9 *NASA image of summer in the northern hemisphere due to Earth's axial tilt*

The tilted rotation of Earth has two other effects:

- The angle at which the Sun's rays strike Earth: the bigger the angle, the greater and more direct the level of heat energy. This gives warmer temperatures. Lower temperatures result from a smaller and less direct angle.
- The length of the day: the bigger the angle, the longer the length of day; the smaller the angle, the shorter the day.

Portfolio 276

Activity 38.2

Question

How can we investigate Earth's tilt?

Equipment needed

Lamp (containing bulb of wattage above 100 W)
A4 black sheet of paper
Metre stick
Protractor
Thermometer
Graph paper

Safety

- Be careful not to shine the lamp in another student's eyes or touch the lamp when it is on.

Conducting the activity

1. Shine the lamp, from a height of 5 cm, at various angles on the sheet of black paper. Here are some angles that you might want to try:
   - 21 June (first day of summer) – 73°
   - Over the equator at summer – 90°
   - 21 December (winter solstice) – 26°
2. Measure the angle by placing the metre stick at the end of the lamp and vertical (straight) to the ground. Use the protractor to record the angle between the lamp and the metre stick.
3. Ensure that you shine the lamp from the *same distance each time*. All you are changing is the angle at which the light is shining.
4. Using the thermometer, record the temperature where the light strikes the black sheet of paper.
5. Record all your results.
6. Repeat the procedure, using the same angles, now shining the lamp on a sheet of graph paper.
7. Draw a line around the outline of the light on the paper.
8. Calculate the area the light covers on the graph paper, by counting the number of full and half squares.
9. Record all your results in a table similar to the following.

Angle	Temperature (°c)	Number of squares the light covers

38.9 For each of our seasons identify the position of the Sun in the sky at midday and the resulting weather conditions.

Did you know?

If Earth did not rotate on a tilted axis we would not have seasons and day and night would be the same length all year round.

What are eclipses?

Earth, the Sun and the Moon are all bodies in space. As we know, Earth and the Moon move around the Sun. But what happens when one of them gets in the way of the Sun's rays of light? When this takes place we call the event an **eclipse**.

There are two types of eclipse:

Lunar eclipse

This happens when Earth passes between the Sun and the Moon, resulting in Earth blocking the Sun's light from reaching the Moon.

A lunar eclipse is not the same as a phase of the moon.

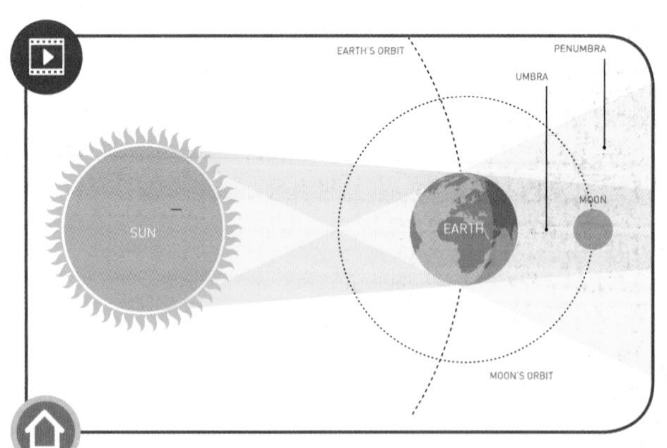

Figure 38.10 *Total lunar eclipse*

38.10 Why is an eclipse different from a phase of the moon?

Solar eclipse

This happens when the Moon passes between the Sun and Earth so that the Moon's shadow falls on parts of Earth.

Figure 38.11 *Solar eclipse from space*

Figure 38.12 *Solar eclipse geometry*

38.11 Why do we need eye protection to view a solar eclipse but it is not necessary for viewing a lunar eclipse?

Figure 38.13 *Eye protection for a solar eclipse*

Did you know?

Earth is the only planet in the Solar System where a solar eclipse can occur.

Each type of eclipse results in shadows being cast either onto the Moon or onto Earth. If the Moon or Earth is in a complete and dark shadow, this shadow is termed the **umbra**.

When the umbra shadow completely covers another body, we call this **totality**. This means the area is in total shadow.

If the Moon or Earth is in a partial or less darkened shadow, this shadow is termed the **penumbra**.

The penumbra is a shadow that we see at the first and final stages of an eclipse.

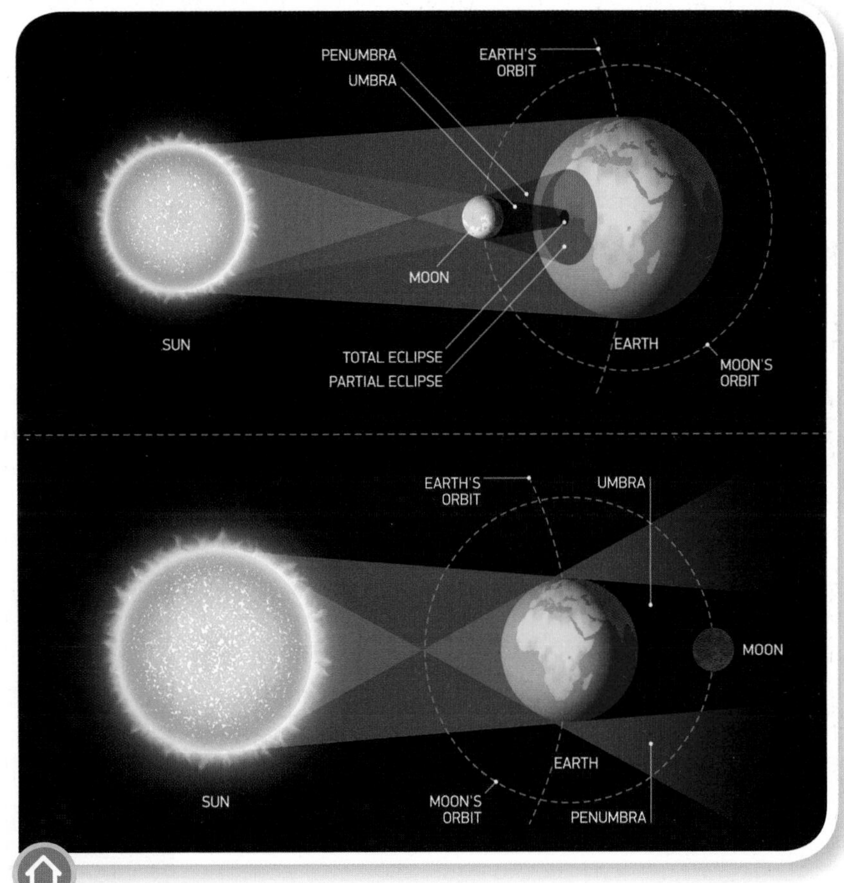

Figure 38.14 *Umbra and penumbra for a lunar and solar eclipse*

Did you know?

When a solar eclipse occurs, darkness falls in the middle of the day. Stars can be seen, temperature falls and birds might stop singing.

Activity 38.3

Question

How does a lunar eclipse occur?

Working in groups of four, three people in the group will represent a particular object in the lunar eclipse, and one person will be noting the results:

- Person 1, shining the torch = the Sun
- Person 2, standing in the middle = Earth
- Person 3, holding the white sheet = the Moon
- Person 4, with the data logger, will measure and record the light levels on the white sheet.

Equipment needed

Torch

White sheet or white sheet of board

Data logger with a light sensor

Safety

- Take care not to shine the torch directly into another student's eyes.

Conducting the activity

1. Persons 1, 2 and 3 stand one behind the other 1 metre apart, with person 1 facing person 2.
2. Person 1 shines the torch directly at person 2's body (not near the eyes!). Person 3 will hold the card directly behind person 2.
3. Person 4 will observe the shadow falling on the white sheet and record the intensity of the light falling onto the white sheet using the data logger.
4. Change your positions to represent a solar eclipse and repeat the investigation.
5. Person 1 shines the torch directly onto the sheet. Measure the light intensity on the card.

38.12 During a lunar eclipse the Moon may sometimes appear red and is given the name of a **blood red moon**. Investigate why the Moon appears to be this colour.

Figure 38.15 *A blood red moon during a lunar eclipse*

38.13 Discuss with a partner whether a lunar eclipse can be observed from all parts of Earth at the same time. Give reason(s) for your answer.

38.14 Name the phases of the lunar cycle.

38.15 Explain how a lunar eclipse and solar eclipse take place.

CHAPTER 39

UNIT 5

The water and carbon cycles – what goes around comes around

Learning outcomes

At the end of this chapter you will be able to:

- Explain the importance of nutrient cycling in the environment
- Describe the carbon cycle in terms of biological and atmospheric changes
- Describe the water cycle
- Examine the importance of water to all living organisms.

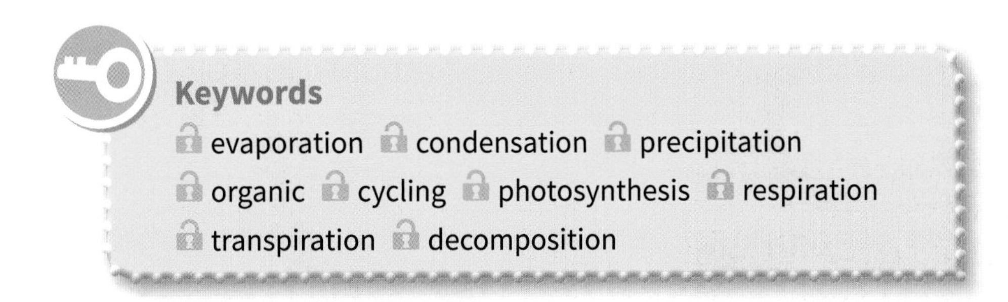

Keywords

evaporation condensation precipitation organic cycling photosynthesis respiration transpiration decomposition

Does nature recycle?

For many households and businesses it is a daily routine to recycle materials such as plastic, aluminium, paper and glass. We do this in order to conserve and protect important resources in our environment.

Figure 39.1 *Our daily recycling*

But what about recycling in nature? How does nature recycle material and nutrients (chemicals that organisms need in order to live)?

Scientists do not use the term 'recycling' in terms of nature. Instead they use the term **cycling** or **cycles**.

Nature excels at cycling vital resources. It has to do so!

Earth has a fixed amount of matter. Matter is anything that occupies space and has a mass. Therefore nature is continually cycling matter to ensure that it can be used time and time again.

Figure 39.2 *Cycling in nature*

In pairs, complete the following research:

39.1 Why it is important for Earth to cycle matter?

39.2 How do cycles in nature maintain the stability of Earth's climate?

39.3 Identify key nutrients that nature cycles.

Two of the key resources that nature cycles are water and carbon. We will be looking at both of these areas in nature and their importance to us and our planet.

What is the water cycle?

When you get a glass of water from your tap you probably don't think of the age of the water. The amazing thing is, although the water in your glass may have fallen as rain last week, that same water has been around since Earth was formed!

Humans cannot live without water, nor can a vast range of organisms in the environment.

Figure 39.3 *How old is water?*

Figure 39.4 *Organisms need water*

Did you know?

By the time a person feels thirsty, his or her body has lost over one percent of their total water volume in their body.

Water can exist in solid (ice), liquid (water) or gas (water vapour) form.

Figure 39.5 *Water can exist in solid (ice), liquid (water) or gas (water vapour) form*

39.4 Give examples, from nature, of water in solid, liquid and gas form.

Water in nature is always in constant motion.

The **water cycle** is the motion or movement of water from the oceans to the atmosphere and back to the oceans.

Figure 39.6 *The water cycle*

What are the stages of the water cycle?

Within the water cycle there are six key stages:

- Stage 1 – evaporation
- Stage 2 – condensation
- Stage 3 – precipitation (rainfall)
- Stage 4 – infiltration (soaking)
- Stage 5 – runoff/collection
- Stage 6 – transpiration.

We will look at each stage individually.

Stage 1 – evaporation

Evaporation is the changing of water in the form of a liquid to water in the form of a gas. Most of the evaporation that takes place on Earth comes from the oceans. Only a small amount of evaporation takes place from inland water (rivers and lakes) and plants.

Figure 39.7 *A boiling kettle, where water is turned into water vapour (a gas)*

Evaporation requires energy in the form of heat. It is the Sun's heat energy that drives this process causing water to change from a liquid to a vapour/gas.

Stage 2 – condensation

Condensation takes place when a gas changes to liquid. Think of steam from the shower hitting a mirror – what do you notice happening?

Figure 39.8 *Condensation on glass*

The higher up you go on Earth the colder it gets – think of snow caps on the tops of mountains. So as water vapour rises it starts to get colder and condenses. The water droplets are still light enough to remain suspended or held in the air. The droplets come together in vast numbers and clouds are formed.

Portfolio 283

Activity 39.1

Question

How can we demonstrate evaporation?

Equipment needed

A piece of material about 30 cm square, cut in half
Zip-lock bags
Basin
Water
Stop watch or timer
Beaker
Open container
Top-pan balance/ weighing scales

Safety

- Ensure that water does not spill on the floor, making another student's area unsafe.

Conducting the activity

1. Measure 50 cm^3 of water into a beaker.
2. Place your two pieces of material in a basin and pour the water from the beaker onto the material.
3. Leave the material to soak in the water for 5 minutes.
4. Remove the material and twist the pieces once for 10 seconds.
5. Place one piece of material on a top-pan balance/weighing scales and record the mass of the material soaked with water. Do the same with the second piece.
6. Place one piece of material into a zip-lock bag.
7. Place the second piece of material into an open container.
8. Leave both the bag and the container in an open, airy place for two to three days.
9. After the two to three days record the mass of each piece of material and note the 'dryness' of the material.

Stage 3 – precipitation/rainfall

As the water droplets held within the clouds continue to rise they carry on getting colder. When the water droplets become too heavy to be held in the cloud, the water falls back to Earth as rain, sleet or snow.

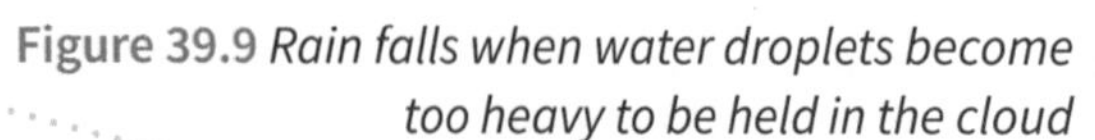

Figure 39.9 *Rain falls when water droplets become too heavy to be held in the cloud*

Stage 4 – infiltration

Infiltration occurs when the rain hits the ground and infiltrates or soaks through the soil and the rocks. This water then collects and forms **ground water**. Ground water is water that is held in the ground and supplies wells and springs.

39.5 When might the level of the ground water increase or decrease?

Did you know?

Water can spend thousands of years locked up in ground water or frozen within the polar ice caps. Yet it can remain within the atmosphere only for a few days.

Stage 5 – runoff/collection

The water eventually runs off the land or out of the soil and collects into the rivers and lakes.

Figure 39.10 *Groundwater runs off the land into rivers and lakes*

Stage 6 – transpiration

Plants are constantly taking up water from the soil through their roots. To continue this uptake of water from the soil, the plants must lose water into the air from their leaves in the form of water vapour. This loss of water is called transpiration.

The water has now completed its full cycle.

What is the carbon cycle?

Scientists know that carbon is the basis of all life. Carbon is the second most abundant substance in living things.

39.6 What substance is found in the greatest quantities in living things?

EARTH & SPACE

Any substance that contains carbon is called an **organic** substance.

We all need carbon for survival. Earth has only a certain amount of carbon and so it is very important that nature continues to cycle it to maintain its supplies.

However, a fine balance must be kept between too much carbon and too little carbon in the atmosphere. We will be looking at this delicate balance in chapter 41.

39.7 Carbon is the fourth most abundant element in the entire universe. What do you think are the top three elements in our universe?

What are the stages of the carbon cycle?

Carbon, like water, is constantly moving in nature from one process to the next. It is this constantly moving carbon that results in the carbon cycle. This is shown in Figure 39.11.

Within the carbon cycle there are six key stages. In these stages carbon moves from:

1. The atmosphere to plants
2. Plants to animals
3. Plants and animals to the ground
4. Living things into the atmosphere
5. Fossil fuels back into the atmosphere
6. The atmosphere into the oceans.

We will look at each stage.

Figure 39.11 *The carbon cycle*

39.8 Carbon appears in many forms, such as coal, diamonds and graphite in pencils. Research these three forms of the same element, carbon, and clearly distinguish between them in terms of:

(a) Appearance
(b) How they are formed
(c) What they can be used for.

Carbon moves from the atmosphere to plants

Carbon, in the form of carbon dioxide gas, is taken from the atmosphere by plants and is converted into food containing carbon. This process, that allows plants to uptake carbon dioxide and make food, is called **photosynthesis** (see chapter 10).

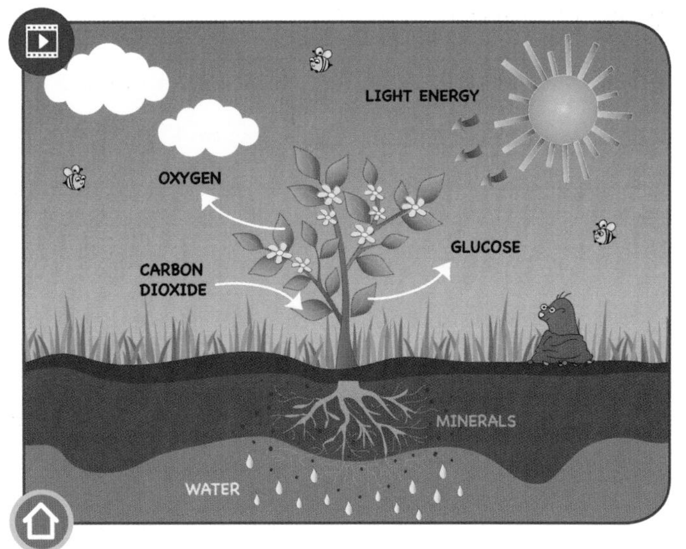

Figure 39.12 *The process of photosynthesis*

Carbon moves from plants to animals

Animals eat plants and other animals in order to get their supply of carbon.

Figure 39.13 *Animals get carbon by eating plants and other animals*

Carbon moves from plants and animals to the ground

When plants, animals and micro-organisms die the remains of their structures will decompose into the ground. Over millions of years the remains may become fossil fuels.

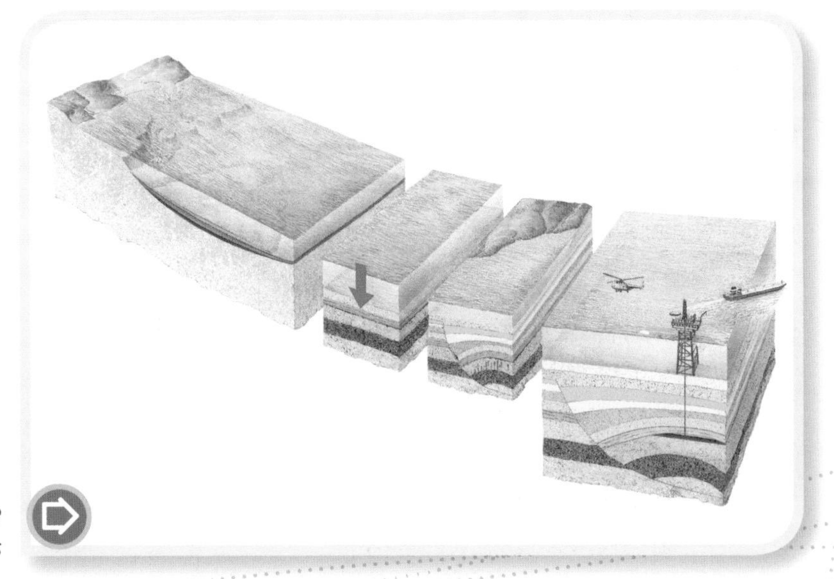

Figure 39.14 *Fossil fuels are the remains of plants and animals*

39.9 What does the word 'fossil' mean?

39.10 What are the main fossil fuels on Earth?

Carbon moves from living things into the atmosphere

Plants, animals and micro-organisms break down food containing carbon in a process called **respiration** (see chapter 10). This process releases energy to the organism but produces both water and carbon dioxide as waste products. The carbon dioxide is released into the atmosphere.

Carbon moves from fossil fuels back into the atmosphere

Fossil fuels contain carbon and hydrogen. Substances that contain both carbon and hydrogen are called **hydrocarbons**.

When we burn fossil fuels they release carbon dioxide and water vapour into the atmosphere.

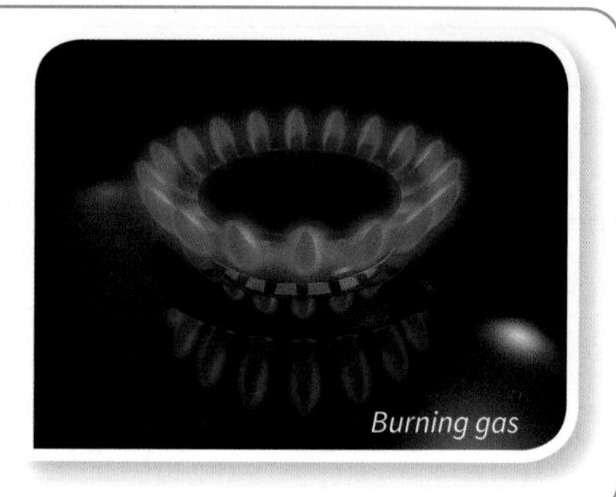

Figure 39.15 *Burning fossil fuels releases carbon dioxide and water vapour into the atmosphere*

39.11 Identify four ways in which humans burn the fossil fuels.

Carbon moves from the atmosphere into the oceans

Most of the carbon that is absorbed from the atmosphere is absorbed by the oceans. Carbon is involved in many processes that take place in the oceans.

Did you know?

The amount of carbon in the oceans is fifty times greater than the amount contained in the atmosphere.

EARTH & SPACE

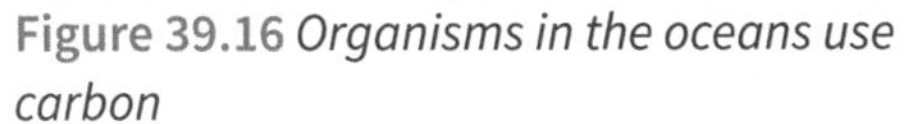
Figure 39.16 *Organisms in the oceans use carbon*

Figure 39.17 *A forest is a carbon sink*

What are carbon sinks and sources?

In nature, places that store carbon are called **carbon sinks** or **reservoirs**. An example of a carbon sink would be a forest full of trees.

39.12 What structures within the trees contain carbon?

Where carbon is given off or released in great quantities, this is called a **carbon source**. An example of a carbon source is a volcano.

Figure 39.18 *A volcano is a carbon source – carbon is released when it erupts*

39.13 What do the words evaporation and condensation mean?

39.14 Draw simple diagrams to show the carbon and water cycles.

CHAPTER 40

UNIT 5

Energy – our use and our need

Learning outcomes

At the end of this chapter you will be able to:

- Identify different forms of energy
- Describe the ways in which energy may be transferred
- Describe different examples of renewable and non-renewable sources of energy
- Consider our future needs in terms of energy.

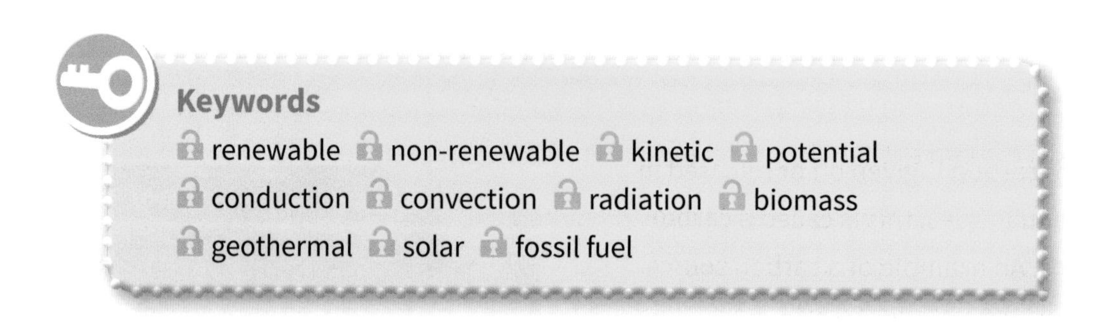

What is energy?

In this chapter we will be looking at how energy is used within our environment. We will also look at what our future holds in terms of energy.

But first, what is energy and what forms of energy are present on a day-to-day basis?

In science we say that **energy is the ability to do work**.

This simply means that, for example, if you pick up a book and put it down in another position, work has been done.

Energy can be stored in one place or it can be transferred or moved from one place to another. Energy is all around us and takes all sorts of forms.

Figure 40.1 *Different devices use different amounts of energy*

What forms does energy take?

Energy takes these forms:

- **Kinetic** – Energy that a moving body has; for example, a ball that is moving.
- **Potential** – Stored energy due to the position of an object, for example when a ball is completely stationary.
- **Heat** – Energy that is transferred between particles at different temperatures; for example, this is how a spoon gets hot when placed into hot water.
- **Sound** – This is energy that is produced by vibrating particles or objects; for example, sound coming from your vocal cords, or a guitar string vibrating.
- **Light** – Energy that moves in the form of waves; for example, the visible light that we can see.
- **Nuclear** – Energy produced from nuclear reactions; for example, energy from nuclear reactions in the Sun.
- **Electrical** – This is energy that comes from the flow of electric charge through an object; for example, electric current running through a wire.

Figure 40.2 *A moving ball has kinetic energy*

Figure 40.3 *Heat energy is transferred between this hot water and the spoon*

From activity 40.1 we can see that energy within a system remains constant but it was changed from one form to another form. This is called **the law of conservation of energy**.

40.1 List other forms of energy apart from those in the list above.

Figure 40.4 *Sound energy is produced by a guitar string when it vibrates*

Figure 40.5 *Nuclear reactions are taking place in the Sun*

Did you know?

A person shouting for eight years, seven months, and six days would produce the same amount of energy that would be needed to heat one cup of coffee or tea!

Activity 40.1

Question

How can we show that sound has energy?

Equipment needed

Tuning fork

Ping-pong ball

Safety

- Take care when striking the tuning fork off the desk.

Conducting the activity

1. Place the ping-pong ball onto your desk, making sure that the ball is not moving.
2. Now strike the tuning fork off your desk. Note the sound coming from the fork.
3. Immediately touch the tuning fork on the ball.

Figure 40.6 *Tuning forks*

Figure 40.7 *A ping-pong ball*

40.2 At step 1, when the ball was not moving, what form of energy did it have?

40.3 What happened to the ball at step 3?

40.4 What form of energy does the ball have at step 3?

In conclusion, energy cannot be created or destroyed, but it can be transformed from one form to another.

Not only can energy be transformed or changed, energy can also be transferred or moved from one place to another.

Heat energy transfer

There are three ways in which heat energy can be moved or transferred:

- Conduction
- Convection
- Radiation.

Figure 40.8 *A saucepan on a hob is heated by conduction*

Conduction

Conduction is the movement of heat energy from one object in direct contact with another object.

Conduction works best in solids such as metals. *Example:* a saucepan heating up on a hot cooker.

40.5 Give five examples of objects that do not transfer heat very well.

40.6 What name is given to objects/substances that do not conduct heat well?

Convection

Convection is the movement of heat energy within a liquid or a gas.

Because particles within a liquid or gas can move, they can transfer the heat within that liquid or gas. This occurs when warmer areas in the liquid or gas rise and are replaced by cooler liquids or gas. *Example:* water heating in a kettle.

Figure 40.9 *Water is heated in a kettle by convection*

Radiation

The hotter an object is, the more heat energy that is emitted or released from that object.

No particles are needed to carry the heat. So this form of heat energy (radiation) can move through a vacuum (a vacuum has no particles in it, like space in the Solar System).
Example: the Sun releasing heat energy into space.

How do we use energy and where does it come from?

What are the forms of energy we use in our homes? Where does that energy come from?

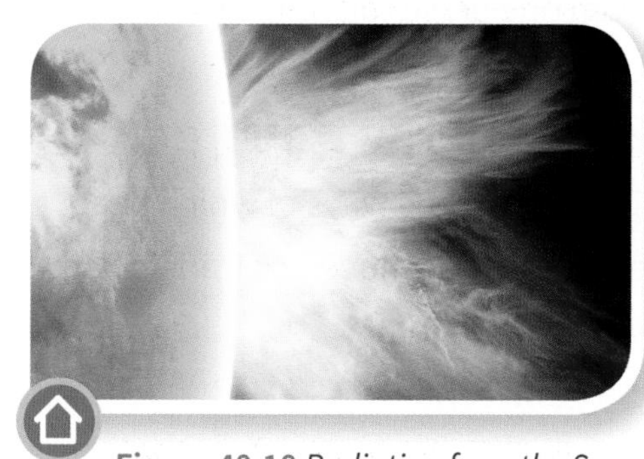

Figure 40.10 *Radiation from the Sun*

We usually flick a light switch without any thought as to what source of energy produces the electricity in the light.

In order to supply homes with energy, some source of fuel or resource must be changed or transformed to electrical energy.

There are two forms of resources available to us: non-renewable and renewable.

40.7 List all the forms of energy that you can identify that are used in your home.

Non-renewable resources

Non-renewable resources are **limited resources** that will run out and we are unable to replace them. In common terms we call them the **fossil fuels**.

What are fossil fuels?

Fossil fuels are the remains of animals and plants from millions of years ago. The remains were squashed/compressed by earth over a long period of time producing the fossil fuel.

The main fossil fuels are:

- Coal
- Gas
- Oil
- Peat.

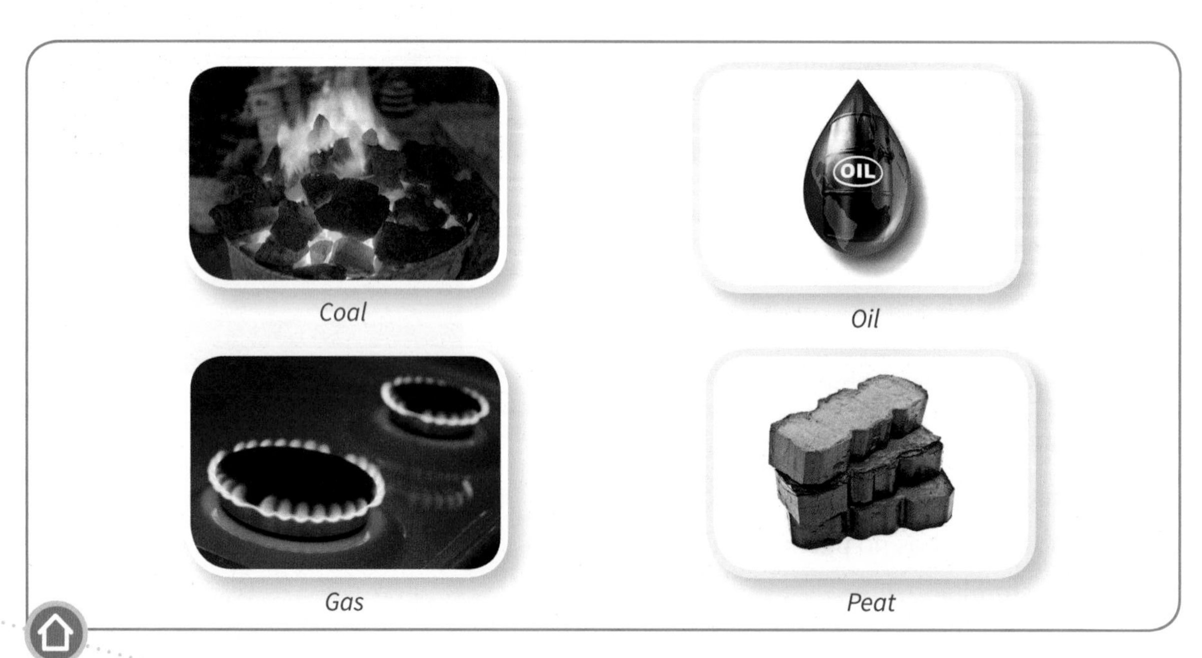

Coal

Oil

Gas

Peat

Figure 40.11 *Different forms of fossil fuel*

Fossil fuels have held energy in Earth for millions of years. For example, coal can be mined and broken into nuggets of a suitable size for our fires.

We are using fossil fuels at a much greater rate than they can actually be produced. More than three-quarters of Earth's energy needs are met by the burning of fossil fuels.

40.8 In pairs or groups explore:

(a) The advantages and disadvantages of the burning/combustion of fossil fuels.

(b) The advantages and disadvantages of the use of nuclear energy.

Renewable resources

Renewable resources can be replaced and will not run out in the short term.

Some examples of renewable resources and their uses are:

- **Wind power** – Turbines/windmills that turn and rotate in the wind, transforming some of the energy in the wind to electrical energy.
- **Water** – This is using the energy within moving or falling water and changing it to electrical energy. Examples of how this is done are hydroelectric stations.
- **Biomass** – The burning of fuel that comes from living things. An example is wood from trees. It is renewable only if the trees that are cut down are then replaced.
- **Geothermal** – This requires us to use the heat that is beneath the ground. Water is pumped underground and warmed from the heat in the rocks. This heat energy is generated and stored in Earth.
- **Solar panels/tubes** – Solar panels heat water that runs through them. The energy source that supplies the heat is the light from the Sun.
- **Solar cells** – These cells are found in devices that transform light energy to electrical energy. An example is a solar-powered calculator.

The fastest-growing source of energy in the world is the wind turbine. One wind turbine, of sufficient size, can supply enough energy to provide all the energy needs to over 300 homes.

Figure 40.12 *Wind turbines convert wind energy to electrical energy*

Figure 40.13 *Energy from falling water is converted to electrical energy*

Figure 40.14 *Biomass can be converted to electrical energy*

Figure 40.15 *Water at the Old Faithful geyser (in Yellowstone National Park in the United States) is heated underground by the rocks*

Figure 40.16 *Solar panels harness energy from the Sun*

Figure 40.17 *Some solar panels are small, like the one on this calculator. These smaller panels are called 'solar cells'*

Did you know?

Enough energy from the Sun falls on Earth every hour that we could power the entire Earth for a full year – if only we could work out how to trap or use it!

40.9 Research the following areas and determine the effect, be it positive or negative, on the energy output of the following renewable sources of energy. Present your findings in your copy.

Solar panels

(a) Can the presence of clouds or solid particles impact the energy output from the panels?

(b) Is the angle and direction in which a solar cell or panel is facing important? Explain your answer.

Wind turbines

(c) Does the number of blades or the length of the blades on a wind turbine affect the amount of energy being produced from that turbine?

(d) Does the direction the wind turbine is facing affect its efficiency?

(e) What are the main disadvantages in using solar panels and wind turbines?

What are our current and future energy requirements?

We have become an **energy hungry society**. This means, per individual on Earth, we have a very high demand and requirement for energy.

Evidence of this is in a satellite image of Earth – look at all the light that can be seen from space coming from cities and people's homes in Figure 40.18.

Figure 40.18 *A satellite image of Europe shows up electric light from cities and towns*

Most of our current energy needs are met by burning fossil fuels. Fossil fuels, along with nuclear energy, supply 93% of the world's energy requirement. The remaining 7% comes from renewable energy sources.

Table 40.1 shows how much fossil fuel is used just to supply the world's electrical demands.

Table 40.1 Percentage of types of fuel used to supply the world's electrical demands

Energy type	% of world electrical supply
Coal	39
Gas	19
Nuclear	17
Oil	16
Hydro	7
Other	2

As economies and countries become more developed, the demand for energy increases dramatically.

A simple example of this is the number of cars that are currently on the world's roads. From a study done in 2014, there are now over one billion cars on the road, with the US having the highest number of cars and China having the second-highest.

In addition the world's population is also expanding – and it is expected to reach about 10 billion people in the next fifty years – and so our energy demands will also increase.

Energy experts expect that by the time we reach 2030 the world energy demand will have increased by 55% compared to today.

Figure 40.19 *Traffic on a road in the USA*

Not only will we have to use renewable energy in greater and greater amounts, we will need to be more efficient about how we use our energy. Energy efficiency is essential as scientists believe that within the next 50 to 100 years our fossil fuels will run out, and once they are gone they are gone!

Did you know?

On average 15% of electricity used in the home is used by devices and equipment that are on standby.

EARTH & SPACE

The European Union has set targets for all member states to help the environment. Ireland has many targets that it has to meet, including:

- By 2020 16% of all energy being used in the country will have to come from a renewable energy source.
- By 2020 10% of transport will have to be from a renewable energy source.

40.10 In pairs or groups, investigate all renewable energy forms that are being used in Ireland. How efficient are they, and how expensive?

Figure 40.20 *Renewable energy*

Figure 40.21 *Wind farm energy*

Did you know?

Scientists believe that it would take only one percent of the world's land area covered in solar panels to supply all of the world's present electrical needs!

We can no longer continue with our current dependency on fossil fuels. Nor can we continue to ignore how important it is for us to begin to use renewable energy in greater amounts.

Our future, in terms of energy, depends on what we do now and what way we begin to plan for our future energy needs.

40.11 Identify five renewable resources.

40.12 Name the fossil fuels.

CHAPTER 41

UNIT 5

Climate change – what is making us so hot under the collar?

Learning outcomes

At the end of this chapter you will be able to:

- Explain the difference between climate change and global warming
- Identify the main greenhouse gases
- Outline how climate change affects certain processes on Earth
- Describe the effects on Earth of global warming
- Determine how humans can reduce the effect of climate change.

Keywords

climate global greenhouse reflectivity absorbed reflected glaciers

What is the difference between global warming and climate change?

Figure 41.1 *The burning of fossil fuel is impacting on Earth*

From chapter 40 we know that we are burning fossil fuels to an extent that it has now begun to impact on the processes that take place on Earth.

You may be more aware of the term 'global warming' than the term 'climate change'. So what is the difference between the two terms?

Climate change is any long-term change, usually in terms of decades, to Earth's climate. Climate means weather over a long period. This means climate change causes weather changes.

Figure 41.2 *Global warming*

Figure 41.3 *Rising global temperatures*

Figure 41.4 *Animals such as the polar bear are losing their habitats because of global warming*

Global warming is the increase in Earth's average surface temperature due to the effect of greenhouse gases.

It is the current global warming taking place on Earth that is causing our climate to change.

Globally, temperatures have risen by approximately 0.8°C over the last one hundred years. Europe is warming faster than many parts of the world – by 1.3°C in the last century, according to EU research.

These increases in temperature may appear small, but they are potentially serious and dangerous to the balance of nature.

What are the factors that are causing our planet to warm up? What are the impacts on our environment? And how can we, as individuals and as countries, make a difference?

What is the greenhouse effect?

The greenhouse effect occurs when gases in Earth's atmosphere prevent some of the heat from escaping into space.

These gases, which trap the heat in the atmosphere and as a result make Earth much warmer, are called **greenhouse gases.**

The main greenhouse gases are:

- Carbon dioxide (CO_2)
- Methane (CH_4)
- Nitrous oxide (N_2O)
- Water vapour (H_2O).

Did you know?

According to the food and agriculture section of the United Nations, agriculture is responsible for 18% of the total release of greenhouse gases worldwide, with methane from cattle being the major contributor.

In describing the greenhouse effect we will look at the most commonly known greenhouse gas, carbon dioxide.

We looked at the carbon cycle in chapter 39, and at how carbon is cycled through nature.

41.1 What processes from nature and from humans release CO_2 into the atmosphere?

Figure 41.5 *Heat being trapped by greenhouse gases in the atmosphere*

Figure 41.6 *Earth is getting too hot*

Earth is surrounded by the atmosphere. This acts like a blanket, trapping heat energy from the Sun. As a result Earth has a surface temperature that allows life to exist. Increasing levels of carbon dioxide in Earth's atmosphere trap more of this heat energy.

Carbon dioxide is released by many natural means:

- Burning
- Animal and plant respiration (how plants and animals break down food to release energy)
- Volcanoes erupting
- Carbon dioxide exchange between the oceans and the atmosphere.

There is a balance of carbon dioxide within the atmosphere:

- Too little and Earth is too cold to sustain life.
- Too much and Earth warms up, and even small temperature rises begin to affect how our planet functions.

Figure 41.7 *Burning fossil fuels releases carbon dioxide into the atmosphere*

EARTH & SPACE

However, due to the increased burning of fossil fuels this balance of carbon dioxide has been dramatically affected. It is this increased level of CO_2 that has resulted in global warming and the resulting changes to our climate.

According to NASA scientists, there has been a 40% increase in the level of carbon dioxide concentration in the atmosphere since the Industrial Revolution in the late 1700s.

It is the 'warming up' due to excess carbon dioxide that is causing the worldwide climate to change.

So how is Earth coping? Many factors are causing the planet to struggle. We will look at three:

- Oceans
- How our surfaces reflect light
- A process called 'global dimming'.

41.2 Identify some of the reasons and uses where fossil fuels are burned.

How do the oceans affect climate?

The oceans are very important to Earth's climate. Oceans trap heat energy from the Sun, which warms the water. This warm water is then distributed around Earth by the oceans' currents. As the warm water passes by land it warms that land.

Therefore our oceans are crucial in maintaining the **heat transfer** around Earth.

The changing acidic nature of Earth's oceans

Another key factor is that the oceans absorb carbon dioxide. Currently the oceans are absorbing approximately 40% of all the carbon dioxide that is being released into the atmosphere. Oceans absorb CO_2 directly from the atmosphere *or* in the form of **acid rain** (rain in which CO_2 is dissolved within the raindrop itself). CO_2 is an acidic gas, which means that when it is dissolved in water it makes that water more acidic.

This will affect how animals and plants live within the oceans.

Figure 41.8 *The oceans affect Earth's climate*

41.3 Examine if there are any areas in Earth's oceans that are currently being affected by this changing chemical nature of the oceans.

41.4 Outline any effect on plant and animals in the oceans as a result of the chemical change in the oceans.

41.5 Identify the pH range (how acidic the water must be) for animals and plants in Earth's oceans to become affected.

Oceans are also absorbing 90% of all the excess heat that is being generated due to the increased amounts of the greenhouse gases.

Did you know?

Earth's oceans have absorbed twenty times more of this increased amount of heat over the last fifty years. This has resulted in Earth's oceans warming up also.

Colder water absorbs carbon dioxide much more easily than warmer water. So as the oceans warm up they will be unable to absorb as much CO_2.

The heat will then be returned to the atmosphere. This in turn will cause more heat to stay in the atmosphere causing the planet to warm up even more.

This increased warming of Earth's oceans is not something that *may* happen in the future – it is happening right now. Scientists have been studying the levels of carbon dioxide in the North Atlantic Ocean for the last thirty years. They have found that there are large sections of the North Atlantic that are currently unable to absorb as much CO_2 as they used to. This has also been observed in the Sea of Japan.

As some scientists have stated, our oceans are doing 'a service to humans'. It is important that we protect them more than we are currently doing.

Surface reflectivity

When sunlight reaches Earth it will either be absorbed or reflected.

The lighter colour an object is – for example, snow, ice, clouds – the more the heat energy is reflected back into space. This helps Earth to remain cool.

The darker colour an object is – for example, oceans, forests and soil – the more of the heat from the Sun is absorbed to warm up Earth.

Figure 41.9 *Deforestation contributes to global warming*

Earth usually absorbs around 70% of the sunlight and reflects the remaining 30%. It is this balance that allows Earth to remain warm but avoid warming up too much.

But what happens if the balance changes? What if, due to global warming, the reflectors like ice and snow begin to melt into the oceans?

What happens when the world's glaciers begin melting and retreating?

41.6 Looking at the questions asked within the previous text, research:

(a) The evidence that scientists have gathered to show that global warming and climate change is *actually* taking place.

(b) The melting of the polar ice caps resulting in more fresh water going into Earth's oceans. Outline the effect this is currently having, and what effects it may cause in the future.

(c) As well as CO_2, water vapour and methane gas are major contributing greenhouse gases. Describe the effects of each of these three gases in terms of climate change, and outline why more and more of these gases are being released into the atmosphere.

Global dimming

When we burn fossil fuels, not only are we releasing greenhouse gases into the atmosphere, we are releasing particles, such as soot and ash, into the air.

These particles allow water vapour to gather on them to create larger clouds.

The more fossil fuels we burn, the more particles there will be in the atmosphere and the greater the amount of water within the clouds.

In simple terms, polluted clouds contain more water than unpolluted clouds.

This means that these clouds act like mirrors, reflecting more sunlight back into space. This is **global dimming**. The result of reflecting more sunlight is a lower temperature.

Scientists had estimated how advanced global warming was. Global dimming may mean that their estimates were wrong. Remember global dimming reflects heat energy. So the effects of global warming may be more advanced than we had originally thought.

Figure 41.10 *The world's sea levels are rising*

What are the effects of climate change?

The effects of climate change are:

- Rising sea levels
- Shrinking glaciers
- Storms and floods
- Heatwaves
- Drought.

Rising sea levels

The melting of glaciers, polar ice sheets and sea ice is increasing the levels of Earth's waters.

Figure 41.11 *Flooding is becoming more frequent – this is Bangkok airport*

Did you know?

If the ice sheet in the country of Greenland melts, the world's sea level will rise by 5 to 7 metres.

Shrinking glaciers

A glacier is a river of ice. Glaciers are formed when snow does not completely melt away in the summer. With each winter extra snow gets laid down, compressing the layers of snow beneath it. Eventually, over thousands of years, the accumulation of these now solid layers forms a glacier.

Glaciers move and flow through the landscape. People who live near glaciers depend on glaciers for their fresh water. This fresh water comes from meltwater from the glaciers.

Figure 41.12 *Glaciers are shrinking*

Glaciers are very sensitive to changes in temperature. Climate change is causing many of the world's glaciers to retreat, or go backwards. Many of these glaciers are retreating so rapidly that they may completely disappear within decades. For example, the glaciers in the Himalayas are shrinking and getting smaller in terms of length by 37 metres every year.

Storms and floods

Warmer waters in our oceans give strength to storms, making them more powerful. Local flooding results when these storms reach land.

Figure 41.13 *Storms are becoming more regular in some parts of the world*

Figure 41.14 *Storms and rising water levels are causing more flooding of homes and businesses*

41.7 What is the name of the category 5 hurricane that hit New Orleans in August 2005?

41.8 Describe any of the effects from the storms that battered Ireland in 2013/2014. These storms were described by Met Éireann as the worst storms to hit Ireland in fifteen years.

Heatwaves

Heatwaves occur when the normal temperatures of a region are much greater than previous temperatures. According to records, nine of the ten warmest years on record have taken place since the year 2000.

Figure 41.15 *Rising temperatures cause heatwaves*

Did you know?

2014 was the warmest year on land and in oceans since records began in 1880.

Drought

As heatwaves take place, drought, or lack of sufficient supplies of water, may result.

The Intergovernmental Panel on Climate Change, which is a group set up by the United Nations to monitor climate change, has stated that by 2020 between 75 million and 250 million Africans will experience water shortages.

Figure 41.16 *Droughts kill crops, animals and people*

41.9 Design a poster to illustrate one of the following:

(a) The effects of climate change on Earth.

(b) How humans have affected the rate at which climate change is occurring.

We are aware that climate change is taking place. It is how we now respond to it that will determine how much we can slow down the process.

Carbon footprint

Carbon footprint is a measure of the amount of carbon that is produced from the activities that we carry out. It can then be a measure of the impact that we have on the environment. For example, the electricity required to power a video game, or the fossil fuel required by the car, train or bus that brought you to school each has a carbon footprint. Carbon footprints can be measured for individuals, businesses, councils and so on.

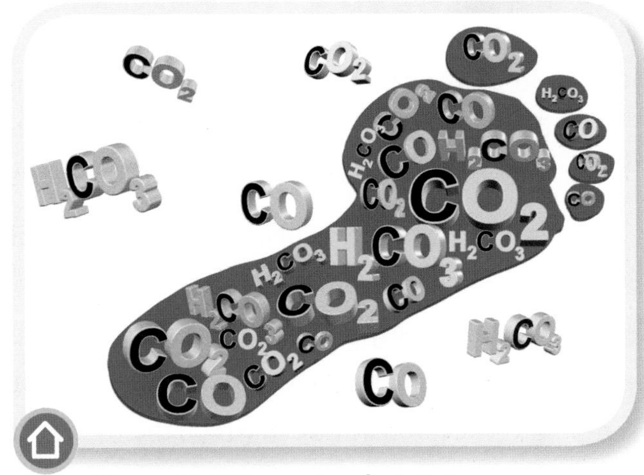

Figure 41.17 *Our carbon footprint*

Having a small carbon footprint is much better than having a large carbon footprint. Reducing the amount of energy you use will lower the carbon footprint that you have.

41.10 Many initiatives have been undertaken across the world to reduce the effects of climate change.

In groups or pairs research:

(a) Any agreements that governments or any countries have made in order to reduce the 'carbon footprint' on Earth. Determine, from your research, if these agreements have been successfully put in place and if they are having any effect.

(b) Outline any initiatives that have been undertaken in your local area *or* school to reduce the carbon footprint of that area.

(c) Make a list of daily activities that you carry out that require energy. Determine from that list if you feel you have a large or a small carbon footprint.

We can look at ourselves and what we are doing on a day-to-day basis to reduce our own carbon footprint. It is not just what governments decide that will reduce the effect of climate change: we all have a role to play.

It may be what we – each of us – do within our daily routine that may have the biggest impact.

Figure 41.18 *Switching away from carbon dioxide*

41.11 Monitor your energy use in your house over the period of a week.
Decide on a particular time in the evening to complete your checks. Keep to the same time frame for the remaining days of the week.

Things that you will need to take account of are:

- The number of lights on in each room.
- How many rooms with no person in them have a light on.
- The electrical devices that are on standby each day.
- The temperature at which the thermostat is set for your heating.

You will also need to make a note of:

- The type of fuel that is being used in your home to generate heat.
- The number of compact fluorescent light bulbs that are currently in use in your home. These are the energy-efficient light bulbs.

41.12 Work out ways that you each, within your daily routines, can be more efficient in terms of your energy use. Refer to the energy checks you did for your homes.

41.13 Give examples of any new types of vehicles that are being manufactured at the moment that use different forms of fuels that are not carbon based.

41.14 Determine whether your school is an energy-efficient building by identifying:

(a) The types of lights that are used in the building.

(b) How many empty classrooms have lights left on in them (choose a particular time of the school day to go around the school checking).

41.15 Identify three ways in which energy use can be reduced in your school.

It is now up to each and every one of us to protect our planet by reducing our carbon footprint. It is one of the most important things for humankind and our very existence may depend on what we do today and how Earth will fare in the future as a result.

41.16 Identify four results of global warming.

41.17 Distinguish between global warming and climate change.

Figure 41.19 *Our planet needs protecting*

EARTH & SPACE

CHAPTER 42

UNIT 5

Space exploration – 'To infinity and beyond!'

Learning outcomes

At the end of this chapter you will be able to:

- Describe the benefits of space exploration
- Explain the dangers of space travel
- Outline the future of space exploration for humans.

Keywords

exploration technology density hazards astronauts

What is out there?

Since the time of the first explorers, such as Christopher Columbus, humankind has been fascinated by the unknown worlds that lie beyond our horizon.

One of our greatest wonders lies in the worlds beyond our planet and what possibly may exist there.

Figure 42.1 *What wonders lie beyond our world?*

Our history tells us that it was during the 'Cold War' – a period of time, beginning in the late 1940s, when the USA and Russia had a very difficult political relationship – that some of our greatest achievements in space exploration took place.

The desire to explore space was called the 'Race to the Moon'. Both Russia and the USA wanted to be the first country to land astronauts on our closest cosmic neighbour.

Figure 42.2 *The USA organisation, the National Aeronautics and Space Administration (NASA), was set up to send astronauts to the Moon*

It was during this time, in 1958, that NASA (the National Aeronautics and Space Administration) was started. Its main mission was to ensure that an American astronaut was the first human to set foot on the Moon.

Even though a Russian, Yuri Gagarin, was the first human to orbit Earth, in 1961, the USA won the 'race' for a human to walk on the Moon eight years later. On 20 July 1969, the American astronauts Neil Armstrong and Buzz Aldrin stepped on to the Moon, announcing to the world 'That's one small step for man, one giant leap for mankind'.

Figure 42.3 *In 1961 Yuri Gagarin was the first human to orbit Earth*

Figure 42.4 *'The first step on the Moon'*

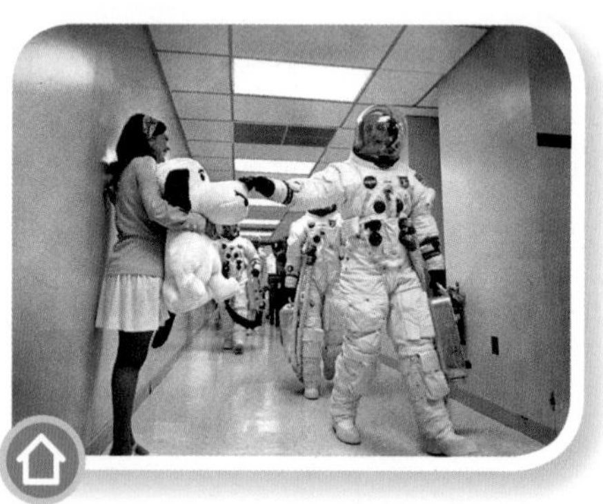

Figure 42.5 *NASA astronauts have Snoopy as their mascot*

Did you know?

All astronauts from NASA use Snoopy, the cartoon character, as their lucky mascot.

Figure 42.6 *'The Apollo 11 Moon landing'*

It is this 'giant leap' – the leap into space exploration – that we will be focusing on in this chapter. We will be looking at what we have learned from our journeys into space.

What are the benefits of space exploration?

In developing rockets and shuttles that could be launched into space, scientists were driven to make computers and digital technology that was small enough and light enough to fit into spacecraft.

Spin-offs of the research into technology for the space programme have benefits for the rest of us on a day-to-day basis.

Table 42.1 gives a small list of technologies that we all now make use of, which came about because of research and development for the space programme.

Table 42.1 Technologies developed by the space programme that are now available to everyone

Nutrition	
Food in space must have a long shelf life. Food needs to be nutritious but not go off for long periods of time. This need led to the development of long-life foods, which we now find on our supermarket shelves. *Example:* Powdered food such as soup.	 Figure 42.7 *Long-life foods used in spacecraft*

Industry

In spacecraft all piping has to be lightweight but high strength and this had to be developed specifically. This form of piping is used now in industry. *Example:* Heat pipes are now used in computer systems.

Along with piping, cordless tools that were developed for space shuttle use are now also widely found in ordinary households.

The use of robotic technology, which was developed for spacecraft, is now also used in industry.

Figure 42.8 *Cordless tools*

Figure 42.9 *Robotic arm used in manufacturing*

Medicine

Heart monitors were developed to observe the heart rates of the astronauts on missions to space. They are now used in all hospitals.

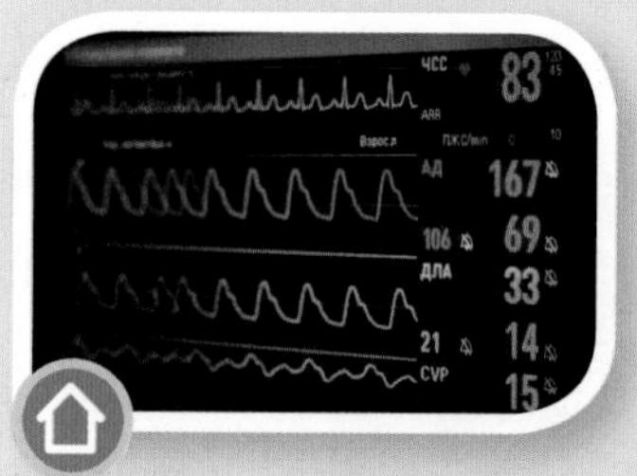

Figure 42.10 *Heart monitor*

Materials

The safety of astronauts was an essential part of all development. Materials that astronauts wore needed to be fireproof. Firefighters now wear protective suits made from material used in space suits.

Spacecraft have to endure some harsh conditions. Materials used in spacecraft to withstand extreme changes in temperature are now used as fire-resistant materials in new homes.

Figure 42.11 *Heat shield for lunar module re-entry to Earth*

Mobile phone cameras

The cameras on our mobile phones are a result of technological developments of cameras in spacecraft.

Figure 42.12 *Camera on a mobile phone*

Computers

To ensure spacecraft were light enough to be launched into space, all computers on board needed to be very lightweight. This lightweight technology has been applied to all computers that we now use.

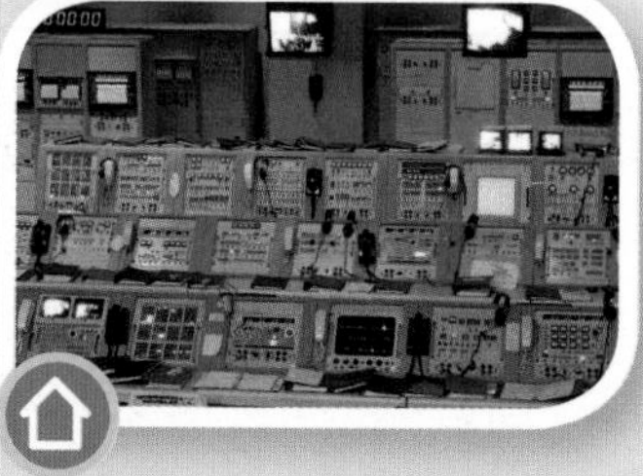

Figure 42.13 *Computers in industry*

42.1 The first satellite in space was launched by the Russians on 4 October 1957. The satellite's name was 'Sputnik'.

Since that date, there have been major developments in the use of satellites and their role. Using the internet and the school library, prepare a PowerPoint presentation on:

(a) Satellite development
(b) The role of satellites in space exploration
(c) Use of satellites in current everyday technology.

Figure 42.14 *Stamp showing a satellite*

Apart from all the amazing technology that has been and continues to be developed, it was the excitement that came from our interest in space exploration that attracted people to study and take up careers in science, technology, engineering and maths, or STEM as it is sometimes called.

Space exploration has also enabled us to use technologies to look into space and from space to monitor what is taking place on Earth and outside our planet.

A range of benefits has resulted from space exploration. But what are the dangers of space travel?

42.2 List any devices or tools in your home that are 'cordless'.

42.3 List any career opportunities, in relation to space exploration, that come from studying STEM subjects.

42.4 List and describe any events in space or any events on Earth that you think we use space exploration technology to keep an eye on.

Did you know?

Astronauts wear orange spacesuits for launch and re-entry (re-entry is when the spacecraft returns to Earth's atmosphere). Orange is easily seen if there is an emergency. Astronauts wear white space suits during space walks.

Figure 42.15 *Astronauts wear orange space suits for launch and re-entry*

Figure 42.16 *Astronauts wear white space suits in space*

EARTH & SPACE

42.5 Why do astronauts wear white space suits when on a spacewalk?

What are the hazards of space exploration?

Throughout the history of all space travel there have been many disasters.

Figure 42.17 *Apollo 1 suffered a fire*

Disasters in space

The most famous and most unfortunate disasters resulted in not only a loss of the spacecraft but sometimes the loss of the crew.

Apollo 1 in 1967 All three astronauts were killed in a fire in the cockpit during pre-launch tests.

Apollo 13 in 1970 An oxygen gas tank exploded on the command module part of the spacecraft. This meant that the astronauts could not land on the Moon, as had been planned. The crew suffered great hardships because of the problems, but they all returned home safely.

Challenger space shuttle in 1986 Just 73 seconds into lift-off the shuttle exploded, killing all seven crew members.

Figure 42.18 *Apollo 13 was badly damaged*

Figure 42.19 *The Challenger space shuttle exploded within two minutes of take-off*

Colombia space shuttle in 2003 The shuttle broke apart on re-entry to Earth, after a two-week mission. All seven crew were killed.

42.6 Within your group, research the above space disasters, or any other disaster that took place on a piloted mission to space. Outline the full details of the event. Present your work as a PowerPoint presentation to the class.

Health risks

It is not only their lives that astronauts risk. There can also be a risk to the condition of their bodies after a mission to space. Our bodies are designed to work on Earth in response to gravity.

42.7 Explain the term 'gravity'.

When we lift up anything our muscles need to apply strength to pull an object against the effect of gravity. This makes our muscles and bones strong. But in space there is a lower effect from gravity.

According to scientists, 'space is not an environment we are evolved to survive in'. Scientists have spent years studying the effect of being in space and the reduced gravity, experienced within spacecraft, on the human body.

Figure 42.20 *The effect of zero gravity*

Figure 42.21 *This is what happens when an astronaut combs her hair in space*

Figure 42.22 *Astronauts float in zero gravity*

Did you know?

You may have heard the term 'zero gravity'. This does not mean there is no gravity, but that it is not the same as on Earth. In spacecraft humans experience 'zero' or 'micro' gravity. 'Micro' means small, so humans experience a much smaller effect from gravity in space. The effect of gravity gets smaller and smaller as a body moves away from another body in space; for example, as a spacecraft moves away from Earth.

Effects of reduced gravity on the body

Bone When astronauts are floating around in a spacecraft they are not using their bones in the same way in which they use their bones on Earth. As a result astronauts will suffer from bone loss in space and so they have to exercise carefully.

Bone loss will begin to occur after only one week in space. Bone loss occurs when the rate at which bone is absorbed into the body is greater than the rate at which bone is being produced. As a result the bone becomes weaker.

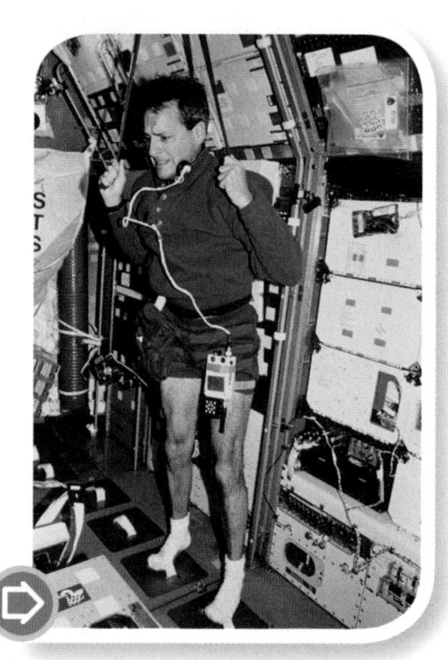

Figure 42.23 *Astronauts have to exercise while in space to prevent bone loss*

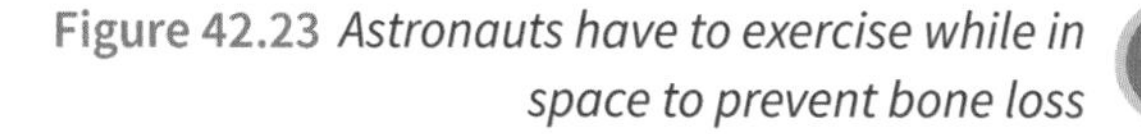

42.8 What is the term that describes the loss of bone density?

42.9 Describe any effects to the body that may result from the loss of bone density.

Did you know?

NASA estimates that a return trip to Mars would result in the same bone loss that you would experience in your whole lifetime on Earth.

Muscle The muscles in the body shrink in space, leaving the body weaker when the astronaut returns to Earth.

Immune system Long missions to space cause the immune system to be less effective at fighting off infections.

Circulatory system NASA says that being in space is 'like standing on your head'. Blood collects in the upper part of the body, resulting in increases in blood pressure.

Heart The heart does not have to work as hard in space as it does on Earth. This may sound like an advantage, but it is very dangerous as the heart may become weaker if it is not worked hard enough.

Sleep patterns There is constant noise and light on a spacecraft, which makes it very difficult to sleep.

Figure 42.24 *Astronauts find it difficult to sleep on a spacecraft*

Radiation Astronauts are exposed to one of the greatest dangers in space: radiation. Astronauts have experienced flashes of light inside their eyelids. This comes from the increase in cosmic rays that are actually passing through them at great speed.

42.10 Looking at the list of difficulties that the body experiences in space, investigate how scientists have developed technology and information for astronauts to overcome the effect of zero gravity.

Activity 42.1

Question

How does being in space affect bone loss?

Equipment needed

Puff cereal (around 150 g)
5 zip-lock bags
Markers
Book
Metre stick
Dust pan for clean up!

Safety

- Be careful when dropping the book on to the bag of cereal.
- Wear goggles to prevent any cereal getting into your eyes.

Conducting the activity

1. Bag 1 – fill the bag full with the puff cereal, leaving very little air in the bag. This bag now represents normal bone density and is equal to 100%.
2. Count how many pieces of cereal you have placed into the bag.
3. Close the bag tightly, removing as much air as possible from it without squashing the cereal.
4. Fill the remaining four bags with less cereal to represent bone density loss:
   Bag 2 – fill to 90% = 10% bone loss
   Bag 3 – fill to 80% = 20% bone loss
   Bag 4 – fill to 70% = 30% bone loss
   Bag 5 – fill to 60% = 40% bone loss.
5. Calculate the percentage bone loss using the total amount you have in Bag 1 and removing the puff cereal to make up the 10%, 20%, 30%, and 40% bone loss.
6. Place Bag 1 on the desk.
7. Drop the book onto the bag from a height of 50 cm noted on the metre stick.
8. Record what happens.
9. Count how many puff cereal pieces remain unbroken.
10. Repeat the procedure for each bag and record the results.

Did you know?

The International Space Station (ISS) was first launched in November 1998 and took thirteen years to build. It is a habitable low-orbit satellite that has been continuously occupied by astronauts since 2000.

The ISS is a joint project involving five space agencies: NASA (USA), Roscosmos (Russia), JAXA (Japan), CSA (Canada) and the European Space Agency (ESA). The ISS has been visited by astronauts from fourteen different countries. Up to November 2014, the ISS had taken part in one hundred Russian launches and thirty-seven space shuttle launches.

The ISS allows us to have a constant human presence in space. It allows crew members to conduct experiments while also allowing scientists to see the long-term effects of zero gravity on the human body.

Figure 42.25 *International Space Station and the space shuttle above Earth*

42.11 The European Space Agency was formed in 1975.

In pairs or groups complete the following activity. Use the internet and your school library to find information on the following:

(a) Name the countries that sit on the ESA's governing council.

(b) Identify any major developments and/or missions that the Agency has been involved in. Outline the main outcomes/results of the topic you have chosen.

(c) Draw a poster showing future missions/projects that the European Space Agency will be involved in.

What is the future of space exploration?

Where do we go from here? What are the next destinations that we are looking to explore?

Mars

The planet Mars is the next big destination. Recently NASA sent probes successfully to the planet. They are hoping to launch the first unmanned mission by 2017 and are looking to have astronauts orbiting Mars by the 2030s.

Figure 42.26 *Probes on Mars*

Figure 42.27 *Mars – the next planet to explore*

Figure 42.28 *A space station on Mars?*

You may wonder why Mars is the next planet scientists want to look at closely. Apart from Earth, Mars is the other planet in the Solar System that could possibly support humans living on it. It is a planet rich in the nutrients carbon, nitrogen, oxygen and hydrogen – all of which we need to survive.

Also Mars has one key element that makes it a good destination: it has water. Although the water is frozen as ice, the key fact for scientists is that Mars has water.

The journey to Mars takes approximately six months. Astronauts would remain on Mars for 30 days or 300 days. These might seem like odd lengths of time, but the orbit of Mars around the Sun does not exactly match that of Earth. So there would be a window of opportunity for astronauts to return to earth at 30 days. If this was missed the astronauts would have to wait for another 270 days for Mars to have completed its orbit around the sun and be in the correct position again to exit Mars and return to Earth.

Scientists are very aware that long stays in space badly affect our bodies. Overcoming this problem could be one of our greatest difficulties for prolonged space travel.

42.12 Discuss with a partner how a mission might remain in space for a long period of time. Explain, in your answer, how you think astronauts could access the required extra oxygen and water that they would need.

EARTH & SPACE

Minerals

Another area of space exploration that scientists are looking at is minerals.

There will come a time in Earth's future when our mineral resources will run out. We need to begin to explore new areas and possibly new worlds that have high quantities of minerals.

Research on meteorite collisions with Earth have shown that these asteroid rocks from space are rich in minerals.

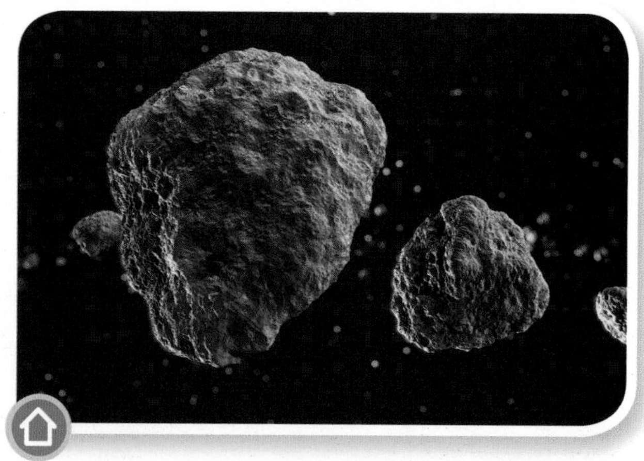

Figure 42.29 *Asteroids are rich in minerals*

NASA has developed the programme called the Asteroid Redirect Mission. It is NASA's intention to move an asteroid close to the moon and allow astronauts to explore it. This mission they hope to have launched by 2020.

42.13 Space exploration has always been enormously expensive for countries that have space agencies and space programmes.

Discuss within groups, whether you would:

(i) Discontinue a space exploration programme, if you were in charge, due to its high financial cost, *or*

(ii) Maintain the programme. If you decide to maintain the programme you must give your reasons as to why you have decided to do so.

Summary

Humans are curious about what exists beyond our planet. We have questioned, explored and discovered vast amounts of knowledge because of this thirst for information.

Yet we still crave and desire to know more. We keep looking outwards towards space and the infinite possibilities that exist there. It is humans' drive to seek out the unknown and it is this that maintains our constant search into the worlds and galaxies beyond our own planet.

Figure 42.30 *We have a huge interest in and curiosity about space*

Our relationship with space can be summed up by a quote from the famous *Star Trek* TV series:

> 'To explore strange new worlds, to seek out new life and new civilisations, to boldly go where no one has gone before.'

Index

	1	2	3	4	5	6	7	8	9	10	11	12	13	14	15	16	17	18
1	1 **H** 1.00794																	2 **He** 4.0026
2	3 **Li** 6.941	4 **Be** 9.01218											5 **B** 10.811	6 **C** 12.0107	7 **N** 14.0067	8 **O** 15.9994	9 **F** 18.9984	10 **Ne** 20.1797
3	11 **Na** 22.9898	12 **Mg** 24.305											13 **Al** 26.9815	14 **Si** 28.0855	15 **P** 30.9738	16 **S** 32.065	17 **Cl** 35.453	18 **Ar** 39.948
4	19 **K** 39.0983	20 **Ca** 40.078	21 **Sc** 44.9559	22 **Ti** 47.867	23 **V** 50.9415	24 **Cr** 51.9961	25 **Mn** 54.938	26 **Fe** 55.845	27 **Co** 58.9332	28 **Ni** 58.6934	29 **Cu** 63.546	30 **Zn** 65.38	31 **Ga** 69.723	32 **Ge** 72.63	33 **As** 74.9216	34 **Se** 78.96	35 **Br** 79.904	36 **Kr** 83.798
5	37 **Rb** 85.4678	38 **Sr** 87.62	39 **Y** 88.9059	40 **Zr** 91.224	41 **Nb** 92.9064	42 **Mo** 95.96	43 **Tc** [98]	44 **Ru** 101.07	45 **Rh** 102.906	46 **Pd** 106.42	47 **Ag** 107.868	48 **Cd** 112.411	49 **In** 114.818	50 **Sn** 118.71	51 **Sb** 121.76	52 **Te** 127.6	53 **I** 126.904	54 **Xe** 131.293
6	55 **Cs** 132.905	56 **Ba** 137.327	57–71	72 **Hf** 178.49	73 **Ta** 180.948	74 **W** 183.84	75 **Re** 186.207	76 **Os** 190.23	77 **Ir** 192.217	78 **Pt** 195.084	79 **Au** 196.967	80 **Hg** 200.59	81 **Tl** 204.383	82 **Pb** 207.2	83 **Bi** 208.98	84 **Po** [210]	85 **At** [210]	86 **Rn** [222]
7	87 **Fr** [223]	88 **Ra** [226]	89–103	104 **Rf** [267]	105 **Db** [268]	106 **Sg** [269]	107 **Bh** [270]	108 **Hs** [269]	109 **Mt** [278]	110 **Ds** [281]	111 **Rg** [281]	112 **Cn** [285]	113 **Uut** [286]	114 **Fl** [289]	115 **Uup** [288]	116 **Lv** [293]	117 **Uus** [294]	118 **Uuo** [294]

57 **La** 138.905	58 **Ce** 140.116	59 **Pr** 140.908	60 **Nd** 144.242	61 **Pm** [145]	62 **Sm** 150.36	63 **Eu** 151.964	64 **Gd** 157.25	65 **Tb** 158.925	66 **Dy** 162.5	67 **Ho** 164.93	68 **Er** 167.259	69 **Tm** 168.934	70 **Yb** 173.054	71 **Lu** 174.967
89 **Ac** [227]	90 **Th** 232.038	91 **Pa** 231.036	92 **U** 238.029	93 **Np** [237]	94 **Pu** [244]	95 **Am** [243]	96 **Cm** [247]	97 **Bk** [247]	98 **Cf** [251]	99 **Es** [252]	100 **Fm** [257]	101 **Md** [258]	102 **No** [259]	103 **Lr** [262]

s
p
d
f